The Bases of Speech

The
Bases of Speech

Third Edition

by
Giles Wilkeson Gray

and
Claude Merton Wise

 Harper & Row, Publishers
New York, Evanston, and London

THE BASES OF SPEECH, Third Edition

Library of Congress catalog card number: 58-13956

Contents

PREFACE   xi

    I. The Social Basis of Speech   1

   II. The Physical Basis of Speech   66

  III. The Physiological Basis of Speech   135

  IV. The Neurological Basis of Speech   200

   V. The Phonetic Basis of Speech   235•

  VI. The Linguistic Basis of Speech   321

 VII. The Psychological Basis of Speech   380

VIII. The Genetic Basis of Speech   455

  IX. The Semantic Basis of Speech   489

BIBLIOGRAPHY   533

INDEX   547

Figures

1. Freely Vibrating Lamella   69
2. Sine Curve   72
3. Derivation of the Sine Curve   73
4. Masses and Springs   82
5. Cruva's Disc   84
6. Action of Tuning Fork on Surface   92
7. The Audible Area   108
8. Highly Complex Sound Waves   112
9. Acoustic Spectra   118
10. Tridimensional Acoustic Spectra   120
11. Comparison of Vocal Resonating Tract with Cylindrical Resonators   122
12. Spectrogram of the Front Vowels   124
13. Spectrogram of the Back Vowels   124
14. Spectrograms of the Most Frequently Used Diphthongs   125
15. Sequence Chart of Vowel Sounds for One Speaker   126
16. First Formant Frequencies for the Vowel (i) as Spoken by 28 Women   127
17. Fundamental and Formant Frequencies for 25 Speakers   128
18. The Lungs, Showing Bronchial Tree with Branches   138
19. Changes in the Thoracic Cage in Breathing   142
20. The Diaphragm   143
21. The Serratus Posterior Inferior   146
22. The Quadratus Lumborum   146
23. Muscles of the Torso, Viewed Obliquely from Front to Side   147
24. Deep Muscles of the Thorax   148
25. The Sternocleidomastoideus   149
26. The Serratus Posterior Superior   149
27. The Levatores Costarum   150
28. The Scaleni Muscles   151
29. Muscles of the Abdomen   157

30. Transversus Abdominis 158
31. Transversus Thoracis 159
32. Schematic Drawing of Action of Muscles in Respiration 160
33. Muscles of the Thorax and Abdomen 161
34. The Glottis 164
35. The Glottis Closed at Beginning of Vibratory Cycle and Open at
    Midpoint of Vibratory Cycle 166–167
36. Section Showing Interior of Larynx 168
37. Muscles of the Pharynx 170
38. Lateral View of Cartilages and Ligaments of the Larynx 171
39. Posterior View of Pharynx and Constrictor Muscles 172
40. Posterior Ligaments of the Larynx 172
41. Anterior View of Cartilages and Ligaments of the Larnyx 173
42. Intrinsic Muscles of the Larynx (Right Wing of Thyroid Removed) 174
43. The Larynx in Relation to the Esophagus 175
44. Posterior Muscles of the Larynx 177
45. The Cricothyroid Muscle 179
46. Interior of the Larynx 180
47. Sagittal View of the Nose, Mouth, Pharynx, etc. 184
48. Muscles of the Tongue and Hyoid Bone 188
49. Graph of the Sine Curve 191
50. Graph of a Sound Wave 192
51. Sagittal Section of the Ear, Showing the Inner Ear 195
52. Partially Diagrammatic Representation of the Organ of Corti and
    the Tectorial Membrane 196
53. Schema of Functional Relationships in Speech Control 202
54. General View of the Nervous System, Showing Brain, Spinal Cord,
    and Nerves 210
55. The Involuntary System of Nerves 211
56. Schematic Representation of Excitatory and Inhibitory Innervation
    in the Autonomic Nervous System 213
57. Diagram Showing Length and Enlargements of the Spinal Cord 215
58. Illustration Showing from Ventral Side Points of Emergence of
    Spinal Nerves from Spinal Cord, also Right Spinal Ganglia 215
59. Schema Showing Relations of Ventricles to Surface of Brain 216
60. Transverse Section of the Spinal Cord Showing Gray Matter and
    White Matter 216
61. Vertical Antero-Posterior Section Through Hindbrain, Showing
    Medulla Oblongata, Pons, and Cerebellum 217

62. Anterior Surface of Medulla Oblongata and Pons   217
63. Metencephalon and Myelencephalon (Hindbrain) Together with
    Mesencephalon (Midbrain), Viewed from Side and Back, Show-
    ing Point of Emergence of Cranial Nerves   218
64. Vertical Transverse Section of the Cerebrum, Showing Thalamus
    and Striate Bodies   219
65. View of Left Side of Adult Human Brain   220
66. Brodmann's Numberings, Selected Illustrations   221
67. Types of Neurons   225
68. A Series of Neurons Showing Synaptic Connections   227
69. Schema of Cross Section Through Spinal Cord, Showing Elements
    of a Reflex Arc   229
70. Diagram of Cell Body of a Neuron   229
71. Vowel Diagram   241
72. Isoglos: Section A, Group 1   336
73. Isoglos: Section A, Group 5   336
74. Isoglos: Section B, Group 2   337
75. Isoglos: Section S, Group 1   337
76. Bimodal Curve of Distribution   427
77. Gaussian (Normal) Curve of Distribution   428
78. Schema Showing Development of Substitute Response from
    Circular Response   483

Preface

In the Preface to the Second Edition of *The Bases of Speech*, which appeared some twelve years ago, attention was called not only to the ancient and honorable heritage enjoyed by the present-day student of speech, but also to the constantly increasing body of knowledge being contributed by modern science and by many zealous workers in our own field. Even the very first edition of the text, published almost a quarter of a century ago, attempted to synthesize the best of what was then known, to provide a broad understanding of the foundations of our discipline, from a number of different points of view. The second edition, appearing twelve years later, sought to bring that synthesis up to date by incorporating into the text as many as possible of the more significant contributions that had accumulated during the interim between the two editions.

A similar period has now elapsed since the second edition came from the press. During that time it again appears that many important contributions have been made to our already extensive body of knowledge. So many and so significant have these been that another attempt seems justified to bring together these more recent additions to our understanding of the fundamentals of speech, and to synthesize them with what was already known. And again, as before, we have tried to incorporate into this, the third edition, as much of that information as can reasonably be incorporated into a single volume.

The changes that have been made will be obvious; there is no need to point them out in detail. To mention only a few: the concept of the social basis of speech has been developed much more extensively to include phenomena that were not recognized in the earlier editions; significant additions have been made to the discussions of the physical, acoustic basis of speech; the neurological chapter has been entirely rewritten; the treatment of the psychological aspects of speech has been enriched by the application of recent thought and inquiry; a new section, on the relation of language and culture, has been added; and the presentation of the linguistic basis shows the influence of current linguistic theory.

The only basic shift in emphasis, however, that has occurred in the work since it appeared in its original form, as six mimeographed chapters, some twenty-five years ago, has been with reference to the academic level for which it has been recommended. At first it was frankly a beginning text, written expressly for the beginning course in speech. In its subsequent development, however, the treatment has become more and more adapted for the higher levels—for advanced undergraduates and graduates. It has become, accordingly, primarily expository in nature. It now attempts to provide basic information on the nature and function of speech, as viewed from the several points of view indicated by the chapter headings.

Yet it can hardly be said that the basic philosophy has been substantially altered. We still hold that, whether for direct application or for broad understanding upon the basis of which applications may be made, the study of speech, to be thorough, requires that the subject be approached from many points of view. We do not believe that anyone who is limited to a single viewpoint, or even two or three, in his understanding of the basic medium of human communication can have a thorough grasp of the broader phases of speech in human behavior. Nor do we believe that one who limits his study of speech to a single aspect of the subject can possibly know very much about speech as a whole. Before one can specialize in the diseases of the eye one must first become a physician; a clinical psychologist must first be a psychologist. Similarly, to become a specialist in some aspect of speech one should know speech itself.

The original version of *The Bases of Speech*, then, was written to provide as broad an understanding as possible of the nature and function of speech in order that one might base upon that understanding a rational process of improvement in the oral aspects of communication. The present edition attempts to broaden that understanding primarily because that understanding is in itself worth while.

It should be obvious that no text, whether of reasonable or unreasonable dimensions, can possibly present all the material that might be included. Different readers will no doubt wish that still other subjects had been treated. But limitations of both time and space have demanded that a corresponding limitation be placed on the topics brought under consideration, and on the amount of space that could be devoted to any of them. The subject has not been exhausted in this or any other text, nor will it be in any shelf of books. Perhaps one happy result of the discussions here presented may be that here and there some student will be stimulated into further inquiry in some phase of the discipline, from one of the points of view here taken, or even from an entirely new approach.

It is difficult to give adequate recognition to all those who have contributed in one way or another, in lesser or greater degree, to this book. We are indebted far more than can be said to a not inconsiderable number of people. Furthermore, it always happens that the sources of many details have become lost, perhaps because those details have passed into the public domain. In the first two editions we acknowledged our indebtedness to a number of people who had made significant contributions to the content, or to other aspects, of the work; we are still obligated to many of them in the present edition, for their influence has been a continuing thing. In particular, we are grateful to Dr. A. T. Weaver, of the University of Wisconsin, and to Dr. Robert West, of Brooklyn College, for generous counsel on the first edition of this text; and to Professor Miles R. Hanley, late of the University of Wisconsin, Dr. Hans Kurath, of the University of Michigan, Dr. Robert T. Clark, late of the University of California, and Dr. A. A. Hill, of the University of Texas, for suggestions on Chapter VIII. In addition, we wish to recognize a few more, whose contributions for obvious reasons were not available twenty-five, or even twelve, years ago.

Among these we include Dr. Gordon E. Peterson, of the University of Michigan, for his helpfulness in connection with Chapters II, III, and IV; Mr. George H. Gunn, Jr., for his major contribution to Chapter IV; to Dr. Irwin Berg, Chairman of the Department of Psychology of Louisiana State University, for suggestions relating to Chapter VI; and to Dr. Charles M. Goss, Head of the Department of Anatomy of the Medical School of Louisiana State University, and editor of Gray's *Anatomy*, and to his colleague in the Department of Anatomy, Dr. Frank N. Low, for their assistance in connection with Chapter III.

GILES WILKESON GRAY
CLAUDE MERTON WISE

Baton Rouge, 1958

Chapter I

The Social Basis
of Speech

Communication in Human Society

The Function of Communication

Within the past few years, relatively speaking, interest in the phenomena of communication has become increasingly widespread. To find evidence of that interest one needs only to look about; it is to be observed on every hand. In fact, it has become one of the most important subjects of inquiry in our time. Psychologists, sociologists, ethnologists, anthropologists, physicists, communications engineers, to say nothing of students in the field of speech itself, have gone deeper and deeper into the practical and theoretical aspects of the media through which human beings interact among themselves. It is through communication that individuals are integrated into societies; it is through communication that the cultures of those societies are established and perpetuated. It was, according to the Biblical account, because of a complete breakdown in interpersonal communication that the building of the great Tower of Babel had to be discontinued and the peoples engaged in that enterprise dispersed. If human beings had no method of communicating with one another, none of the human institutions—industry, religion, government, education—would be possible; there would not even be any human beings.

There are of course other ways of communicating than through the use of language. Two or more people can set up any system they want to by which it is possible to carry information from one individual to another. Pictographs, smoke signals, drum beats have been and are used to convey complicated messages to great distances. It was signal lights, "One if by land and two if by sea," that sent Paul Revere on his famous ride on the night of April 18–19,

1775. But it is generally agreed that of all the media of communication, language is the most important. In this text we shall consider communication as it is carried on through the use of language, particularly the spoken forms.

Communication through language, which may be thought of as a systematized code of arbitrary symbols, basically vocal, but reinforced by visible bodily activity, has enabled individuals to adjust themselves to their physical and social environment and to learn the customs, the background, the mores —in short, the culture—of the groups into which they have come. It has made it possible for groups to unite themselves into socially organic units and to carry on their normal activities with a minimum of friction and a maximum of effectiveness; it has provided a means by which one individual may exercise a measure of control over the behavior of those about him; it has provided man with a vehicle for thought itself and for the expression of his innermost feelings.

It is through language, furthermore, that men are enabled to share their experiences and culture with one another, and to hand those experiences and that culture down to their successors.

It is quite impossible to conceive of either the origin or the development of culture apart from language, for language is that part of culture which, more than any other, enables men not only to make their own experiences and learning continuous, but, as well, to participate vicariously in the experiences and learning of others, past and present, who are or have been members of the group. To the extent that a culture as a whole is made up of common understandings, its linguistic aspect is its most vital and necessary part.[1]

The problems of achieving mutual understanding, of language barriers, of propaganda and advertising, of education, of the technique of managing human affairs without undue friction, of an intelligence in human relations that can keep pace with the changes brought about by the physical sciences, all run afoul of this matter of language and thought.[2]

Bram expresses the socializing function of language thus:

Language is related to [the process of socialization] in a number of ways. In the first place, acquiring a mastery of speech and, in more advanced cultures, the techniques of reading and writing, constitute a prerequisite to full participation in one's society. Second, language is the principal channel through which social beliefs and attitudes are communicated to the growing child. Third, language describes and clarifies the roles which the child will be called upon to identify and to enact.

---

[1] Harry Hoijer, "The relation of language to culture," in *Anthropology Today: An Encyclopedic Inventory*, A. L. Kroeber (ed.), Chicago, University of Chicago Press, 1953, pp. 554–573.
[2] Benjamin Lee Whorf, *Language, Thought, and Reality*, New York, John Wiley & Sons, 1956, p. 82.

Finally, language initiates the child to the *esprit de corps* of his speech community or any special subdivision of it, and provides the feeling of belonging.[3]

In the child of today language develops partially as an avenue of self-expression; throughout his life it will retain its usefulness in the expression of his feelings as well as of his ideas. Even more extensively and significantly, however, language develops in the child as the medium by which he fits himself into his social environment, integrates his thinking and activities into the thinking and activities of those about him, and lets other people know what he wants. His awareness of others and of his own place in the social order develops as his speech develops, and he learns gradually, chiefly through speech, to take his place in that order.

No child is fully adopted into human society unless and until he makes progress in picking his way through the labyrinth of language. Of all the achievements of the infant, none is more commented upon, at least in our civilization, than the first intelligible sounds and the subsequent acquisition of language skill. From the earliest days, our proficiency in speech not only serves the simple utilitarian end of signalling for food or protection; it is a measuring stick constantly applied to our personality as a whole. Language facility usually carries with it a stream of indulgence from members of the home circle and beyond, while failure shrivels the self.[4]

Hockett states the principle somewhat differently: "A newcomer to the community, e.g., a newborn child, assumes a position in the social structure, and changes that position from time to time; the pattern for such transformations of social position is socially inherited, and the main mechanism for the enculturation is language."[5]

These functions of language are not separate and discrete; they overlap to such an extent that it is impossible to know where one leaves off and another begins. Integration and adaptation, for example, come about partially through social control, and adequate adjustment is to a great extent dependent on complete integration.

The integrative, adaptive, adjusting, and controlling functions are all perfectly normal and legitimate, provided that legitimate uses are made of them. They are among the basic objectives of the entire educational system. Problems of social adjustment have for years occupied the attention of educators, psychologists, and psychiatrists; and sociologists are profoundly

[3] Joseph Bram, *Language and Society*, Garden City (N.Y.), Doubleday & Co., 1955, p. 19.
[4] Harold D. Lasswell, Nathan Leites, and Associates, *Language of Politics: Studies in Quantitative Semantics*, New York, George W. Stewart, 1949, pp. 5–6.
[5] Charles F. Hockett, "Biophysics, linguistics, and the unity of science," *American Scientist* (1948), *36*: 558–572.

concerned with the question of social integration and social control. These functions are recognized to be among the most powerful factors in human society; they are, indeed, among the things that make society possible. What language performs for the human community may readily be compared with what the nervous system does for the individual organism.

The desire and need for more effective means of social interaction have motivated the creation of all our elaborate systems of communications: the telegraph, telephone, radio, television, postal systems, newspapers, magazines, books, and so on. The history of the world might well be written in terms of the development of our facilities for more effective communication. Such a history would give an account of the many forms and media of communication which have been invented, of the improvement in those forms directed toward increasing the effectiveness with which we are able to transmit our meanings to others, and of the effects which each new development has had on human society in the course of human progress.

It is recognized that the degree to which we are able to integrate ourselves into our social environment and to get people to think, feel, and act as we want them to do, is determined in great measure by our ability to convey to others clearly and forcefully what we have in mind, whether directly through face-to-face meeting or through the use of the various media of "distance" communication. If the telephone is not working, we cannot use it to order groceries or to call the doctor or to hold pleasant converse. If a radio tube is burned out, we cannot tune in on an interesting program or follow the course of events as they are broadcast throughout the day. If anything interrupts the transmission or reception of a favorite television program we feel a deep sense of frustration. Occasionally a letter gets lost; the intended recipient may never know what the writer tried to tell him, or that he even wrote. Not infrequently an important verbal communication is totally misunderstood because the speaker has failed to make his words and meanings distinct and unmistakable. Vast sums of money and long years of effort are expended in the attempt to make the material channels of communication more reliable and effective; it would seem reasonable to expect that a comparative effort should be exerted toward making the vocal methods of communication equally reliable.

Isolation

Sociologists recognize various types of isolation, that is, factors that contribute to the failure of individuals, communities, peoples, and nations to meet on a common ground of understanding and mutual tolerance. As the term is commonly used, it refers essentially and simply to exclusion from communication. One of the most obvious factors contributing to isolation is the geographical, which is sociologically significant to the degree that it prevents freedom of communication. Language barriers are even more difficult to overcome.

Until such inventions as the telegraph, the long-distance telephone, the radio and television came into being, information traveled slowly. It took twenty-one days for a courier to carry a message from Caesar in Britain to Rome. At the time of the election of Lincoln in 1860, the Pony Express carried the news from St. Joseph, Missouri, to San Francisco in seven days. Today we can listen to eye-witness descriptions of events anywhere in the world. "News as it happens" is no exaggeration. In driving about the countryside one is surprised to find television antennae rising from so many unprepossessing, even wretched dwellings here and there. The phenomenon illustrates a principle ascribed by many writers to the human species, not shared by the lower orders, that there is an inherent impulse to communicate, to establish and maintain a social relation with one's fellows, to break through the barriers to free intercourse. As Wiener expresses the idea, "There are animals besides man which are social, and live in a continuous relation to their fellow creatures, but there is none in whom this desire for communication, or rather this necessity for communication, is the guiding motive of their whole life." [6]

Geographical barriers have in the past made travel tedious and difficult; but fast trains, automobiles on more or less adequate highways, and the airplane have enabled most people to mingle with others; they have permitted both temporary and permanent migrations. With improved methods of communication and better transportation facilities, a wider participation in the affairs of the larger community has been made possible despite natural barriers. Geographical obstacles are not the contributing factors to isolation that they once were.

But there are other types of isolation much more difficult to overcome. Language differences prohibit free social intercourse and may even reduce communication to the limitations of gesture. Many types of isolation arise from group attitudes—those attitudes held in common by a great majority of the group—which may have developed for one reason or another over a period of many years. Typical of these are class distinctions, religious sectarianism, racial segregation as opposed to integration, extreme nationalism, and political

[6] Norbert Wiener, *The Human Use of Human Beings*, Boston, Houghton Mifflin Company, 1950, pp. 2–3.

partisanship. It has been only within the past very few years that travelers have been permitted to visit in Soviet Russia. Sometimes the very existence of such groups as religious sects, social castes, or organizations controlled by a dictatorial leadership, depends upon the maintenance of isolation. Freedom to admit ideas from the outside world would in such cases speedily destroy the foundations upon which the group is established and maintained.

No implication is intended here that all these attitudes, in their moderate forms, are essentially and inherently pernicious, but rather that any attitude may become so when it is combined with such extremes as snobbishness, bigotry, intolerance, exclusion from normal human activities, chauvinism, and rigid domination. The point is that extreme attitudes isolate those who adhere to them from normal contacts with other people.

In alleviating these forms of isolation, communication may again play its part in providing the means for deeper understanding, by stimulating more tolerant attitudes, and by creating more profoundly genuine sympathies.

Still another type of isolation is individual rather than group isolation, but again this develops largely from emotional attitudes and failure in common understanding. Many years ago James pointed out that people tend to believe that which coincides with beliefs they already hold, logical or otherwise, and to close their minds to propositions which, they feel, may conflict with their "convictions," regardless of the mass of evidence in support of the rejected idea. The battles over evolution, woman suffrage, birth control, the treatment of venereal diseases, and desegregation have been fought and are being fought with emotional biases already firmly entrenched on both sides and with many minds closed to objectivity.

Illogical, rationalized emotional attitudes result in an isolation often far more effective and far more tragic than that imposed by physical or geographical obstacles. "None is so blind," we are told, "as he who will not see." The difficulty here is often semantic (see Chapter IX) in its nature and can largely be overcome through a more careful, accurate use of language itself. Through communication attitudes can often be changed, emotional and semantic blocks removed, and minds opened to the calm and objective consideration of most problems.

The meaning of all this is simply that communication, the purposes of which are social adjustment, social integration and adaptation, and social control, is recognized as an extremely important activity in the life of every individual and in the life of the social organization itself. Although there are nonverbal forms, most communication among human beings is carried on through the medium of language. Where communication is severely curtailed or restricted, social and personal isolation is the result.

Speech the Universal Mode of Communication

"Actually, the oldest known systems of graphically recording human speech do not go beyond the third millennium B.C., whereas there are good reasons to believe that the spoken word was at least within the capabilities of some of the earliest representatives of our species, such as *Pithecanthropus erectus* (the man of Java) or *Sinanthropus Pekinensis* (the Peking man) who lived more than 500,000 years ago."[7] Alphabetic writing of connected speech does not go beyond the second millennium B.C., although alphabetic symbols were known much earlier than that. Even so, the great mass of the peoples of the world are still illiterate. It has been only within the past two centuries or less that the idea of universal literacy, even within a single country, has been the announced aim of education. Speech has been for thousands of years the universal medium of communication; it still is.

Not everyone has the opportunity of using extensively many of the available media of communication; relatively few people write books, magazine articles, or newspaper stories. Most of us have occasion now and then to write letters, but the printing presses are not utilized by the great majority of people for the purpose of initiating communication; and for increasing numbers radio and television, which are essentially extensions of speech, are replacing reading.

But everyone from the age of about two years onward speaks—much and often. Most of our social contacts are made through speech; we receive much of our education through lectures and discussions in the classroom. We use that particular mode of communication daily in adjusting to our fellows, in solidifying our social relations, and in getting other people to think, feel, and act as we want them to do. For every man who writes a book, thousands are day after day talking quietly among themselves. The actual human voice, together with the appropriate visible bodily activity in direct face-to-face contact, is still the universal medium of social exchange, even among the highly literate. "Linguistic change, it would seem, is . . . influenced relatively little by the circumstance of writing, even though, to those who are literate, writing and language are often regarded as synonymous. Yet beyond the written forms are the spoken ones; and language, expressed in speech, constantly changes. . . . Writing, though one of the great achievements of mankind, follows rather than determines changes in the speaking habits of

[7] Bram, *op. cit.*, p. 3.

peoples who employ it."[8] We need, says Whorf, "to free ourselves from that vague innuendo of inferiority which clings about the world 'talk,' as in the phrase 'just talk'; that false opposition which the English-speaking world likes to fancy between talk and action. There is no need to apologize for speech, the most human of all actions. . . . 'talk' *ought to be* a more noble and dignified word than 'think.' Science begins and ends in talk; this is the reverse of anything ignoble."[9]

It is not surprising, therefore, that some of the most significant inventions of the century have had to do with recording and transmitting as much of speech as possible—of the human voice itself and of the accompanying postures, gestures, facial expressions, and general movements that are highly expressive, and which aid in giving words meaning. The telegraph of a century or more ago increased the speed of communication, but it still lacked the effectiveness supplied by the telephone. The wireless telegraph was not enough; wireless telephony—radio—had to follow. Even the voice alone as it is transmitted over the radio with its present high fidelity is not enough for complete speech; television, by which visual cues may be added to the auditory for more complete speech, has grown immeasurably within the past decade; at the beginning of 1949 there were no more than fifty stations in twenty-nine cities in the country. Something was missing in the silent pictures of three decades ago, and talking pictures came into being. All of these have been improved until they have reached an exceedingly high degree of efficiency and of fidelity to the original speech which goes into the microphone or is caught by the camera. They are all extensions of the different aspects of speech, together with an attempt, highly successful, to bring all these aspects together to record and preserve and transmit the whole act of speech, in so far as the speaker is concerned. The means of bringing information, entertainment, and other cultural influences instantaneously to great masses of people have been among the most important developments of the past century. The telephone of Alexander Graham Bell and the triode tube of Lee de Forest have been milestones in the development of communication.

While these inventions have succeeded to a great degree in dispelling or at least mitigating isolation for the individual, they have, according to more than one observer, "weakened the habit of more direct and intimate forms of interpersonal communication."[10] "The commercialization of mass communication has led to a depersonalization of human relations and to a glorification

---

[8] Melville John Herskowitz, *Cultural Anthropology*, New York, Alfred A. Knopf, 1955, p. 300.

[9] *Op. cit.*, pp. 207–219.

[10] Bram, *op. cit.*, p. 5.

of clichés and slogans. The standardized response begins more and more to substitute for a deeply felt, personalized expression. . . ."[11]

The Cycle of Communication

"Feedback"

Communications engineers and group dynamicists make much use of the phenomenon known to them as feedback. Wiener describes it as

. . . the control of a system [of communication] by reinserting into the system the results of its performance. If these results are merely used as numerical data for the criticism of the system and its regulation, we have the simple feedback of the control engineers. If, however, the information which proceeds backward from the performance is able to change the general method and pattern of performance, we have a process which may well be called learning.[12]

Ruesch and Kees go a step further in applying the principle to human interactions:

When a person has expressed an idea in words to another, a reaction is necessarily expected. And this reaction contributes to clarify, extend, or alter the original idea. Feedback, therefore, refers to the process of correction through incorporation of information about effects received. When a person perceives the results produced by his own actions, the information so derived will influence subsequent actions. Feedback of information thus becomes a steering device upon which learning and the correction of errors and misunderstandings are based.[13]

Miller differentiates between *primary information*, "the message that the group is trying to circulate," and *secondary information*, or "knowledge about who knows what, knowledge of which pattern of information exists at the moment. . . . Secondary information is given to the talker by the recipients' responses." A statement of fact, or opinion, made to another constitutes "primary information"; but awareness by the speaker that the recipient received the message constitutes "secondary information," which "must somehow return to the original talker."[14] "Reciprocal communication," according to Révész, is "the basic condition of all forms of communication, inclusive of language."[15]

[11] Jurgen Ruesch and Weldon Kees, *Nonverbal Communication*, Berkeley, University of California Press, 1956, p. 4.

[12] *Op. cit.*, p. 71.

[13] *Op. cit.*, p. 7.

[14] George A. Miller, *Language and Communication*, New York, McGraw-Hill Book Company, 1951, p. 252.

[15] G. Révész, *The Origins and Prehistory of Language*, tr. by J. Butler, New York, Philosophical Library, 1956, p. 131.

The complete act of communication includes not only the presenting of the stimuli, but a response, real or imagined, as it comes into the awareness of the initiator of the process. It is not sufficient that we present the stimuli or that the desired response is elicited. For the cycle to be complete we must be made aware, either directly or indirectly, of that response. If we speak to someone who gives no evidence of having heard, the act of communication has not been completed; we must have knowledge that he has heard and has responded in some way. He may ignore what we have said without breaking the cycle, but he cannot ignore the fact that we have said it. When A's behavior is affected by B's response to A's initial stimulus, the cycle may be said to have been completed.

Immediacy of either the response or of our awareness of that response is not an essential condition for the completion of the cycle, although immediacy may be thought of as a relative term. We write a letter; the communication is not complete until we have an answer of some kind. Often the fulfillment is delayed over a period of time; many people answer last year's accumulation of mail only at Christmas time, and sometimes not at all. Actually, such communications as Christmas greetings, birthday congratulations, and the like are primarily expressions of personal attitudes, and serve mainly to maintain psychological contacts. But in any continued change of messages immediacy is highly desirable, and often contributes significantly to the final effectiveness of the whole process. This is why in times of crisis, or when matters of vital importance, such as international relations, are at stake, men resort to the personal conference, in a face-to-face situation. In such instances immediacy of response, of "feedback," in this sense, is imperative.

The particular manner in which the response comes within the knowledge of the initiator is likewise basically unimportant. A letter ordering a bill of goods may result in a shipment of the desired articles; a telegram may be answered by the personal appearance of the recipient. Knowledge of compliance with a request may be relayed through several hands before finally coming back to the originator. None of these variations affects in the least the fact that the response has been made and that knowledge of that response has come back to complete the cycle.

Often the completion of the cycle is not obvious; sometimes no direct knowledge of the response comes back to the initiator of the communication. We write letters with no expectation of an answer; we write an article without knowing who if anyone will read it. We assume that there will be a response, although we cannot predict what that response will be. Often it is an imagined one; we imagine the feelings and actions of the recipient, basing our imagination upon what we know of the individual in more or less similar situations. We base the content of our letter upon assumptions that may be totally wrong, and a breakdown in communication may result. Then, too, we sometimes misinterpret the response that has been made. A jocular remark which we think has been well received may not have had anything like the effect we thought it had.

Even though in such instances the cycle is apparently broken, our own behavior is affected by the assumed or imagined response or by the response as we have interpreted it. We go on our way, shaping our course according to what we thought the effect of our communication probably, or actually, was. But an erroneous assumption, or an imagination that does not consider all the possibilities, or a misinterpretation, can lead to a considerable amount of embarrassment to all concerned; it can result in misunderstandings that have tragic results.

The Senses in Communication

The Relative Importance of the Senses in Communication

All kinds of stimuli may be used for communication; they are limited only by the number of senses that we possess. Visual symbols obviously mean nothing to the blind; auditory stimuli excite no responses in the deaf. But to normal persons possessed of all the senses, both of these are extremely important. The cutaneous or pressure senses may be used to convey meanings—a gentle touch of the hand, or a firm grip may have any one of a number of meanings, depending on the situation. There are, as has been pointed out, many kinds of nonverbal communication.[16] But of all the possible avenues of stimulation, the senses of vision and audition are undoubtedly of the greatest value for communication. Let us see why this is so.

Distance Reception.   All the other senses depend on physical proximity, actual physical contact, with the object perceived. We cannot touch an object farther away than the reach of our fingers; we can detect an odor only by the presence of gases brought into contact with the olfactory sense organs. We cannot taste until the substance is taken into the mouth where it can reach the taste buds.

In sight and hearing, on the other hand, objects may be at some distance from us, so long as there is enough light or acoustic energy left to affect the

[16] See Ruesch and Kees, *op. cit.*

sense organs concerned. The actual stimulus consists of sound or light waves coming to us from the source, which then becomes the object perceived. It is true that these waves do impinge upon the sense organs, so that in a restricted sense, there is contact; but we see the stars not at the eye but out in space. We hear the sound not at the ear but somewhere away from us. The object perceived, which provides the stimulus, does not need to be in physical contact, or even in proximity with the sense organs of sight and hearing.

Because sight and hearing are "distance senses," it is possible for people to use them to communicate over distances without coming into physical contact, as in the case of the "contact" senses. In this connection, it may be pointed out that sound not only carries to some distance, but may be made loud or soft to suit that distance. For example, speakers find that it is easily possible to vary the loudness of the voice to accommodate it to the physical conditions under which they are speaking, the size of the auditorium, or the distance to the listeners.

Furthermore, sound is only slightly obstructed by partial barriers and can turn corners easily. Pillars in an auditorium, although annoying because they shut off the speaker from view, do not interfere seriously with the sound of the voice. It is often fortunate that we can hear a sound before being able to see its source, as in the case of an approaching train or an automobile; on the other hand it is often difficult if not impossible to shut off many sounds even when we want to; we cannot entirely close our ears. It is this characteristic of sound—that it carries around and even through obstacles—that makes it of special usefulness in a country obstructed by trees, variations in contour, and the like. We can talk to someone in the next room or hear an automobile horn signaling to us from the street. Sound is roughly directional, although in this regard it is usually supplemented by vision for the sake of more definite localization of the source.

Fine Distinctions.   Another reason for the importance of sight and hearing for communication is that through them we are able to make finer distinctions than through the contact senses. Through vision we are able to detect fine movements, delicate adjustment of muscle, facial expression, bodily sway, and so on. Form, movement, distance, and color are all revealed to us through the sense of vision. The eye can distinguish approximately 1000 shades of whites, blacks, and grays alone, and more than 30,000 color qualities. The ear can distinguish more than 10,000 "qualities" of tones.[17] Through hearing

[17] Madison Bentley, *The Field of Psychology*, New York, Appleton-Century-Crofts, 1924, pp. 52, 69.

we can differentiate pitch, loudness, quality of tone, duration, with all their infinite variations.

Furthermore, and what is perhaps more important, this ability to make fine distinctions is a readily usable one. The mechanism is at hand, so to speak, and developed in the human adult, for both producing and receiving minute shadings without the use of external equipment. There are thousands of tastes and smells, but we do not have within our physical makeup the facilities for using them; we must resort to elaborate and complicated matériel for their use. The fine distinctions made possible by visual and auditory symbols, however, in addition to being readily usable, are also easily combined into rapidly successive forms, making possible the development of words and of fluent continuous discourse. A contributing factor in the development of human intelligence was the acquisition of the capacity for and the mechanism of articulation, without which it is probable that "the human race would not have made much psychological advance upon the Anthropoid apes."[18] "Man has evolved language from what originated as simple cries and calls. A rise of intelligence is essential in every instance for the elaboration of a vocal code, but at the same time the acquisition of powers of vocal communication [has] given a great spur to the advancement of the intelligence. This is particularly noticeable in the case of Man."[19]

Transmission.   A third reason for the superiority of these two senses in communication lies in the transmissibility of auditory and visual stimuli, especially as they have been utilized, singly and together, in such devices as the talking pictures, the radio, television, the telephone. Writing itself may be considered essentially an extension of speech, in that modern forms of written language make some attempt, at least, to represent the oral forms.[20]

The property of transmissibility has made it possible to reach visually and aurally millions of people simultaneously; it has permitted us to talk personally with friends, relatives, and business associates, and to carry on diplomatic conversations over thousands of miles of wire and more thousands by air. And we are told that we may soon be able to see our friends' faces over the telephone, as well as to hear their voices.

Record.   Still a fourth reason for the importance of these two senses in communication is the possibility of record. Writing, known to be more than

[18] Romanes, quoted by V. E. Negus, *The Mechanism of the Larynx*, London, Wm. Heinemann, 1929, p. 295.

[19] Negus, *op. cit.*, p. 343.

[20] Cf. A. J. Ayer, "What is communication?" in *Studies in Communication*, A. J. Ayer and Others, London, Martin Secker & Warburg, 1955, pp. 11–29.

5000 years old, has come down to us; how much older writing actually is we can only conjecture. Certainly it had already undergone a process of development covering thousands of years before it was set down in a form that even approximately represented speech. Early in the Egyptian monarchy men had constructed an alphabet; that is, they had symbols for the individual sounds, twenty-four of them. But they did not know how to put them together to represent *speech*. Although the earliest specimen of writing extant is alphabetic, and although even at that remote period the Egyptians were attempting to represent the individual sounds of speech, it has been only within comparatively recent years that speech as it actually sounds has been recorded so that it could be heard again much as it was heard the first time.

Transmission and recording have made possible communication over periods of time as well as over distances in space. The "historic age" of man begins with the recording of language, and from the records which go back thousands of years we are able to reconstruct the life and conditions of those times. Because of them, communication need not be direct or immediate in point of either time or space. People need not be in either physical or temporal proximity to make communication possible.

The four characteristics of both auditory and visual symbols, then, which make them particularly adaptable to human communication, are as follows:

1. They are "distance" rather than "contact" senses.
2. They are susceptible of fine distinctions which may be rapidly combined, by using mechanisms within the physical makeup of the normal individual.
3. They lend themselves to mechanical and electrical methods of transmission.
4. They are susceptible to recording for permanence, and often to facilitate transmission.[21]

---

[21] Negus, *op. cit.*, pp. 293 ff., gives eleven points of superiority of sound over other types of stimulus as media of communication. Among those not touched upon directly in the present discussion he lists the following:
1. The use of sound leaves the movements of the face and limbs free.
2. The use of sound leaves the eyes free, allowing the animal to look for danger in one direction while listening in another.
3. Sound will travel up wind, though impeded slightly.
4. Sound is equally useful in the dark and in the light. It has been pointed out, however, that certain primitive tribes, whose meager vocabulary is supplemented with much gesture, cannot converse in the dark.
      [This common belief is not supported by Hoijer: "We frequently hear . . . of very primitive folk whose languages possess at most only a few hundred words. This is obvious nonsense for even the simplest culture requires a far greater number of words merely to enumerate the many objects and acts dealt with in the course of every-day occupations."

It is of no little interest that almost a half-century ago Cooley, the sociologist, pointed out four factors that mainly contribute to the efficiency of the mechanism of intercourse:

Expressiveness, or the range of ideas and feelings it is competent to carry.
Permanence of record, or the overcoming of time.
Swiftness, or the overcoming of space.
Diffusion, or access to all classes of men.[22]

Cooley's analysis is surprisingly accurate even today, despite the fact that many of the "mechanisms of intercourse" which have even more positively verified his analysis were still in the future when he wrote. The significance of the changes in these mechanisms he presents thus:

It is not too much to say that these changes are the basis, from a mechanical stand-point, of nearly everything that is characteristic in the psychology of modern life. In a general way they mean the expansion of human nature, that is to say, of its power to express itself in social wholes. They make it possible for society to be organized more and more on the higher faculties of man, on intelligence and sympathy, rather than on authority, caste, and routine. They mean freedom, outlook, indefinite possibility.[23]

The Significance of the Senses in Speech

What is the significance of these four characteristics, and of those mentioned by Negus, in relation to speech as a mode of communication? Do they find special application in speech which makes them of particular importance in social interaction?

Significance of Distance Senses. The advantages of the distance senses, and of distance communication as distinguished from contact, are obvious. In much of their speaking, people can go on about their work or play without serious interruption. Their freedom of action during the process of communication is relatively unhampered. Compare this freedom with the restrictions placed upon such handicapped people as, for example, Helen Keller, whose

---

—Harry Hoijer, "Language and writing," in *Man, Culture, and Society*, Henry L. Shapiro (ed.), New York, Oxford University Press, 1956, pp. 196–223.]
It is for these reasons, and possibly others, that sound is so widely used, even among lower animals, not only for the expression of their general bodily states and emotional reactions, but also for establishing and maintaining contact with and influencing the behavior of others.
[22] Charles Horton Cooley, *Social Organization*, New York, Charles Scribner's Sons, 1912, p. 80.
[23] *Ibid.*, p. 81.

only mode of receiving communication is through contact. When she "listens" she places her fingers on the lips and throat of the one speaking.

Distance communication is effected through writing as well as through speech; but in a very real sense he who reads may *not* run. He must stop whatever he is doing and devote his entire attention to reading, if he is to get the full meaning of the material. His activities are limited to that one thing just as much as are Helen Keller's. Much the same restriction is imposed by television as compared with radio. One can do many things while listening, even to speech, so long as those activities are more or less habitual; but television demands both auditory and visual attention.

Significance of Diffusion.   It is possible through distance communication to stimulate a number of people at the same time. One can speak to as many as will come within the hearing of his voice. This advantage has been enormously increased with radio, television, and talking pictures, although these have limitations which will appear later. "Public speaking," as it is called, is essentially a performance of this type, in that it is a process of stimulating many people simultaneously.

Ordinarily in this type of communication some freedom of activity on the part of both speaker and listeners is sacrificed. People assemble in groups of varying sizes to form audiences. For the time being, that is all they are doing; it is difficult if not impossible for them to engage in other activities as long as they are part of the actual audience and not merely physically present, although people do, it is true, occasionally perform certain types of habitual manual acts which have been practiced so much that they require no attention, at the same time listening attentively to the speaker. Women may sometimes be seen knitting while attending a lecture.

In this particular, writing is somewhat comparable to speaking, with this difference, that whereas in the ordinary audience situation where listeners are gathered in numbers the people who are being stimulated form of themselves a distinct social group, in graphic communication, on the other hand—that is, in writing and reading—each person maintains his individuality in the sense that he has no essential social relations with the other people who are being stimulated at the same time. Writing is perhaps more nearly parallel to radio speaking, although even here a number of people may listen to the same loudspeaker and thus form a social group among themselves, whereas it is seldom that more than one will read the same page at the same time. Writing most nearly approaches public address when it is projected on a screen before a group for all to read simultaneously, as in the case of election returns, or when it appears as news bulletins in a newspaper office window.

Significance of Fine Distinctions. The fine distinctions which are possible through the medium of the auditory and the visual senses give speech a tremendous advantage over other means of communication. Through speech with its appeal to the ear and the eye, it is possible to communicate the finest shades of meanings as well as the whole range of human experience, if not in a single language, then in other languages.

Consider the matter of vocabulary alone. The latest unabridged dictionaries list some 600,000 English words and phrases. The actual meanings of these words, as will be shown in Chapter IX, can be numerous in each case, depending on a number of factors, such as manner of utterance, context, individual associations, and so on. Whenever human experience enlarges, symbolic expressions are soon found for the new experience, if it is to be treated ideationally at all. One peculiar advantage of speech over all other forms of communication lies in the relation of meaning to the manner of utterance. Extensive vocabulary is available to the writer, but he has no sure way of indicating the inflection or duration of a single sound, or the particular quality of voice with which his material should be read.

Rapid silent reading gives little opportunity for vocal elements to play any part in the meanings which the writer would convey if he could. Whenever one reads silently at the rate of from 400 to 600 words per minute, or even more, vocal or subvocal processes have no time to exert their proper influence on the finer shades of meaning. This deficiency is of special importance in the reading of literary works where the author is attempting not only to convey logical meanings but to arouse attitudes as well, and where the emotional content is fully as important as the uncolored thought. Much of the beauty of a passage depends on its sound, as well as upon the images it stimulates. "It is a fact of human nature which the poets have always recognized that the sound and the pronunciation of words can be made to comport with meaning in a way which is more subtle than we usually recognize when we think of words as symbols of ideas." [24] And much of this is entirely lost when we read silently without permitting the vocal mechanism, at least implicitly, to fill in, so to speak, the more delicate shades of meaning. "A poem is not primarily a series of printed word-signs addressed to the eye; it is a series of sounds addressed to the ear, and the arbitrary symbols for these sounds do not convey

[24] Charles Hubbard Judd, *The Psychology of Human Institutions*, New York, The Macmillan Company, 1926, p. 107.

the poem unless they are audibly rendered."[25] "Every bit of literature so called that history has to show is intended not for the eye primarily, but for the ear. Every line of Shakespeare, every line of Milton, is meant to be pronounced, cannot be duly appreciated until it is pronounced."[26]

Importance of the Appeal to the Visual.   Speech in its truest and most complete sense appeals to both the auditory and the visual senses. In the ordinary situation the speaker is "a thing to be seen, shown to the sight, a being of action to be noted and read through the eye."[27] What the speaker is doing reinforces the meanings which he is conveying vocally, or, as sometimes happens, negates them. Even more, what the listeners see the speaker doing contributes significantly to the meanings themselves, and makes them more specific.

Meaning for speech has an emotional as well as a logical component. If we think about things at all, we also feel about them. "It is not enough that a speaker use a type of expression that carries only a logical meaning: he must show the hearer *how he himself feels about the matter*. He must not only let the hearer know *what the idea is*, but *how well or ill he himself thinks of it*."[28] The emotional reactions are difficult to localize; they are characterized by their all-over nature. A part of our emotional activity involves deep-seated mechanisms—the glandular system, the vascular system, the heart beat, the respiratory apparatus, the vocal apparatus itself. But part of it emerges as overt behavior affecting the vocal elements described in the preceding section, as well as such visible elements as posture, gross bodily movement, the use of the hands, facial expression, and so on. Those who watched the Senate investigations into widespread crime, as they were made available over television, will recall the intense nervousness of some of the men under investigation, as it was expressed by the involuntary movements and tensions of the hands alone.

When people see these overt signs of an emotional state they read meanings into them on the basis of their own past experiences with such signs. Some of these overt expressions may be voluntary, deliberately assumed for the purpose of conveying to the audience one's state of mind. These may be brought under control, as an experienced actor must learn to control his expressive behavior in order to portray the various characters he is required

[25] Bliss Perry, *A Study of Poetry*, Boston, Houghton Mifflin Company, 1920.
[26] Lane Cooper, *Two Views of Education*, New Haven, Yale University Press, 1922.
[27] Charles Henry Woolbert, *The Fundamentals of Speech*, rev. ed., New York, Harper & Brothers, 1927, p. 5.
[28] *Ibid.*, p. 195.

to delineate on the stage or screen. But some of them are so faint and fleeting that we ourselves are unaware of them, even though they contribute to the total impression received by the audience. These are much more difficult, sometimes even impossible, to control.

In any event, the speaker's meanings are conveyed to his listeners by three means: the words and the manner in which they are organized into contextual relations; the variations in the vocal elements, which aid in crystalizing and making more specific the meanings of the language; and the visible bodily activity, which completes the process of clarifying and intensifying those meanings. Speech is the only form of communication in which the two senses of sight and hearing can be completely combined and synchronized into a unity. Since the variations in both are well-nigh unlimited, the meanings which can be conveyed in their logical and emotional aspects by the use of appeals to both senses are almost infinite in number.

Significance of Transmissibility.   The development of our vast networks of communication systems has been for the most part in the direction of perfecting the means of transmitting speech, the human voice, and the accompanying visible bodily activity; and with these, since the same type of system will transmit both, music. Our telephone system, by which one can speak to persons thousands of miles away, is an outstanding example. From one's own telephone one is within reach of 92 per cent of the world's telephones. Radio and television, through which one man can speak at one time to most of the population of the United States and to great numbers of people in foreign countries, has enormously broadened the scope of social interaction through speech.

The essential difference between the telephone and the typical radio or television "broadcast," as these have been developed, seems to be this: whereas the former is a means of extending social contacts as between individuals, the latter is primarily a means of diffusion or mass interaction. One does not use the telephone to address a large gathering or a number of individuals simultaneously; neither does one ordinarily use the radio in personal, individual communication. Attempts have been made, with some success, to make the radio more personal by means of directional beams, "scrambled speech," radio-telephone hookups, and such devices; but these have hitherto been essentially applications of the telephone principle rather than limitations of radio broadcast. On the other hand, developments during the past decade or so point to the possibility of an extensive use of the radio, by means of the "walkie-talkie" and other adaptations, to individual communication. These have not as yet seen extensive adoption. One application has been the increasing use of radio for the control of train movements, and for the control of fleets of trucks, police cars, and taxicabs.

Significance of Recording.   In the matter of recording, speech has not fared so well in the past as has writing. From the beginnings of preserved writing conventional symbols have been set down for the representation of individual sounds; but that is not making a record of speech itself. Nor has the recording of visible action been any more successful. Photography has been known and practiced for more than a century; but early photography could not show the body in action. Two inventions by Edison made possible the first recording of both audible speech and visible action. These were the phonograph in 1877 and the "kinetoscopic camera" in 1891. The first of these made possible the recording of the voice, and the second, the recording of motion. The early attempts were crude and unsatisfactory, but they have been improved until at the present time it is possible to make recordings which reproduce the tones of the voice and the movements of the body, even the delicate, involuntary shadings which contribute so much to meaning, with remarkable fidelity. In the past few years application has been made of another invention by Poulson, by which an electrical impulse, varying with the sound energy impressed on a microphone, produces a magnetization on a wire or a specially prepared paper or plastic tape. Instruments utilizing this principle have been so refined that they are widely used for recording speech and music.

Up to the time of talking pictures most of the recording done was of music, although there are extant records of the speech of a considerable number of famous men and women made during the last part of the nineteenth century. With the invention of the process of using a variable light beam to record sound waves on a photographic film, and its application to the talking pictures, speech has come in for a far larger share of recording. Now the voice can be recorded with high fidelity, and preserved for future listening, or sent to distant places for playing back. The same speech can be copied, somewhat like printing, for reproduction in a number of places simultaneously to suit the convenience of the listeners. It may also serve as valuable documentation in relation to significant events.

The visible aspects of speech are likewise being recorded for preservation to any undetermined showing. Recordings of both sound and visible speech are being made an important aspect of documentation for deposit in archives for posterity to examine and analyze. Television programs are being filmed

for later telecasting. Educational television is making constant u
filmed production; through the distribution of such films to the
television stations in the area of general influence of the institi
wherever they may be wanted, it is possible to cover much more territory
than it would be by original "live" telecasting. This practice, of course, has
been common in commercial television for some time. Except for the absence
of "feedback," the lack of face-to-face contact, these "canned" programs may
have a high communicative value.

The Significance of Confrontation.[29] Speech has still another point of
advantage over other methods of communication, growing out of the other
points, yet distinct from any of them. It has been pointed out that proximity,
physical or temporal, is unnecessary in order for communication to be effected
through an appeal to the auditory and the visual senses. Recording has
provided for that. But it is also true that such proximity leads to a more
effective type of communication.

Other things being equal, the stimulus situation which makes an appeal to
more than one of the senses is the more effective. The case of motion pictures
has been mentioned; television is for many types of program more effective
than radio. People do not ordinarily like to have to listen to a speaker whom
they cannot see. To most people, listening to a football game over the radio
does not give the thrill that comes from seeing it over television or from
actually being in the stadium and watching it. Speech which appeals to both
the visual and the auditory, when it is done with reasonable skill, is more
effective than that which is purely auditory. Up to the present time, as has
also been said, the most effective way of providing this combination of
auditory and visual stimulation is through direct speech. Let us see why this
is so.

Communication, it should be remembered, is a two-way process; it is a
cycle, not complete when the stimuli have been presented, nor yet when the
response has been made. For the fulfillment of the communicative process that
response must come within the knowledge of the one who initiates the process, the one who provides the original stimulus.

The physical and temporal proximity provided by direct speech makes the
completion of this cycle more positive, the fulfillment of the process more
effective, by providing for its immediate feedback. A lapse of time between the
initiation of the communication and the knowledge or awareness of the

[29] For the use of this term, as applied to the concept described herein, we are indebted to
Dr. C. H. Woolbert, who discussed it in class and lecture, but never set down his development
of the concept in writing.

response inevitably reduces the effectiveness of the process. Ordinarily people prefer to shop over the counter rather than by mail. The limitation of the talking picture lies precisely in this fact: the response is not made directly to the actors but to the picture; the actors themselves cannot possibly get an immediate benefit from that response while they are making the picture. They know of it sooner or later, only indirectly if at all, and through box office receipts.

Contrast this with the experience of Otis Skinner in his interpretation of Haaj in *Kismet*. Mr. Skinner started out with the intention of presenting the old beggar as a tragic character. In an early performance of the play, however, during one of his assassination scenes, someone in the audience tittered. What could there possibly be of a humorous nature in murder? the actor asked himself. He studied the part over and over, and finally began to see why this one person had laughed. Those who saw him, either on the stage or on the screen, will remember the richness of the comedy which Mr. Skinner finally put into the character of the old rogue, all as a result of the *immediate response* which he himself had received from one of his copartners in the dual process of communication. This sort of reversal of interpretation would be impossible in motion pictures without a complete retake of the whole play.

Action on the screen is and must be static; a role cannot grow and develop as a result of the audience reactions. Once it has been recorded it is a thing of permanence, fixed, unchangeable. For this reason there are still a few actors and actresses who rarely leave the flexible, living action of the stage for the static performance of the screen. Much the same principle operates in television.

The biggest thing in living theatre is the fact that it actually is "living." When you see a stage show through a television screen, it is like trying to kiss a pretty girl through a plate glass window—not at all satisfactory.

The experts haven't figured out any substitute for the elusive sparks which makes (*sic*) living theatre ignite, the two-way interplay of actors and audience, the dynamic interaction of the players themselves. . . .

The simple magic ingredient lost on TV is person-to-person communion. Through that, theatre makes ordinary material live, and superior material becomes unforgettable.[30]

Something of the same type of limitation is imposed on radio and television. Temporal proximity is achieved, it is true. But here again, when the President,

[30] William Glover, "Movies," Theatre Section, *Times Picayune New Orleans States*, September 18, 1955, p. 9.

for example, talks to millions of listeners, he has no possible way of getting from his audience an immediate reaction—in fact, he has no way of knowing who or how many are listening. It is a fair assumption that he will have a very large audience, but the people in his audience cannot respond directly to him at the time he is talking, and in such a way that his speaking will be in any way affected by the way they are responding. A reference to the discussion of "feedback" (pp. 9–10) will serve to clarify the point. Speaking into a microphone with no one listening is as unnatural and artificial as is speaking to a mirror. Most broadcasting stations provide for actual audiences directly in the studio, and the responses it gives to the performers undoubtedly influence the performance itself. But the radio or television audiences cannot participate in those responses in any way to affect the performers. William Jennings Bryan once said, "I cannot talk to an audience I cannot see."

Two-way closed-circuit television may solve the problem when only a small group is involved. But it would obviously be impossible for any performer to get a picture of all his audience, such as his listeners might be able to get of him. Recent developments which make it possible for persons speaking over the telephone to see as well as to hear each other may help to solve the problem for individual, personal conversation.

Physical proximity makes it possible both to give and to receive stimuli at the same time. It is this simultaneous, reciprocal giving and receiving of stimuli which makes speech preëminent as a mode of communication. It is the factor of *confrontation*, the face-to-face directness of speech, that still impels nations to assign diplomats to all the recognized capitals of the world and consuls to all the chief cities, to represent them in international political and commercial relations. There is no substitute. Because confrontation is significant, special conferences are called, to which all the nations involved send their duly accredited delegates. "Notes" may be important in leading up to the conference and in preparing the way, but the time comes when correspondence is entirely unsatisfactory. So important is this factor that even prime ministers frequently leave their home duties and visit corresponding officials in other countries to hold "conversations" on weighty problems. Even our own Presidents, from Wilson to Eisenhower, have all made such trips to engage in personal conferences with the leaders of other nations.

All the learned societies publish their journals; but in addition, they hold periodic conventions at which the members may meet and talk together, read papers, reëstablish contact with one another, and hold informal, extramural conferences on matters of prime interest. Few business transactions of great importance are decided solely through correspondence. An industrial merger, for example, is not formed without the officials getting together and ironing out difficulties and coming to agreement through personal conference. Business houses send out their representatives, knowing that in the keen struggle for trade nothing can quite take the place of personal contact with their customers.

"The communicator's [speaker's] perceptions of the interpreters [listeners] may determine the character of the content he produces. . . . Where communicator and interpreter are physically in each other's presence, the produced content is more likely to be adjusted to the immediate responses of the interpreter." When they are separated, "the communicator produces content on the basis of assumptions about the interpreter" which he may not be able to modify, and "communication may break down completely."[31]

"The more personal the media, the more effective it is (*sic*) in converting opinions. This means (other things being equal) that personal conversation is more effective than a radio speech, and that a radio speech is more effective than a newspaper account of it. The greater the amount of 'personalism' the communication act contains, the more effective it presumably is. Recent analyses have confirmed the critical importance of personal contacts between the individual and his fellows."[32]

The Aims of Speech

Speech is much more than a medium of social control. It is a useful outlet for the expression of emotion; and it is in great measure the principal avenue of social adaptation and social integration. The function of speech in self-expression will be discussed in Chapter VII, "The Psychological Basis of Speech."

[31] Franklin Fearing, "Toward a psychological theory of communication," *Journal of Personality* (1953), *22*: 71–88.
[32] Wilbur Schramm (ed.), *Communications in Modern Society*, Urbana, University of Illinois Press, 1948, p. 172.
It should be observed that Walter Lippman (*The Public Philosophy*, Boston, Little, Brown and Company, 1955) uses the term *confrontation* in a quite different sense from the way it is used here. As he uses the term it refers to a challenge, an opposition of ideas and opinions leading often if not usually to argument; and "the modern media of communication do not lend themselves easily to confrontation of opinion" (p. 128). In our usage two people may agree perfectly, yet maintain confrontation. In either sense of the word, it is still true that confrontation is difficult if not impossible in the modern media of mass communication.

Social Integration [33]

Language, and particularly speech, is the principal mechanism by which individuals are bound together into a society. Speech may serve to isolate one group from another; but it is also a powerful factor in creating cohesiveness. When young people bind themselves together in search of union and secret brotherhood, they develop peculiar rites and a peculiar speech in order to strengthen the feeling of belonging together with their fellows.

In such a phenomenon speech serves a ritualistic purpose. For example, we say "Good morning; fine weather!" We teach the child to say "Good morning," because such greetings are polite when one meets another in the morning. In such a case a word patently has the purpose of creating a contact between different people, the creation of an atmosphere of community. One shows through these polite expressions that one desires to stand in good relations with those with whom one comes in contact. One stands well with those whose language one speaks.

Speech, then, creates a feeling of belonging, a "Wir-Gefühl," a "we-feeling," which is of great significance for the continuance of the group.

Thus it is that smaller groups in a community, whether it be a school class, a military group, or the personnel in a large business firm, feel the need of creating a special jargon. This jargon lends a feeling of cohesion, "Wir-Gefühl," that contributes to security. One does not stand so alone against the feared teacher, the commanding officer, or the head of one's department.

Behind this function of speech stands also the fact that two people who use the same speech must also apply the words as symbols of identical common situations. For words stand, according to our conception, as symbols not only for a certain thought or a certain idea, but for feeling, volition, and behavior.

Social Control

Since language is closely related to the social order and is a primary mechanism of social control, its functions have to do with the type of response which it elicits. Allport speaks of language as "social stimulation."

Making and responding to language stimuli, oral and written, has become deeply rooted in our most vital interests. . . .

In conversations we strive to impress upon others our experiences, attitudes, and feelings. In letters we do the same, and we politely request our correspondents to

[33] This discussion is adapted freely from Torgny T. Segerstedt, *Die Macht des Wortes*, Zürich, Pan-Verlag, 1947, pp. 153 ff.

perform services for which we "feel ourselves deeply indebted." The novelist and dramatist control the flow of emotion and imagery in their auditors to suit their own purposes. Even the professor in delivering a scientific lecture controls the thought processes of his students; for communication of ideas is a form of social control.[34]

If the various responses to what has been called "instrumental" language are analyzed, it will be found that they can be classified into certain groups or types. And as we desire to arouse one type of response or another, the purposes of speech may be classified accordingly. Strictly speaking, and from a psychological point of view, all speaking, all communication, except for the purely expressive forms of utterance, has but one purpose, namely, to get a response. Now all types of response involve, somewhere along the line, a neuromuscular or a neuroglandular activity of one kind or another, a pattern of behavior. And so it may truthfully be said that the one objective in all speech, as in all communication, is action: that the basic purpose in "social stimulation," to use Allport's term, is the influencing of behavior.

But there appear many kinds of behavior. Some of them are observable only by the individual doing the "behaving," some of them not even by him. These we call "covert" or "implicit" actions. Other forms are observable to other persons; these we call "overt" or "explicit." Thinking is ordinarily a covert form of action, but language itself, as used in communication, is an overt form. Moreover, covert behavior or action tends ultimately to emerge as overt behavior; so here again we may say that the purpose of speech is action of one sort or another.

Again, we may think of behavior as being general or specific. One may determine upon a general course, such as "Honesty is the best policy," or he may decide upon some specific act, such as going to the play or voting for a certain candidate. From this point of view it may be said that there are as many purposes to speaking as there are responses which it may be desired to elicit.

In most forms of speaking, especially that form known as "public speaking," which may include reading, interpretation, and acting, the speaker must be definite in his attempt to arouse any of these types of behavior. It is not enough that the speaker have some vague, undefined objective; he must know not only what sort of behavior he wants from his hearer or hearers, but precisely what specific response he is desirous of arousing.

The purposes of speaking have been the subject of much inquiry ever since the time of Aristotle, when speaking, the art of rhetoric, was mainly per-

[34] Floyd Henry Allport, *Social Psychology*, Boston, Houghton Mifflin Company, 1924, pp. 197 f.

suasive; it is so defined by Aristotle himself. In our modern age, however, not all speaking may be so classified; argumentation is by no means the only form of discourse. At present there is some disagreement over the "general ends" of speech, but except for the expressive forms, from a theoretical as well as a practical point of view, we can consider these ends as five in number. These relate only to *general ends*; the *specific purposes* are different for nearly every speech.

1. In the first place, we may speak *to give understanding*. When a professor delivers a scientific lecture or a lecture in history, his audience lacks experience in, or knowledge about, what he is presenting; their understanding of those things is incomplete, if not entirely negligible. His intent is primarily to add to their experiences by giving them information which they have not hitherto possessed. What use his students may make of that information is of secondary interest, although he may incidentally give them further understanding of the possibilities and implications in their newly acquired experiences and in their use of them. A complete understanding of the social aspects of speech carries with it implications regarding its potency as an influence on human behavior. If one is interested in problems of social value, those implications have a particular significance, as indeed they should have.

Let us suppose, for example, that the professor mentioned above is an engineer and the subject of his lecture is "Erosion in the Mississippi River Valley." He will probably discuss the various factors influencing erosion—the velocity of the stream, the soil characteristics of the banks, the influence of wide or sweeping bends, vegetation, the effect of rainfall, and so on. He may suggest some of the ways in which erosion has been checked or stopped entirely. As a result of his lecture new experiences, new understanding have been added to the lives of his listeners; they now have new information, new knowledge.

2. In the second place, we may speak *to entertain*, to divert. In this situation the speaker is attempting to arouse pleasant attitudes, not so much toward the subject under discussion, although he may do this, as toward the general situation, toward himself, and among the listeners themselves. His purpose is enjoyment, pleasure, amusement—possibly to remove the thoughts of his listeners from the cares and worries of their workaday lives and give them a period of relaxation, of freedom from stress and strain, to relieve their tensions.

Let us use our engineer professor again as an illustration. He is this time giving a lecture to a heterogeneous audience on the same subject as before. He tells them of the many battles that have been waged against "Ol' Man River," of how those battles have sometimes been lost, sometimes won. He narrates amusing incidents, draws pictures of interesting characters who have participated in the struggle, and describes picturesque scenes. He will inevitably have given information, but that has not been the basic purpose of his lecture. He has sought mainly to entertain, to divert his listeners.

Many examples of those types of speech known as storytelling, oral interpretation, drama, and even conversation fall under the general end of entertainment.

3. In the third place, we may speak *to influence belief*. For some years there has been a warm controversy over whether there is any essential difference between influencing belief, and the fourth general end.

4. We may speak *to influence action*. Perhaps it will serve to clarify any distinction that exists if numbers three and four are discussed together and if some attempt is made to show points of correlation and of difference.

It has been argued that belief, if it is a true belief and not mere verbalization, leads to action. Woolbert insists that all the other forms of response are themselves actions, and that the four general purposes (to divert, to stimulate, to inform, to convince) all lead to action. He says that action, to be action, need not be overt, like raising the hand or getting out the pocketbook, or signing on the dotted line. For him, deciding to vote, deciding not to give, laughing, feeling, grasping an idea, being "stirred with a great truth," are all actions, just as truly as those which we can see people performing.[35]

From a psychological point of view all this is perfectly correct; as has been said, there is no response without neuromuscular or neuroglandular activity, which means action, either overt or covert. Behavior patterns are undoubtedly involved. There is, however, considerable difference between deciding which candidate one believes will be the better public official and actually going to the polls and voting for him. In fact, a person may believe in the superiority of one candidate even though, for some reason, he may be ineligible to vote at all. His ineligibility does not in the least impair the strength of his conviction.

One acts upon his belief, where action is called for, it is true, but his specific action is quite another matter. To be consistent, one must argue that since complete information contributes to belief there is no distinction between these two as ends of speech; or that since understanding is a form of behavior it is essentially the same as overt action.

But we all know that knowledge does not always give rise to beliefs, which are often, if not usually, strongly influenced by emotional attitudes, and these are not easily swayed by a logical presentation of fact. A person whose dis-

[35] Woolbert, *op. cit.*, pp. 311–312. See also "Conviction and persuasion: some considerations of theory," *The Quarterly Journal of Speech* (1917), *3*: 249–264.

belief in a theory is based on the idea that the theory necessarily conflicts with his religious convictions will not be easily convinced that the facts in the case establish the theory with reasonable or acceptable certainty.

Furthermore, even when knowledge does give rise to beliefs, the knowledge itself does not necessarily determine what those beliefs shall be. Even with the most objectively minded persons many factors enter into belief besides knowledge and understanding. Attitudes which have grown out of antecedent experiences play a role we sometimes fail to recognize; in extreme cases they may be uncovered only through a long process of psychoanalysis. Even though all nine members of the Supreme Court have access to the same briefs, the same Federal Constitution, and the same body of law, they seldom reach unanimity in their decisions. Two equally learned scholars, say in the field of economics or political science, having access to the same body of factual data, may disagree violently in their beliefs regarding the basic causes of the economic and political ills of society. And even though they may hold the same beliefs with respect to the causes of these ills, they may still disagree over the proper remedies to be applied. ". . . even when a man's belief is so fixed that he cannot think otherwise, he still has a choice in regard to the action suggested by it, and so cannot escape the duty of investigating on the ground of the strength of his convictions. . . ."[36]

The gist of the matter seems to lie in the answer to this question: What, if anything, is to be done about it? If we argue that some theory is valid and succeed in convincing our adversary of the truth of that principle, we still have not indicated to him what he is to do about it—nor is it necessary, in many instances, for us to go this far. The acceptance of the theory on his part may not call for any overt action; and even if it does there may be any number of things he might do, the choice among which we are quite willing to leave to him. In fact, we may not be concerned about whether he does anything at all. If, however, we are arguing with a legislator in an attempt to persuade him to vote for a certain bill, we are not willing to leave the choice of action to him. Of course, we give him much information regarding the facts; we go further and seek to arouse his belief that the bill will be beneficial. But we do not stop there; we propose *a specific action*—we try to persuade him just what he ought to do in the matter.

THE "PROCLAMATION" AND THE "COMMAND." The basic distinction between these two general purposes in speech is suggested by de Laguna, who,

---

[36] W. K. Clifford, "The ethics of belief," in *Lectures and Essays*, vol. II, New York, The Macmillan Company, 1901.

in discussing the development of human speech from the simple cry, names, as possible responses which might be appropriate to the situation, the "independent alternatives (1) of proclaiming the presence of particular kinds of objects in their particular states and relations, and (2) of commanding the performance of particular acts and combinations of acts relatively independent of the specific situation." In the growth of speech from the animal cry to its present highly organized status, the essential factor is the "differentiation of the proclamation as such from the command." As long as the announcement of danger, for example, could result in but one possible response, as long as the group was capable of but one mode of reaction in a given situation, the mere announcement of the existence of that situation was enough to call forth the response and no differentiation could be made.[37]

When, however, owing to a developing complexity in the neuromuscular system, there came to be a capacity for variation in the response, when there were several things that could be done to meet the situation, then the mere announcement was not enough; it only prepared the group for action or incited a readiness to act, without determining specifically what that action was to be. Although it made the members of the group aware of a new, possibly disturbing and even dangerous element in the situation, the additional factor of command was necessary to excite the specific response to that new situation. The group needed to be told more than that the danger existed or that a supply of food was near; they must be told what to do about it if any specific or concerted response was desired. The mere knowledge of the existence of danger or of the presence of food was no guarantee that the group would all do anything definite, or that they would all do the same thing.[38]

The difference between conviction, the influencing of belief, and persuasion, the influencing of action, is based upon this distinction, which is fundamental. We may argue that there are certain defects in our existing social order, our argument being comparable to the primitive announcement of imminent danger to the group; but because of the infinite human capacity for varied responses we do not necessarily have to outline a specific remedy for the evils that presumably threaten us, in order to arouse in our listeners a belief that something is radically wrong. On the other hand, we may argue for the adoption of a certain type of social organization, which is comparable to the primitive command, with this difference, that there being no tribal chief, each member of the group has his own plan of social organization which he thinks

[37] Grace Andrus de Laguna, *Speech: Its Function and Development*, New Haven, Yale University Press, 1927, pp. 49–50.
[38] *Ibid.*, pp. 55–56.

should be adopted, and no one individual (at least in those countries where a measure of political and economic thought and action exists) has the power or the authority to decree the change. Lacking such authority, we seek to persuade our fellows that the action which we propose, and which we would command if we could enforce obedience, is the best one to follow.

ARGUMENTATIVE PROPOSITIONS.   The basic distinction between conviction and persuasion is to be noted in the types of argumentative propositions. Practically all writers on argumentation and debate differentiate sharply between what are called "propositions of fact" and "propositions of policy." A proposition of fact affirms or denies the truth of the statement as given; and argument for or against the proposition has as its purpose to convince the listeners of the truth or falsity of the statement. Conduct may be involved only indirectly or by suggestion. To argue, for example, that the country needs a new political alignment is primarily to announce that the present situation is such that something ought to be done. No one in particular is urged to do anything about it, even though there is a general indication as to what might be done. "Our climate is changing" might be argued indefinitely without ever suggesting that there is anything that can be done about it, so far as control of the weather is concerned. Agreement with the proposition involves no more than a recognition of a progressive alteration in the total situation as regards the climate.

If, on the other hand, one urges Congress, as a proposition of policy, to take specific steps leading to the establishment of a world supergovernment as a guarantee of lasting peace, a definite course is proposed. An announcement, a proclamation, of existing or unsatisfactory conditions is necessary, but in addition the specific response to that disturbing element in the international situation is laid out. The adoption of the proposition constitutes obedience to the command.

Now back of every proposition of policy, of every proposal for action, is a psychological assumption based upon motives for action, upon human goals. *Assuming* the desirability of a certain outcome, is the proposed plan the most efficient and certain way to bring about that result? The question as to whether a world supergovernment should be set up as a guarantee of peace is based on the assumption that peace itself is a desirable state among nations. Among peoples who do not believe that peace is desirable, any proposal leading to lasting amity among nations would fall upon deaf ears. But *assuming* that the peoples of the world desire a cessation of wars among nations, the argument resolves itself into a question of fact: Is it true that the proposed plan would bring about this highly desirable result without bringing also a series of objectionable effects which are even less desirable than war itself?

From the practical point of view the distinction is very useful. It aids the speaker to determine much more precisely the response he wants from his hearers, because it defines his general purpose. Even more important, it aids him in defining more clearly his specific purpose. He can determine with more certainty just how far he wants to go into the development of his argument in relation to the response he hopes to get from his listeners. Suppose, for example, our lecturer, speaking on the subject of erosion in the Mississippi River Valley, takes for his thesis the proposition of fact, "The depredations of the Mississippi River through erosion can be curbed." Once again he brings his material together, discussing the factors influencing erosion, and then shows what has been done to counteract those factors—the building of dams and jetties, straightening the river bed by cutting new channels, setting out vegetation, and all the other methods that have been used to stop the erosive nature of the stream. He gives information, it is true, and it is not at all impossible that his lecture has been highly entertaining. But primarily he has convinced his audience of the truth of the proposition that "Ol' Man River" can be tamed, as in part it has been. He is not asking his hearers to do anything about it; if they live along the banks under the levee they may and probably will act upon his assurance and their new belief in their safety. But, going back to de Laguna's distinction, he has announced, in such a way that his announcement arouses acceptance, that a change has come about in the general situation—this time a beneficent change. He may incite a *readiness* to act, but he leaves to his individual hearers the choice of action, or whether to do anything at all.

Suppose, however, he is appearing before a legislative committee which is considering an appropriation for the purpose of carrying on the struggle against the effects of erosion. Here he argues the proposition of policy, "Your committee should approve the appropriation of certain moneys for curbing erosion by the Mississippi River." Once more he brings his facts together to show that in many places erosion has actually been stopped. But, he argues, the work is not complete; vast economic losses are incurred each year from the inroads of the stream, and these losses ought to be ended. He shows the committee how erosion has been stopped in many places and how it can likewise be stopped elsewhere. His line of argument may be something like this: (1) The Mississippi is causing enormous losses annually through erosion. (2) In many places the cause of erosion has been removed or counteracted, showing that erosion can be controlled. (3) There are still many places, however, where these losses are continuing. (4) These losses ought to be stopped all along the river. (5) To carry this work out, funds are needed. (6) This body ought to recommend the appropriation of sufficient funds to complete the work.

He has in this case not only made a number of announcements relative to the changing situation, both disturbing and reassuring, but he has also issued what in de Laguna's theory amounts to a command, namely, "Appropriate sufficient funds." The fact that there is still further argument among the members of the committee does not alter in the least the essential nature of the case; neither does the fact that opposing "commands" will be issued nor that he has no authority to enforce compliance with his command. Having stated the situation he proposes a specific response, not being satisfied to leave the nature of that response to his hearers.

The distinction between these two instances of argument, then, is not only a theoretical one but a very practical one as well. It would obviously be futile to argue seriously that a certain policy ought to be adopted by the listeners, when they have neither anything authoritative to say about it nor any power to do anything about it. Conversely, there would be little use in arguing a mere question of fact when a question of action is before a group who have the authority to act, and are already in a condition of readiness to act.

Throughout the foregoing discussion the term *argument* has been used frequently with reference to both conviction and persuasion, because both are argumentative. They seek to make a *change* in either the attitudes, or the beliefs, or the course of action of the listener. They are based on two assumptions; if one does not start out with them, then any attempt to influence either belief or action is a waste of time. The first of these assumptions is that our listeners do not agree with us; they do not accept our point of view. They may not violently oppose our stand; they may even be neutral. But they certainly do not agree with us. Obviously, unless there is opposition of viewpoint, unless there is disagreement, there can be no argument. We may discuss the subject, but unless people take opposing sides on a given proposition, they cannot argue.

The second basic assumption in an argumentative situation is that we want our hearers to agree with us. Except in forensic exercises, designed to develop the techniques of argument, there is no point in arguing merely for the sake of arguing. If one does not care whether his listeners will agree with him, there is no purpose in the effort. In the usual situation we are keenly desirous of obtaining an acceptance of the proposition of fact which we are upholding, or the adoption of the specific policy we are advocating. Given these two assumptions, an argument may easily result.

5. The fifth general purpose of speech is *to stimulate*. The preacher who goes into his pulpit every Sunday morning and delivers a sermon has this purpose uppermost in his mind. The congregation agrees with him in the main; they are quite willing to accept the truth of what he says, and they are not averse to following out the course he advocates. But people often become "weary in well-doing" and need stimulation, prodding, reminding. In the press of living, ideals and sentiments and beliefs are removed from the focus of attention and need to be brought back occasionally. In this type of speaking the basic assumptions operative in argumentation do not function because there is already fundamental agreement.

Such a purpose is not unworthy of the best efforts of the speaker. Stimulation is necessary as often as either outright conviction or persuasion. Most of us are honest; we are actuated by worthy motives; we want to live wholesome, happy lives. But sometimes "the spirit is willing, but the flesh is weak," and we need to be reminded of our duty to ourselves, our neighbors, our country, and the world at large. We need now and then to have our attitudes crystallized into action, into beliefs that will arouse us to activity.

Some writers give *impressiveness* as one of the ends of speech. But whether one uses the term impressiveness or stimulation to designate the fifth general end is unimportant. Both words refer to a type of objective which is widely used in speech, and the differences in meaning between the two are here negligible.

There is much overlapping among these five purposes of speech. Information will creep into almost any type of discourse. Understanding leads to beliefs and beliefs to action. Many propositions of policy demand for their acceptance the establishing of beliefs. Stimulation crystallizes beliefs and thus indirectly as well as directly leads to overt action. It is quite legitimate for several purposes to appear in a discourse, provided that one of them is dominant and the others subordinate and supporting. But the basic distinctions do exist, and an understanding of their differences is of considerable importance to the one who would understand the nature and function of speech as a medium of social control.

Not only is there often, if not usually, considerable overlapping among these various purposes of speech, but a distinction must sometimes be made between a speaker's apparent purpose and his real purpose, or between his ostensible goals and his ulterior ends. Mark Antony, in his funeral oration, never once lets the mob know that he wants it to "rise and mutiny"; ostensibly he is giving information about Caesar's attitude toward the Roman people, and arousing sympathy for the fallen leader. Actually, the effect of his oration, the uprising of the mob, is precisely what he has intended from the outset. A speech apparently for the purpose of giving information may have the intended effect of changing beliefs, as a result of which only one course of action is logical. A speech seemingly given solely for entertainment may in fact have as its purpose profound stimulation involving crystallization of attitudes and resulting in specific overt behavior.

Communicativeness

"Communication may be said to occur when the perception of [the content of the communication] brings communicator and interpreters into dynamic relationship. . . . The act of producing content is *directed* rather than random or aimless, and implicitly or explicitly assumes future effects. . . . In the act of producing content, the interpreters are always in the psychological field of the communicator." [39]

In directing his communication to his listeners ("interpreters"), as Fearing indicates, the speaker achieves what is called communicativeness or, simply, directness. This relation in speaking arises entirely from the attitude of the speaker and is especially essential in what has been called instrumental speaking.[40] It is based on three factors: (1) a keen appreciation of the exact purpose in speaking; (2) a strong sense of personal contact with the listeners; and (3) a full understanding of the significance of the words being uttered.[41]

There is a vast difference between having something to say and having to say something. If we have something to say, in all probability we will have some reason for saying it. A student may rise in a meeting of his classmates or social group to support or protest a proposed course of action. He feels keenly that this course would not be a wise move at this time, and he has a strong desire to lend the weight of his opinion to the side he is advocating. He will probably feel in close contact with the group; the rapport is very strong; their interests and his interests are held in common. And the result is, probably, that he will find himself talking directly to them with a high degree of communicativeness. His very attitude and manner of speaking are conducive to a high degree of feedback. He has something he feels ought to be said and his purposes in saying it are quite obvious to him.

1. It is difficult to speak directly if one's aim is not clear. If we want to entertain we must be perfectly clear in our minds that that is just what we

[39] Fearing, *op. cit.*

[40] Leon Festinger, "Informal social communication," *Psychological Review* (1950), *57*: 271–282.

[41] See James Albert Winans, *Public Speaking*, rev. ed., New York, Appleton-Century-Crofts, 1922, p. 31.

have set out to do. If our purpose is to inform we must know what it is that we want to make clear to our hearers. When we undertake to stimulate or to inspire we must not be vague on the principle we want to crystallize into a course of action or on the attitude or belief we want strengthened. In seeking to influence the beliefs of an audience we ourselves must know the precise statement we wish the listeners to accept as true or false. If we want some definite action from our hearers we must be certain that we know exactly what we want them to do. We must not put ourselves in the position of the speaker about whom it was asked by one who did not hear him, "What did he talk about?" The reply was, "He didn't say."

2. A sense of personal contact, a rapport, with the audience is dependent upon a realization of the relation between speaker and listeners. None of us likes to hear a speaker, even in conversation, who ignores us, who gazes out of the window or at the floor or up at the ceiling. There is, however, a manner of speaking sometimes very effective, in which the speaker seems to be thinking aloud, turning a topic over and over in his mind, yet apparently not addressing the listeners directly. He seems to be soliloquizing. It is conceivable that the great soliloquies of Shakespeare's dramas may be considered in this light. True, the listeners may not enter actively and verbally into the "dialogue," but by their alert interest, their smiles and nods of approval or frowns of disapproval, their quizzical expressions of doubt or uncertainty, they are responding to the speaker in such a way that he is, if he himself is alert, fully aware of their reactions. Without this participation there is no rapport, no feedback; the listeners, or the "interpreters," as Fearing uses the term, are not made to feel that the speaker is talking directly to them. The cycle of communication is not completed.

3. Communicativeness is impossible unless we have a full realization of the meanings we are trying to convey to the listeners. We must be keenly conscious of those meanings as we utter the words; for through words our listeners become aware of meanings. One phase of this requirement of directness is the matter of logical arrangement of ideas. It is difficult if not impossible to maintain a sense of word meanings unless the word interrelationships are clearly defined in our own minds, for, as we shall see in Chapter IX, context is one of the most important determinants of meanings. Understanding of these interrelationships demands a careful preliminary planning and organizing according to accepted principles of rhetorical and psychological and logical construction.

Communicativeness is the direct opposite of exhibitionism or "expressive" language, which are themselves not the same. We may give a splendid exhibition of technical skill in bodily and vocal control, even in the choice of words for emotional effect, and yet fail utterly to establish a contact with the listeners. That was largely what happened to the elocutionists of the late nineteenth and early twentieth centuries. In their concern for technical virtuosity they ignored the principle of reading, as of acting, which is "to hold, as 'twere, the mirror up to nature." Orators, so called, became so enthralled by their own eloquence that they were, as has been said, "intoxicated by the exuberance of their own verbosity."

Technical excellence in speaking, however, is not to be considered lacking in value. But, as between two speakers approximately equal in technical skill, the more successful will invariably be the one who succeeds in getting into close communicative rapport with his hearers, which itself demands a certain skill. Proficiency in the techniques of speaking will add immeasurably to the power and effectiveness of the speaker who is able also to establish and maintain that rapport. The ideal is to develop all the factors of effective speaking to as high a point as possible. The close contact with the audience is not the least important of these factors.

Speaking in Groups

Those interested in the study of social interaction in its various aspects are today paying increasing attention to the phenomena of group behavior, and to the behavior of individuals in groups. A not inconsiderable number of concepts have been built up around these phenomena, designating different types of groups and certain aspects of group behavior. Thus we have *primary groups, play groups, work groups, family groups, task-oriented groups, action groups, study groups, problem-solving groups, coacting groups,* and so on. Not that these so-called types are mutually exclusive; at one time a given number of people may well be placed in one category, at another time in another, or even in two or more at the same time. A primary group, for example, may well be a problem-solving group at one stage of its progress and an action group at a subsequent stage. Somewhat similarly, there are such concepts of group behavior as *group dynamics, group discussion, group action, group attitudes, group mind, group therapy,* and numerous others.

Definition

Perhaps the first consideration in such a presentation is an understanding of what is meant by the group. Although the widespread interest mentioned above is relatively recent, as early as 1909 Cooley described what he called primary groups as "Those characterized by intimate face-to-face association and cooperation." Primary groups are "fundamental in forming the social nature and ideals of the individual. The result of intimate association, psychologically, is a certain fusion of individualities in a common whole, so that one's very self, for many purposes at least, is the common life and purpose of the group. Perhaps the simplest way of describing this wholeness is by saying that it is a 'we'; it involves the sort of sympathy and mutual identification for which 'we' is the natural expression." [42]

Homans defines a group as "a number of persons who communicate with one another over a span of time, and who are few enough so that each person is able to communicate with all the others, not at secondhand, through other people, but face-to-face." [43] Since it is only in the small group that the essential characteristics of the primary group are found, it seems evident that they are basically the same thing. Hence the two terms will be used interchangeably.

Bales defines a small group as

. . . any number of persons engaged in interaction with each other in a single face-to-face meeting or in a series of such meetings, in which each member receives some impression or perception of each other member so that he can, either at the time or in later questioning, give some reaction to each of the others as an individual person, even though it be only to recall that the other person was present. . . . [But] a number of persons who have never interacted with one another do not constitute a small group. [44]

Mere physical presence without interaction is not enough to provide the essentials for group integrity; furthermore, if the number of persons is so large or so widely scattered that they can establish contact only through intermediaries, they do not constitute a group. Bales further recognizes that in some assemblages there may be a few or many who are quite unaware of the presence of others, and therefore do not interact with them. It is only those who remember and are recognized by the others who constitute the group. One might easily infer that the larger the number of people involved, the weaker the interaction among the members.

Perhaps the following statement will meet our needs as a definition of the

[42] Cooley, *op. cit.*, pp. 23 f. The Preface to this text is dated 1909.

[43] G. C. Homans, *The Human Group*, New York, Harcourt, Brace and Company, 1950, p. 1.

[44] Robert F. Bales, *Interaction Process Analysis*, Cambridge, Addison-Wesley Press, Inc., 1950, p. 33.

term: A group consists of any relatively small number of persons meeting either a single time or more or less regularly, and establishing a mutual interaction among the members in a face-to-face situation, in order, through a reciprocal process of exchanging and pooling significant information, opinions, attitudes, to accomplish some mutually desirable objective or to repel some mutually undesirable outcome.

The Group Situation

An analysis of the group situation reveals three major aspects, all of which are necessary to an understanding of group processes. These are (1) the essential characteristics of the group itself, (2) the types of group organization, and (3) the dynamics of the group.

Essential Characteristics.   Throughout nearly all definitions of the group, as well as in all descriptions of the group situation and of group processes, certain basic characteristics of the group seem to be common.

1. The first of these is that the members actually meet; that is, they come into each other's physical and temporal presence. As Bales points out, "a number of persons who have never interacted with each other do not constitute a small group." Furthermore, as was pointed out, when the individuals are so scattered that interaction is only indirect they do not constitute a group.[45] Over and over the "face-to-face" relation is included as an integral phase of the definition of the group. Obviously, this can only mean that the individuals comprising the group have assembled or do assemble at a definite time and in a definite place.

2. The second characteristic is that each of the members of the group is in a position to communicate, in the face-to-face situation, directly with each of the other members. Note again Homans' definition; Bales emphasizes the interactions between each member and every other member. "Recent analyses have confirmed the critical importance in opinion formation of personal contacts between the individual and his fellows. The individual's opinions are formed in the context of his formal and informal group associations."[46]

3. Third, the effectiveness of the group process is a function of participation by all the members of the group. " . . . it may easily be demonstrated that for all classes of tasks any hope of success depends upon an effective flow of

[45] *Ibid.*

[46] Bernard Berelson, "Communications and public opinion," in *Communications in Modern Society*, Wilbur Schramm (ed.), Urbana, University of Illinois Press, 1948, pp. 167–185.

communication."[47] According to Benne and others, participation means that "the individual must play an active part in the planning processes." Certain values accrue to the individual and to the group by such participation. Among the values they cite are the following:

1. Decisions and actions are enriched by the knowledge, insight and imagination of many different people.
2. The plans made and the actions taken are more likely to meet all the varied needs of the people involved and to fit the unique features of the situation. . . .
4. Participation provides opportunities for each individual to learn from his activities. Passivity doesn't lead to growth. As individuals participate in the activities that concern them . . . and learn from this participation, they become more competent and mature. . . .

Democracy must be in the hands of mature and competent people who have grown through responsible participation in their affairs to carry responsibility in ever wider and larger affairs.[48]

Equally important is the fact that in face-to-face exchange of ideas the members of the group learn not only from, but about each other.

Types of Group Organization. Various studies have been made of different types of group organization, based largely upon the nature of leadership and degree of participation. Bradford and Lippitt report on one of these studies. Four types of work group are described, with the reactions of the members to each, and the general effect on production. Of these four the one in which the members were encouraged to participate fully in the deliberations and the decisions with respect to planning work showed the highest enthusiasm for the work, the highest quality and quantity of production, closer teamwork, and "fewer problems of employee performance and motivation."[49]

Similar findings were made by Kurt Lewin and his associates in a study of three groups of ten- to twelve-year-old children in handicraft classes. These three were designated as *autocratic*, in which the children were told exactly what to do; the *anarchistic*, in which they were left to work out all their own problems and make all the decisions themselves; and the *democratic*, in which the leader retained a measure of control, but the children made most of the decisions. In the autocratic group there was a great deal of internal friction;

[47] Alex Bavelas, "Communication patterns in task-oriented groups," *Journal of the Acoustical Society of America* (1950), *22*: 725–730.

[48] Kenneth D. Benne and others, "Participation and democracy," *Adult Leadership* (May, 1952), *1*: 25–27.

[49] Leland P. Bradford and Ronald Lippitt, "Building a work group," *Personnel* (November, 1945), *22*: 142–148.

some of the children left, and as soon as the adult leader withdrew the group began to fall apart. The anarchistic group disintegrated almost immediately. But the democratic group, though it began slowly, built up so much internal stability that it continued to function even after the adult leader withdrew. "The experiment demonstrated that participation and so-called 'permissive' leadership make a stronger, more productive group than either autocratic leadership or a policy of everyone for himself." [50]

McBurney and Hance describe four kinds of groups, the distinctions among them being based in part on the nature of the respective situations, in part on the method of application of the principles of discussion, in part on the purposes of the group. The *learning group* is concerned not only with imparting and discovering knowledge, but also with developing attitudes, skills, social attitudes, self-confidence, and sociability of the individuals of the group. The *policy-determining group* is "one seeking to arrive at a decision which can be translated into group action." From its very nature it "must reach a conclusion which can be set down as the decision of the group," or fail in the purpose which brought it into being."

Coacting groups arise from a situation in which the number of persons in attendance is so large that face-to-face interaction among all members is impossible, in which case a small number are chosen to carry on the discussion, with the others constituting an audience. Often a question-and-answer period follows the discussion itself. In this type of situation the face-to-face factor is maintained among the discussants, but at the same time there is an awareness among them of the presence of a larger group of listeners, who may themselves establish a confrontation with the members of the panel, so that there is a certain amount of feedback from audience to speakers. There are several different subtypes of coacting group situations: the panel discussion, the dialogue, the symposium, and the forum lecture. Each of these has its own characteristics, and its own sphere of usefulness.

The fourth type is the *forum*, which seems to be essentially an extension of the coacting group: information and directions of thought are presented to an audience by means of a speaker or speakers, after which the audience is given the opportunity of participating more or less freely through a question-and-answer period. The forum itself is a long-established institution in America, having taken in its history a number of forms. [51]

Howell and Smith recognize the *round table* and the *symposium* as the two

[50] Stuart Chase, *The Proper Study of Mankind*, rev. ed., New York, Harper & Brothers, 1956, p. 248.
[51] James H. McBurney and Kenneth G. Hance, *Discussion in Human Affairs*, New York, Harper & Brothers, 1950, pp. 271–349.

basic types of discussion conducted by small groups. Each of these has special forms. They constitute fairly definite types of groups in which the element of discussion is predominant. The round table may be used either by a private group, such as a labor-management conference, a study group, a "conference of educators," who are attempting to solve their own problems among themselves, or a group of discussants, similar to the panel, appearing before an audience to present some problem and the various points of view or solutions of that problem to a group of listeners permitted to "listen in" on the discussion.[52]

In all these types of groups the characteristics of the group situation prevail: the face-to-face factor, the interactions among the members, and the participation by all the members, if not overtly, at least implicitly through the operation of feedback.

Group Dynamics.   It is impossible to present here a complete discussion of all the aspects of group dynamics as they have developed during the past quarter of a century or so. The most that will be attempted is an introduction to the subject. It is generally agreed that the pioneer in the movement was Kurt Lewin; he is credited with having originated the term *group dynamics* in 1945. Not that there has been a slavish copying of the principles which Lewin enunciated; but his efforts seem to have opened up the field for later investigators. It cannot be said that as yet any large number of positive principles or "laws" have been objectively established, but there seems to be little question that up to the present time much of the work that has gone into the problem has been fruitful.

At present, research in group dynamics is being conducted in a number of universities, including Harvard, Massachusetts Institute of Technology, Boston University, Cornell, Rochester, Chicago, Minnesota, and the New School for Social Research.[53] Specific training and research centers have been established, such as the Research Centers for Group Dynamics at the University of Michigan and the Massachusetts Institute of Technology; the Sociometric Institute in New York City; The National Training Laboratory for Group Development at Bethel, Maine; The Institute for Social Research at the University of Michigan; the Human Dynamics Laboratory at the University of Chicago; the Tavistock Institute of Human Relations in London, England. One of the best reviews of the literature on the sub-

[52] William S. Howell and Donald K. Smith, *Discussion*, New York, The Macmillan Company, 1956, pp. 161–175.

[53] Herbert C. Kelman, "Group dynamics—neither hope nor hoax," *The Quarterly Journal of Speech* (1950), *36*: 371–377.

ject up to the time of its publication is Haiman's "Materials in group dynamics." [54]

THE SCOPE OF GROUP DYNAMICS.   Just what is encompassed under the term "group dynamics?" A few years ago the complaint was made that "despite the fact that so-called dynamicists are assiduously engaged in doing things together, it is not entirely clear whatever it is they do." [55] But one definition of the term is that of Jenkins: "Essentially, the term group dynamics describes an area of study and research in the social sciences, an examination of the 'dynamics of the group,'" the dynamics of the group describing "the forces in the group situation which are determining the behavior of the group and its members." Among these forces he mentions the motivation of the members of the group, both stated and underlying, the direction which the members want the group to take, the relationships among the members (friendly or antagonistic), any status problems among the members, the question of hierarchy, the goals or purposes of the group as a whole, and so on. Selection of appropriate techniques for any particular group depends on knowing "(1) *the dynamics of the group at this particular time, (2) the goals, values and ethics of the group and its members, and (3) the dynamics of the particular techniques we are considering.*" [56]

Workers in the field of group dynamics recognize that "a fact can be established only through careful use of objective methods of observation, measurement, and experimentation. . . . The use of such methods has accelerated rapidly within very recent years. . . . Perhaps the most important reason for this development is the simultaneous acceptance of two propositions—that the health of democratic society is dependent upon the effectiveness of its component groups, and that the scientific method can be employed in the task of improving group life." [57] Of course, it is also recognized that before engaging in the task of improving group life, a great deal of theoretical and experimental research must be carried on to determine objectively the major facts regarding group life. [58] Before techniques can be developed to improve group life, research techniques must be developed and utilized for

[54] Franklyn S. Haiman, "Materials in group dynamics," *The Quarterly Journal of Speech* (1954), *40*: 201–206.

[55] Robert Gray Gunderson, "The group dynamics furor," *School and Society* (August 18, 1951), *74*: 97–100.

[56] David H. Jenkins, "What is group dynamics?" *Adult Education Journal* (April, 1950), *9*: 54–60. Italics in the original. To these three factors might conceivably be added the persuasive potentials of the members of the group.

[57] Dorwin Cartwright and Alvin Zander, *Group Dynamics: Research and Theory*, Evanston, Ill., Row, Peterson and Company, 1953, p. ix.

[58] Kelman, *op. cit.*

the study of how groups function. Techniques for observing, recording, measuring, and classifying the essential processes of group activity, however, have been and are still being worked out. Only the most dogmatic will insist that these procedures have reached their highest effectiveness; but there seems to be ample evidence that much progress is being made.

PROBLEMS IN GROUP DYNAMICS.   Among the problems in the study of group dynamics is, first, the definition of the group. This subject was taken up many years ago; it has already been discussed here.[59] Another problem has to do with what is called group "cohesiveness." What are the aspects of group behavior which cause the individual to react to it favorably or unfavorably? What are the factors that bring and hold a group together, or cause it to disintegrate? Here again the problem is in part one of definition. Just what do we mean by the cohesiveness of the group? Cartwright and Zander, after reviewing a number of approaches to definition, summarize thus: "At least three rather different meanings may be distinguished: (a) attraction to the group, including resistance to leaving it; (2) morale, or the level of motivation of the members to attack their tasks with zeal; and (3) coordination of the efforts of members." So far as the determinants of cohesiveness are concerned, these writers recognize that much additional research is needed before it will be possible to say specifically what are the conditions that influence cohesiveness itself. Two major sources of attractiveness seem to be recognizable: (1) Does the group satisfy the needs of the individual, and (2) Does the group provide avenues for further satisfaction outside the group itself? But many if not most of the studies which have attempted to refine these inquiries further seem to have encountered problems which for the time being have not been solved.[60]

Other studies that have been made include Bavelas' "Communication patterns in task-oriented groups," already referred to. How and to what extent does a fixed communication pattern affect the life and work of a group?

Do some patterns have structural properties that limit group performance? It may be that among several communication patterns, *all logically adequate for the successful completion of a specified task*, one gives significantly better performance than another. What effects can pattern, as such, have upon the emergence of leadership, the development of organization, the degree of resistance to group disruption, the ability to adapt successfully to sudden changes in the working environment?

[59] Pp. 37–39.
[60] Cartwright and Zander, *op. cit.*, pp. 78 ff. See also Leon Festinger, "Group attraction and membership," *ibid.*, pp. 92–101. In fact, the whole of Part II, pp. 72–133, is an excellent presentation of the problem of cohesiveness, up to the time the book was published (1953).

Such differences in pattern as in all probability do exist are

. . . with respect to (a) the location in the pattern of recognized leadership, (b) the probability of errors in performance, and (c) the general satisfaction of group members. . . . in patterns with a high localized centrality, organization evolves more quickly, is more stable, and errors in performance are less. At the same time, however, morale drops. It is unconceivable that morale should not, in the long run, affect stability and accuracy negatively.[61]

Another significant study is that of Bales, who points out that

. . . it is . . . clear that direct, face-to-face interaction takes place in all . . . groups and there is little reason to doubt that human interaction on a face-to-face level has at least certain formal similarities wherever we find it. Probably it will be recognized also that some more or less identical *problems* of first-hand skills and ethics in human relations are involved for the participants in all. The scientific relevance of the present procedure is based on these minimum assumptions.[62]

Jones, as a result of an experiment in group discussion at Ohio State University, concluded that students with a high school speech background, especially in discussion, seemed to engage more actively in discussion at the college level than did those without. The group which planned its own discussion and chose its own leader was more active than the group whose leader and discussion were given to it.[63]

Haiman suggests still other problems undertaken by various workers in the field. Among these may be mentioned Asch's study of group pressures, Thelen's work on "emotional subgrouping," and others. As Haiman points out, in controversy over "questions of educational and social philosophy raised by *training* programs . . . a very substantial aspect of the study of group dynamics is being lost in the shuffle. It is the part that has to do with the *research* attempts by social psychologists, whether labeled 'group dynamicists' or not, to build a scientifically tested and testable body of laws and hypotheses regarding the behavior of small groups."[64]

Cartwright and Zander have organized their treatment of the general subject, group dynamics, into six major "parts," each indicative of a major area. These are Approaches to the Study of Groups, Group Cohesiveness, Group Pressures and Group Standards, Group Goals and Group Locomotion, The Structural Properties of Groups, and Leadership. Each part develops one of

[61] Bavelas, *op. cit.*
[62] Bales, *op. cit.*, pp. i ff.
[63] R. Stewart Jones, "A procedure for the appraisal of the mechanics of group discussion," *Progressive Education* (January, 1951), *28*: 96–99
[64] Haiman, *op. cit.*

these areas by chapters written by outstanding workers in group dynamics and social interaction.[65]

EVALUATIONS.   The whole concept of group dynamics has been severely criticized by Gunderson, primarily on the basis that "(1) group dynamics is based upon theoretical assumptions which are open to serious challenge; (2) much of the experimental work in group dynamics suffers from subjectivity, inadequately defined terminology, and the use of unprecise measuring instruments; (3) the application of group dynamics to non-laboratory situations (in Lewin's terminology, 'action research') has often produced weird manifestations, if not downright quackery."[66]

As Kelman has pointed out, however, students of group dynamics themselves recognize that for either research or application their field is new in that it deals with an area that had not been explored before. New techniques and tools, both of which are being continually revised and refined, have been necessary.

On the theoretical side, the aim is to develop a conceptual framework which will be adequate for the explanation and prediction of group phenomena. On the methodological side, it is necessary to perfect techniques of observation, recording, and content analysis, which will yield information about social interaction. In all of this work only one assumption is added to the usual assumptions made in psychological experimentation: that the behavior of groups, and of individuals in groups, is predictable and measurable. . . . To be sure, some of the early work is inadequate in certain respects; it represents, after all, the first efforts in an entirely new area. The more recent work is methodologically and theoretically sound. In all of this work, however, the objective is clearly one of developing scientific knowledge about groups.[67]

Chase insists that a body of principles has already been developed, listing six which have been particularly helpful.

1. Identify oneself with other members of the group, rather than play a lone hand.
2. Encourage maximum participation in activities and discussion.
3. Practice democratic or "permissive" leadership.
4. Protect the emotional security of others. Never let a member feel ridiculous.
5. Keep communication lines open.
6. Encourage better listening.[68]

[65] Cartwright and Zander, op. cit.
[66] Robert Gray Gunderson, "Group dynamics—hope or hoax?" The Quarterly Journal of Speech (1950), 36: 34–38; "More dynamics," ibid., pp. 245–246; "The group-dynamics furor," School and Society (August 18, 1951), 74: 97–100.
[67] Kelman, op. cit.
[68] Chase, op. cit., p. 251.

Few of these findings will come as a surprise to one who has been studying and teaching the techniques of group discussion for any length of time. It is in this connection that Chase quotes someone as saying, "There is no adequate substitution for some actual verbal participation of each member."

SUMMARY.   One might summarize the present situation with respect to group dynamics thus: While the study of groups as such is by no means new—it is doubtful if Cooley in 1909 was the first to call attention to their existence and importance—the examination of the forces which influence the behavior of groups themselves or of the individuals *as members of groups* has come to the fore only in relatively recent years. Since techniques for such studies have not heretofore existed, new ones have had to be devised and tested in order to accumulate the objective data necessary to arrive at valid descriptions, analyses, measurements, and predictions. Even terminology, which has been borrowed from various sources, must be refined and given specificity, as in any other science. The assumptions that the behavior of groups and of individuals in groups is measurable and predictable are as valid as any assumptions regarding human behavior would be, in the light of our present knowledge. There would seem to be no insurmountable obstacles to applying the techniques of research that have been established in other fields of inquiry to the problem of the dynamics of groups, that is, of the forces and influences operative in group activity. The fact that such application is being made is evidence that still further application in the foreseeable future may be confidently predicted.

As with many other areas involving the study of human behavior, one problem has been, and will continue to be, the avoidance of cultism and dogmatism. Group dynamics, like general semantics, personality, and communications, is not something to be "believed in" as a matter of faith, but something to be studied with an objective, scientific attitude, in an effort to discover the facts of group behavior, and to learn how those facts may be applied most effectively in the group situation to the end that the goals of people working together may be achieved the more readily. The apostolic concept of faith should not be applicable in such an area of inquiry.

Speech in the Group Situation

It may have been observed that throughout the discussions of group activity certain concepts and principles have been very much in the foreground. Practically all writers emphasize the face-to-face aspect of the group itself as an essential element in its existence. Numbers of persons too widely distributed to come before each other personally, in physical presence, do not, in the opinion of most writers, constitute a group; they must have established "dynamic relationship"; they must be within the "psychological field" of one another; they must be "engaged in interaction with one another in a single face-to-face meeting or a series of such meetings." In other words, an indispensable requirement for the existence of the group is the element of *confrontation* as the term has been explained (see pp. 21–24).

Another essential to the effective proceedings of the group, which has been emphasized over and over, is the element of participation, that is, participation in a situation of confrontation. Effective democratic organization, according to comparisons of different types of leadership, requires that all members take an active part in the deliberations of the group. Participation obviously involves discussion, formal or informal, a term frequently used in describing a major aspect of group activity. Bales' technique includes specific provision for observing the nature and extent of each individual's participation in the activities of the group; at least seven of his twelve "categories" have to do directly with discussion; the others are indirectly related. He speaks of "the issues being discussed." The work of the Bethel Laboratory emphasizes discussion. One is almost forced to the inference that there can be no group activity on the ideational level without discussion in a face-to-face situation.

All of this, of course, leads up to the significance of speech in the activities of the group. Discussion, participation, in a situation of confrontation, *means* speech, for there is no other medium of communication which permits such interaction among individuals. It is true that Bales includes as media of communication such things as "facial expressions, gesture, bodily attitudes, emotional signs, or nonverbal acts of various kinds." [69] And Meerloo points out, "The result of discussion is only partly decided by the spoken word. Gestures, clothing, prejudices, suggestions and pauses play their part."[70] But the visible aspects of speech, particularly when they are directed toward other people as communicative acts, have for generations been included under the general rubric of speech. The Fifth Canon of classical rhetoric, *Pronuntiatio* or *Actio*, was an integral part of the ancient art of speaking. Many of the nonverbal symbols of Ruesch and Kees have similarly been included under speech for a long time. It was Woolbert who pointed out that the manner in which words are uttered, including changes in vocal expression and visible

[69] Bales, *op. cit.*, p. 38.
[70] Joost A. M. Meerloo, *Conversation and Communication*, New York, International Universities Press, Inc., 1952, p. 127.

activities of the body, are not something added to language for purposes of effect, but constitute an integral aspect of spoken language itself, and contribute significantly to the meanings of the words uttered.[71]

Few writers on group activity, however, include a discussion of speech *per se* as one of the basic elements in the "dynamics of the group." Although they emphasize the elements of confrontation (though not by that name), participation, discussion, they generally omit a consideration of the specific medium through which these elements are brought into operation. The effectiveness of speech is a basic problem of group dynamics, as it is of all social interaction. But aside from the literature on group discussion as such, the role of speech in group dynamics has not as yet been treated adequately by those interested in the mechanisms of group behavior.

Perhaps the most complete catalog of criticisms of the delivery of participants in group discussion and debate has been presented by Baird. These criticisms center about voice, action, general manner, and emotional "set" or attitude. Fortunately, no one is likely to have faults in all these areas; but faults in any of them will interfere more or less seriously with the effectiveness of participation in the deliberations of the group. The fifteen suggestions which Baird offers for the improvement of delivery are directed toward the improvement of that effectiveness. Many of them are stated or suggested in the following discussion.[72]

Characteristics of Good Speech

In order to make the most of speech as a means of social interaction, principles of effectiveness must be applied to speech itself quite as rigorously as to other media of communication. We talk glibly of "freedom of speech" without appreciating the fact that the degree of freedom to do anything is determined not so much by legislative enactment as by our own ability to exercise that freedom. Participation in the deliberations of the groups to which we may belong is urged as a vital factor in the democratic processes; but that participation is limited by our own personal control of the means of participation. The most tragic limitation that can be placed on our freedom of utterance is not that imposed by any external restriction; it is that which we place upon

[71] Ruesch and Kees, *op. cit.* This is the point of view of Woolbert's whole book, the subtitle to which is *A Textbook of Delivery*. James Burgh had advanced the same principle almost 200 years ago.

[72] A. Craig Baird, *Argumentation, Discussion, and Debate*, New York, McGraw-Hill Book Company, Inc., 1950, pp. 235–249.

ourselves when we fail to develop within ourselves the maximum effectiveness in our own speech. To the extent that we are unable to use the facilities of our own mechanisms, to that extent do we fall short of realizing the full function of speech as a medium of social adjustment, social integration, and social control.

We do not always appreciate the fact that the modern mechanical and electrical media of communication are effective only to the degree to which the speech that is put into them is effective. The pronunciation of local radio announcers often presents a case in point. *Xavier* is regularly spoken of as *Gzavier* or *Exavier*, rather than *Xavier*, the accepted pronunciation; but when the great French port of Le Havre was called *Le Have-ray*, with the accent of the second syllable, it was nothing short of shocking! Mechanical and electrical devices for the transmission of speech over great distances and to great numbers of people are highly effective in that they will carry with reasonable fidelity and intelligibility just what goes into the mouthpiece or transmitter. But there is as yet no invention that will change a muffled, shrill, harsh, or nasal voice, grossly incorrect mispronunciation, or indistinct articulation, into clear, correct speech. If speech does not start right it will not be right when it reaches the listener.

When we analyze good speech, the speech of educated people, the speech that most adequately contributes to social interaction, we discover that it possesses certain characteristics. Each of these characteristics makes its peculiar contribution to the total impression, so that he who would make the most of his speech in his relations with others about him will do well to develop as many as possible of his good speech characteristics to the highest degree to which he is capable.

It must not be thought that the principles of good speech to be discussed in the following pages are applicable only to public speaking, or to any type of public performance. They apply equally to that sort of personal, conversational speaking that all of us use every day. They hold true regardless of the type of social situation in which we speak or of the particular social objective which may motivate our speaking. It is important, then, that we develop our greatest effectiveness in this medium of social intercourse. The principles are not presented in any particular order of importance; all are important. A shortcoming in one detracts by just so much from the general effectiveness of speech.

Two of these characteristics, purposiveness and communicativeness, have already been discussed in another connection,[73] and will not be further

[73] See pp. 24–37.

developed here. They should, however, be reviewed in relation to their significance as characteristics of good speech.

Agreeable Voice Quality

To be most effective as an instrument of communication the speaker's voice should be of good quality. It should not be harsh, or shrill, or excessively nasal, or possessed of any of those characteristics that will arouse feelings of unpleasantness. Good voice quality is quite often a specific requirement for employment.

Whether we realize it or not, we gain much of our impressions of people, and they gain theirs of us, through the voice. In fact, much of what has been called personality is found, when carefully analyzed, to be resident in the voice. After all, the social significance of personality lies essentially in the way we impress people, and the only way we can impress them is by what we allow them to see and hear us doing. In other words, personality, in its social aspects, is gauged by the favorable or unfavorable reactions we arouse in others. To have pleasing personalities, therefore, is to arouse favorable or pleasing reactions.

In general, it may be said that a pleasing quality of voice consists in the absence of unpleasant characteristics. Among these less desirable qualities may be mentioned briefly the following.

Breathiness.   This has been referred to as a "sort of 'feather-edge' quality; the tone has a fuzziness rather than a 'knife-edge.'"[74] It is probably caused by a failure to bring the edges of the vocal bands together closely enough, either along the whole length of the glottis, or along a substantial part of its length, so that some of the breath escapes without being vocalized. A greater degree of tonicity, especially in the region of the larynx, should help to bring the bands into closer approximation. If this quality is not a matter of habit, but is caused by some substance or growth that impedes the free vibration of the bands, the opinion of a qualified clinician or physician should be sought.

Huskiness.   Sometimes called hoarseness, huskiness is the effect not so much of a specific quality of resonance as of the addition of certain noise elements to the tone, resulting in a lack of clearness. It is entirely possible that some foreign substance is interfering with the normal vibration of the vocal

[74] Charles Henry Woolbert and Andrew Thomas Weaver, *Better Speech*, rev. ed., New York, Harcourt, Brace and Company, 1929, p. 351.

bands. Excess mucus may lodge there, particularly when one is afflicted with a "cold," or with laryngitis, or with some other inflammation of the vocal mechanism. Occasionally small processes, somewhat like corns, form on the edges of the bands, preventing free vibration and resulting in huskiness. Williamson found that "the most common cause of hoarse voice was the throat tensions resulting from the effort to speak at a level far below optimum pitch."[75]

Muffled Tones.   What is called "muffled voice" is usually accompanied by indistinct articulation. The voice lacks carrying power; it seems "swallowed," is dull and lifeless, and lacks the upper tones which give brightness and richness. Precision of articulation will aid in removing the "swallowed" effect. Emphasis on the consonants will inevitably affect the vowels as well, particularly those formed by the lips or front part of the tongue. Shakespeare's advice to the players, "Speech the speech, I pray you, . . . trippingly on the tongue," is as sound today as it was in the time of Elizabeth I.

Shrillness, Harshness.   Shrillness or harshness is almost the opposite of the muffled tone, and results from overtensions in the throat and neck; it is often if not usually accompanied by hypertensions of the whole body. A shrill voice is often found with high pitch, which is also the result of overtension. General relaxation should help to overcome this difficulty.

Nasality.   Many theories regarding the cause of nasality have been advanced.[76] Most of them center about the opinion that it is caused by improper use of nasal or nasopharyngeal resonance. Probably the most common causes, except for such pathological conditions as cleft palate, are (1) insufficient closure of the velum or soft palate against the back wall of the pharynx, and (2) too narrow a mouth opening. A certain amount of nasalization may not be offensive; the conspicuous quality often called "twang" is disagreeable, however, and should be corrected if present.

Optimum Pitch

For every voice there is a general pitch level at which the voice will be found to be most comfortable and most effective. This level will vary for

[75] Arleigh B. Williamson, "Diagnosis and treatment of seventy-two cases of hoarse voice," *The Quarterly Journal of Speech* (1945), *31*: 189–202.
[76] See Joseph P. Kelly, "Studies in nasality," *Archives of Speech* (January, 1934), *1*: 26–42.

different individuals, and each person will find it easily possible to make considerable variation from this general level. The approximate median of the range at which the voice functions most easily and most effectively is called the optimum pitch; it has been found to be about one-fourth the way up from the lowest note one can produce to the highest, in terms of the musical scale.[77]

This "pitch level" is not a fixed tone, by any means. The best voices have, in fact, a wide range; but within this range is a median above and below which the voice rises and falls, always tending to return to the general vicinity of the median. A fairly high or low pitch level is not of itself a handicap to effectiveness; but it is reasonable to presume that this is true only if such a level represents the optimum for that particular voice. It is observedly true that more badly pitched voices are above the optimum than below it. Normally, then, one would expect to find his optimum pitch below, rather than above, his habitual pitch.

Flexibility

It will be recalled that, according to Cooley, many of the advances in the efficiency of the mechanism of communication have to do with "expressiveness," or the range of ideas and feelings it is competent to carry.[78] Since meanings are determined not only by the words themselves but also by the manner in which they are uttered, it follows that a flexible voice will carry a much wider range of meanings and make finer distinctions than one that is monotonous.

Flexibility as a principle of expressiveness is applied in any or all of the tonal elements—pitch, rate, force or loudness, or quality. Lacking such flexibility the voice becomes monotonous.

1. Monotony of pitch may take the form of speaking on the same pitch or in a very narrow pitch range, or of using constantly repeated pitch patterns. Flexibility has the psychological value of stimulation in the form of *change* from a set background—a variation in the pattern of stimulus. When the voice maintains a constant pattern, whether it be of a narrow range of pitch, or of an often repeated inflectional movement, it loses its stimulus value. Furthermore, by uttering all sentences, clauses, or phrases in the same manner, the voice loses much of its meaningful variability.

2. Monotony of "force" or loudness is another type of violation of the

---

[77] Grant Fairbanks, *Voice and Articulation Drillbook*, New York, Harper & Brothers, 1940, p. 169.
[78] *Op. cit.*, p. 80. See also this chapter, pp. 12–13, 15, 17–18.

principle of flexibility. We have all heard speakers who, five minutes after they began to speak, were shouting at the tops of their voices; and they kept up that shouting throughout their speeches. Even as a stimulus to our attention, such a voice soon loses its effectiveness and within a very short time we have lost interest.

Force, as the tonal element is usually called, is applied in three ways: First, by giving to certain syllables in polysyllabic words an extra stress called *accent*. Accent is primarily a matter of convention; it is concerned with correctness in word pronunciation. Placing the accent on the "wrong" syllable results in mispronunciation. Second, a certain word or group of words in a sentence may be uttered with extra stress called *emphasis*. Emphasis has to do with meaning; the emphasized words are deemed somewhat more significant than others; they stand out more sharply. Third, the whole speech may be spoken loudly or softly, depending partly on the requirements of the physical surroundings (size of auditorium, outside distractions, and so on), often because the subject itself and its treatment seem to call for a vigorous or mild approach. Part of the heightened vigor is increased force, as we may achieve a mildness of tone by reducing the force.

3. Again, there is monotony of time. A speaker may use, for example, 120 words per minute; but that does not mean that every second he is uttering two words, no more and no less. Yet some speakers seem to follow that plan. Emphasis may be secured by holding a word or phrase, or an entire passage, somewhat longer than the rest of the utterance. Variations in time may be achieved (1) by varying the "quantity," that is, the length of time a word or syllable is held; (2) by varying the general rate of speaking, increasing, for instance, from 120 to 160 words per minute; (3) by varying the number of pauses, that is, by varying the length of the word-groups; and (4) by varying the length of pauses between word-groups. Adequate variations in the time element are perhaps the most difficult and subtle to acquire, since they are measured in thousandths of a second.

Adequate Projection

The voice must be sufficiently strong to carry to the last row of the audience. Making the voice easily audible to all listeners without apparent expenditure of unnecessary effort is called projection. It is, of course, possible and quite common to speak more loudly than the conditions demand; it is also possible, and equally common, to speak so softly as to be almost inaudible except to the first few rows of listeners.

Projection arises in part from a good voice mechanism properly used; it is influenced also by the attitude of the speaker. It is sometimes interpreted by the audience as indicative of interest, animation, and enthusiasm on the part of the speaker. It suggests an alertness, an eagerness to establish and maintain the contact which is necessary if the speaker is to keep the interest of his listeners. But mere loudness does not of itself constitute projection.

Inadequate projection is often the result of failure to open the mouth far enough to permit the sound to be emitted with sufficient energy to carry. The tone is muffled, rumbling, and though we may observe that the speaker is talking, we are unable to distinguish what he is saying. Failure to provide an adequate breath stream to activate the vocal bands with sufficient force may also be a cause of poor projection. Indistinct articulation, often related to inadequate "breath support," is another possible cause.

Good speech must be more than merely audible; it must be intelligible as well. Adequate projection contributes to both of these desiderata.

Adequate Articulation and Enunciation

For writing to be legible, the letters and words must be distinguishable. For speech to be intelligible, the sounds and words must be clearly articulated. Words must be unmistakable, and instantly so, for speech to be intelligible. Every sound in every word must be given its proper value: the vowels must be clearly enunciated, the consonants sharply articulated. This does not mean that all the sounds must be given equal stress; in rapid speech many sounds, both vowels and consonants, are elided, particularly and only, as a rule, in unaccented syllables. In stressed syllables the vowel should be clear and distinct; consonants should always be sharp when not elided entirely. *And*, for example, is often acceptably shortened to simply *'n'*, as in *men and women*, *give and take* (*men 'n' women, give 'n' take*). One cannot be too free in the matter of such clipping, however; indistinctness is largely made up of such elisions carried to the point of unintelligibility.

A most common social situation in which careless utterance is particularly irritating is in introductions. A name is spoken hastily or mumbled so that it is impossible to catch it clearly, and we are forced to make further inquiry or go through an evening wondering what the name was.

The intelligibility of speech is dependent more on the consonants than on the vowels, whereas the "carrying power" of the voice depends more on the vowels. The difference lies in the fact that the consonants are, most of them, inherently weaker in energy than the vowels. It takes an extra effort, therefore, to make them as easily understood as the vowels, since the latter may be distinguished at intensities, or degrees of loudness, at which the former cannot be heard.[79] Loss of distinctness resulting from loss of control over the organs of articulation appears early in many mental disorders, and to the psychiatrist it has certain diagnostic values. It is also common in alcoholic intoxication, and signifies a marked decrease in the control of one's higher faculties.

Distinctness of speech requires flexibility and agility in the organs of articulation, that is, the tongue, jaw, and lips. Positions and movements of these organs must be precise and definite, with accompanying breath pressure. Furthermore, the sounds must be formed in the right positions. Indistinctness is caused by inadequate movements or positions, incorrect positions, inadequate breath pressures, weak occlusions, or laxity or slowness in moving from one position to the next.

"Correct" Pronunciation

Correct pronunciation may be defined as the pronunciation of the educated, careful speakers of the general region in which a person happens to have formed his speech habits. This definition allows for the differences in pronunciation which we hear in different regions of the English-speaking world; it allows as well as for the variations which we hear within the particular regions themselves. "Correctness," or acceptability, if one prefers the latter term, is essentially a matter of agreement among speakers as to the particular manner in which they prefer to utter words; different general regions have arrived through linguistic processes at different agreements, any one of which, for its respective region, is entirely acceptable. It follows, then, that there can be no "correct" pronunciation except in terms of its acceptability. Actually, the major modes of speech, which are described in detail in Chapter IV, are acceptable anywhere. We commonly speak of "Eastern," "Southern," or "General American." But most characteristics found in one region are also widely current in the other two. All we can possibly mean by these terms is that certain forms are heard somewhat more frequently in those respective areas than in either of the other two. Only a very few forms used in one section are rarely heard in either of the others.

A good dictionary is probably the best guide for the student—or for anyone else, for that matter—in acquiring good pronunciation. Listening to good speakers will give additional ideas as to current tendencies, for pronunciations are constantly, though slowly, changing. As a general rule, the pronunciation

[79] Miller, *op. cit.*, pp. 60 f.

indicated by any good dictionary should be acceptable; if the speaker follows one of them, his pronunciation is virtually certain to be recognized as "correct"; but a pronunciation not sanctioned by any dictionary is less likely to be so.

Animation

Good speaking is characterized by a certain liveliness, an animation, indicative of the fact that the speaker is wide awake, alert, and interested in what he is saying as well as in the saying of it. Audiences like to feel that the speaker is earnest, sincere, honest, both with himself and with them. Animation grows out of the speaker's attitude toward the general situation. It is indicative of keen interest, deep feeling, and a strong desire to share that interest and feeling with his hearers. It shows itself in the general bearing and in the voice. It means an alert, active body; expressive face and eyes, clear, resonant, flexible voice; and clean, distinct, intelligible utterance. The whole physical mechanism is engaged in conveying to the audience those logical and emotional meanings which are at the time paramount. There is no place in any type of situation for dull, lifeless, uninterested speaking.

Ease of Bearing

Perhaps ease of bearing can best be explained by descriptions of violations of the principle. Some speakers are awkward, stiff, unbending, revealing thereby a condition of being ill at ease. Some are immovable; they stand as if glued to the floor; the body is inflexible, the shoulders and arms fixed, the head held rigidly, the eyes fixed and staring. Then there is the speaker who paces to and fro like a caged animal. There is no coördination between what he is saying and what the body is doing. Another type is the slump: the skeletal muscles lack tonicity, apparently, to hold the body erect; the speaker lacks life and animation.

Such speakers make audiences uncomfortable, nervous, ill at ease themselves; the listeners are distracted from what they are saying by what they are doing; their empathic reactions are unpleasant.

One's posture may be formal or informal, depending on the occasion; smoothness of movement is appropriate where smoothness suits the mood, and vigor where vigor is demanded. In any event the posture should be erect, suggesting self-respect though not arrogance; alert but not rigidly tense; relaxed but not slovenly. Unaffected freedom under control characterizes the best speaking.

Absence of Excessive Fear and Timidity

A certain degree of tension is common to all speakers, even the most experienced. Many of the best speakers are, in fact, acutely uncomfortable when anticipating coming before an audience. The inexperienced speaker is likely to feel that his is a unique experience, and that his feelings are indicative of some pathological condition. The truth is more nearly that such tensions, arising at times to the degree of fright, are common, normal, and may even be beneficial, in that they tend to key the speaker up and serve as a challenge to his best efforts. Speaking is not something to be approached with nonchalance, with overweening self-confidence; to be successful it demands the best efforts one can put into it. Absence of all feelings of tension is often due to failure to realize the social significance of the speaking process, to a lack of appreciation of the real problems in presenting a case successfully, or to a wholly wrong attitude toward the intelligence of the audience.

Being nervous, even frightened, before an audience is of itself of little importance; what is important is the degree to which one is able to rise above this feeling, through a keen desire to achieve the social objectives which good speaking makes possible. "Stage fright," if we choose to call it that, is of immediate concern only when it serves *to prevent the speaker from doing what he sets out to do.*

A realization of the fact that such nervousness is common, that it is normal, and that it can be overcome as it has been overcome by all good speakers from the time of Demosthenes, may help to create a wholesome attitude toward the experience, and a determination not to let it dominate one's speaking efforts. Preparation is perhaps the best practical aid in overcoming its effects. Movement, action, are also helpful, provided they are not too vigorous. The tensions in rigid muscles can often be relieved by putting them to easy, gentle work. The development of wholesome attitudes toward the act of speaking should be a further aid in relieving oneself of the effects of excessive tensions.

Semantic Soundness

Language, whether in speech or in writing, is used to arouse meanings in the minds of the recipients of the communication. We hope these meanings will approximate those which we ourselves have in mind when we select and use words. For many of our words there is enough community of meaning that we have little difficulty in being understood; without such a community no communication would be possible. But many of our words do not arouse such correspondence of meaning in our listeners; the associations which have been built up about the words themselves are so different that we cannot be precisely certain what is meant by such words as *truth, beauty, honor, justice*; indeed, it is often difficult for the person who uses such terms to know exactly what they mean to him. Many of these words are so charged with emotional content that they serve only to arouse emotional reactions rather than objective reference. The words are powerful because of the strength of the emotional reactions they arouse.

Our language contains many "stereotypes," terms which are accepted by otherwise intelligent people for their emotional content, with little or no effort to analyze objectively their material referents. Stereotypes call forth judgments often quite at variance with actuality. In stimulating or entertaining speech these often do no harm, so long as they are used to stimulate attitudes generally considered wholesome. When they are used deliberately, with the specific intention of beclouding the understanding and concealing the actual paucity of ideas, the absence of a constructive program, and the presence of unworthy bias on the part of the speaker, they become reprehensible and even pernicious. When stereotypes, or even other terms—words of vague, indeterminate meanings, emotionally surcharged terms—are used deliberately with the intention of concealing the purpose and clouding issues and facts, the speech is semantically and ethically unsound. The problem of semantics in its ethical aspects will be discussed at some length in Chapter IX. For the present let it suffice to say that good speech should be semantically sound.

Among the techniques of group behavior, as of all social interaction, speech must then be accorded a place of major significance. It is the principal medium of social adjustment and adaptation, social integration, and social control. Just as other techniques depend for their maximum effectiveness upon the application of certain minimum characteristics, so also does speech demand that certain requirements be met in order that it may be used to its greatest degree of success. These requirements, as they have been presented in the preceding pages, may be summarized as follows:

Good speech is both purposive and communicative; it has agreeable voice quality; it is pitched at a level which is best for that particular voice; it is highly flexible and has sufficient strength to be heard easily. It is clearly and distinctly articulated and is correct, but not pedantically so, in pronunciation and usage. It is characterized by animation and ease of bearing, and by the absence of excessive fears and tensions. Finally, it is semantically sound.

Listening

Except for almost purely expressive utterance, speaking implies a listener or listeners. It has been pointed out that the purpose of instrumental speaking is to elicit a response. Whenever anything interferes with that process so that the intended response is not forthcoming, it is said that there has been a breakdown in the communication. Such a breakdown may occur in the initiation, the transmission, or the reception of the stimulus, as in the case of hearing losses; or it may take place between the physical and physiological impingement of the stimulus on the sense organs and the motor responses as a result of that impingement.[80] Recent studies have shown that a prolific source of ineffectiveness in communication stems from the listening itself, that is, in the adequate reception, recognition, and interpretation of the speech symbols.

Again, except for expressive utterance, the two most important factors in any speaking situation are what is being said and the person or persons to whom it is being said. The speaker is the medium by which idea and listener are brought together; he "is clear and effective only when the listener understands and responds to him."[81] It is obvious, therefore, that listening is a most vital function in oral communication, taking the same place with reference to speaking that reading takes to writing. We speak, it is true, far more than we write; more than that, however, we listen. Rankin found that for children in Grades Three through Eight, 29.5 percent of the total waking time, or 42.1 percent of the time spent in verbal communication, is spent in listening. Somewhat less time is spent in talking—21.5 and 31.9 percent respectively; in reading, the figures are 10.0 and 15 percent; and in writing 6.9 and 11.0 percent.[82] Heilman found that children in Grades One through Seven spend an average of two and one-half hours, or 57.5 per cent of their daily school time, in listening. Yet with only a few exceptions, writers on educational psychology are hardly aware of the existence of a problem.[83] Evidence that listening continues to be a problem throughout the educational system may be found in the fact that of all college graduates responding to a specific inquiry, one-fourth reported difficulty in listening. In another study "Thirty percent of 1335 college graduates, 39 percent of 703 high school

---

[80] See Wendell Johnson, "The fateful process of Mr. A. talking to Mr. B," *Harvard Business Review* (1953), *31*: 49–56.

[81] Harlen M. Adams, "Listening," *The Quarterly Journal of Speech* (1938), *24*: 209–211.

[82] Paul Tory Rankin, "The measurement of the ability to understand spoken language," Ph.D. Dissertation, University of Michigan, 1926. University Microfilms, Ann Arbor, Michigan, 1952. Publication No. 4362.

[83] Arthur Heilman, "Listening and the curriculum," *Education* (1955), *75*: 283–287.

graduates, and 34 percent of 577 grammar school graduates reported difficulties in listening in interviews and conferences."[84]

College courses in communication "emphasize that the process of communication is predominantly composed of four skills: reading, writing, speaking, and listening."[85] Whether listening is or is not the most important of the four, the fact remains that we do more of it than of any of the others. It would seem, therefore, that it merits more emphasis than it has received. There is an old proverb to the effect that man has two ears and one mouth, so that he can hear twice as much as he speaks.

Yet despite the great amount of literature on the subject of listening, as indicated by the extensive bibliographies, the actual amount of objective information obtained as a result of careful research employing rigorous scientific procedures is so meager that any generalizations with reference to the process would be precarious if not in most instances actually invalid.

Probably the major difficulty in making such studies has been the inadequacy in analyzing the process of listening itself. Inadequate analysis makes definition impossible. J. I. Brown has pointed out that listening consists of not one but many skills. "This opens the way for specific experimentation to determine exactly which of these listening skills are most amenable to training and how they may best be taught."[86] But what these listening skills are we are not informed, except in a very general way.

Inadequate analysis has led to at least three major difficulties in studies of listening. The first of these is the matter of the basic concepts involved, including definitions and terminology. Listening has been defined as "the adequate reception, recognition, and interpretation of spoken symbols." Each of these three components offers a wide field for inquiry in itself. But to many, the term listening refers to little more than the first of these three factors, and might apply equally to hearing the singing of a bird, or the soughing of the wind through the trees, or the clanging of a fire truck bell. Some years ago Wiksell pointed out that "very little recorded effort has been found which attempts to define listening *per se*."[87]

In an attempt to meet the need for a term designating a more comprehensive, yet more specific concept, the word *auding* has been proposed. It seems first to have been used in an unpublished manuscript by Donald Pardee

[84] Wesley Wiksell, "The problem of listening," *The Quarterly Journal of Speech* (1946), *32*: 505–508.

[85] Ralph G. Nichols, "Factors in listening comprehension," *Speech Monographs* (1948), *15*: 154–163.

[86] James I. Brown, "The objective measurement of listening ability," *The Journal of Communication* (1951) *1*: 44–48.

[87] *Op. cit.*

Brown, but received its first publication in an article on listening by Anderson.[88] Subsequently it was made the subject of at least three doctoral dissertations.[89] There does not seem to be in any Indo-European language a word which "denotes hearing, listening to, recognizing, comprehending, and interpreting spoken language."[90] Nor is there "in an unabridged dictionary a word to complement *speak* as *read* complements *write*."[91] It was to supply this need, to designate this specific meaning, and no other, that the term has been coined. Caffrey urges the use of the newer term on the basis that there are too many different meanings for the word *listening* for it to be usable in any specific sense, such as that for which *auding* is advocated, and which centers about the comprehension of orally presented material. ". . . if I read aloud a short factual article from a current magazine, answer questions from the floor, discuss it briefly, and then follow my reading with an objective quiz on the contents of what I have read, I am testing the students' auding." The studies developed from the concept seem to be the first to consider the process of "listening to, recognizing, and interpreting spoken symbols" as a discrete linguistic function, or to examine the basic factors in that process apart from the external conditions affecting it.

Brown, in fact, insists that auding is the primary language ability, out of which all the others develop.[92] His point of view is given support by Révész, who argues that ". . . with children the linguistic function is not first expressed by means of sound or gesture language. It is expressed in the understanding of language . . ."[93]

In view of the diverse meanings attached to the word *listening*, it is possible that a term is needed to denote the more precise delimitation of the concept which would result from a more adequate analysis; certainly such an analysis would tend to clarify the meaning of such term as is finally agreed upon. That the newer term has not been accepted widely, however, may be indicated by the fact that in the past five years of the *Psychological Abstracts* the word

[88] Harold A. Anderson, "Teaching the art of listening," *School Review* (February, 1949), 57: 63–67.

[89] John G. Caffrey, "Auding ability as a function of certain psychometric variables," Ph.D. Dissertation, University of California, 1953; Donald Pardee Brown, "Auding as the primary language ability," Ed.D. Dissertation, Stanford University, 1954. University Microfilms No. 10,347. *Microfilm Abstracts, 14*: 2281; George Bryan Welsh, "An investigation of some predictive factors in auding ability," Ph.D. Dissertation, University of Pittsburgh, 1954. University Microfilms No. 9995. *Microfilm Abstracts, 14*: 2407.

[90] John G. Caffrey, "An introduction to the auding concept," *Education* (1949), 70: 234–239.

[91] D. P. Brown, *op. cit.*

[92] *Ibid.*

[93] *Op. cit.*, p. 44.

auding appears in the Subject Index once, while *listening* appears forty-seven times, almost half of them in 1955 alone.

As a second major problem arising from inadequate analysis, the probability that listening, or auding, involves not one but many skills leads to the further probability that many of the "skills" attributed to listening may not be integral components of listening at all. Either probability introduces potential variables that make any measurement of listening as a single phenomenon difficult. It is conceivable that in measuring some of these skills, and in attempting to improve listening competence, one is measuring or improving not listening *per se* but external factors which may or may not be conducive to effective listening.

That attempts to evaluate and improve these external factors may be entirely worth while no one can deny, provided they are made with due regard for recognized scientific method; no suggestion is intended that the end product of listening—comprehension and retention—might not be improved by increasing the efficacy of these external factors. But careful studies in listening, or of auding, if one prefers the latter term, need, among other things, further research in the analysis of listening as a "discrete linguistic function"; they need, moreover, further research rather than subjective guesses on the influences which affect the process, be they intrinsic or extrinsic.

Such analyses as the following, however, would seem to indicate that efforts are being made to arrive at a more fundamental description of the processes involved in the reception, recognition, and interpretation of speech symbols. The "ten components of effective listening" listed by Nichols are, for the most part, directly involved in listening itself, although in the development of some of them a number of external factors are introduced:

1. Previous experience with difficult material.
2. Interest in the topic at hand.
3. Adjustment to the speaker.
4. Energy expenditure of the listener.
5. Adjustment to the abnormal speaking situation.
6. Adjustment to emotion-laden words.
7. Adjustment to emotion-rousing points.
8. Recognition of central ideas.
9. Utilization of notes.
10. Reconciliation of thought speed and speech speed.[94]

[94] Ralph G. Nichols, "Ten components of effective listening," *Education* (1955), 75: 292–302.

Fessenden does not list such components but presents "levels" of listening:

(1) isolation of sounds, ideas, arguments, facts, organization, and the like; (2) identification, giving meaning to those aspects isolated in Level One; (3) integration of what we hear with past experiences; (4) inspection of the new, and a "general configuration of the new and the old data"; (5) interpretations of what we hear; (6) interpolation of comments and statements that we hear; and (7) introspection.[95]

D. P. Brown approaches the problem somewhat differently, in discussing the attributes of the "ideal" auder:

1. Excellent hearing.
2. Superior powers of phonetic discrimination.
3. Superior intelligence.
4. A disciplined and extensive auding vocabulary.
5. A broad acquaintance with roots and suffixes.
6. A wealth of interests.
7. Habits and techniques of effective inquiry.
8. A method of phonemic notation.
9. Skill in listening.
10. Semantic orientation.
11. A capacity to compensate for emotional and prejudicial distortion.
12. Tolerance for differences in regional and social-class dialects.[96]

Such different approaches as these to the problem of listening are certain to result in different descriptions, which at present are probably not significant.

The third major difficulty arising from the as yet inadequate analysis of the problems involved in listening becomes apparent in attempts to improve listening ability. Most, if not all, programs directed toward the improvement of listening seem in fact to be efforts to better the conditions of listening— the external factors conducive to listening. Unless the basic elements are isolated, it is difficult if not impossible to control the variables that are inevitably present, since listening, even though it may be a "discrete function," is still complex—how complex is indicated by the analyses that have been attempted. Until these basic components are established, it would seem that improvement programs are certain to be superficial. Furthermore, the external factors themselves introduce a number of variables that need to be brought under rigorous control if generalizations with regard to improvement are to be valid. In the present state of inquiry it is not always possible to know

[95] Seth A. Fessenden, "Levels of listening: a theory," *Education* (1955) *75*: 288–291.
[96] D. P. Brown, *op. cit.*

whether those reporting improvement in listening have actually succeeded in raising the proficiency of listening itself, or have succeeded in modifying and improving the conditions that make listening possible.

That the reception, recognition, and interpretation of speech symbols is an important aspect of communication no one can question. That it may be analyzed into its basic components is more than probable. Moreover, it is also possible that as a form of voluntary human behavior it can be improved, as can any other skill. But both analysis and improvement of listening *per se* depend primarily upon a clarification of the concept of listening, together with an objectively determined description of the process. Although significant steps have been taken in those directions, neither has as yet been fully achieved. It has not yet been fully recognized that listening, or auding, is in fact a skill in itself, simple or complex, apart from the external conditions affecting the processes involved, or that as a skill in itself it is susceptible of either analysis or improvement. It is entirely possible that programs of improvement will continue to be limited to bettering the outward conditions of listening, that the "psychometric variables" of which auding is suspected of being a function are themselves unimprovable.

After editing the several articles that went into the "Listening Number" of *Education* for 1955, Hackett arrived at the conclusion that *"There is not enough evidence that listening can be taught."* He continues:

1. We know almost nothing about listening outside the field of acoustics; the valid studies number less than 20, compared, for example, with probably 3000 for reading.
2. There is no basic research because few of us have the training to form testable hypotheses, to prepare the instruments for testing, or to evaluate what we have tested. We lack the scientific rigor; we even lack the scientific inclination.
3. Most of our instruction in listening is of the "hoo-rah" or as John Caffrey says the "chatsy-patsy lend-me-your-ears, folks, variety; much of this instruction consists of 'Listen, damn it!' No wonder," he continues, "so much of our communications research . . . is either regurgitive or soothingly and unarguably platitudinous." [97]

It is probable that many of those in the field of communications, particularly in studies in listening, will feel Hackett's conclusions somewhat harsh and unduly pessimistic.

[97] Herbert Hackett, "A null hypothesis: There is not enough evidence," *Education* (1955), 75: 349–351.

Chapter II

The Physical Basis
of Speech

THE HUMAN ACTIVITY which we call speech consists of the presentation of certain conventionalized vocal symbols, which through long usage have come to have more or less specific meanings to the person using them and to the person or persons addressed. These vocal symbols are often accompanied by visual signs, such as gesture, facial expression, posture, and the like, which in the main are expressive of attitudes, feelings, and emotions, though in addition they often make more specific the logical meanings of the words we use.

Without in the least minimizing the importance of the visible phases of speech, let us for the sake of convenience in the present discussion consider only the vocal, or audible, phases. Even a perfunctory examination of these aspects will show that speech consists of *sounds* of different kinds, which are produced by the vocal mechanism—the vocal bands, tongue, lips, teeth, oral and nasal passages, etc.

These sounds are essentially just like those produced by other sound-producing instruments; that is, they follow the same principles and are subject to the same sort of analysis. They may be described in the same terminology. We do not as yet know everything with respect to the actual manner in which the vocal mechanism operates to produce certain effects; but once the sound is produced, we find that we may describe it according to definite laws of physics and physiology.

The phenomena of sound are important to both the physicist and the psychologist. Because the vocal part of speech is made up of sounds, a study of sound should be of prime importance to the student of speech as well. We cannot study voice and its production or the formation of correct speech sounds without some reference to the phenomena of sound in general; on the other hand, with an understanding of some of the basic facts regarding these phenomena, a study of speech will be more intelligible than it would be otherwise.

Although the physicist and the psychologist both are keenly interested in sound, they describe it from different points of view; they use different terminologies. The physicist thinks of it as an aspect of matter, of motion, of energy; he uses complicated mathematical formulae to determine the relationships involved. The psychologist, on the other hand, thinks of sound as an experience, as it affects the human ear, as it influences human responses, human behavior. His descriptions are based on the way we hear and respond to the physical·stimulus, upon our interpretation of that experience which results from the impinging of that stimulus on our sensory apparatus, rather than upon the physical nature of the stimulus itself.

To the physicist sound consists of physical vibrations of a sound "source," or of disturbances in some propagating medium which have certain characteristics making possible the reception of these disturbances as an auditory stimulus. Whether they are actually so received or not makes no difference whatever in the phenomenon itself. The "information theory," in which communications engineers are at present so deeply interested, is not concerned, according to those dealing with its development and use, with "information" as the term is commonly used, but primarily with problems of the transmission of the signals of communication. Semantic significance of these signals is not involved. To the psychologist, however, sound consists of the perception of vibrations actually received and experienced through the ear.

But while these two points of view are different, there are certain close interrelations between them: what the physicist thinks of sound may or may not be determined by the hearing of it; but what the psychologist thinks of sound is always affected by its physical attributes. As students of speech, we shall more often take the psychological point of view. However, an understanding of this point of view is largely dependent upon some knowledge of the physical factors; in fact, psychologists are coming to realize more and more the importance of a basic knowledge of the physical aspects of sound as a foundation for an understanding of the psychological aspects.

Basic Aspects of Sound

Vibration

However one may consider it, sound always has its source in some vibrating body. The vibrations of this body set up disturbances or "waves" in some transmitting medium such as air. These waves are propagated through the medium and thus carried to the ear, to be interpreted by the listener as sound.[1] What do we mean by vibration, and what are the conditions which may give rise to the phenomenon? What properties of air or other media permit sound waves to travel through these substances?

Elasticity and Inertia.   As the word is used in the study of sound, vibration is an oscillatory motion of some body or substance, caused by certain properties within the substance itself. These oscillations are due to the operation of two principles, *elasticity* and *inertia*. The term *elasticity* refers to that tendency of many substances, when distorted in shape or size, to resume their original form or dimensions after the removal of the distorting force. If the shape of a lump of wet clay or putty is distorted, the lump will retain the new shape without noticeable tendency to go back to its original form; it has volume, but no "shear" elasticity. Loose earth, especially if it is damp, can be tamped into a much smaller space and will remain there. It likewise has very little or no elasticity to cause it to resume its former shape.

If a rubber ball, however, is dented without being cut, it will resume its roundness once the pressure is removed, because of its elasticity. It will bounce from a hard surface for the same reason. A baseball or a golf ball, when struck, will resume its shape so quickly that the resultant force will cause it to travel several hundred feet. Very peculiarly, just as the golf ball has more elasticity than a tennis ball, a steel ball, even though it cannot be distorted so easily as the other, will resume its original shape much more quickly; hence we say that it has much more elasticity. If a thin tongue of steel, such as a hacksaw blade, is bent to one side, it will upon release spring back and become as straight as it was before. Under great pressures many of these substances can be compressed, but once the pressure is removed they will resume their original volume and shape.

Gases also have the property of elasticity. Although they will freely assume the shape of any container into which they may be put, because of "volume elasticity," they may be compressed when pressure is applied and they expand again when the pressure is removed. No matter how many times a gas may be compressed, it never loses its tendency to expand when the external pressure is released. Moreover, the molecules of a gas such as air tend to maintain approximately the same intermolecular distances under any given

---

[1] Under certain conditions, stimulation of the auditory nerve will produce "psychological sound," without the usual physical vibrations. These cases, however, are outside the scope of the present discussion.

pressure. If the total mass of the gas is compressed into a smaller volume, these distances will be reduced, but they will still tend to remain equal. This is generally true, regardless of the space which the given mass is required to occupy. If the space is increased, the gas will expand; that is, the inter-molecular distances will increase, still tending to remain approximately equal. If, by the application of some external force, some of these molecules are pushed closer to their neighbors, they will likewise give those neighbors a similar push, but will also rebound and again tend to resume their former condition of "equilibrium" in spacing, in which the pressures from all sides remain in balance.

The term *inertia* refers to that property described by Newton, by which matter at rest or in motion remains at rest or in motion unless acted upon by an external force. A ball lying on the table will stay there unless it is picked up or pushed to one side. If it is thrown, it will continue through the air until the resistance of the air causes it to slow down and the force of gravity (both external forces) brings it finally to earth. The distance it will go depends on *momentum*, which is a function of the mass and the velocity,[2] and on the resistance (friction) it has to overcome.

Now let us apply these two properties of elasticity and inertia to some elastic body, such as a thin tongue of spring steel, to see how vibrations are set up. If we clamp one end of the spring firmly in a vise, as in Figure 1, and pull the other end to one side (to position *B*), it may be observed that the farther we pull, the more force we have to put on it. That is, the elastic force pulling the spring back into its original position, or the *restoring force*, is proportional to the distance it is pulled aside, or to the *displacement*. This is the principle of spring scales used for weighing: the heavier the weight, the farther the indicator is swung. If we know how far the indicator will swing for each added unit of mass, we can determine the weight of a quantity of drugs, beans, nails, or whatever we may be weighing.

Figure 1. Freely Vibrating Lamella.

If our spring, which is now in position B, is suddenly released, its elasticity will cause it to resume its former shape, which was straight, and it will swing back in that direction, gaining speed as it approaches its "point of rest"

---

[2] The momentum may be determined by the familiar formula, Kinetic Energy equals one-half the Mass multiplied by the Square of the Velocity:

$$K.E. = \tfrac{1}{2} mv^2.$$

(position *A*). But because of its inertia its momentum will carry it beyond that point. As its displacement increases, the restoring force also increases, so that it will gradually slow down until it reaches its maximum excursion on the other side of the midpoint (position *C*), where the restoring force of elasticity overcomes the momentum. Again it starts back toward its point of rest and again its momentum carries it past *A* to *B*. These back and forth oscillations continue with diminishing amplitude, because of internal friction within the steel itself and the friction of the air, until all its momentum is lost and the spring comes finally to rest.

This oscillatory motion of the spring is called vibration; if one considers the separate oscillations, they may be thought of as *vibrations*; the steel spring itself is said to *vibrate*.

The Pendulum. The pendulum is a good example of "slow motion" vibration. In this case the restoring force is not elasticity but gravity. When it is not moving, the bar hangs perpendicularly, the weight remaining in one position. Since there is no displacement, all the forces are in equilibrium. But if it is set in motion, certain characteristics of its movement may be observed as it swings first to one side, reverses its direction, and then swings back to the other side, to begin the cycle all over again.

Just what happens, and how does its motion compare with that of the steel spring described above? Let us start from the extreme position at one end of the swing. As the weight has been displaced to one side, it has also been raised somewhat, because the bar acts as the radius of an arc. The restoring force, gravity, is again proportional to its displacement. As the weight is released, it starts downward and forward, gathering speed and momentum until it reaches the midpoint of its excursion, which is its normal point of rest. Its momentum, however, carries it past that point; but immediately because of the increasing displacement to the other side and consequent application of greater and greater restoring force (gravity), it begins to slow down. It proceeds more and more slowly until it reaches the farthest point at the other end of the swing, where the restoring force overcomes its momentum and it immediately starts back. Again its speed accelerates until it reaches the midpoint; again its momentum carries it past this point of rest to that from which it originally started; whereupon the cycle begins again, each excursion becoming shorter and shorter until it "dies down" and comes finally to rest at the midpoint. We are all familiar with the youthful practice, while swinging, of "letting the cat die."

It was Galileo who first discovered the fact that, regardless of the length of the swing from one side to the other of the hanging lamps in the cathedral at Pisa, the time required for each swing, or its *period*, was always the same. It has since been discovered, also, that the weight on the end of a pendulum does not affect its period. It is only the length of the pendulum (the distance from the point of suspension to the center of gravity of the weight) that has any influence on the time it takes for the swing to complete its cycle. Two pendulums, each suspended by a cord of negligible mass 30 inches in length— that is, with the center of gravity of the weight 30 inches from the point of suspension—but one with a weight of 1 pound and the other with a weight of 1 ounce, will swing with exactly the same period, approximately 1.72 seconds; and if the excursion of one is 2 inches and the other 1 inch, they will still have the same period.

The period of a pendulum may be calculated from the formula,

$$T = 2\pi \sqrt{\frac{L}{G}}$$

where T is the period, L the length of the pendulum in feet and G the force of gravity (32.2), or where L is the length in centimeters and G is the force of gravity in centimeters (980). (This value represents an acceleration each second, due to the force of gravity, of 980 centimeters per second.) The formula also means that in order to double the period of a pendulum its length must be increased four times. Thus, a pendulum 24.8 centimeters long will swing with a period of exactly 1 second; one 12 inches, or 1 foot, long, will have a period of 1.10 seconds. To have a period of 2 seconds, the length must be four times 24.82, or 99.28 centimeters, approximately 1 meter.

Problems [3]

1. Find the period of a pendulum whose length is 64 cm; 20 in. How long must a pendulum be to give a period of 0.75 sec?
2. A brass rod expands .0000193 times its length for each degree C. rise in temperature. What will be the gain or loss in the indicated time of a clock the pendulum of which ticks once each second, if the temperature rises 20° C.?
3. If a pendulum 100 cm long has a period of 2 sec, how long must a pendulum be to have a period of 0.8 sec?
4. A Foucault pendulum hangs 20 m from a ceiling. What is the time of each swing? How many swings will it make in one day? As the earth turns under it, what is the angle between successive swings?

[3] The problems included in this chapter are primarily for the purpose of clarifying and fixing the principles discussed. They may be omitted if the instructor prefers.

The motions of the pendulum and the steel spring are essentially identical. For the elasticity of the spring substitute the gravity of the pendulum, and there is no basic difference between the vibrations of the two. If tracing points were attached to the tip of each and a curve were traced on a paper moving at uniform rate in a direction perpendicular to the backward and forward movement, both curves would be something like that in Figure 2. Mathematically this curve is known as a *sine curve*, because it can be constructed from certain trigonometric functions of right angles. It may also be thought of as a *curve of displacement*, in that it represents the displacement of the steel spring or of the pendulum to one side or the other of the point of rest, at successive instants throughout the cycle. The maximum displacement on either side of the point of rest is the *amplitude*. In Figure 2 the amplitude is indicated by the distance *Aa* or *Cc*.

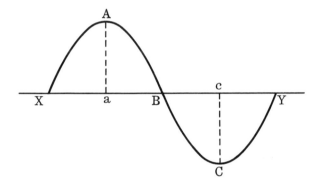

Figure 2. Sine Curve.

Harmonic Motion.   The backward and forward motion described by a pendulum or other vibrator like the steel spring is called by physicists *harmonic motion*, because it resembles the backward and forward movement of a point on the circumference of a uniformly revolving circle when that movement is projected on the diameter. It is beyond the scope of this discussion to show the mathematical derivation of this similarity; [4] it is enough here to point out that both the movement of the pendulum (or other simple vibrator) and that of the projected point on the circle may be represented by the sine curve. The derivation of the sine curve itself from the movement of a point on a circle, as described above, is illustrated in Figure 3. In this figure the successive radii of the circle set off equal angles. Any number of such

[4] If the student is interested in pursuing the question, he will find an adequate explanation in any good textbook on physics.

angles might be taken; here there are 24, each one being 15°. Now let us drop perpendiculars from the intersections of these radii with the circumference to the diameter AC, making a number of successive right triangles around the circle.

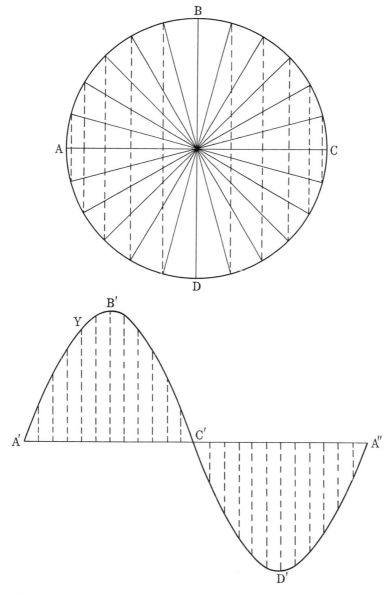

Figure 3. Derivation of the Sine Curve.

The sine of an angle of a right triangle is defined as the ratio between the side opposite that angle and the hypotenuse. Since a radius of the circle forms the hypotenuse of each of the triangles that have been formed and is therefore the same in all of them, the values of the respective sines of the successive angles about the center may be expressed proportionally by the lengths of the sides opposite, that is, by the perpendiculars themselves.

On the horizontal line $A'A''$, therefore, let us erect equidistant perpendicular lines equal to the perpendiculars in the circle. Since these equidistant lines are proportional to the respective sines of the successive angles, the curve joining their ends is called a *sine curve*.[5] The resemblance of the curve in Figure 3 to that in Figure 2 is evident. If a stylus were fastened to the end of one prong of an electrically driven tuning fork, whose movement is very similar to that of the vibrating spring which has already been described, it would trace on a moving smoked paper a curve identical with that in Figure 2 or Figure 3.

FREQUENCY.   Practically all vibrators have a motion comparable to that of the pendulum, except that those which produce sounds vibrate at a much higher rate or *frequency*. The term frequency refers to the number of complete cycles a vibrator makes in one unit of time. With reference to sound this unit is the second. Frequency is the reciprocal of the *period*, a term which refers to the length of time or duration of one complete cycle. If the period of a vibrator is 0.01 second, its frequency will be 100 cycles per second. If its frequency is 1000 cycles per second, its period will be 0.001 second. Frequency is occasionally indicated as *periods per second*, or *pps*; it is usually indicated as "double vibrations" (d.v.), or "cycles per second" (cps).

The minimum number of cycles which can produce audible sound is about 16. That is, if the length of our steel spring (Fig. 1) could be shortened or lengthened at will, thus varying the rapidity with which it vibrated, we should find that an adjustment which would result in about 16 complete vibrations or cycles per second would be the lowest that would give us the sensation of sound. Vibrations slower than this would produce only successive puffs, not tone, and sometimes barely audible.

Phase.   An understanding of simple harmonic motion and its representation by means of the sine curve will make more easily comprehensible the principle

---

[5] The equation for the sine curve in its simplest form is $y = a \sin \theta$, where a may be any constant, usually depending on values within the problem. In the construction of a curve for the sines of consecutive angles, any arbitrary value may be used for a.

of *phase*, which is of considerable importance in the study of certain aspects of sound. Phase may be defined as the portion of a cycle which has been passed through up to a given instant, measured in degrees of the circle.

The points on the curve drawn according to the conditions described above can be given corresponding values in degrees. At point A', which represents A on the circle, we have passed through no portion of the cycle; hence the phase is $0°$, or it is at zero phase. At B' we have passed through one-fourth of the cycle, hence the phase is $90°$, or it is at $90°$ phase. The phase at any point Y on the curve may be determined by dropping a perpendicular from Y to the line $A'A''$, intersecting at Y', and then applying the formula

$$\phi = \frac{A'Y''}{A'A''} \times 360°,$$

where ϕ is the phase in degrees.

If two such curves, or two waves which may be represented by such curves, are at a given instant at the same degree of advancement from a point which has been chosen as the zero point, or zero phase, they are said to be *in phase* at that instant. If two waves, or two curves, coincide throughout, they are in phase throughout: or if they start with a given phase difference, e.g., if one is $90°$ in advance of the other, they will maintain this same phase difference, or phase relation, as long as they last, *provided* they are of the same frequency. Two or more waves having different frequencies are constantly changing phase relations. The importance of these points will be shown later in the discussion of wave form and timbre or quality.

Types of Vibrators.   The kinds of objects or bodies which will vibrate and thus generate sound are innumerable. Most of the more common may be classified in rather well-defined groups, as utilized by many of the familiar musical instruments.

STRINGS.   Typical of instruments with strings are the piano, violin, guitar, harp, violoncello.

MEMBRANES.   The snare drum and the bass drum have stretched membranes which ordinarily are not "tuned" to definite pitches, whereas the kettledrum has a stretched membrane which is "tuned."

REEDS.   The woodwind instruments make use of reeds; the clarinet, saxophone, oboe, bassoon, and English horn, are examples with single or double reeds. The mouth organ (harmonica) and the old-fashioned cabinet or parlor organ make use of a separate reed for each note.

AIR COLUMNS.   A pipe or tube, or any sort of rigid or semirigid container, may enclose a body of air which can be set into vibration. The organ makes use of a separate pipe for each note, whereas the flute and piccolo have holes and stops for varying the length of the column; brass instruments have valves. All make use of the principle of the vibrating column of air.

BARS.   The xylophone and marimbaphone are made up of tuned bars, the former of metal and the latter of wood. In many chimes the tones come from bars rather than from bells.

PLATES.   Cymbals are metal plates struck together.

In addition to these familiar instruments there are a great many other objects which produce sounds: the whistle, for example, the escaping jet of steam, the striking of heel and toe in a tap dance, the drawing of a file across the teeth of a saw, the blade of a saw when a violin bow is drawn across its back edge, and so on. There is a world of variety in the sources of sounds as well as in the sounds themselves as they strike our ears.

Sources of Energy.   It is obviously not enough, in order to produce sound, that we have a vibrator. The vibrator must be set in vibration—there must be a source of energy. This is the second requisite for the production of sound. Let us see how this is applied in the various instruments.

Strings are set into vibration (1) by striking, as in the piano; (2) by plucking, as in the banjo, guitar, or harp; (3) by stroking, as in the violin.

Membranes are set into vibration chiefly by striking, as in the case of the drums. The cone of a radio loud-speaker is a membrane set into vibration by the pulsating action of an electric current.

Reeds are set into vibration usually by forcing a stream of air over them.

Air columns may be made to vibrate either by setting up periodic eddies through the action of a stream of air forced over a thin lip at one end of the column, as in the organ pipe and the whistle, or by interrupting the stream of air by means of a reed, as in the clarinet, oboe, or bassoon.

Bars may be struck or stroked.

Plates may be activated by striking, or, as in the case of the telephone receiver, by the fluctuation of an electric current.

The action of the voice has been thought to resemble the brass instruments more than any other type of sound-producing mechanism, although the opinion is subject to considerable objection. The vocal bands, according to this interpretation, have their counterpart in the lips of the player, and the column of air in the pharynx, mouth, and nose is analogous to the column of air in the tube of the instrument.[6]

Types of Vibration; Damping. The various methods of applying the energy to vibrators, together with the nature of the vibrators themselves, give rise to different types, so to speak, of vibration.

FREE VIBRATION. When a pendulum is set to swinging, it will continue to swing for some time without the further application of force. This type is known as *free vibration.* Eventually, however, it will "die down" and come to rest. Similarly, a tuning fork when struck will sound for as much as two minutes or more; it will also finally stop. On the piano each string (or set of strings) is struck once for each note, and the tone will last for a considerable time if the key is held down. Every elastic system has its own natural period of vibration; if it is set into motion and no interfering force is applied, it will vibrate only in its particular frequency. *Free vibration may be defined, therefore, as the vibration of a freely elastic system in its own natural period, "after all driving forces have been removed from the system."* [7] Its continued vibration is the result of its own elasticity and inertia.

No free vibration can continue indefinitely. Its energy is lost in heat, in overcoming friction, in setting up sound waves, and in various other ways. Some of these vibrations are short, others are of long duration. The vibration of a column of air dies out very rapidly. This dying out of a free vibration is known as *damping.* If the duration of the vibration is long, we say that it has very small damping; if very short, it has large damping. A swinging pendulum, especially if it is long and the bob is heavy, has a very small damping; the cone of a loud-speaker has a large damping, for it will cease to vibrate almost as soon as the electric current which sets it into motion is broken. In fact, its vibration dies so quickly that its movement can hardly be termed free vibration at all.

Three conditions are essential for free vibration.[8] The system must have (1) sufficient elasticity to restore it to its original equilibrium once it has been

[6] But see later discussions in this chapter, and in Chapter III.
[7] "American standard acoustical terminology," *Journal of the Acoustical Society of America* (July, 1942), *14*: 84–101.
[8] Arthur Tabor Jones, *Sound, a Textbook*, Princeton, N.J., D. Van Nostrand Company, 1937, pp. 130 f.

displaced; (2) enough inertia to carry it past that point, and thus back and forth a number of times; and (3) absence of such interfering forces as would entirely prevent that oscillation. In other words, the damping must be small. If the friction which has to be overcome is very nearly equal to that of the restoring force, that is, if the damping is very large, the pendulum will simply swing slowly back to its point of rest and stop there. It will not swing very long in water, for example.

MAINTAINED VIBRATION.   So long as no additional force is applied to the pendulum, as has been said, its swinging will gradually die down and finally stop altogether. If the pendulum is put into a clock, however, and provided with some means by which a small amount of force can be applied each time it swings, and in the direction of the movement at the time the force is applied, it will continue to swing for as long as that force is continued, that is, as long as the spring or weight which supplies the repeated force is wound up. (There are clocks which have been running for generations.) The escape mechanism, actuated by a chain of gears, by the mainspring, or by the weight, gives the pendulum just enough push to balance the factors which would cause it to die down. It is important to note, however, that the pendulum continues to vibrate in its own natural period. *Maintained vibration may be defined as that type in which repeated impulses are given to the vibrator so that it continues to vibrate in its own natural frequency, or approximately so.*

The violin string affords another example of maintained vibration. It has its own natural period and, when the bow is drawn across it, will vibrate in that period. It is fairly highly damped, however, and in order that the tone may be sustained there must be a continued application of energy, which is supplied by the bow. In the *pizzicato* the strings are plucked with the finger; although the pitch of the note is definite, the sound dies out very quickly. The vibration of a column of air of proper length when a vibrating tuning fork is held over it is another illustration of maintained vibration. So long as the fork is held over the open end, the column will continue to vibrate at its own frequency;[9] once the fork is removed the vibration of the column stops. The vibration of the air in the vocal cavities is probably maintained vibration actuated by the movement of the vocal cords. In fact, the action of the vocal cords themselves is in a sense maintained vibration.

FORCED VIBRATION.   *Forced vibration may be defined as that type in which the vibrator is caused to vibrate in the period of an applied force rather than its*

---

[9] But see the discussion on "Coupled Systems."

own. If the stem or yoke of a tuning fork is held on a flat surface, such as a board of some size, the surface will vibrate as long as the vibrating fork is held there. Furthermore, it will vibrate with the approximate frequency of the fork. The diaphragm of a telephone receiver or the cone of a loud-speaker will also vibrate with the frequency of the electric current; as soon as the current is stopped the vibration will cease. It is this characteristic of such apparatus that makes the telephone and the radio possible. "All methods of recording and reproducing sound depend on forced vibrations." [10]

When the frequency and phase of the impressed force approach those of the forced system, the resultant amplitude is increased. Since both the diaphragm of the telephone receiver and the cone of the loud-speaker have their natural periods, "distortion" results when those frequencies, among all others that occur in speech and music, are impressed upon them. A similar distortion may occur in the forced vibration of the diaphragm of a microphone, which in most cases is actuated by waves of pressure coming through the air from a sound source. The frequencies in the complex waves which are near the natural frequency of the diaphragm will cause a disproportionately large amplitude of those components in relation to the amplitudes of other components, so that the fluctuations in current from the microphone do not correspond to the variations in energy in the sound wave.

The sounding board of a piano, which must respond to an extremely wide range of frequencies and still maintain its quality of tone, represents forced vibration. Variations in the excellence of violins are due in part to the skill with which the violin maker has produced an instrument that will produce the particular combination of frequencies, at the particular combination of amplitudes, that are judged to be most pleasing.

It is significant to note that in either maintained or forced vibration, the vibration continues only as long as the external force is applied. Maintained vibration is, in fact, a special kind of forced vibration. Once that force is withdrawn, the vibration becomes, in a sense, free vibration, and will die down at a rate determined by the damping. In most recording and reproducing apparatus this damping is large, so that these free vibrations will not be recorded or reproduced.

Coupled Systems.   Whenever two elastic systems, each capable of independent vibration in its own period, are so juxtaposed that the vibration of each affects that of the other, we have what is called a *coupled system.* It was said

---

[10] Stanley Smith Stevens and Hallowel Davis, *Hearing, Its Psychology and Physiology,* New York, John Wiley & Sons, 1938, p. 9.

above that a tuning fork held over a column of air of proper length will set up a maintained vibration in that column. For maximum amplitude of vibration the natural frequencies of the fork and of the column must be the same; but even if they are a little different, maintained vibrations will still be set up. Not only will the vibration of the fork affect that of the column, but the vibration of the column will in turn affect that of the fork. In fact, "the resonating air column affects the frequency of the fork rather than vice versa." [11]

When this mutual influence is slight, the system is said to be *loosely coupled*, in which case the "pitches of either may be pulled just a little out of tune by the presence of the other." [12] That the length of the air column affects the frequency of a vibrating reed to which it is coupled has been known for more than a hundred years. [13] This influence may be very strong, in which case it is said to be *closely coupled*.

The organ pipe affords a good illustration of close coupling. As the air passes over the thin lip of the pipe, alternating eddies are formed inside and outside the pipe. Those on the inside produce what are known as *edge tones*; in addition, they also set up vibrations in the air column. "The energy of the latter vibrations is so much greater than that of the edge tones that the latter may almost be disregarded, and the vibrations of the whole structure treated as simply those of the air in the pipe. Nevertheless, the edge tones are just too strong to be disregarded entirely, and exert a certain slight influence on the tone of the pipe as a whole." [14]

Other types of wind instruments make use of closely coupled systems. As has been indicated, the air column of a clarinet or an oboe has as much influence on the vibration of the reed as the reed has on the column. Similarly, the lips of the trumpet player are affected by the vibration of the air in the tube of the instrument. According to some writers, the vocal mechanism constitutes a closely coupled system, in which the vibration of the vocal bands influences and is influenced by the cavities in the throat, mouth, and nose. Furthermore, it is also thought that the cavities themselves form a coupled system in which the relationships in the sizes, shapes, and connecting passages contribute significantly to the peculiar timbre of the different sounds of speech, especially of the vowels.

[11] George Walter Stewart, *Introductory Acoustics*, Princeton, N.J., D. Van Nostrand Company, 1933, p. 178.
[12] Sir James Jeans, *Science and Music*, New York, The Macmillan Company, 1938, p. 132.
[13] Cited by E. G. Richardson, *Technical Aspects of Sound*, vol. I, Amsterdam. Elsevier Publishing Company, 1953, p. 506.
[14] Jeans, *op. cit.*, p. 132.

Sound Waves

We have said that the vibrations of various bodies set up disturbances, or waves, which are carried in some transmitting medium to the ear. Since the nature of these waves may easily be misunderstood, some explanation is necessary for a clear concept of what goes on in the transmission of sound. The most common medium through which sound is propagated is air; we shall, therefore, confine our explanation to a description of sound waves in air.

We are all familiar with the effect when we throw a stone into a quiet pool of water. The pattern of ripples, beginning at the point where the stone enters the water, moves outward in concentric circles until it is broken up either by the shore or another interfering body, or until it dies out because all the energy has been used up in the "work" of moving the successive particles of water. Most of us are also somewhat familiar with the usual "pictures" of sound waves, which consist of certain types of curves—some of them simple, smooth curves, others highly irregular. These pictures more or less resemble the waves produced on the surface of the water; and partly for this reason it is very easy to get the erroneous impression that sound waves themselves are similar to those of water.

In at least one particular, however, sound waves do resemble waves in water. As we look at the ripples moving outward from the point of disturbance, it appears as if the water itself were moving outward, when as a matter of fact it is not moving forward at all. If some small, light object is placed on the surface, it will rise and fall with the movement of the water; but when the ripples have died down, the object will be just where it was in the first place. It is the *wave* and not the water which travels over the surface. In a somewhat similar manner the particles of air in a sound wave simply oscillate back and forth; they do not travel forward with the wave. When the sound dies down, each particle is just where it was before it was disturbed. Again, it is only the *wave* which is transmitted through the air. It is a longitudinal wave, in that the particles in the medium are displaced to and fro in the line of propagation of the wave itself. In a *transverse* wave, as in a vibrating string, the displacement is perpendicular to the line of propagation.

The customary curves used by the physicist and the psychologist to represent sound waves are not true "pictures" of sound waves at all. They do not give a visual reproduction; a sound wave would not look like one of these curves, even if we could see it. The curve is merely a graphic representation of the movement of the vibrator itself, or of certain conditions in the air while the sound wave is passing through it.

Compression and Rarefaction

Consider a series of equal masses separated by springs of equal character-istics (Figure 4). If mass A is moved forward closer to B, unequal stresses are set up among the several springs. In order to restore an equilibrium in these stresses, this movement of A will be communicated to B and cause it also to move forward. The forward movement of B is communicated through its spring to C, which in turn is moved closer to D, and so on to the end of the series. Since each mass starts to move only when the spring has been com-pressed slightly, the result is a series of consecutive movements of the masses, or a *wave*, which, starting with the movement of A, travels all the way down the line. Since these successive approximating movements of the masses were produced by compressions in the springs separating them, the wave is called a *wave of compression*.[15]

Now if, instead of moving mass A closer to B, we pull it away slightly, the

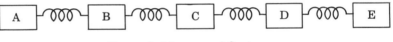

Figure 4. Masses and Springs.

distance between A and B will be increased and again unequal stresses in the springs will be created. But the pull of the spring will tend to restore that equality and will therefore exert a pull on B, causing it to move backward. This movement will increase the distance between B and C, resulting in a backward movement of C, and so on down the line. The resulting series of consecutive separating movements of the masses may be thought of as a *wave of rarefaction*, since the masses are moved farther apart, the spaces being, so to speak, "rarefied."

When mass A is moved closer to B, an additional effect may be observed. Not only is B moved forward by the compression of the spring, but if all the masses are free to move to and fro, except for the push or pull of the spring, the same compression also causes a rebound in mass A, so that after it has given its impulse to B and started a wave of compression down the line, it swings backward, increasing the distance to B. Its momentum carries it past its normal point of rest and its backward movement creates a backward pull on B. This pull, added to the rebound from C, causes B likewise to move backward past its point of rest, separating it from C. Thus a wave of rare-

15 Adapted from Alpheus E. Smith, *The Elements of Physics*, New York, McGraw-Hill Book Company, 1938, pp. 184 f.

faction is started down the line closely following the original wave of compression. By this time the pull on the spring between A and B has caused A again to move forward past its point of rest, starting another wave of compression; and again its rebound sets up a following wave of rarefaction, each mass being alternately pushed and pulled on either side of its normal point of rest until all the energy is lost, as in the case of the pendulum or the vibrating steel spring. The masses finally come to a stop at their points of rest and the springs are in equilibrium, with all their stresses balanced.

In this sort of apparatus the masses represent the minute particles of which a gas, or any other elastic substance in which sound waves may be set up, is composed, and the springs the elasticity, or tendency of the substance to maintain the same relative distance between the particles. If in such a gas as air, for example, one particle is pushed closer to the next one, its movement will be communicated through elasticity to its neighbor, and so on down in a wave of compression until something takes place (usually friction or reflection) to stop the movement. Similarly, if one of these particles is pulled slightly away from the next one, its backward movement will also be communicated down the line in a wave of rarefaction.

Sound waves are composed of these alternating waves of compression and rarefaction in some elastic medium such as air, or metal, or wood, or glass. A vibrator, such as a tuning fork, being set into vibration, gives to the particles surrounding it, in the case of air, alternating pushes and pulls, thus setting up conditions readily represented by those in the masses and springs. The air particles oscillate back and forth because of elasticity and inertia, and the resultant wave or pattern moves outward from the source, not in circles, as in the case of waves in water, but in concentric *spheres* of alternating condensation and rarefaction.

The backward and forward movement of the air particles in a sound wave follow very closely the backward and forward movements of the vibrator itself. If the vibrator moves in simple harmonic motion, the particles in the transmitting medium will also move in simple harmonic motion; if the motion of the vibrator is more complex, as it is in most sound-producing mechanisms, the movements of the particles will be correspondingly complex. For the present we are concerned only with simple harmonic motion; more complex types will be discussed later in this chapter.

Cruva's Disc.   An interesting little device known as Cruva's Disc shows very effectively how these alternating waves of condensation and rarefaction occur. It represents a cross section of the spheres mentioned above, and consists simply of a series of eccentric circles of increasing diameters, with the successive centers taken about the circumference of a very small circle, itself at the center of the whole pattern. As the disc is slowly revolved, the circles, seen through a narrow slit along a radius, seem to move alternately to and from one another in much the same way as do the particles of air in a sound wave; but the total *pattern* of approach and withdrawal moves slowly outward to the circumference of the disc, or inward toward the center, depending on the direction of rotation of the disc (see Figure 5).

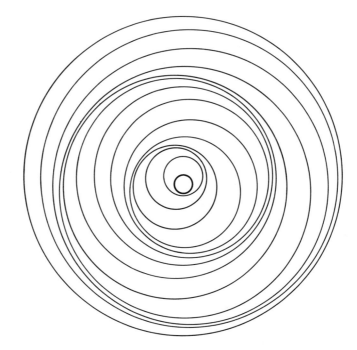

Figure 5. Cruva's Disc.

The Ripple Box. Another interesting method of showing how these patterns are formed is by the use of what is known as a *ripple box*. This is simply a shallow box of fairly large dimensions filled with water. A strong light from above is so directed as to throw a reflection from the surface of the water to a screen or wall. As the surface of the water is disturbed, alternating patterns of light and shadow move across the screen. The shadows may be considered as representing the phase of compression, and the highlights the phase of rarefaction.

The Helix.   Still a third instrument will aid further in forming a conception of the true condition within a sound wave. This consists of a long helix, or open coil, of spring wire, suspended horizontally at each turn of the coil from a solid support. If the end coil is given a light blow there will be seen, moving down the length of the helix, a pattern of alternating approach and withdrawal which represents very clearly the pattern of condensation and rarefaction. If a small light is attached to each coil, the movement of the lights back and forth clearly suggest the movement of the particles of air in a sound wave.

Sound Wave Curves

The curves used to represent sound waves are really graphs, which may indicate any one of various conditions in the wave. In discussing the sine curve in connection with the motion of a pendulum or a simple spring vibrator, it was pointed out that such a curve could be used to graph the *displacement* of the pendulum or of the spring to one side or the other of its point of rest. Such a curve could also be used to represent the displacement of a single one of the particles of air on either side of its point of rest, from the time it was given its initial push, through its forward swing, its rebound, and back to its original starting point. In Figure 2, X would represent the position of equilibrium, A its farthest forward movement, B the position when it passed through the point of rest on the rebound, C its farthest backward excursion, and Y the position when it again passed through the point of rest on the way forward. To indicate a series of such vibrations or waves, the curve would be repeated as many times as necessary.

It will be observed that the above description applies to the movement of a single particle through the duration of one complete cycle. The line XY in this case represents one period, or the time it takes for one cycle. The same curve could also be used to graph the displacement of all the particles in a wave at a given instant. The particle at X is in equilibrium, or at its point of rest, moving in the direction in which the wave is traveling. At A the particles are displaced their greatest extent forward. At B they are again in equilibrium but moving backward, and at C they are at their farthest backward displacement, that is, opposite to the direction in which the wave is moving. At Y they are again in equilibrium and again moving in the direction of the wave. In this case the line XY indicates the distance between identical phases, or one wave length, of the cycle.

Again, the curve may represent conditions of *pressure* at successive instants of time. Obviously, when the particles approach one another there is greater pressure; when they are closest the pressure is greatest, and when they are farthest apart the pressure is at its minimum. Let the line XY represent the period of the cycle. The point X, then, represents normal pressure when the particles are in a state of equilibrium. As the particles approach one another the pressure increases, as indicated by the rising curve. At A the pressure is at its maximum. At B the particles have again swung back to equilibrium, coming to their minimum pressure at C. At Y the pressure is again normal.

The curve may also indicate a simultaneous condition of pressure throughout the entire length of the wave. Let the distance XY represent the length of the wave, that is, the distance between identical phases of the wave. At point X the pressure is normal. As we approach A along the length of the wave the pressure gradually increases until at A it is at its maximum. As we move farther along the wave the pressure gradually decreases until at B it is normal again. It continues to decrease until we get to C, where it is at its minimum, or where rarefaction is greatest. From there it begins again to increase until at Y it is normal once more and the cycle begins all over again.

It will not be necessary to go into full details of all the different aspects of the wave such a curve may represent; the few examples which have been given will help to clarify the point that these curves which are used to describe sound waves are not in any sense pictures of the wave; they do not represent reproductions of waves, but are merely graphic descriptions of the varying conditions of displacement, pressure, and so on, in the wave.

Velocity

We are all familiar with illustrations of the fact that sound is not transmitted instantaneously, but that it takes time for a sound wave to travel from its source to the listener. We see the flash of lightning, and a few seconds later comes the rumble or crash of the thunder, depending on how far away the phenomenon occurred. At a distance a column of marching soldiers may appear to be entirely out of step with the band, and the band itself is not keeping time with the drum major at all. As they approach us, all three—marching men, music, and drum major—gradually get closer together until, when they are passing immediately in front of us they are in perfect time. None of them has changed; from their points of view, or rather of hearing, they have been together all the time. We have experienced a nice example of relativity. We have seen the beat of the baton and the step of the men in a column an appreciable time before the corresponding notes from the band could reach us.

A sound wave, as has been pointed out, consists of a pattern of alternating compressions and rarefactions, traveling through a propagating medium, such as air. It was noted that in the case of the series of masses connected by springs, it took a short time for the initial impulse given to mass A to be communicated to mass B, and so on down the line. In much the same way, it takes a little time for the initial impulse given to the particles of air by a vibrator to be communicated to the next one, and so on. Hence it takes an appreciable time for the total pattern of compression and rarefaction to be transmitted for any distance. The speed at which this propagation takes place is known as its velocity. *Velocity may be defined, therefore, as the distance which a sound wave will be transmitted or propagated through a given medium in a single unit of time.* The customary unit of time is the second, and the velocity itself is usually expressed in feet or meters per second; in the case of light it is expressed in miles per second.

Different media transmit sound at different velocities, depending on the density and what is called the *volume elasticity* of the given medium. Under normal conditions, sound is propagated through the air at a velocity of approximately 1135 feet per second. According to Stewart, the velocity of sound in air at 0° centigrade (usually written 0° C.) is very nearly 331.5 meters per second.[16] Other authorities give figures of 331.41, 331.45, and 331.6 meters per second.[17] According to Miller, the evidence from the most careful investigations indicates a velocity of 331.36 meters per second "under standard conditions," that is, at 0° C.[18] Miller also gives evidence that the velocity of very loud sounds decreases at great distances. In liquids the velocity is much greater: in distilled water at 31° C. it is given as 1500 meters per second, and in sea water at 13° C. it is given as 1492.3.[19] In most metals the velocity is still greater. In copper at 20° it is 3560; in cast steel at 20° it is 4990; whereas in lead, which has a high density but a low elasticity, it is only 1229. (These data are in meters per second.) Many of us are familiar with the effect produced when a section gang several hundred yards down

[16] Stewart, *op. cit.*, p. 17.
[17] To convert meters to feet approximately, multiply by 3.3. For a closer approximation, multiply by 3.28.
[18] D. C. Miller, *Sound Waves, Their Shape and Speed*, New York, The Macmillan Company, 1937, pp. 147 ff.
[19] See Richard K. Brown, "Measurement of the velocity of sound in the ocean," *Journal of the Acoustical Society of America* (January, 1954), *26*: 64–67. According to Brown, the velocity varies from 4750 to 5050 ft/sec, depending on pressure and temperature, as well as on salinity.

the track is driving spikes. We can hear the blow through the steel almost instantly, but it takes fifteen times as long for the sound to come to us through the air!

Normally, all sounds, regardless of pitch, travel through the air at the same velocity. This can be observed by listening to a marching band. Except for the fact that some frequencies do not carry so far as do others, still, if it is a good band, it loses none of its harmony as it approaches or recedes. If the sounds at different pitches traveled at different velocities, there would be times when the harmony would be destroyed because the tones from the various instruments, the piccolo and the tuba, for example, would reach us at different times. This point will be seen even more clearly when, in our study of timbre or quality, we realize that the tone from a single instrument really consists of a great many different tones blended together.

Under certain conditions, however, the velocity of sound varies from the figures given. Thus, sounds of extremely high intensity may travel faster than do those of normal intensity. The sound of an explosion, as of a large gun, has a higher velocity near the gun than it has at some distance away.[20] Similarly, the sound from an electric spark of high intensity travels at a greater velocity near the spark than farther away. But since the sounds of speech do not reach these high intensities, this fact is of no more than passing interest. We may assume the velocity of sound, as used in speech, to be, under the usual conditions under which we speak, very close to 1135 feet, or 346.03 meters, per second. At 72° F., or 22.2° C., it will be 1130.46 feet, or 344.65 meters, per second.

Apparently the only factor which causes an appreciable change in the velocity of such sound waves is temperature. It has been determined, both theoretically and experimentally, that for each degree centigrade rise in temperature, the velocity increases by about 0.6 meter per second. That is, assuming the velocity at 0° C. to be 331.36 m/sec (meters per second), at 27° C. it will be $331.36+(0.6\times 27)$, or 347.56 m/sec. For each degree Fahrenheit rise, the velocity increases by about 1.09 ft/sec. Thus, if the velocity at 32° F. is 1086.86 ft/sec, at 90° it will be $1086.86+(58\times 1.09)$, or 1150.08 ft/sec.[21] This effect of temperature on velocity is of special importance in the measurement of cavity resonators or in the tuning of a pipe organ.

---

[20] Miller, *op. cit.*, chap. VIII, gives an interesting account of experiments with the sounds from large caliber guns.

[21] In scientific work measurements are usually in a metric system; temperatures are measured in degrees centigrade, in which water freezes at 0° and boils at 100°. To convert centigrade to Fahrenheit, apply the formula $F=9/5\ C.+32$. Conversely, to change Fahrenheit to centigrade, the formula is $C=5/9(F-32)$.

Problems

1. A hunter at the bottom of a canyon whose walls are 8000 feet apart fires a shot. He hears the echo from one side $2^1/_2$ sec later than the echo from the other side. If the temperature is 87° F., how far is he from each wall?

2. A band is marching with a cadence of 128 steps per minute. How far will it be from the listener when the right foot of the marchers, instead of the left, seems to the listener to be exactly with the down beat of the music? The temperature is 72° F.

3. The sound from a section gang working on the steel rails of a railroad reaches the listener through the air 2.5 sec after it has reached him through the rail. How far away are the workmen ($t = 0°$ C.)?

4. How long before a sound is started down the steel rails must another sound be started through the air in order for both to reach the listener a mile down the road at the same time?

5. Sound waves are reflected from the bottom of the ocean in order to determine the depth of the water. If it takes 5 sec for a wave to be reflected back to the ship, how deep is the water?

6. A workman strikes a blow with a hammer on one end of a steel pipe 750 m long. Another workman at the other end hears two sounds, one through the pipe and the other through the air. How far apart are the two sounds in time ($t = 25°$ C.)?

7. At what temperature is the velocity of sound 346 m/sec? 1145 ft/sec?

Wave Length

Assume a velocity of sound in air to be 1100 ft/sec and a sound having a frequency of 200 cps. (What would be the temperature?) It is obvious that by the time the first wave has traveled the distance of 1100 feet, the vibrator has sent out some 200 waves, all traveling at the same velocity. There are in those 1100 feet some 200 waves of compression and rarefaction, all spaced equally over the entire distance. From the point of maximum compression in one wave to the point of maximum compression in the next wave must be therefore 1/200 of 1100 feet, or 5.5 feet. Similarly between *any* two homologous points on adjacent waves the distance must be the same, 5.5 feet. *This distance between points of identical phase in two adjacent waves is the wave length of that particular sound.* That is, in Figure 2 (p. 72), the distance XY represents one wave length.

The wave length is dependent on, first, the frequency, and second, the velocity. It is found from the formula, $l = v/f$; in which case $f = v/l$ and $v = l \times f$, where l is the wave length (sometimes expressed by the Greek letter λ), v the velocity of sound, and f the frequency. The higher the frequency the shorter the wave length; a sound with a frequency of 500 cps, if the velocity were 1100 ft/sec, would be 2.2 ft. One of 440 cps would have a wave length of 1100/440, or 2.50 ft.

The frequency of a sound wave does not change in passing through different transmitting media. The pitch of the note is the same, whether we hear it directly through the air, or through closed windows, or through a wall. But the sound will travel through most of these other media with different velocities. If the velocity increases, the wave length increases also. Thus, a sound of 440 cps transmitted through steel, which would have a velocity of 4990 meters per second, would have a wave length of 11.34 meters, or more than 37 feet. Again, since the velocity increases with temperature, so also does the wave length. At 0° C. the wave length of a sound of 256 cps would be 331.36/256, or 1.294 m; at 27° C., when the velocity is 347.36 m/sec, the wave length would be 1.36 m.

Problems

1. What are the wave lengths of the tones at the lower and upper limits of audible sound (temperature 72° F.)?
2. Find the wave lengths for frequencies of 256, 384, 440, 750 cps at temperatures of 54° F., 67° F. 90° F., 29° C.

Resonance

While for the production of sound only two elements, a vibrator and a source of energy, are necessary, in most musical instruments as well as in the voice a third element is required. An unaided vibrator, such as a clarinet reed or a piano string, will produce a sound, but it is often very weak and unsuited for musical purposes. Some method must be adopted to make possible the translation of the energy given off by the vibrator into air waves that are more audible. If the energy in the vibrating string, for example, can be used to activate some sort of additional vibrator that will give off a more powerful tone, we may say that the sound of the string has been resonated. The principle of resonance may be stated thus: *When a periodic force is applied to an elastic system, the system will tend to vibrate with the frequency of the applied force. The nearer the periodic force is to the natural frequency of the elastic system, the greater will be the resulting amplitude of vibration.* When this amplitude is at its maximum so that the sound is at its loudest, we have what is commonly called resonance. "Resonance occurs whenever there is impressed upon a body the frequency at which it would vibrate if set in motion and then left to itself." [22]

A company of marching troops, keeping step with regular cadence, may set a strong bridge to swinging with such vigor that the limits of safety are passed and the bridge will collapse. For that reason troops always break step when crossing a bridge.

The principle as stated above is commonly applied in three different ways and these are often given different names.

Sympathetic Vibration

If one of two tuning forks of equal frequency placed near each other is struck and then its vibration is stopped, a sound can be heard from the second fork. It has been set into *sympathetic vibration* by the very small amount of energy in the sound waves from the first fork. Similarly, if one holds down a piano key, sympathetic vibrations may be induced in the released string by singing a loud note in the same frequency as that of the string, even though the latter has not been struck by the hammer. Although sympathetic vibrations do occur, they are not ordinarily of sufficient loudness to be significant.

The "Sounding-Board" Effect

A second application of the principle of resonance may be noted in forced vibration, in what has been termed the *sounding-board effect*. The waves from the oscillating tuning fork are of low amplitude; they disturb the air only a little. But if the stem of the fork is placed on a table or other resilient surface of considerable dimensions, setting this body into vibration, the air is disturbed over a larger area and the resulting tone is made much louder. Consider the vibrating fork illustrated in Figure 6. At rest the prongs take the position indicated by *AA*, and the yoke is in the position of the solid arc at *O*. As the prongs move inward together, toward *BB*, the arc at *O* is forced downward by a powerful leverage action and the surface on which the stem rests is pressed downward from *A'* to *B'*. When the prongs move toward the position *CC*, the yoke is brought upward, and the surface on which the stem rests comes to the position *C'*. The resulting vibration of the surface brought about by the leverage of the yoke of the fork sets into vibration the air over a large area, with the result that the sound as heard is very strong.

[22] Stevens and Davis, *op. cit.*, p. 8.

The strings stretched tightly across the bridge of a violin operate in much the same way. Although their transverse movement is not great, when they are bowed they exert tremendous variations in force on the bridge, and through it set into powerful vibration the body of the instrument. The strong tones of the piano are made possible by the action of the strings on the sounding board.

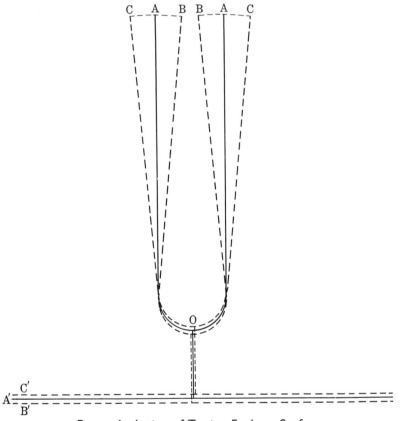

Figure 6. Action of Tuning Fork on Surface.

In the forced vibration of a surface or sounding board, the vibration of the fork or the strings is communicated directly through some rigid but elastic body, such as the bridge, to the "sounding-board," so that the body vibrates with approximately the frequency of the impressed force. It is the sounding board itself which gives out the tone of great power. The phenomenon is considered by some to constitute amplification, but not resonance in the strict sense of the word. However, as commonly used, the word *resonance* may apply to amplification either by cavity resonance or by the sounding board.

Cavity Resonance

The principle of resonance is applied in a third manner known as *cavity resonance*, which is a case of maintained vibration. A vibrating tuning fork held in the hand will give a barely audible tone. But if it is held over the open end of a tube of proper length or over the mouth of a jar or bottle of the right size, the resulting tone will be quite strong and can be heard for some distance. The tube or bottle is a resonator. In it is a body of air capable of vibrating with a definite frequency, which may be determined by blowing across the mouth of the container. The very small energy from the fork is enough to set the air column or body into vibration, just as the marching of troops may be enough to set a bridge to swinging. As a result of the two vibrations being superimposed one upon the other in the same phase, the forces are released into the air with considerable vigor. The waves from the fork, too weak to be heard, are added to those from the body of air, producing a resulting wave of much greater amplitude.

A resonator does not add energy; it merely permits the energy of the vibrator to be used up more rapidly. A tuning fork without a resonator may sound for as long as a minute and a half; in the presence of a resonator it may vibrate no longer than ten seconds.[23] The reason why the presence of a resonator reduces the duration of vibration is obvious. When a vibrator or any other source of energy acts upon a mass so that an acceleration in the mass results, the vibrator itself is doing "work" and is using up energy. The greater the mass or the greater the acceleration, the more rapidly the energy is used up. Hence a free vibrator with a resonator will vibrate for a shorter time than will one without a resonator.

When the vibrating tuning fork is held over a tube open at both ends, one end of which is immersed in a jar of water, it will be found that by moving the tube up and down in the water a certain length will be found which will give the maximum loudness amplitude of the sound. If a fork of different frequency is used, another length of the tube must be found to give the maximum resonance. In fact, for each frequency a certain length will be found to be most effective in producing the greatest intensity of tone. If bottles or flasks are used, each frequency will have its own most effective size. This law can therefore be stated: *For every frequency there is a certain size of resonator that*

[23] Stewart, *op. cit.*, p. 87.

will give the maximum resonance; *the lower the frequency, the larger the cavity.*[24] This law, with its modifications to be explained below, tends to explain the principle of the optimum pitch of the voice.[25] Since the principal resonator of the human voice, the pharynx or throat, is of a given size for each individual and is subject to only small adjustments in size to retain a balance in muscular tensions, it is evident that the individual's average vocal pitch should be chosen at the frequency level at which the pharyngeal cavity can resonate with maximum efficiency, or without undue tensions in the muscles governing its size. (But see the discussion of resonance in Chapter III, pp. 183–188.)

Resonance in Tubes.   The natural frequency of a tube may be determined from its length. If one end is closed, it will resonate with maximum amplitude a tone whose wave length is four times that of the tube itself.[26] It will be recalled that, because velocity varies with temperature, so also does the wave length. It follows that the frequency of a tube will also vary with the tempera-ture. Thus, to give maximum resonance to a tone having a frequency of 256 cps (end correction omitted), a tube closed at one end must have a length of 32.35 cm at a temperature of 0° C., whereas at 25° C. its length will be almost 1.5 cm longer, or 33.8 cm.

A tube open at both ends, on the other hand, resonates with maximum amplitude a sound having a wave length twice that of the tube itself. There-fore, at the temperatures mentioned above, in order to give maximum resonance to a tone having a frequency of 256 cps, a tube open at both ends must have a length of 64.7 cm at 0° C., or 67.6 cm at 25° C., the end cor-rection again being ignored.

Problems

1. An open organ pipe 128 cm in length is tuned correctly when the temperature is 18° C. What will be the change in frequency when the temperature rises to 28° C.? (Disregard end correction.)
2. An open pipe is 48 cm in length. Find the lengths of two closed pipes that will give frequencies 5/4 and 6/4 times that of the open pipe. (Disregard end corrections.)

[24] But see below, "Resonance in Flasks."
[25] See Chapter I, pp. 52–53.
[26] For greatest accuracy an end correction must be made of 0.3 of the diameter, which is added to the length of the tube. If the tube is open at both ends the correction must be made at both ends.

3. An open pipe is 30 cm in length and 2 cm in diameter. How long would a closed
   pipe 1.75 cm in diameter have to be to give a tone an octave lower (one-half the
   frequency), if end corrections are made?
4. It is desired to have two open tubes of as low frequency as possible, which when
   sounded together will give 48 beats in 10 sec. The larger piece of tubing has a
   diameter of 1 in. and is 18 in. long. The smaller piece has a diameter of $3/4$ in.,
   and is shorter than the other. Figuring end corrections, how long will the smaller
   tube be?

The variation in the length of tubes due to changes in temperature makes
it necessary to have fairly constant temperature in tuning the pipes of an
organ. If one were to begin in the cool of the morning and finish in the heat
of midday, the organ would be very badly out of tune when the work was done.

Resonance in Flasks.   The resonance of cavities where the diameter is
somewhere near the length, as in a flask or bottle, involves somewhat more
complicated calculations. Three factors determine the frequency of cavities
of this sort: the volume, the size of the aperture, and the length of the neck.
The larger the volume of the cavity, the smaller the aperture, and the longer
the neck, the lower is the resonating frequency.[27] The influence of these
factors, according to Stewart, explains "the possibility of securing low natural
frequencies with but relatively small volumes of air. . . . A deep bass note
sung by a man would require a 10-foot organ pipe to produce."

It is not at all unlikely that this principle is utilized to some degree in
changing the pitch of the voice. As will be seen in Chapter III, there are
various ways in which not only the resonating cavities but the apertures as well
may be made larger or smaller. The position of the epiglottis or the uvula may
have a significant influence on the frequency; the position of the tongue most
certainly does, because it modifies the length and caliber of the aperture; and
the size of the opening at the lips makes a larger or smaller orifice between
the mouth cavity and the outer atmosphere.

Further aspects of resonance will be discussed later in this chapter, in the
treatment of timbre and quality as well as in connection with the sounds of
speech.

The Basic Factors of Sound in Speech

All sounds, including those of the human voice, can be described in terms
which have been generally agreed upon. These terms differ for the psycho-

[27] The formulas required for calculating the resonance frequency in such cavities may be
obtained from Stewart, *op. cit.,* pp. 89 f.

logist and the physicist, but, as has been pointed out, there are certain definite interrelations among those used by the two groups of scientists. Students of speech are perhaps more likely to use the psychological than the physical terms, but some understanding of the latter is necessary in order to comprehend fully the former.

Erickson has listed the "basic factors of the human voice" as follows: *pitch, intensity, timbre, volume,* and *time.*

All thought, feeling and action that may be embodied or suggested in vocal utterance is expressed or appreciated through the medium of one or more of these factors. And any scientific or practical rating of voice must be made with reference to one or more of these elements. The factors of pitch, intensity and time are fundamental attributes of all sound, and hence they are inherent elements of vocal tone. Timbre is essentially a pitch complex, but it denotes the clang or character of a tone as the attribute of pitch itself does not do. Likewise volume, while it is dependent on or correlative with pitch, intensity and timbre, also characterizes a vocal tone in a way that each of the three inherent factors does not.[28]

Let us see just how these factors are correlated with their corresponding physical attributes, and what their significance is in relation to speech.

Frequency and Pitch

The physicist in describing sounds speaks very often of *frequency*. The psychologist in his descriptions talks about *pitch*. What do these terms mean and what is their relation one to the other?

The pendulum, from the time it starts one forward swing to the time it starts the next forward swing, passes through one complete cycle. Similarly, a tuning fork or a taut string, vibrating at a much greater rapidity, passes through a certain number of complete swings or cycles each second. The number of such complete cycles per second through which a vibrator passes is the frequency of its vibration. A freely swinging pendulum one meter long will have a frequency of approximately $1/2$ cycle per second. A column of air 32 ft long, open at both ends and at a temperature of 82° F., will vibrate with a frequency of approximately 18.5 cps; one of 16 ft in length will vibrate with a frequency of about 37 cps; one of 8 ft, 73.5 cps.

The frequency of a vibration or a sound wave is a purely physical phenomenon. It has, however, a very definite effect on the psychological experience, or the way we hear the sound. This experiencing of frequency we call pitch.

---

[28] Carl I. Erickson, "The basic factors in the human voice," *University of Iowa Studies in Psychology, 10, Psychological Monographs* (1926), *36*: 82–112.

That is, we hear the pitch of a sound and not the number of vibrations. But the pitch is directly affected by the frequency; the higher the frequency, the higher the pitch. As we go up the musical scale, for example, the frequencies of the successive notes increase by definite, fixed ratios. In the "tempered scale," which is used for all pianos, each note has a frequency 1.059463 times that of the note just below it. If one is multiplied by this figure 12 times cumulatively, the resulting products will be the ratios for all the notes of the scale. For example, if $A = 440$ cps is taken as the starting point, and if it is multiplied cumulatively 12 times by this figure, the actual frequencies of the notes of the chromatic scale will be obtained. [29]

The range of frequencies which can be heard by the human ear is from approximately 16 cps to about 20,000 cps. These are the generally accepted limits of audibility for the ordinary ear. Occasionally someone is found whose limits extend beyond these frequencies, but such persons are comparatively rare.

The dependence of pitch on frequency may be shown by playing a phonograph record at different speeds. Three turntable speeds are now in common use—78, 45, and $33^1/_3$ revolutions per minute. The startling effect produced when a record recorded at one speed is inadvertently played at either of the other two is common to all of us. It provides a striking illustration of the relation between frequency and pitch. Reducing the speed from 78 to 45 rpm lowers the pitch by approximately a sixth, in musical terminology, or about as far as from C to the E below; whereas reducing the speed from 45 to $33^1/_3$ rpm lowers the pitch by about a fourth, or from C to G below. For example, if a tone having a frequency of 440 cps were recorded with a turntable speed of 78 rpm and played back at 45 rpm, the resulting frequency would be 254. A note with a frequency of 440 at 45 rpm would have a frequency of 326 if played back at $33^1/_3$ rpm.

Tones and Noises.   Another factor which enters into the question of sound is the distinction between tones and noises.

Generally speaking, *tones* are made up of sounds which have periodic vibrations. A tuning fork, for example, having a frequency of 100 cps vibrates with the utmost regularity. So regular is the period of vibration, in fact, that it can be used in very fine instruments for marking off time intervals; some

---

[29] Although it is apparently true that the pitch rises as the frequency rises, it does not seem to be true that "equal ratios of frequency give rise to equal intervals of pitch." " . . . musical intervals become subjectively larger as frequency increases up to the fourth octave above middle C. . . . " Stevens and Davis, *op. cit.*, p. 84. See also *infra*, p. 69. The relation between pitch and frequency is discussed at some length by Stevens and Davis, pp. 76–84.

forks marking off intervals of one-thousandth of a second have been used with entire confidence in the reliability of the measurement. In simple periodic vibrations of constant frequency the wave length in a given medium is constantly the same. If the amplitude is also constant, the curve of such a vibration is a true sine curve.

It is, of course, possible to have tones of changing frequency without altering the essential regularity of the vibration. The pitch characteristic is easily identifiable, and the tones are such as might be made useful for musical purposes. Examples of this phenomenon may be found in the glissando of the violin, the sliding tones of the trombone, and the inflections of the voice. In singing, the *portamento* illustrates this type of pitch change. The tonality of the sound is not affected by the fact that the frequency is not constant. A tone of varying frequency, in which is maintained what has been termed above "regularity," is quite a different thing from a sound which has no periodicity to begin with, and hence no such "regularity."

Sounds which do not have such regularity of vibration, which have no periodicity and no identifiable pitch, are usually classified as noises. The scraping of sandpaper, the crash of a falling tree, the clicking of a typewriter, the sounds which fill the air in a busy street—these are all noises. They have no regularity of vibration.

There is no sharp dividing line between tones and noises. Some sounds which under certain circumstances may be considered as tones may be noises under other conditions. Striking the individual keys of a piano will produce tones; certain combinations of keys will produce pleasant tones in the form of harmony. Other combinations will produce what is known as discord; three or four adjacent keys struck simultaneously will result in distinctly unpleasant sounds. Some chords in one progression will be quite satisfactory; the same chords in other progressions will be jarring. A bundle of sticks dropped on the table will make a noise; yet these same sticks, if cut to proper lengths, may be dropped one at a time in proper order to produce a musical scale. One might not be expected to get much music from a pile of discarded tomato cans; but they can be so tuned that a melody can be played on them. From one point of view, any undesirable sound, whether it has a definite pitch or not, may be thought of as noise. From another point of view, any sound which "masks" another sound that we want to listen to, to such an extent that the latter can be heard only with difficulty, may be considered noise.

Furthermore, there are what might be called low-pitched and high-pitched noises. The deep rumbling of distant thunder, even though no definite pitch can be identified, is quite different from the shattering of glass, the ticking of a clock, or the hiss of escaping steam. Aperiodic waves may be so far apart that the effect is of low pitch, or so close together that they produce an effect of high pitch.

Some of our speech sounds have noise characteristics as well as tone characteristics. This is particularly true of the consonants. The fricative sounds of such consonants as [f], [v], [s], [z], voiceless *th* [θ], voiced *th* [ð], *sh* [ʃ], *zh* [ʒ], and the plosive sounds of [p], [b], [t], [d], [k], [g], either consist of or contain speech noises, although some of their characteristic high frequencies have been determined. Other speech noises are produced by "air blades"—sheets of air forced out of narrow oral (mouth) apertures under pressure, and thus set into violent fluttering vibration, as in the production of the fricative [ɹ], as in *drill*, [j] as in French *fille* [fij], etc. Vowels should not be, but often are, accompanied by speech noises.

Factors Influencing Frequency. Frequency of vibration is affected by certain characteristics of the vibrator. Some of these may be varied in certain musical instruments and fixed in others. In the voice, with its great variety in pitch, it would seem obvious that the determinants of pitch are flexible indeed. The aspects of cavities that affect frequency have already been presented; their application to the voice will be treated later in this discussion.

MASS. Consider a taut string or wire. The bass strings on a piano are heavy, massive wires, wound with smaller wire to give them greater mass [30] per unit of length. The result is a slower vibration and a lower pitch. For the same reason the G string on a violin is larger and heavier than the E string. Some people's vocal bands are heavier and thicker than those of others, and their voices are lower in pitch than the voices of those with thinner, lighter bands. The mass of a vibrator is the least susceptible to alteration in changing the pitch on a given instrument. The greater the mass the lower the frequency, and hence the lower the pitch.

LENGTH. Slower vibrations result also from lengthening the vibrator. The bass strings on the piano are much longer than those at the other end of the scale. A long organ pipe, as we have seen, produces a much lower tone than a short one of the same type. Whereas on the piano a separate string or set of strings is required for each note, the violinist can produce different notes (pitches) by varying the length of the strings through fingering. A clarinetist

---

[30] *Mass* may be defined as volume times density. For our present purposes, the mass may be considered as equivalent to the weight of one unit of length, 1 cm. or 1 ft.

varies the length of the air column, and thus the pitch, by means of the stops and keys. A man's voice is about a sixth lower than a woman's, partly because his vocal bands are longer and heavier.

The distressing "change of voice" which many boys are said to experience in early adolescence is presumed to be due, at least in part, to a sudden, rapid growth in the larynx, resulting in an increase in the length of the vocal cords without immediate muscular adjustment, which comes somewhat later. It is doubtful whether these breaks are so frequent or so devastating in their psychological effects as has been implied.[31]

TENSION.   As tension increases, frequency increases and the pitch rises. A kettledrum, for example, may be tuned by tightening or loosening the head. A violinist tunes his instrument by altering the tension of the strings, while the mass and length remain the same. When a piano tuner tunes a piano, he makes delicate adjustments in the tension of the strings until he has secured the exact frequencies required.

The relationships between each of these three factors and the frequency are expressed in the formula,

$$F = \frac{1}{2L}\sqrt{\frac{KT}{M}};$$

in which case,

$$M = \frac{KT}{4F^2L^2}; \quad L = \frac{1}{2F}\sqrt{\frac{KT}{M}}; \quad \text{and} \quad T = \frac{4F^2L^2M}{K}.$$

These formulas, which are all variations of the same relationship among the several determining factors, show that the frequency of a taut string or wire varies inversely with the length, L, in centimeters or feet; directly with the square root of the tension, T (times 980 if T is in grams and by 32.2 if T is in pounds); and inversely with the square root of the mass, M, in grams per centimeter or pounds per foot of length. That is, to reduce a frequency by one-half, we may double the length, or multiply the mass or divide the tension by four.

Problems

1. A steel wire 40 cm in length and having a mass of 0.03 gm/cm is stretched by a tension of 50 kg. What is its frequency?
2. What changes in frequency would result if you reduced the length of a wire by

---

[31] Charles Paul Pedrey, "A study of voice change in boys between the ages of eleven and sixteen," Ph.D. Dissertation, Louisiana State University, 1944. See also Eldon K. Jerome, "Change of voice in male adolescents," *The Quarterly Journal of Speech* (1937), *23*: 648–653.

one-half? If you doubled the mass? If you reduced the tension by one-half? What change would occur if you did all three of these?

3. If a steel wire 100 cm in length has a tension of 15 kg and a frequency of 440 cps, what will be its frequency if the tension is increased to 20 kg?

4. The frequency of a stretched wire 180 cm in length is 320 cps. What is the tension if the total mass is 3.60 gm?

5. Given: $M = .006$ gm/cm; $L = 24$ cm; $T = 2.0$ kg; find F.
   Given: $F = 440$ cps; $L = 32$ cm; $M = .004$ gm/cm; find T.
   Given: $F = 64$ cps; $T = 15$ kg; $M = .64$ gm/cm; find L.

6. If the tension of a wire is doubled, how much and in what direction will the length have to be altered to maintain the same frequency?

According to Erickson, ". . . the [vocal] cords are the ultimate determiners of pitch. Their frequency at any given time is the frequency of the resultant tone. And . . . the same general structure of the cords seems to·be the determining factor in the range of frequencies that may be produced." [32] This point of view is indirectly supported by Drew and Kellogg,[33] who, in a study of the time required for a vocal tone to reach its full intensity, found that only one or two vibrations were necessary. They concluded that "the human vocal cords are not like a cornet, where a return wave from an air column would control the vocal cords and thereby establish when the next pulse comes. If a strong resonance of some kind were involved, [such] sudden beginnings would not be possible. The voice mechanism seems more like a relaxation oscillator that does not carry over any energy from one cycle to the next."

On the other hand, it has been argued that the entire vocal mechanism is a coupled system and that it is highly probable that the action of the vocal cavities influences the frequency of the vocal bands almost, if not quite, as much as they are influenced by them.[34]

This diversity of opinion is one illustration of the fact, as indicated on the first page of this chapter, that "we do not as yet know everything with respect to the actual manner in which the vocal mechanism operates to produce certain effects."

In the discussion of optimum pitch (Chapter I) it was pointed out that for each voice there is a general pitch range or level at which that voice will be found to be most effective. This level, it was also noted, varies for different

[32] Op. cit.

[33] R. O. Drew and E. W. Kellogg, "Starting characteristics of speech sounds," *Journal of the Acoustical Society of America* (July, 1940), *12*: 85–103.

[34] Robert Curry, *The Mechanism of the Human Voice*, New York, Longmans, Green & Company, 1940, pp. 44–50. See also Lee Edward Travis, W. R. G. Bender, and Archibald R, Buchanan, "Research contribution to vowel theory," *Speech Monographs* (September, 1934), *1*: 65–71.

individuals, and each person makes considerable variation from his own general level. In fact, the most effective voices seem capable of fairly wide ranges in pitch. Cowan, investigating the speech of ten contemporary actors and actresses, found an average pitch range for all ten, of two octaves, ranging from 1.28 to 2.56 octaves. Median pitch levels for the men's voices ranged from 134 cps to 146 cps, with an average of 141 cps; the average pitch level for women's voices was 233 cps, about a sixth higher than the average for the men's voices, and ranged from 188 cps to 295 cps.[35] However, Cowan also concluded, "There is no evidence to indicate that any voice has a normal or fixed pitch level." Still, his data show that the median pitch level for some men is higher than that for others, and that for some women it is higher than for some others, which is essentially the principle of optimum pitch.

Pitch and Laryngeal Measurements.   The relationships between pitch and laryngeal measurements suggested above have been substantiated by Hollien, who measured general laryngeal size, vocal fold cross-sectional area, elevation of the vocal folds at different pitches, vocal fold length, and "tilt" or the slope of the superior border of the folds toward the midline. He found that

1. Individuals with low pitch levels exhibit larger, more massive vocal folds and generally larger laryngeal structures than do individuals with higher pitch levels. This is true at least for the dimensions of general laryngeal size, vocal fold cross-sectional area, vocal fold thickness, and vocal fold length as measured in this study.
2. As the fundamental frequency of an individual's voice is raised, there is a strong tendency for the vocal folds to be reduced in cross-sectional area, to become thinner. The rate of change of these dimensions with changes in frequency is more marked in the low frequency part of the subject's range.
3. Cross-sectional dimensions of the vocal folds seem to be correlated with absolute frequency level to a greater degree than with relative frequency within the subject's singing range. This tendency is evident no matter what a given individual's pitch level or laryngeal dimensions may be, e.g., a baritone and soprano singing the same pitch would tend to have vocal folds of about the same thickness. It appears that one of the most important determiners of vocal pitch may be the mass of the folds or thickness as shown by cross-sectional areas and thickness measures.
4. As the fundamental frequency of voice is raised, there is a tendency for the vocal folds to lengthen.

---

[35] Milton Cowan, "Pitch and intensity characteristics of stage speech," *Archives of Speech Supplement*, Iowa City, Iowa, December, 1936.

5. There is a tendency for the vocal folds to be progressively more elevated with successive rises in pitch. . . .

6. There is a tendency for tilt of the folds to become greater with successive rises in pitch except at the falsetto pitch. . . . [36]

Intensity and Loudness

Amplitude.   Another characteristic of sound waves in which the physicist is interested is *amplitude*, which may be illustrated by the swing of the pendulum, in which the distance from the point of rest to the point of its farthest swing—that is, to the outer limit of its excursion in one direction— is the amplitude. If the curve in Figure 2 (page 72) is used to represent the displacements of the air particles, the distance *Aa* or *Cc* will represent the amplitude of the wave.

The amplitude of a wave does not depend on the frequency of that wave, although some of the same factors may affect both. Obviously a long pendulum can have a wider excursion than a very short one; it will also have a slower movement. But a pendulum of a given length will swing with the same frequency, whether the excursion is large or small. This can be shown in the following manner: Attach a light stylus to the bottom of the bob of a pendulum and allow it to touch lightly the surface of a smoked paper on a uniformly revolving drum. The swinging pendulum will mark off equal distances on the paper, regardless of the extent of the excursion. An exception to this principle may be observed if we pluck or strike a taut string very strongly. The pitch for the first few hundredths of a second will be higher than the natural, but the frequency will soon settle down to the normal; and these vibrations will have a greater amplitude than if the string were struck lightly in the first place.

Intensity.   Strictly, intensity refers to the rate at which energy is given off by the sound source, or the energy with which a sound wave strikes an object such as the eardrum or a microphone, some distance away. The amount of energy thus produced is dependent upon (1) the amplitude, and (2) the frequency. This dependence may be explained by the fact that a body in motion possesses a kinetic energy equal to one-half the product of its mass and the square of its velocity ($KE = \frac{1}{2}MV^2$). If the frequency of oscillation of a particle of air is doubled, the particle must travel twice as far in the same

[36] Harry Francis Hollien, "A study of some larnygeal correlates of vocal pitch," Ph.D. Dissertation, State University of Iowa, 1955. *Microfilm Abstracts*, 15: 2340, Publication No. 14,119.

period of time. Its velocity, then, must be twice as great, and the average kinetic energy, which varies with the average square of the velocity, will be four times as great. Similarly, if the amplitude of vibration is doubled, the particle must likewise travel twice the distance in the same time, and again its velocity will be doubled. Its kinetic energy will again be four times as great. If both the frequency and the amplitude are doubled, the kinetic energy will be 16 times as great. The formula $I \propto A^2 \times F^2$ simply means that the intensity, that is, the energy in a sound wave, is proportional to the square of the amplitude times the square of the frequency.

Although the pressure of a sound wave is proportional to the amplitude times the frequency, the *energy* is proportional to the square of the pressure, and hence, again, to the square of the product of the amplitude and the frequency.[37]

It was pointed out (page 81) that the wave pattern, if allowed to spread uniformly in all directions, travels outward from the source in concentric spheres of alternating condensation and rarefaction. The total amount of energy is distributed, so to speak, over the entire surface of the sphere, which forms the *wave front*. As the sphere expands, its area will increase as the square of the radius. But, assuming that none of the energy is lost as the wave moves outward, since the total amount of energy must still be distributed over this increased area, then for any given portion of that area, for example, one square centimeter, the amount of available energy will be smaller and smaller as the sphere expands. That amount will obviously decrease in an inverse ratio as the total area increases; that is, as the radius is doubled, the total area will be increased four times, and the amount of available energy on any portion of that surface of a given area will be decreased to one-fourth. In other words, the intensity of a sound, or its energy, is inversely proportional to the square of the radius or distance from the source.

This description assumes an uninterrupted flow of energy outward in all directions. Actually, such a condition is rarely encountered. It does not hold true, for example, where reflecting surfaces may reinforce the sound from the source, or where interferences may cause undue diminution of the sound. In the absence of such interrupting factors, however, it is generally true that the intensity of sound is inversely proportional to the square of the distance from the source.

The amount of energy in sound is actually very small. Conversational speech has been estimated to have an energy of 125 ergs/sec.[38] Slightly softer

---

[37] Stevens and Davis, *op. cit.*, p. 28.

[38] Stewart, *op. cit.*, p. 121. The magnitude of an erg may be appreciated from the fact that 1 watt is the equivalent of 10^7 (10,000,000) ergs/sec, so that an electric light bulb of 40 watts

speech of 100 ergs/sec represents 10 microwatts or 10 millionths of a watt. It has been estimated that the change in pressure on the eardrum membrane from a fairly loud musical note is approximately equivalent to the change in atmospheric pressure if we raised our heads above the earth's surface about a third of an inch![39] Fletcher cites measurements indicating that the total speech power for six men ranged from 10 to 90 microwatts, with an average of 34, and for five women ranged from 8 to 55 microwatts, with an average of 18.[40]

Even though the actual energy is very small, the range of energy in the sounds which we hear about us daily is very great. The ratio of energy in very loud speech to that of a soft whisper is of the order of 1 million to one. Some of the common sounds may have an energy several billion times as great as that necessary for minimum audibility. These ratios are so great that the figures required to indicate them would be cumbersome; furthermore, they would give no indication of the relative loudness of the sounds. For these reasons other units have been devised which are far more usable than the absolute values of the energy in sound waves.

Loudness.   In listening to sounds we are not so much interested in the actual energy as we are in how loud they are. Loudness is, in general, the psychological correlate of intensity; the term refers to the "strength of the sensation received through the ear." [41] Generally speaking, of two tones, the one having the greater intensity will sound louder if the pitches are not too far apart. But there is not the close relationship between intensity and loudness that there is between frequency and pitch. The difficulties in constructing and validating a reliable scale for loudness have been discussed by Garner, who concludes that "Whatever the ultimate solution to the loudness scaling problem may be, it is clear that the problem is not a simple one. Certainly it is not as simple as asking somebody what sounds half, or a quarter, as loud as something else."[42]

THE DECIBEL.   There is an old law of psychophysics, known as the Weber-Fechner Law, which states that the minimum perceptible increment in the intensity of a stimulus is a logarithmic function, or that the strength of

---

would require energy equivalent to 40×10^7 or 400,000,000 ergs/sec. Accordingly, conversational speech would have a speech power of 12.5 microwatts.

[39] Jeans, *op. cit.*, p. 218.

[40] Harvey Fletcher, *Speech and Hearing in Communication*, Princeton, N.J., D. Van Nostrand Company, 1953, p. 76.

[41] D. C. Miller, *The Science of Musical Sounds*, New York, The Macmillan Company, 1922, p. 53.

[42] W. R. Garner, "A technique and a scale for loudness measurement," *Journal of the Acoustical Society of America* (January, 1954), *26*: 73–88.

a sensation increases not as the intensity of that stimulus itself, but as the logarithm of the *ratio* of the greater intensity to the lesser.[43] It should be clear that the strength of a sensation increases much more slowly than the intensity of the stimulus.

Although more recent investigations have shown that this "law" is far from being rigidly true, it does offer a starting point for establishing a relation between intensity and loudness. If we take the *ratio* between two intensities, the logarithm of that ratio will give a value which can be used in applying the Weber-Fechner Law, or some approximation of it, to such a relation. Communications engineers have adopted for this value the term *bel*, named for the inventor of the telephone. *The bel is, then, the logarithm of the ratio between two intensities.* But since a difference of 1 bel, as between 8 and 9 bels, represents an intensity ratio of 10:1, a unit representing a smaller ratio must be used. The bel has been divided, therefore, into 10 *decibels*, each of which is equal to one-tenth of a bel. There are thus 10 times as many decibels as bels in a given difference.

The decibel is not an absolute unit of measurement, like the inch or the gram or the watt. It is a relative unit, somewhat like the degree of temperature; it measures the intensity of sound in comparison with some other sound, or with some arbitrarily chosen "reference intensity." The relation between decibels and the ratio of two intensities is indicated by the following formula:

$$\text{db} = 10 \log_{10} \frac{\mathcal{J}_1}{\mathcal{J}_2},$$

where $\mathcal{J}_1$ and $\mathcal{J}_2$ are the intensities of the two sounds. Usually the larger of the two is taken as the numerator. If pressures are used, the formula calls for 20 log, instead of 10 log.

Problem

1. A sound is measured 2 ft from the source, and again at some distance away. If the difference in intensities is 40 db, how far away is the second measurement?

In the field of hearing the basis for comparison is the barely audible sound, as measured by a large number of normal ears. In terms of the sound wave

---

[43] The logarithm of a number N is the power x to which a given "base" a must be raised to give the number N. Thus, if $a^x = N$, then $\log_a N = x$, to be read the logarithm of N to the base a is x. The law stated above simply means that the least noticeable change in the intensity of a stimulus must be a given *proportion* of the original intensity, rather than a given *amount*. That is, if the weight of an ounce must be increased by $1/16$ to be just perceptible, then the weight of a pound must also be increased by a like proportion, one-sixteenth.

pressure a reference level of .0002 dyne per cm² has been agreed upon. Under the most favorable conditions the human ear can detect sounds having a pressure of one-half this value, or .0001 dyne/cm².[44] Physically, the "reference intensity" for a pure tone of 1000 cps has been defined by the American Standards Association as 10^{-16} watts per square centimeter. This value is equal to 1 preceded by 15 zeros and a decimal point! This reference level is considerably below that agreed upon for hearing. Miller points out further:

A very low whisper at 5 feet from the talker's lips averages about 20 db. The general level of background noise in a well-designed radio broadcasting studio is between 25 and 30 db. The audience noise in a motion-picture theatre is about 45 db. Noise in a large store runs around 60 db, and the average factory noise is about 75 db. The noise in a subway station when an express train passes is about 100 db. The point at which sounds cause pain to the listener is about 140 db. The report of a 12-inch cannon, at 12 feet in front of and below the muzzle, is about 230 db.[45]

How much greater must the intensity be to make a difference of 1 decibel? Since the logarithm of 10 is 1, an intensity ratio of 10:1 would mean a difference of 1 bel. For a 1 db difference, the logarithm must be .1, and the ratio itself is found to be approximately 1.259:1. That is, if one sound has about 26 percent greater intensity than another, there is a difference in intensity of 1 db.

The "talker levels"—the "intensity level produced at 1 meter distance from the lips and directly in front of the talker"[46]—of a large number of persons have been measured. It was found that 7 percent of the people talking into the telephone in a conversational tone spoke so softly that their speech measured only 54 db, corresponding to a total speech power of 2 microwatts. About 40 percent had levels "within 3 db of the average 66 db, and no person had a talker level greater than 75 db."

"A round figure of about 0.01 microwatt probably represents the faintest sound and of about 5000 microwatts the peak value of the loudest sound that will be encountered in conversation. This represents a range in intensity of 500,000 to 1 or 56 db."[47] But "If the measuring microphone is placed 18 in. directly in front of the talker's lips, conversational speech registers about 76 db above the standard reference pressure of 0.0002 dyne/cm²."[48]

[44] George A. Miller, *Language and Communication*, New York, McGraw-Hill Book Company, 1951, p. 28.
[45] *Ibid.*, p. 31.
[46] Fletcher, *op. cit.*, pp. 76 f.
[47] *Ibid.*, p. 88.
[48] G. A. Miller, *op. cit.*, p. 32.

What has this physical unit, the decibel, to do with loudness? It was pointed out that in listening to sounds we are interested not so much in the amount of energy in the sounds as we are in the effect of the energy on the sensation of loudness, which is a function of hearing—in general, the psychological correlate of intensity. Referring again to the Weber-Fechner Law, which, as has been indicated, is no more than an approximation, we can say that the decibel, measured as a logarithmic function of intensity, provides a convenient unit for the measurement of loudness as well. Not only can the minimum and maximum limits of audibility for pure tones over the audible frequency range be measured in terms of decibels, but the threshold of loudness difference as well can be indicated through the use of this unit. Furthermore, any two tones or sounds can be compared in loudness with each other, and any given sound can be given a value of loudness in comparison with the generally accepted "reference intensity" which is taken as "zero loudness." A given sound may thus be said to be 40 db louder than another, or 40 db above the threshold of audibility.

THE AUDIBLE AREA.   Above the threshold of hearing on the one hand and the upper limit where the threshold of feeling begins is a large area in both frequency and intensity. At the lowest frequencies a much greater intensity is

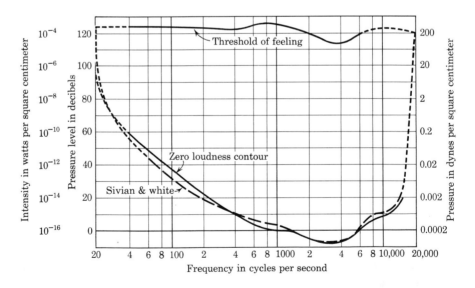

Figure 7. Auditory Area Between Threshold of Feeling and the Threshold of Hearing. (From Harvey Fletcher, *Speech and Hearing in Communication*, 2nd ed., p. 134. Copyright, 1953, D. Van Nostrand Company, Princeton, New Jersey.)

required for a sound to be barely audible than is necessary for higher frequencies. The requisite intensity decreases as the frequency rises until at a frequency of around 2000 cps it is at its minimum. With further rises in frequency, however, the necessary intensity again rises until at about 15,000 cps it has reached the maximum, so far as measured data indicate. The graph in Figure 7 shows these relations. It also shows that somewhere above 120 db, again depending somewhat on frequency, the intensity of sound stimulates a sensation of feeling rising to actual pain. In Figure 7, the area bounded by the curve of minimum audibility and the curve marking the beginning of the level of feeling is known as the *audible area*.

THE LOUDNESS OF THE SOUNDS OF SPEECH.   The intensity level of speech in general has been discussed (page 107); but what of the individual sounds of speech, particularly in relation to one another? The speech power of each of the sounds has been measured, and tabulated in order from the greatest to the least.

TABLE 1[a]

ɔ	680	u	310	ʧ	42	k	13
ɑ	600	ɪ	260	n	36	v	12
ʌ	510	i	220	ʤ	23	ð	11
æ	490	r	210	ʒ	20	b	7
oʊ	470	l	100	z	16	d	7
ʊ	460	ʃ	80	s	16	p	6
eɪ	370	ŋ	73	t	15	f	5
ɛ	350	m	52	g	15	θ	1

[a] From Harvey Fletcher, *Speech and Hearing in Communication*, 2nd ed., p. 86. Copyright, 1953, D. Van Nostrand Co., Inc., Princeton, New Jersey.

These relative values probably are not fixed. The intensity of a vowel varies significantly from word to word when uttered in separate, isolated words, probably because of the influence of varying phonetic context. There may be still other factors involved as well, such as emphasis, accent, and semantic differences.[49]

PITCH AND INTENSITY.   Studies of the relation of pitch and intensity have not always agreed. Stevens found that "For low tones, the pitch decreases with intensity, but, for high tones, the pitch increases with intensity. For

[49] Grant Fairbanks, Arthur S. House, and Eugene L. Stevens, "An experimental study of vowel intensities," *Journal of the Acoustical Society of America* (July, 1950), *22*: 457–459.

certain tones in the middle range, both effects are present to a slight degree. Thus at 2000 cycles, the pitch, for this observer, increased up to about 60 db above threshold and then decreased. At other frequencies this point of reversal occurred at different intensities. In general, the higher the frequency, the higher the intensity at which the reversal takes place."[50]

In a later study, however, Morgan, Garner, and Galambos concluded:

Perhaps the first thing to note about our results is how little, in general, pitch changes with intensity. The median or typical change never exceeds two percent. . . . For some subjects, however, there is a good deal of change of pitch with intensity. . . . we find that pitch often changes by as much as five percent between the lowest and highest intensities. . . . So, in extreme, atypical cases we find large changes, but in the general, more typical case, the pitch changes are very small.[51]

These accounts may illustrate the importance of consistency and specificity in the use of terms. It is often difficult to avoid confusions arising from uncertainty in differentiating such parallel terms as frequency and pitch, intensity and loudness, in distinguishing between physical and psychological concepts.

Wave Complexity and Timbre

Thus far the discussion of sound waves has proceeded upon the general assumption that vibrations are as simple as the swing of a pendulum or a tuning fork, that they follow the pattern of simple harmonic motion. Actually, this type of vibration is rare, being seldom found outside the laboratory. As a matter of fact, vibrations are usually exceedingly complex; sound waves are ordinarily made up of simple waves blended together into what may be called the *tone-complex*.

Consider again a taut string. If it is struck or plucked smartly, it will vibrate in its full length, the rate of vibration being determined by its mass, length, and tension. It gives out a note which we say has a certain pitch. The pitch of this note is determined by the frequency of the string vibrating throughout its full length.

Segmental Vibrations. While this vibration is proceeding, if we touch lightly with a fine brush the exact midpoint of the string, the halves will continue to vibrate, but at a frequency twice that of the string in its full

[50] Stanley Smith Stevens, "The relation of pitch to intensity," *Journal of the Acoustical Society of America* (1935), *6*: 150–154. Cited in Stevens and Davis, *op. cit.*, pp. 70–73.

[51] C. T. Morgan, W. R. Garner, and Robert Galambos, "Pitch and intensity," *Journal of the Acoustical Society of America* (November, 1951), *23*: 658–663.

length, and at a pitch one octave higher than its former tone. If we touch the string at exactly one-third of its length, the three segments will continue to vibrate, but this time the frequency will be three times that of the original frequency, and the pitch will be an octave and a fifth above its former tone. If it is touched at one-fourth its length, the fourths will vibrate at four times the natural frequency, and the pitch will be two octaves above that of the string vibrating in its full length. The string can similarly be "stopped" at any point that will mark off a common fraction of its length, and its segments will continue to vibrate at a frequency equal to that of the full-length string multiplied by the number of segments, and at pitches determined by the *frequency ratios* of the segmental frequencies in relation to the *fundamental frequency*, or that of the full-length string.

Isolating in such a manner these higher tones out of the tone-complex demonstrates that they are present in the total sound emanating from the string when it is vibrating freely. These tones all contribute to the sound as we hear it. That is, while the string is vibrating as a whole, it is simultaneously vibrating in halves, thirds, fourths, etc., and each vibrating segment is contributing its sound to the whole blend of tones. There may be as many as twenty or thirty, or even double the latter number, of these segmental vibrations, all entering into the tone-complex. The frequencies of the segmental or partial vibrations which enter into the sounds of speech and music may be as high as 16,000 cps, although it is commonly thought that frequencies as high as 10,000 cps are high enough for great fidelity of reproduction. A system of transmission that includes 8000 cps gives a very good quality.

Segmental Vibration in Other Vibrators.   Strings are not the only bodies that vibrate in segments; columns of air, membranes, diaphragms, plates, bars, bells, in fact, practically all types of vibrators produce segmental or partial vibrations. In the discussion of resonance (pages 93–94) it was pointed out that a column of air will give maximum resonance to a tone whose wave length is twice or four times its own length, depending on whether the tube is open or closed at one end. It will also give resonance to integral multiples of those frequencies, with this exception, that a closed tube will respond only to the odd-numbered multiples, whereas an open tube will respond to both odd and even multiples of the fundamental frequency.

Segmental Vibrations and Wave Complexity.   Segmental vibrations also produce complexities in the wave form itself, these complexities becoming

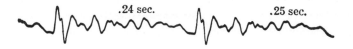

.24 sec.   .25 sec.

<u>a</u> [ɑ] as in father

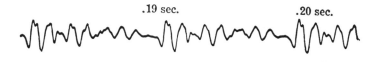

.19 sec.   .20 sec.

<u>a</u> [ɑ] as in father

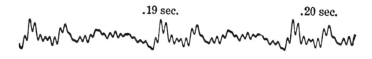

.19 sec.   .20 sec.

<u>u</u> [ʊ] as in put

.14 sec.   .15 sec.

<u>o</u> [ʌ] as in ton

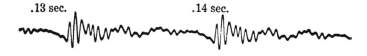

.13 sec.   .14 sec.

<u>i</u> [ɪ] as in tip

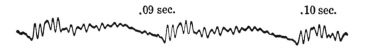

.09 sec.   .10 sec.

<u>ee</u> [i] as in lee

Figure 8. Highly Complex Sound Waves. (From I. B. Crandall, "The sounds of speech," *Bell System Technical Journal* [October, 1925], 4:586–626.)

apparent when we try to show the waves visually, as in "photographs" of such waves, or by exhibiting them on a cathode ray oscillograph screen. In such visual "pictures" there is no smooth sine curve like that in Figure 2 (page 72), but a curve which is a composite of a large number of sine curves—that is, the curves of all the segmental vibrations that enter into that particular sound. Figure 8 shows some of these highly complex waves.

TONES FROM SEGMENTAL VIBRATIONS. The tone which results from the vibration of a string or a column of air or any other vibrator, in its full length or size, is called the *fundamental*. It is the fundamental which identifies the pitch of the note; the pitch of a given tone is always the pitch of the fundamental. This is true even though there is no energy in the fundamental frequency. It is obvious that the total energy in a tone-complex is distributed among the partials in certain proportions. It not infrequently happens that the upper partials receive all the energy, leaving none for the fundamental. Despite this missing component, we still identify the pitch of the complex tone as the pitch of the missing fundamental; we hear a tone that is not present.

Various explanations have been offered for the phenomenon just described. Perhaps the simplest is that the *frequency of the wave*, which determines the pitch, depends not on the common difference between adjacent partials, but on the *greatest common divisor* of the frequencies present. Thus, as Stevens and Davis point out, when the components have frequencies of 400, 600, and 1000 cycles, the pitch "appears to be that of a 200-cycle tone." [52] If to these are added components having frequencies of 500, 700, and 900 cycles, the pitch drops one octave, or to that of a 100-cycle tone. Neither the addition of a 100-cycle nor the elimination of the 400-cycle and the 500-cycle components would alter the frequency of the wave nor the pitch at which the tone would be heard.

Segmental vibrations are called *partials*, the first partial being the vibration in the lowest frequency of which that particular vibrator is capable. This first partial is also sometimes designated as the *fundamental*, and its frequency the *fundamental frequency*. The tones which result from segmental vibrations above the first partial or fundamental are called *overtones*, the term referring to the resulting *sound*, and the term *partial* to the segmental vibration itself. Thus, the fundamental is produced by the string or other body vibrating in its first partial. The first overtone is produced by the body vibrating in its second partial, and so on.

[52] Stevens and Davis, *op. cit.*, p. 99.

When the frequencies of the partials are integral multiples of the lowest or fundamental frequency they are called *harmonics*. Arranged in order, they may be 1, 2, 3, 4, 5, 6, and so on, times the fundamental frequency. This simply means that if the fundamental frequency is 120 cps, that of the second partial or harmonic, or the first overtone, is 240; that of the third partial or second overtone is 360, of the next one 480, and so on. What is called the *harmonic series* or the *harmonic ratio* may be expressed in a series of values:

$$1:2:3:4:5:6....$$

In many types of vibrators the partials do not fall into any such harmonic series. Bell tones, for example, are very complex, with no consistent ratios among the partials, which are, on that account, *enharmonic*. According to a well-known mathematical theorem, however, any periodic wave may be broken down into a number of simple sine waves having frequencies in ratios integral to the fundamental frequency, and also having definite amplitudes and phase relations.[53]

Practically all tones which we hear are made up of these fundamentals and overtones in varying combinations. There are three factors which affect the form of any wave: the frequencies, the amplitudes, and the phase relations of the partials. If any partial is eliminated or a missing partial restored, the wave form will be altered. If the amplitude of any partial is altered, it will also alter the wave form. If the phase relations of any of the partials are changed, the wave form again will be affected.

Quality and Timbre. The *quality* or *timbre*[54] of a tone is a correlate of its wave complexity. Apparently it depends solely upon the frequencies and the relative intensities of the partials present. We are able to distinguish the tones of a violin from those of an organ because of the differences in the relative intensities of the partials. The basic differences in the sounds of speech are due to differences in these same relations. That is, different vowel sounds, for example, are different because they are composed of different blends of relatively strengthened or relatively damped partials. People's voices

[53] These successive frequencies are sometimes written n, $2n$, $3n$, $4n$, $5n$, and so on, or, in terms of their wave lengths, l, $l/2$, $l/3$, $l/4$, $l/5$. . . .

[54] The terms *quality* and *timbre* are frequently interchanged but they are as often confused. As the two terms will be used in this text, quality will refer to subjective evaluations of tones, whether they are good or poor, pleasing or displeasing. Two voices of equal quality may differ in timbre; two instruments, such as the French horn and the 'cello, may be quite unlike in timbre, but equal in quality of tone. Timbre has no connotation of evaluation; it refers to those characteristics of tones which differentiate one instrument from another, one voice from another, one vowel such as [i] from another such as [u].

are distinguishable from one another for the same reason. Moreover, voices are good or poor because of the differences in the relative strengths of the overtones present, often together with the addition of noise elements.

Although, as has been said, the wave form is determined by the frequencies, amplitudes, and phases of the components, timbre or quality apparently does not depend on the shape of the wave form. It is determined only by the frequencies and relative intensities of those components. It is possible to shift the phase of any partial by any amount without altering the sound itself; we are unaware of any difference. It would be possible, therefore, to have two sounds identical so far as the ear could tell, yet with wave forms so different that they could not be identified as the same. The two waves for the *a* in *father* (Figure 8), illustrate how different the waves of the same vowel can be. It is impossible to identify a sound by its wave form or to use the wave form of a given vowel, for example, as a "model" for that particular vowel. Miller[55] reproduces the photograph of a violin tone taken at the moment the direction of the bow is reversed. The phases of the components are exactly reversed, but the ear can detect no change in the tone quality or timbre at such an instant.

The problem of the effect of phase relations has been attacked by a number of investigators.[56] It appears that for a complex tone of only a few components (three or four), phase changes do affect the timbre of the tone. But for the more complex tones such as are heard in music and speech, there seems to be no phase effect unless the sounds are very loud.[57] Jeans likewise insists that "the ear cannot distinguish phase differences in the constituent vibrations out of which a composite tone is formed. In brief, it does not inform the brain as to the mathematical shape of the sound curve it is hearing, but only as to the way in which the energy is distributed over the different pure tones.[58]

TIMBRE, QUALITY, AND RESONANCE.   In the discussion of resonance it was brought out that through the operation of that principle, applied in one or more of the different ways, the tone is made stronger. Strengthening of the tone, however, is not the only effect of resonance; the timbre or quality of the tone is also affected materially. In the case of stringed instruments the vibrations are communicated through the bridge to the body of the instrument,

[55] *The Science of Musical Sounds*, p. 197.
[56] See Stevens and Davis, *op. cit.*, pp. 205–206; J. D. Trimmer and F. A. Firestone, "An investigation of subjective tones by means of the steady tone phase effect," *Journal of the Acoustical Society of America* (July, 1937), 9: 25–29.
[57] Jones, *op. cit.*, pp. 262 ff.
[58] Jeans, *op. cit.*, pp. 249 ff. *Pure tone* refers to the tone produced by a single vibrator, vibrating in only one segment, without overtones, such as that of a tuning fork.

and tones of great power result. Furthermore, the material of the body is so carefully selected, and its size and shape so expertly determined, that the instrument makes a selection of partials which produce tones subjectively evaluated as having good quality.

In wind instruments the shape of the tube or pipe, and the texture of the material of which it is made, also have an influence on the relative intensities of the partials, so that differences in these factors produce differences in wave complexity. Manufacturers of musical instruments are constantly at work to improve the quality of tone.

The timbre and quality of the voice, as a wind instrument, are determined not only by the vibrations of the vocal bands, but also by the size of the air column, by its shape, by the coupling of two or more cavities of different sizes and shapes, and by the texture of the pharyngeal (throat) walls. Tense, rigid walls will emphasize the higher frequencies, resulting in high, sharp voices; lax muscles will permit the lower frequencies to "come out," thus contributing to depth and richness. Excessive laxity may result in heavy, dull, muffled tones. Although most of the energy of the voice is carried in the lower partials, at the same time both high and low frequencies are necessary for the best quality of voice. A certain degree of tonicity, without overtenseness, is therefore a requisite for tones of maximum richness.

SOUND RANGE PREFERENCE. The importance of the overtones, especially the upper ones, in speech and music may be appreciated when one considers the prevailing emphasis on "high fidelity," or "hi-fi," in radio, television, motion pictures, and phonograph recordings. It has been widely thought that for reproduced sound a restricted frequency range is generally preferred to the full range. Olson, however, tested some 1000 subjects ranging from 14 to 65 years in age, with direct "live" music and speech. An acoustic filter was interposed between the sound source and the listeners in such a way that it could be turned on or off at will. A cutoff frequency of 5000 cps was used; that is, when the filter, consisting of a series of baffles, was turned on, the listeners heard no frequencies above 5000 cps; when it was turned off, they heard the sound as it came directly from the source without distortion.

For popular music, 69 percent of the 1000 listeners preferred the full frequency range, and 31 percent the 5000 cps low pass. For semiclassical music, 66 percent out of 150 listeners preferred the full range; for speech, most listeners likewise preferred the full range, although percentages were not given.

For the different age groups, the preferences were as follows: ages 14–20 years, 59 percent for the full range and 41 percent for the restricted; from 20 to 30 years, 67 per cent and 33 percent respectively; from 30 to 40 years, 75 percent and 25 percent; and from 40 to 65 years, 69 percent and 31 percent respectively.[59] It would be interesting to investigate the effect on such preferences of different cutoff frequencies, such as 8000 or 10,000 cps.

Harmonic Analysis.   In the study of complex sounds, especially those of speech and music, it is often necessary to break them down, so to speak, into their components to discover what frequencies are present and what their relative intensities are. We may even want to know their phase relations. This process is known as *harmonic analysis, which is a method of isolating and determining the essential characteristics of the constituents in a complex tone.* These essential features consist of the frequencies, the amplitudes or amounts of energy, relative or absolute, and sometimes the phase relations of the partials. Several such methods are known. Some of these require that a curve of the sound wave be traced and then analyzed graphically or mechanically. These methods usually give data on all the characteristics of all the partials.

Since phase relations enter but little or not at all into a complex sound as it strikes the ear, other methods of analysis are often used which give direct readings of the frequencies and intensities of the components, the latter being read in terms of decibels. By this method, the sound itself may be put through an electroacoustical device which operates somewhat on the principle of the radio tuner, on which, by turning a dial, we are able to tune in on the various broadcasting stations whose radio waves are constantly on the air. But instead of the very high frequencies of radio waves, the instrument measures the frequencies within the audible range. This method of analysis gives, not a wave-to-wave indication of the structure of the sound, but a "cross section" of its composition, assuming a steady state of all the constituents—that is, that they are not fluctuating in either frequency or intensity. For many purposes such a cross section is all that is needed, and the method is entirely usable for these objectives.

When either of these methods of analysis is used, the data assembled provide the basis for a graph, in which the frequency is plotted against either amplitude or intensity in decibels. Such a graph is known as an *acoustic spectrum.* It is useful in revealing to the eye the entire harmonic composition of a sound, within the limits of the instrumentation. But unless an elaborate and time-consuming procedure is followed, it exhibits speech (or other sound) as a

[59] Harry F. Olson, "Frequency range preferences for speech and music," *Journal of the Acoustical Society of America* (July, 1947), *19*: 549–555.

static phenomenon rather than as a dynamic function. It presents all the components within the total range of frequencies and intensities covered by the particular procedure used, whether all these components are significant in the recognition and identification of the sounds involved or not, or whether they contribute, in the case of speech, to the comprehension of the content.

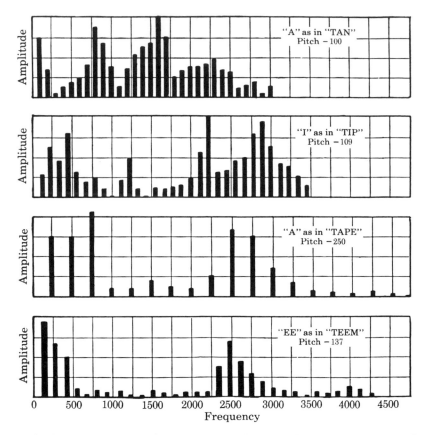

Figure 9. Acoustic Spectra. (From Harvey Fletcher, *Speech and Hearing*. Copyright, 1929, D. Van Nostrand Company, Princeton, New Jersey.)

For a complete examination of the harmonic composition of sounds such techniques are undoubtedly of value: they may permit a comparison of voices deemed to have good or poor quality, or an inquiry into the factors that differentiate one voice from another. But such detailed descriptions of the sounds involved in speech contain considerably more information than is essential for an understanding and examination of the basic distinguishing characteristics of the several sounds employed in oral communication. Figure 9 shows the harmonic spectra of some of the vowels.

While these analytical procedures have yielded much valuable information on the total structure or harmonic composition of the sounds of speech, both vowels and consonants, they still have not indicated the essentially dynamic nature of these sounds, which has long been recognized as an integral aspect of their formation. It has been shown repeatedly that while sustained speech sounds can readily be recognized, the typical sounds change materially from their initiation to their ending, these changes aiding in defining them in continuous speech.[60]

What is needed, therefore, is a method which will (1) provide a method of making an instantaneous record of the detailed composition of any selected sound at a certain instant, but also (2) isolate and record only those frequencies which are essential to the recognition and understanding of the sounds involved in speech, and (3) exhibit these identifying characteristics as a dynamic, continuously changing function in more or less connected speech.

One of the earliest attempts to show the changing pattern in speech sounds was that of Black,[61] who developed a tridimensional spectrum in which the frequencies and "relative energy" of the partials were plotted against each other and also against time, the time factor being represented by showing the respective spectra for the successive waves in the sound being studied, from its beginning to its end. He was able to show that speakers produced vowels of slightly different overtone structures, but also that "each vowel is a succession of different structures." Perhaps more significantly, he showed that "Even the most constant factors, the three frequency bands which characteristically contain centroids of energy, must be expressed in terms which permit considerable latitude." (See Figure 10.)

The procedure involved in such an investigation, however, requiring as it did a wave-to-wave analysis of from thirteen to twenty-two waves for each utterance, and as spoken by the same speaker a number of times as well as by different speakers, required an enormous amount of time. The labor necessitated by such a method would be wellnigh prohibitive in the description of continuous discourse. When it is considered that the analysis of a single wave of up to thirty components takes as much as three hours or more, it becomes obvious that the analysis of even a very short sentence would take weeks or months to complete.

[60] Gordon E. Peterson, "Systematic research in experimental phonetics: 4. The evaluation of speech signals," *Journal of Speech and Hearing Disorders* (1954), *19*: 158–168.
[61] John W. Black, "The quality of a spoken vowel," *Archives of Speech* (July, 1937), *2*: 7–27.

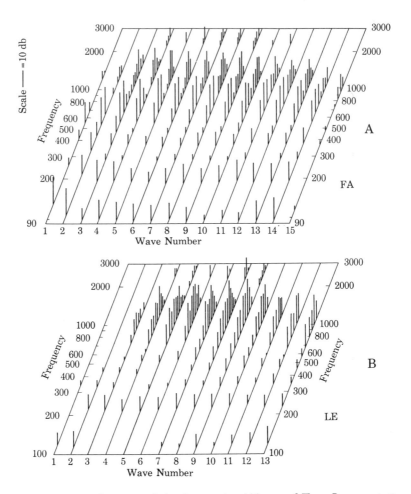

Figure 10. Acoustic Spectra of the Successive Waves of Two Pronunciations of the Vowel as Spoken by FA and LE. (From John W. Black, "The quality of a spoken vowel," *Archives of Speech* [July, 1937], 2:10.)

To meet the requirements as set forth above, the sound spectrograph has been developed.[62] According to Peterson, "the sound spectrograph was the first truly dynamic device developed for the analysis of speech." [63] It "has

[62] Ralph K. Potter, George A. Kopp, and Harriet C. Green, *Visible Speech*, Princeton, N.J., D. Van Nostrand Company, 1947.
[63] Peterson, *op. cit.*

provided a means of observing the dynamical characteristics of speech in its acoustical form." [64]

THE FORMANT.   The significant aspect of the spectrograph is that it produces a readily usable graph of the "frequency bands which characteristically contain centroids of energy" of which Black wrote, and to which has been given the designation of *formants*. The formant, in other words, consists of "two (sometimes three, seldom one) frequency regions of prominence in the speech sound as observed in the outside air. The frequency location of these regions of accentuated intensity, known as formants, is an important characteristic lending individuality to the various periodic sounds." [65]

The existence of such characteristic frequency regions for the different sounds of speech has been known for many years. They were observed in principle by Helmholtz, and described in part by D. C. Miller and others almost a half-century ago; they have been accepted as a significant aspect of speech sounds. But the observations made by earlier investigators entailed long and arduous processes and, while important, did not meet all the needs felt in the study of speech as a dynamic function. The spectrographic technique permits a rapid recording, observation, and analysis of all the formants that characterize the sounds being studied. In addition, it may be used to graph a complete spectrum, showing the relative intensities of all the partials, including those involved in the formants as well as those lying outside them.

The presence of these formants apparently arises from the peculiar characteristics of the resonating system in the throat and mouth. The vocal tract may be thought of as "a series of cylindrical sections, with acoustical mass and compliance uniformly distributed along each section." [66] Together with connecting tubes, these sections form a coupled system (see pages 79–80) which receives the energy supplied from the action of the vocal cords.

The vocal bands themselves serve to modulate the outgoing stream of air, referred to by Fletcher as a *direct current*, or d-c, by superimposing upon it a vibrating or fluctuating current, designated as an *alternating current*. This alternating current, or a-c, has frequencies ranging, with fundamental and harmonics, from approximately 80 cps to 8000 cps or more. "It is the ability

[64] Gordon E. Peterson, "Phonetics, phonemics, and pronunciation: spectrographic analysis," *Georgetown University Monograph Series on Languages and Linguistics* (July, 1954), *16*: 7–18.

[65] Fletcher, *op. cit.*, p. 10.

[66] H. K. Dunn, "The calculation of vocal resonance, and an electrical vocal tract," *Journal of the Acoustical Society of America* (November, 1950), *22*: 740–753.

of the [vocal] cavities selectively to reinforce various groups of harmonics (formants) at will that enables one to produce various speech sounds." [67]

Dunn's theory has been adapted by George A. Miller to illustrate the parallel between the physiological and the acoustical mechanisms (see Figure 11). The two major resonating cavities, the throat and mouth, with their connecting passages, are shown to be analogous to the cylindrical sections, with their joining tubes. Changes in the dimensions of the cylinders and tubes correspond to changes in the sizes and shapes of the vocal resonating

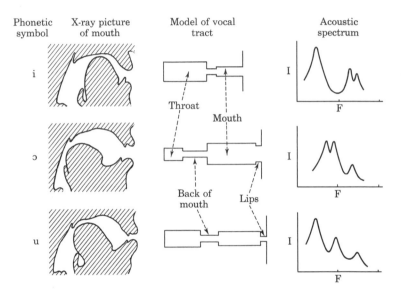

Figure 11. Summary Figure Showing the Phonetic Symbols, the Positions of the Speech Organs, the Sizes of the Resonating Cavities, and the Resulting Acoustic Spectra. (After Dunn. From George A. Miller, *Language and Communication*, p. 40. Copyright, 1951, McGraw-Hill Book Company, New York.)

cavities, and to the alterations in the connecting passages, both caused by the action primarily of the tongue and lips.[68] According to Fletcher, these changes follow very closely the progression of the vowels from the high-back [u] down through the low vowels, and up again to the high-front [i], as these vowels are located in the familiar vowel diagram.[69] Each of the cavities thus

---

[67] Fletcher, *op. cit.*, pp. 6 ff.

[68] Miller, *op. cit.*, pp. 39 f.

[69] Fletcher, *op. cit.*, pp. 1–3. D. C. Miller, *Science of Musical Sounds*, pp. 230 f., recognized and described the same progression as an acoustical as well as a phonetic phenomenon. However, his analysis revealed only a single formant for the back vowels, and two formants for the front vowels. See also Chapter IV.

created, the throat and the mouth, produces one formant, the coupling between them probably producing another.[70] In other words, it is the existence in the vocal tract of these two major resonating cavities, together with the narrow passages connecting them with each other and with the external air, that produces the "frequency regions of prominence" in the speech sounds, and differentiates them one from another. It is obvious, therefore, that no two sounds should have identical formants or relations between or among their respective formants. On the other hand, the differences that exist between voices are not sufficiently great to make identification of the different sound patterns difficult, so long as the speech itself is intelligible.[71]

The spectrum for each of the front vowels from [i] to [a] is shown in Figure 12. The presence of the three formants for these sounds is readily observable. Furthermore, the progression of .these formants as one moves from the high-front position to the low-front is clear. The first formant moves up from its lowest position in [i] until it is at its highest for [a]. On the other hand, the second and third formants, starting in their highest position for [i] move downward, in somewhat different amounts, until they are at their lowest for [a].

For the back vowels (see Figure 13), on the other hand, the first formant moves downward from [a] through the successive vowels to reach its lowest position in the high-back [u]. The movements of the other formants are somewhat less clear, but their presence is unmistakable, except that in these back vowels the third formant, and a fourth if present, either are so weak as not to be noticeable, or they blend in with the third so that it practically disappears.[72] The distinct pattern of each of the vowels is demonstrated in the spectrograms. Figure 14 shows the movement of the formants in six diphthongs.

In the consonants the total energy is distributed more widely, so that their characteristic patterns are not so readily distinguishable. But most of the voiced consonants, especially the voiced continuants and vowellike consonants, such as [l], [r], [m], [n], [ŋ], and the like, show fairly definite formants.

Potter and Steinberg [73] have charted the movements of the formants for the different sounds both for a single speaker and for twenty-five different speakers. Using a fundamental frequency of approximately 125 cps throughout, the single speaker showed for [i] a first formant of about 250 cps, a second

[70] *Ibid.*; see also Dunn, *op. cit.* This separation of first and second formants holds true only if they are well separated.

[71] Potter, Kopp, and Green, *op. cit.*, pp. 44–46.

[72] *Ibid.*, pp. 66, 69. See also the spectrograms on pp. 54–56.

[73] R. K. Potter and J. C. Steinberg, "Toward the specification of speech," *Journal of the Acoustical Society of America* (November, 1950), 22: 807–820.

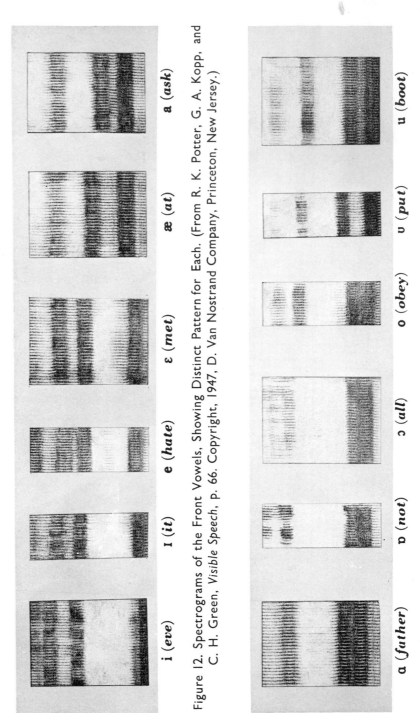

i (*eve*)   ɪ (*it*)   e (*hate*)   ε (*met*)   æ (*at*)   a (*ask*)

Figure 12. Spectrograms of the Front Vowels, Showing Distinct Pattern for Each. (From R. K. Potter, G. A. Kopp, and C. H. Green, *Visible Speech*, p. 66. Copyright, 1947, D. Van Nostrand Company, Princeton, New Jersey.)

ɑ (*father*)   ɒ (*not*)   ɔ (*all*)   o (*obey*)   ʊ (*put*)   u (*boot*)

Figure 13. Spectrogram of the Back Vowels, Showing Distinct Pattern for Each. (From R. K. Potter, G. A. Kopp, and C. H. Green, *Visible Speech*, p. 69. Copyright, 1947, D. Van Nostrand Company, Princeton, New Jersey.)

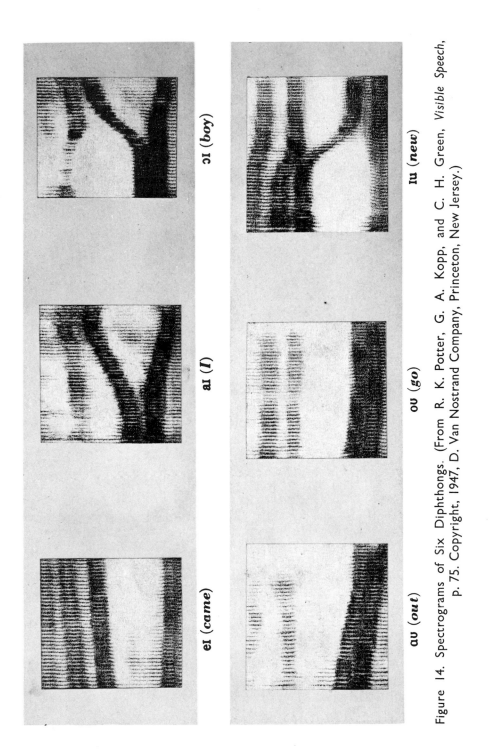

ɔɪ (*boy*)

aɪ (*I*)

eɪ (*came*)

ɪu (*new*)

ou (*go*)

aʊ (*out*)

Figure 14. Spectrograms of Six Diphthongs. (From R. K. Potter, G. A. Kopp, and C. H. Green, *Visible Speech*, p. 75. Copyright, 1947, D. Van Nostrand Company, Princeton, New Jersey.)

of about 2250 cps, and a third of somewhere near 2800 cps. For [ɪ], the first rises to 400, the second drops to 2000, and the third to 2500 cps. The formants for [ɑ] are close to 750, 1100, and 2600 respectively, and those for [u] are about 250, 800, and 2250 respectively (see Figure 15).

The figures given for these formant frequencies must be thought of as approximations only, for they are not constant for any one speaker, or for a

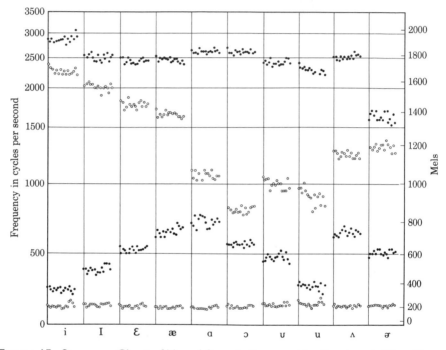

Figure 15. Sequence Chart of Vowel Sounds Repeated by Speaker A. The Observations for each vowel are plotted in the order of the repetitions. (From R. K. Potter and J. C. Steinberg, "Toward the specification of speech," *Journal of the Acoustical Society of America* [November, 1950], 22:815.)

number of different speakers. Moreover, formants cover not any single frequency, but bands of frequencies; they consist of *regions* of prominence rather than specific partials. Their width has been studied by Bogert, who found that "the band width was essentially constant and independent of the particular vowel. The mean values for bars [formants] 1, 2, and 3 were 130, 100, and 185 cps, respectively. Ten percent of the 300 band widths measured were less than 90 cps, and 10 percent greater than 260 cps."[74] However, as Peterson and Barney have pointed out, " . . . the difference between succes-

[74] B. P. Bogert, "On the band width of vowel formants," *Journal of the Acoustical Society of America* (July, 1953), 25: 791–792 (Abstract).

sive utterances of the same sound by the same individual is much less significant statistically than the difference between utterances of the same sound by different individuals." [75]

Illustrative of the variations in a single formant of a vowel spoken by a single person on two different "callings," and by a number of different

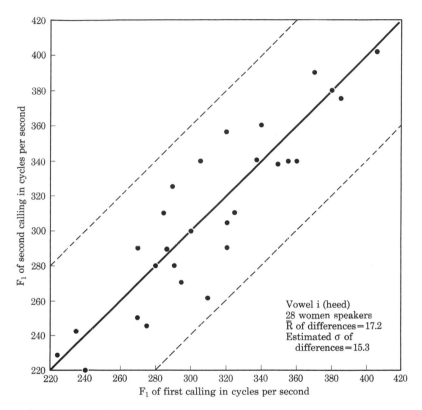

Figure 16. Accuracy-Precision Chart of First Formant Frequencies of [i] as Spoken by 28 Women. (From Gordon E. Peterson and Harold L. Barney, "Control methods used in a study of the vowels," *Journal of the Acoustical Society of America* [May, 1952], 24:181.)

individuals, is the chart drawn by Peterson and Barney, showing the first formant frequencies for the vowel [i] as spoken by twenty-eight women (see Figure 16). The position of the dot at the extreme left shows that for the individual represented here the first formant at one calling had a frequency

[75] Gordon E. Peterson and Harold L. Barney, "Control methods used in a study of the vowels," *Journal of the Acoustical Society of America* (May, 1952), 24: 175–184.

position of approximately 225 cps, and at the second calling of about 230 cps. That is, the two utterances of the vowel were quite consistent with regard to the frequency of the formant. The same consistency is shown by the speaker

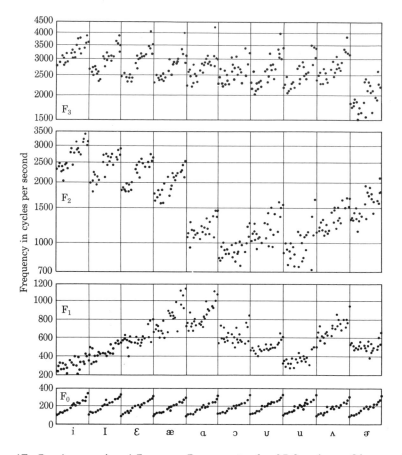

Figure 17. Fundamental and Formant Frequencies for 25 Speakers. Observations plotted in order of increasing average fundamental frequency for each speaker. First ten observations beginning at the left for each sound are for men, next ten are for women, and the last five are for children. (From R. K. Potter and J. C. Steinberg, "Toward the specification of speech," *Journal of the Acoustical Society of America* [November, 1950], 22:816.)

represented by the dot at the extreme right, whose first formant on one calling had a frequency of about 405, and on the other calling of close to 405 cps. The proximity of all the dots, representing the two utterances of the vowels for all the speakers, indicates a high correlation between the frequency positions for the two utterances by the twenty-eight women. Of 2280 points similarly plotted for the ten vowels measured in the study reported here, only thirty fell outside the limits of three times the standard deviation of 15.3 cycles, and twenty of these thirty "were the result of the individuals having produced pairs of sound which were unlike phonetically, as shown by the results of the listening tests." [76]

When the formants of the vowels produced by a number of different speakers are charted, the results show again that there is a wide range in the frequency of the formants when spoken by twenty-five speakers. In Figure 17, the speakers in each block representing a particular sound are arranged in the order of ascending frequency of the fundamental. The first ten speakers, from left to right, were men, the next ten were women, and the last five were children.

Although the same general pattern of movement of the formants as a whole is the same as that for a single speaker, the frequency range for each formant, for all twenty-five speakers, is markedly different from the range for a single speaker, as can be seen in Figure 16. While it is difficult, if not impossible, to establish from the graphs specific frequencies in any instance, the wide range of frequencies for all formants for all vowels, as contrasted with the range for a single speaker, is obvious.

It may be observed, also, that from left to right in each block representing a separate vowel, there is an unmistakable tendency for the frequency of each formant to rise with the frequency of the fundamental. In general, the frequencies of the formants are higher for the women than for the men, and still higher for the children.

Table 2 shows the averages of the fundamental and the formant frequencies, together with the formant amplitudes, of vowels as spoken by seventy-six speakers, including men, women, and children. Again it will be noted that for all vowels, the average frequency of the fundamental and of all the formants is higher for the women than for the men, and higher for the children than for the women. However, for some of the vowels the differences between the frequencies of the first formant for the men and the women are probably so small as not to be significant.

The formant amplitudes are based on the amplitudes of the first formant of the vowel [ɔ] (see Table 1, page 109), which has the highest phonetic power of all the vowels.

The ratios of pitch among the formants, measured in *mels*,[77] appear to be

[76] *Ibid.*

[77] The *mel* is defined as a "unit of pitch." (Stevens and Davis, *op. cit.*, p. 453.) A pitch of 1000 mels, the pitch of a 1000-cycle tone at an intensity of 40 db above the threshold of audibility, is twice as high as a tone of 500 mels. (*Ibid.*, pp. 80–81.)

TABLE 2. AVERAGES OF FUNDAMENTAL AND FORMANT FREQUENCIES AND
FORMANT AMPLITUDES OF VOWELS BY 76 SPEAKERS[a]

		i	I	ɛ	æ	ɑ	ɔ	U	u	ʌ	ɝ
Fundamental fre-	M	136	135	130	127	124	129	137	141	130	133
quencies (cps)	W	235	232	223	210	212	216	232	231	221	218
	Ch	272	269	260	251	256	263	276	274	261	261

Formant frequencies (cps)

		i	I	ɛ	æ	ɑ	ɔ	U	u	ʌ	ɝ
	M	270	390	530	660	730	570	440	300	640	490
F_1	W	310	430	610	860	850	590	470	370	760	500
	Ch	370	530	690	1010	1030	680	560	430	850	560
	M	2290	1990	1840	1720	1090	840	1020	870	1190	1350
F_2	W	2790	2480	2330	2050	1220	920	1160	950	1400	1640
	Ch	3200	2730	2610	2320	1370	1060	1410	1170	1590	1820
	M	3010	2550	2480	2410	2440	2410	2240	2240	2390	1690
F_3	W	3310	3070	2990	2850	2810	2710	2680	2670	2780	1960
	Ch	3730	3600	3570	3320	3170	3180	3310	3260	3360	2160

		i	I	ɛ	æ	ɑ	ɔ	U	u	ʌ	ɝ
Formant amplitudes	L_1	−4	−3	−2	−1	−1	0	−1	−3	−1	−5
(db)	L_2	−24	−23	−17	−12	−5	−7	−12	−19	−10	−15
	L_3	−28	−27	−24	−22	−28	−34	−34	−43	−27	−20

[a] From Gordon E. Peterson and Harold L. Barney, "Control methods used in a study of the vowels," *Journal of the Acoustical Society of America* (May, 1952), 24: 183.

"fairly constant over the range of speakers, including men, women, and children. Within limits, the ratios tend to characterize certain groups of vowels. For example, the ratio (between the mel values of the third and second formants) is significantly different for the two groups, front and back vowels." [78]

To summarize: Different sounds of speech are distinguished by the presence of characteristic frequency regions in which the partials lying within those regions receive a significantly greater portion of the total energy of the sound involved than do the other components. These characteristic regions are known as formants, and are produced by peculiarities in the size and shape of the resonance cavities in the vocal tract, and of the connecting passages resulting from the different movements and positions of the tongue and lips

[78] Peterson and Barney, *op. cit.*

primarily. In passing from the high-front vowel to the low-front, the first of three formants shows a gradual rise in frequency, while the second and third exhibit a gradual fall, the second showing the greater drop. From the high-back vowel to the low-back, the first and third formants show a general lowering of pitch, while the second rises. The central vowel [ʌ] shows all three formants having a frequency above those of the back vowels, 725, 1000, and 1160, while [ɝ] has formants with frequencies of 600, 1200, and 1350 respectively, all these figures being approximations. The formants of women are in general higher than those of men, and those of children highest of all. The mel ratios of the formants are fairly constant for all speakers.

Time, Duration

The factor of time in relation to speech has not been explored as extensively as the three just described. It is, however, a significant aspect of speech, as it is of sound in general. The physicist uses units of time in measuring frequencies; he determines the duration of the reverberation in a room in time units; he knows that it takes time to build up reverberation, and that the phenomenon of damping is largely a function of time. He measures velocities in terms of so many meters or feet per second, and so on. Time is therefore an indispensable aspect of sound for both physicist and psychologist, even though it is not of itself a physical phenomenon.

Neither is time a direct product of the functioning of the vocal mechanism, as are frequency, intensity, and wave complexity, except where there are certain time limitations, as in the production of a continuous tone or of a succession of tones when the replenishing of the breath supply is involved.

Time values are manifested in three ways: first, in the duration of tones; second, in the frequency of the pauses between tones or phrases; and third, in the duration of such pauses. The significance of these three values will be shown in a later chapter in connection with the problem of meaning and its relation to the manner of utterance. In 1781, John Walker made the pause one of the bases of an elaborate system of speech delivery, then called elocution; about a century and a quarter later, S. H. Clark again began his discussion of the art of reading aloud from the printed page with a treatment of the pause as a significant aspect of the problem of the meaning of the passage to be read.

Time and Dialectal Differences.   In a study of dialectal differences made more than twenty-five years ago, Bailey compared the speech of native-born

Easterners and Southerners as to pitch and time. With respect to the time factor, she concluded:

1. Southerners have a slightly longer average net total time for speaking the same material than do Easterners.
2. In accordance with this, Southerners have:
    a. A greater average time of significant phonation.
    b. A greater average duration of phonations.
    c. A shorter average time for pauses and voiceless consonants.
3. The characteristic vowel and diphthong "differences" seem to be due to the factor of duration. The Southerners prolong the [ɔ], [ɪ], [eɪ], and [aɪ], while the Easterners prolong the [æ] and [ɑ] and retain the final "r" in more cases than do the Southerners.[79]

Minimum Perceptible Differences.   The varying rates of speech have been studied and reported by a number of observers. These rates range from somewhere near 100 words per minute to several hundred words per minute, with an average duration of sounds from 0.1 second to somewhat less than 0.02 second. The question has been raised in this connection and in others as to just how short a sound can be and still be recognizable. A number of studies of the minimum perceptible duration have been discussed by Gemelli and Pastori,[80] who themselves concluded that a minimum of two complete cycles was sufficient to enable the listener to identify any one of five Italian vowels. Further, it was concluded that the minimum duration of time varied from 1/245 to 1/130, or from 0.04 to 0.077 second.

Peterson, however, has indicated that vowels of even shorter duration may be recognized. He reports that in an early study made by himself he obtained as high as 40 percent recognitions of vowels having a duration of only 4 milliseconds (0.004).[81] In this study he was able to obtain over 50 percent recognitions at an interval (duration) of 0.0031 second, which at the frequency used gave 0.298 cycle. It should also be pointed out that observers vary in their ability to recognize sounds of such short durations, and sounds themselves vary in their recognizability.

[79] Nina Virginia Bailey, "Pitch and time variations in certain American regional dialects," Unpublished Master's Thesis, State University of Iowa, 1930.

[80] Agostino Gemelli and Giuseppina Pastori, "La durata minima di un fonema sufficiente per la sua percezione," *L'Analisi Elettroacustica del linguaggio*, Milano, Italia. Universita Cattolica del Sacro Cuore (1934), *1*: 149–162.

[81] Peterson, *op. cit.* See also his "The significance of various portions of the wave length in the minimum duration necessary for the recognition of vowel sounds." Unpublished Ph.D. Dissertation, Louisiana State University, 1939.

Tiffany has concluded that "It appears that vowel recognition varies as a function of duration, in ways which depend upon 'natural' or habitual durations of vowels in speech . . . the nearer a given vowel is to its 'natural' duration the better will be recognition for that vowel."[82]

According to an investigation by Fry, the duration ratio is of greater significance in listeners' judgments of stress than is the intensity ratio. While both are significant, the former is the more effective cue.[83]

Volume

The fifth of the basic factors of sound discussed by Erickson[84] is *volume*. Some sounds seem to fill space; we think of them as *big* sounds. The deepest notes of an organ, the rumbling of thunder, the tolling of a large bell, all seem to have a spatial volume, a size that is not characteristic of the shrill notes of the fife, the twitter of birds, the crackling of paper, or other sounds of higher frequency. Ordinarily, the lower the pitch, the greater the volume; and with a given tone, the greater the intensity, the greater the volume. Deep tones seem more massive than high ones.

Volume and intensity differ in this particular, namely, that whereas intensity varies with both amplitude and frequency, volume apparently varies with the amplitude, but approximately inversely as the frequency. Furthermore, although reasonably reliable measurements have been made of loudness through the use of the decibel as a measure of intensity difference, no reliable measurements of volume have been made. Judgments of volume are much cruder than those of loudness. Some observers insist that they detect no effect of space at all. The physicist does not use the term. It is doubtful whether the relation between pitch and volume is very close; certainly they bear no inverse linear relation.

The term "extensity" is sometimes used to refer to this spatial attribute of tones, volume representing a combination of attributes, of which extensity is one. Seashore[85] mentions as components of volume (1) *extensity*, or spatial bigness; (2) *intensity*, as heretofore described; (3) *timbre*, or richness, the rich tones with low overtones having greater volume; and (4) *reduplication*

---

[82] William R. Tiffany, "Vowel recognition as a function of duration, frequency modulation and phonetic context," *Journal of Speech and Hearing Disorders* (1953), *18*: 289–301.

[83] D. B. Fry, "Duration and intensity as physical correlates of linguistic stress," *Journal of the Acoustical Society of America* (1955), *27*: 765–768.

[84] *Op. cit.* This factor is fourth in Erickson's list, fifth to be presented here.

[85] Carl Emil Seashore, *The Psychology of Musical Talent*, New York, Silver, Burdette & Company, 1919, pp. 163–167.

and reflection, the effect of "rapid repetition or simultaneous sounding of several tones or tone elements." Volume may be any one of these four kinds, or it may be any combination of these components in any degree of complexity.

Since volume is a function of both pitch and intensity, no specific mechanism is required for its production and control.

Chapter III

The Physiological Basis
of Speech

IN THE preceding chapter the statement was made that the audible phenomena of speech could be described according to physical and psychological principles. That chapter discussed some of the simpler and more fundamental of these principles, in order to furnish background for an understanding of the physical basis of speech and to relate that basis to our experience of sound. The present chapter describes the human mechanism by which those sounds are produced and the functioning of that mechanism, so far as it is known.

For the production of sounds, it was pointed out, only two things are necessary: a source of energy and a vibrator. In most musical instruments, it was further noted, a third element is added: a resonator, to improve the sound and to give it the distinctive timbre of the instrument. These three elements are all used in the production of vocal sounds; but for the formation of the sounds of articulate speech, an additional element is needed: the articulatory mechanism, with which we form the vowels and consonants and combine them into words, phrases, and sentences. All four of these elements are included in the speech mechanism.

Source of Energy: Respiration

In the various sound-producing instruments the vibrators are actuated in many different ways. The strings of the piano are struck, those of a harp are plucked, and those of a violin are bowed or, as we have said, stroked. Metal bars may be struck or stroked with resin-covered gloves. The air column of a wind instrument may be actuated by the vibration of a single reed, as in the clarinet; by a double reed, as in the oboe or bassoon; by the setting up of eddies in the air as it passes over a thin lip, as in the flute or organ pipe; or by the vibration of the human lips when the player blows through them, as in the trumpet, trombone, or other brass instrument. In some sound-producing instruments an oscillating or pulsating electrical current sets a metal membrane or thin plate into vibration. In the dynamic loud-speaker of a radio, such a current actuates a coil of wire to which is attached a paper or parchment cone to produce the sound.

In the voice, the column of air in the throat, mouth, and nasal cavities is set into vibration by the passage of a stream of air over the *vocal cords* or *vocal bands* or *voice lips*, thus causing them to vibrate. This action has been compared with the action of the lips of a brass instrument player, although there is no instrument which parallels the vocal instrument in every particular.[1]

Whatever may be the exact action, it is certain that the immediate source of energy is the stream of breath as it passes over the vocal bands. But since air is in a sense inert, incapable of acting of its own accord, we must look back of that for some activating mechanism. This mechanism we find in the respiratory apparatus, which has the power, under proper stimulation, of forcing the breath over the bands and causing them to vibrate.

General Structure

The body, that is, the torso, is divided into two cavities, upper and lower, separated by a muscular and tendinous wall. The upper cavity, called the thorax or thoracic cavity, is almost entirely filled with the lungs and heart; the lower, or abdominal, cavity contains various glands, the organs of digestion, and, in the case of females, the organs of reproduction. There is practically no air space in either of these cavities, outside the lungs.

The Thorax. It is in the upper cavity, the thorax, that are found the lungs and chief muscles of inhalation, as will be explained later.

THE FRAMEWORK. The bony cage or framework of the thorax consists of the vertebrae (spinal column), the sternum (breast bone), the ribs, the scapulae (shoulder blades), and the clavicles (collar bones). This framework

---

[1] The comparison has been called into question by Drew and Kellogg ("Starting characteristics of speech sounds," *Journal of the Acoustical Society of America* (July, 1940), *12*: 85–103), who conclude that because of the suddenness of the starting of speech sounds, the air column could not react on the vocal bands, as the column of air in a trumpet reacts on the lips of the player. The action of the vocal bands, they suggest, is more of a relaxation oscillation. See Chap. II, p. 101, and the section on *Phonation* in this chapter.

is so jointed together that a certain amount of movement is possible. The most important skeletal movement for breathing is that of the ribs.

The ribs, which are twelve in number on each side, are so articulated to the vertebrae at the back and to the sternum and to each other in front that when they are pulled upward there is also an increase in the horizontal distance between the corresponding ribs on either side, resulting in a lateral expansion of the thorax. There is also an increase in the distance between the front of the chest wall (the sternum) and the back (the spinal column). If one places the tips of the fingers together about fifteen inches from and in front of the shoulders, with the elbows down, and then gradually raises the elbows, keeping the hands in the same vertical position, it will be evident how the distance between the elbows increases. This roughly illustrates the action of the ribs and how their rise affects the lateral as well as ventrodorsal dimension.

THE LUNGS. The lungs, like all the other so-called organs of speech, were not originally developed for speech at all. They were, and from a strictly biological standpoint still are, for the much more basic and vital purpose of ventilating the blood. Their use in speech is what has been called an "overlaid function." [2] Biologically, the lungs are the chief organs of respiration. They lie in the thoracic cavity, almost filling it, and surrounding the heart. There are two lungs, a right and a left, each being further divided into lobes, the right having three and the left two. The lungs "rest" upon the upper surface of the diaphragm, which is the partition that separates the thoracic from the abdominal cavity.

The general shape of the lungs is conical, with the apex of the cone extending slightly above the upper end of the sternum. The sides conform to the shape of the internal walls of the thorax, and the base is deeply concave, following the shape of the diaphragm.

The lungs themselves consist of a light, spongy, porous tissue, made up of countless air tubes and minute air sacs, which are enclosed by elastic tissues and blood vessels. This tissue is almost purely passive, having in it but few minute muscular fibers. For this reason it cannot exert any force other than that provided by the elasticity of the tissue itself.

It is from the millions of tiny air sacs that the oxygen is taken up by the blood and carried to the tissues of the body. The sacs open up into tubules;

[2] An "overlaid function" may be defined as one which has been superimposed upon the primary, biological function which a given mechanism performs. The definition has been made to imply that the mechanism itself never becomes modified, through the processes of evolution, to perform more efficiently such a superimposed function, however vital that function might be to survival. See Chapter VIII, pp. 474–476.

these converge to form the bronchioles, which in turn lead into the bronchi. The bronchi converge finally to form the trachea, or windpipe, which connects, through the larynx, throat, mouth, and nasal passages, with the open air. Through the branches and subdivisions of these air passages, the air is brought into and from the remotest portions of the lungs.

Biologically the lungs are important because it is here that the oxygen from the air is taken into the blood and exchanged for the carbon dioxide and other gases which are the products of the work done by the muscles. This exchange

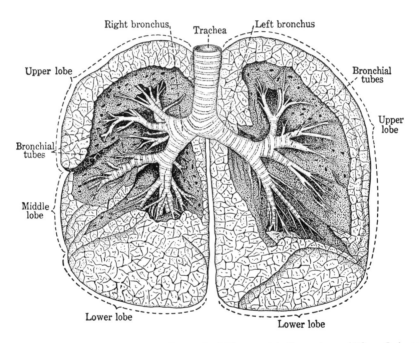

Figure 18. The Lungs, Showing Bronchial Tree with Branches. (After Sobotta.)

takes place by the law of diffusion of gases, a process which in this case resembles osmosis, in that the oxygen must go from the air to the blood, and the carbon dioxide from the blood to the air, through the semipermeable tissues which constitute the walls of the air sacs and capillaries. It is in the lungs that under proper conditions a fresh supply of oxygen is always available, and it is from the lungs that useless or harmful products are carried away from the body.

From the standpoint of speech, the lungs are important because they provide a sort of reservoir for the breath which is to be used in setting the vocal bands into vibration, much as the bellows of an organ provides the reservoir for the air which is used to set the reeds (of the old parlor organ) or the columns of air in a pipe organ into vibration.

The capacity of the lungs varies considerably among different people. A fair average for men is perhaps 225 cubic inches (approximately 3700 cc) and for women from 50 to 75 cubic inches less. That is the volume of air that can be inhaled and exhaled in a single cycle of respiration, and it is called the *vital capacity*. There is in addition a small volume of air, amounting to perhaps 100 cubic inches, that cannot be entirely expelled. It is called the *residual air*. Some men have a capacity of 350 or even 400 cubic inches or more, while others have not more than 150. Some women may have as much as 275 or even 300, and others not more than 100 or 125.

Despite the fact that formerly much attention was given to increasing the capacity of the lungs, there is no evidence that the amount of the vital capacity is of any significance in the production of voice. There is, moreover, no evidence that either quality of tone, strength of tone, or ability to control the strength is in any way dependent upon the total amount of air that one can draw into the lungs. Correlations between vital capacity and audibility are so small as to be negligible (0.12 for normal intensity of voice and 0.22 for loud speaking). As for quality, the correlation, though still too small to be significant, is *negative*; that is, the tendency is for quality to decrease as the vital capacity increases.[3]

Although the vital capacity may be anywhere between the figures given, or even beyond them, the amount of air actually used in breathing is quite small. The average quantity of air which passes into and out of the lungs in a single respiratory cycle is no more than about 30 cubic inches, or about 13 percent of the vital capacity. This figure again varies considerably, ranging from perhaps 5 to 35 percent. Furthermore, the amount of air used in uttering a single phrase (that is, the amount that is actually taken into the lungs at one time in reading or speaking) is generally little if any more than in casual breathing. In fact, more than one-half of a group of 140 subjects breathed more deeply for "life purposes" than for normal speech.[4] However, an individual who uses a large percentage of his vital capacity in casual breathing is likely also to use a large percentage in speaking as well.

[3] Harriett R. Idol, "A statistical study of respiration in relation to speech characteristics," in *Studies in Experimental Phonetics*, Giles Wilkeson Gray (ed.), Louisiana State University Studies, No. 27, Baton Rouge, Louisiana State University Press, 1936, pp. 79–98. See also Charles F. Lindsley, "The psychophysical determinants of voice quality," *Speech Monographs* (1934), *1*: 79–116; and John Barnes, "Vital capacity and ability in oral reading," *The Quarterly Journal of Speech Education* (June, 1926), *12*: 176–181.

[4] Idol, *op. cit.*

But here again there is no evidence that those people who use a large amount of *tidal air*, as it is called, either in actual volume or in proportion to vital capacity, have any better voices or are any better speakers than those who use smaller actual or proportionate amounts of breath, the correlations being again too small to be significant.[5]

Another interesting fact is that not everyone requires more breath to speak loudly than to speak in a normal voice. In fact, in a study of this subject, almost one-third of the 140 people studied used even less breath in speaking loudly than in speaking normally.[6] Increase in loudness in such cases seems to be achieved by adjustments in resonance, resulting in a greater audibility of the tone without corresponding increase in volume of breath used.

Adequate and accurate techniques for studying the mechanics of respiration are still in process of development. Heretofore, most theories of breathing have been based on studies of the expansion and contraction of the torso at different levels during inhalation and exhalation. While data obtained from these techniques have yielded valuable knowledge, they do not of themselves, and apart from such inferences as can be drawn from those movements which can be seen and measured, give us a great deal of precise information about the actual movement of the ribs and the muscles, such as the diaphragm, during the process of respiration. The application of X-ray photography to the study of these movements, so devised as to give images of movements and positions at successive instants in the respiratory cycle, offer possibilities for a much more thorough investigation of the process of breathing. Such studies provide some evidence that the peripheral measurements are in fact closely correlated with the actual movements of the ribs and muscles involved in the processes of inhalation and exhalation.[7] Principles presented here are valid only in the light of such objective data as are currently available.

The Process of Respiration

Respiration is, as has been said, a biological function; that is, it was originally and primarily concerned with the maintenance of life in the organism. But somewhere in the course of animal development it was discovered that if a given animal did certain things to certain tissues in the region of the throat while the air was being expelled, sounds would ensue that would

[5] *Ibid.*
[6] *Ibid.*
[7] Harlan Bloomer and Hide H. Shohara, "The study of respiratory movements by Roentgen kymography," *Speech Monographs* (1941), *8*: 91–101.

have definite effects on other animals.[8] And so, even though this may not have been a "conscious" discovery, vocal and other sounds have been made for countless generations by both animals and men for the expression of their emotional states and for the effect they may have on other animals and men.

Breathing for speech is essentially the same process as breathing for life. It consists of two phases: *inhalation*, in which the air flows into the lungs, where it feeds the blood with refreshing oxygen to be carried to the tissues to aid in doing work; and *exhalation*, in which the air flows out again into the open air, laden with carbon dioxide and other waste matter.

Consider again the cone-shaped thorax, with the lungs (surrounding the heart) entirely filling it, into which the breath rushes in inhalation and from which it is expelled in exhalation. This alternating process, repeated throughout life at the rate of from twelve to twenty times a minute, is carried on by increasing and decreasing the capacity of the thorax once for each respiratory cycle. The dimensions of the thoracic cavity are enlarged, creating a partial vacuum, and the atmospheric pressure forces air into the lungs. On exhalation, one of two things may happen: (1) the natural elasticity of the muscle and lung tissue may cause it to resume its condition of comparative flaccidity, thus gently forcing, or perhaps permitting, the air to flow out; or (2) the dimensions of the thorax may be decreased by positive action of certain muscles of the torso, more forcibly expelling the breath.

Inhalation.   To increase the volume of a cone, one or both of two things may be done: increase the altitude or vertical dimension or increase the area of the base. In such an irregular cone as the thorax, with its more or less movable walls, we may also, in this case, pull out—or bulge, so to speak—the walls themselves without appreciably enlarging the area of the base of the cone or increasing its altitude.

Usually, all of these things happen simultaneously in inhalation. Particularly, the altitude is increased by pulling down on the concave base, and the lateral dimensions are increased by the upward and outward movement of the ribs. These movements are performed by the action of certain muscles of the thorax.

ENLARGING THE THORAX.   The lateral dimensions of the thorax are increased by the upward and outward action of the ribs, with a slight forward and upward movement of the sternum, particularly the lower end (see

[8] In fact, lower animals use many different kinds of sound-producing apparatus. Even among the insects, such as the cricket, the katydid, and others, sounds are produced partly if not largely for their effect on other members of the species.

Figure 19). There is, of course, no way of thrusting the ribs outward, but since their slope is in general downward, any movement that will pull them upward will move the curved edges farther apart. This expansion is accomplished by a number of muscles of the shoulders and chest. Most of these

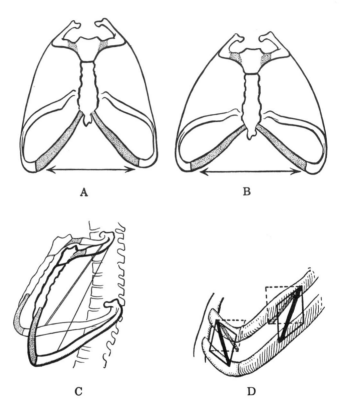

Figure 19. Changes in the Thoracic Cage in Breathing. (A) In exhalation; (B) in inhalation; (C) both positions viewed from the side; (D) shows that the intercostal space is decreased when the ribs are raised. (From Alfred Benninghoff, *Lehrbuch der Anatomie des Menschen*, 4th ed., München–Berlin, Urban & Schwarzenberg, 1949, vol. I, p. 197.)

muscles have a dual function—that is, they do other things as well—but for our purposes we shall consider them only in relation to breathing.

In the following descriptions of the mechanism of respiration there is no intention of implying that the muscles here named are the only ones involved in the process. In quiet, unforced breathing a minimum number of them are active; whereas in deep, forced breathing, as many as eight or ten, or even more, additional muscles may be called into play.[9] As to the specific muscles involved in either quiet or forced respiration, there is no complete agreement among authorities.

THE DIAPHRAGM. One of the important muscles of inhalation is the *diaphragm*. It constitutes the floor of the thorax and the roof of the abdomen, and its movements up and down, or rather diagonally forward and down, provide for the changes in the vertical dimension of the thoracic cone.

The diaphragm is in general somewhat double-dome-shaped, with the right

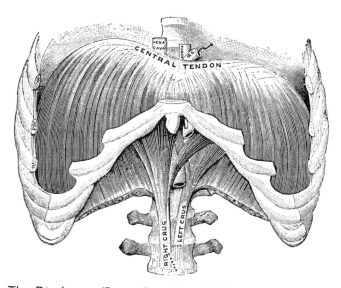

Figure 20. The Diaphram. (From Gerrish in Wilbur P. Bowen and Henry A. Stone, *Applied Anatomy and Kinesiology*, 6th ed., Philadelphia, Lea & Febiger, 1949, p. 226. Courtesy of Lea & Febiger.)

hemidiaphragm rising a little higher than the left. At the center is a large, relatively flat, thin tendon, the "central tendon," shaped somewhat like a lima bean. From the edges of this tendon, entirely around its periphery, is a muscular rim, the fibers extending downward from the edge of the tendon to the body walls and attaching to the lower ribs and the spinal column. At the front they are attached at about the base of the sternum, while at the back the attachment is somewhat lower.

When the muscular fibers contract, they pull upward on the lower ribs and

[9] Lyman Spicer Judson and Andrew Thomas Weaver, *Voice Science*, New York, Appleton-Century-Crofts, 1942, chap. I.

downward on the central tendon. The ribs being to some extent "anchored," as will be shown later, the resulting downward movement of the central tendon increases the vertical dimension of the thorax. It has been commonly supposed that when the muscular rim of the diaphragm contracts, the whole structure is pulled downward, with a consequent flattening of the "dome." X-ray observations indicate that this supposed "flattening" accounts for a very small percentage of the increased volume of the lungs.[10] The anterior portion of the diaphragm descends very little and may even rise as the ribs to which it is attached are elevated. The greater part of the increase in volume is caused rather by a forward and downward movement of the posterior portion, so that differences in the relative heights of the two hemidiaphragms, and the median depression between them, become appreciably smaller. The cavity being thus enlarged, a partial vacuum is created, and the outside air rushes in from atmospheric pressure, expanding the spongy tissue of the lungs to take up the added space.

At the same time, the downward and forward movement of the diaphragm exerts a pressure on the digestive organs of the abdomen. There is a great deal of space in the abdominal region surrounded not by a bony cage but by flexible tissue—muscle, tendinous membranes, and the like. When the diaphragm pushes the contents of the abdomen or the abdominal viscera downward, they must give way in some direction. At the back is the spinal column; at the bottom of the abdominal cavity is the pelvic girdle, a firm, bony floor. Two possibilities for expansion are presented:

1. When the ribs rise, and the horizontal (lateral and ventrodorsal) dimensions of the thorax are increased, the circumference of the upper part of the abdomen is also increased, and the viscera have room to expand without any great increase in the circumference of the lower portions of the abdomen. The diaphragm can thus exert its pull downward, the viscera filling the space created in the upper abdomen by the general increase of the midtorso. In fact, during the maximum raising of the thorax the abdomen is somewhat drawn in at the sides.[11] When this movement and expansion are predominant near the base of the sternum, as compared with the thoracic and lower abdominal expansion, the type of breathing is called "medial." In such movement, the lower abdomen, as has been pointed out, may not expand much, if at all.

[10] H. H. Bloomer, "A roentgenographic study of the mechanics of respiration," *Speech Monographs* (1936), *3*: 118–124.

[11] Alfred Benninghoff, *Lehrbuch der Anatomie des Menschen*, drei Bände, Berlin, Urban & Schwarzenberg, erster Band, 1949, S. 220.

2. If the action of the ribs does not create such an increase in the circumference of the upper abdomen, then the movement of the abdominal viscera presents a somewhat different aspect. In this case, there is only one possible direction for these organs to expand, and that is downward and outward. The result is an outward expansion of the lower abdominal walls, the movement extending down even as far as the pelvis.

The importance of the action of the diaphragm has probably been greatly overestimated. Bloomer estimates that the downward movement of the diaphragm accounts for approximately 40 percent of the vital capacity.[12] Its movement actually is not great. The maximum excursion of the tendon is only about two and one-third inches, while for normal respiration, either for life breathing or for speaking, it is probably little more than one-fourth or one-third of that. It seems probable that more adequate and more accurate measurements of the actual movement of the muscles involved will be necessary before a final determination of the specific role played by any of them in respiration can be made.

THE THORACIC MUSCLES OF INHALATION.   While we are going into some detail regarding the muscles of the thorax, let us at the same time get a general picture of what takes place in inhalation in addition to the "descent" of the diaphragm. The diaphragm itself is attached at the sides to the lowest ribs. When it contracts it might, instead of pulling the central tendon downward, pull the ribs upward with little or no increase in the vertical dimension of the thorax, were it not for a few other muscles which exert a downward pull on those ribs, thus providing a partial anchorage against the pull of the diaphragm. One of these, the *serratus posterior inferior* (Figure 21), extends from the thoracic and lumbar vertebrae to the lowest four ribs. Another is the *quadratus lumborum* (Figure 22), extending from the region of the ilium (the point of the hip bone on which one's belt hangs) up to the lowest rib. While these do not assist directly in the enlarging of the thoracic cavity, they do indirectly and are therefore of some importance in inhalation. It seems probable, however, that their function in pulling the ribs downward in exhalation is even more important.

According to Cunningham, the action of the diaphragm in elevating the ribs and thus increasing the transverse and ventrodorsal dimensions of the thorax is of greater importance than its downward movement increasing the vertical dimension.[13] Bowen and Stone, however, maintain that the

[12] Bloomer, *op. cit.*
[13] D. J. Cunningham, *Textbook of Anatomy*, 3rd ed., Baltimore, William Wood & Company, 1909, p. 419.

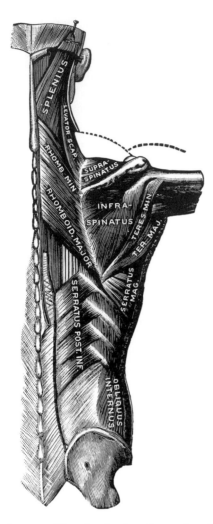

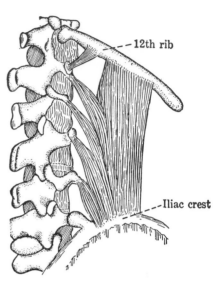

Figure 21. *Left*. The Serratus Posterior Inferior Muscle. (From Gerrish in Wilbur P. Bowen and Henry A. Stone, *Applied Anatomy and Kinesiology*, 6th ed., Philadelphia, Lea & Febiger, 1949, p. 99. Courtesy of Lea & Febiger.)

Figure 22. The Quadratus Lumborum. (After Sobotta.)

diaphragm lifts the body ribs only slightly, its principal movement being to depress the central tendon.[14]

At the same time that the diaphragm is descending, other muscles are at work raising the ribs. Some of these are anterior (front), others are posterior (back), and still others are lateral (sides). They are paired; that is, there is one on each side of the body.

The front or anterior muscles include the *pectoralis major* (Figures 23, 29)

[14] Wilbur Pardon Bowen and Henry A. Stone, *Applied Anatomy and Kinesiology*, 6th ed., Philadelphia, Lea & Febiger, 1949, p. 227.

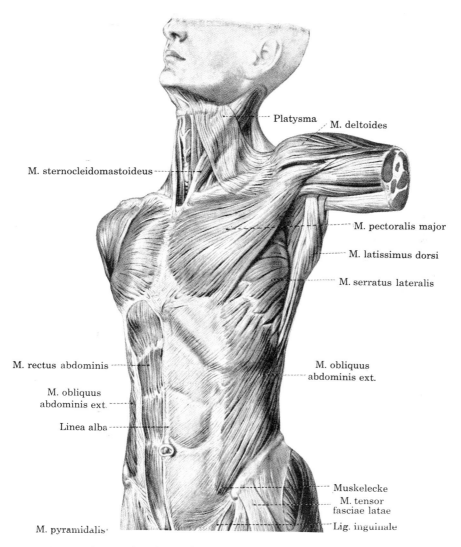

Figure 23. Muscles of the Torso, Viewed Obliquely from Front to Side. (From Alfred Benninghoff, *Lehrbuch der Anatomie des Menschen*, 4th ed., München-Berlin, Urban & Schwarzenberg, 1949, vol. I, p. 175.)

and *pectoralis minor* (Figure 24). The first of these extends from the collar bone and sternum down to the upper five or six ribs, and the latter extends from the shoulder blade down to the third, fourth, and fifth ribs. Their action, when the arm and shoulder are firmly fixed, is to pull these ribs upward. The first rib is elevated primarily by the *subclavius* (Figure 29), which extends up to the collar bone. In some forms of breathing, which are generally not to be recommended, the *sternocleidomastoideus* (Figure 25), which, beginning with the mastoid bone back of the ear and reaching down to the collar bone and the sternum, serves to exaggerate the elevation of these two bones. It is probably most active in what is known as clavicular breathing.

At the back, or posteriorly, certain other muscles attached to the vertebrae

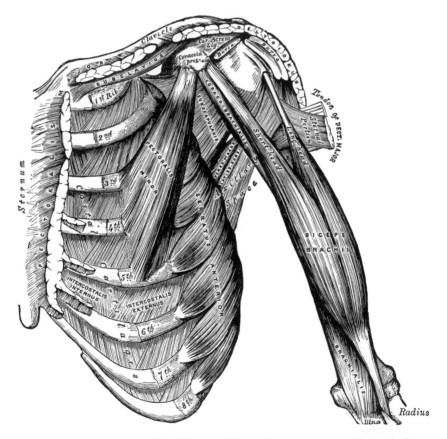

Figure 24. Deep Muscles of the Thorax. (From *Gray's Anatomy*, 26th ed. Courtesy of Lea & Febiger.)

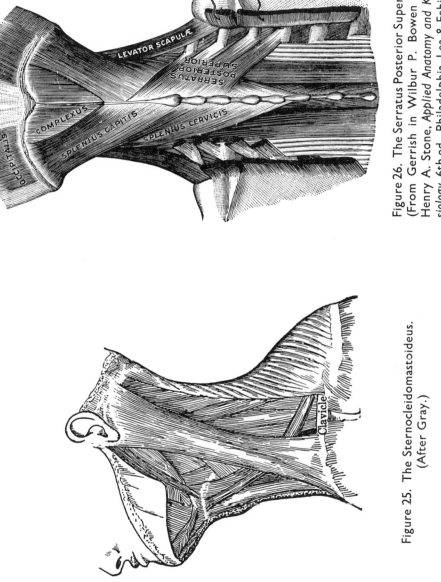

Figure 26. The Serratus Posterior Superior. (From Gerrish in Wilbur P. Bowen and Henry A. Stone, *Applied Anatomy and Kinesiology*, 6th ed., Philadelphia. Lea & Febiger, 1949, p. 216. Courtesy of Lea & Febiger.)

Figure 25. The Sternocleidomastoideus. (After Gray.)

and to the ribs are also important in increasing the lateral dimensions of the thorax. Among these are the *serratus posterior superior* (Figure 26), which helps to raise the second to fifth ribs; the *levatores costarum* (rib elevators, Figure 27), fibers of which extend from each of the vertebrae down to the

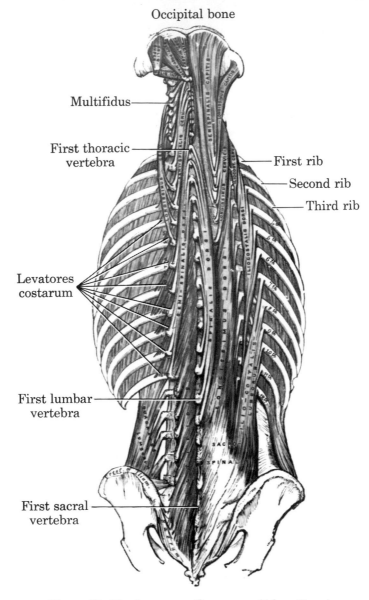

Occipital bone

Multifidus

First thoracic vertebra

First rib

Second rib

Third rib

Levatores costarum

First lumbar vertebra

First sacral vertebra

Figure 27. The Levatores Costarum. (After Gray.)

first and second ribs below the points of origin, and are thus instrumental in raising all the ribs together.

Side or lateral muscles include the *scaleni*, of which there are four pairs: the *scalenus anterior, scalenus medius, scalenus minimus,* and *scalenus posterior* (Figure 28). They have their origin in the second to sixth cervical vertebrae (in the neck), and are attached to the superior surfaces of the first and second ribs. Their action, with the *subclavius*, is to raise these two ribs, whose

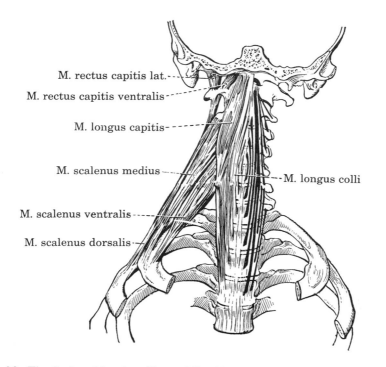

M. rectus capitis lat.
M. rectus capitis ventralis
M. longus capitis
M. scalenus medius
M. scalenus ventralis
M. scalenus dorsalis

M. longus colli

Figure 28. The Scaleni Muscles. (From Alfred Benninghoff, *Lehrbuch der Anatomie des Menschen,* 4th ed., München-Berlin, Urban & Schwarzenberg, 1949, vol. I, p. 170.)

angular movement, according to Bloomer, is at least as great as that of the lower ribs.[15] Other lateral muscles include the *external intercostals* (Figure 29), which extend between adjacent ribs and probably assist in the pull upward; and the *serratus anterior* (Figure 24), although the importance of this muscle has probably been overestimated.[16]

[15] Bloomer, *op. cit.*

[16] Just what part the intercostals play in respiration is not positively known. That they have some function seems to be indicated by the fact that paralysis or removal reduces the movement of the related ribs (Bloomer, *op. cit.*). According to Bowen and Stone (*op. cit.,* p. 225), "it is now generally agreed that the external intercostals act to lift the ribs in inspiration."

THEORIES OF INHALATION.   There is thus provided the means for increasing all the dimensions of the thoracic cone, and thereby increasing the volume. Many theories of correct breathing have been based implicitly on speculations as to whether it is more important, or more efficient, to increase the vertical or the lateral (and ventrodorsal) dimensions—in other words, whether it is more important that the diaphragm be lowered, or that the ribs be raised—or whether both should occur simultaneously. This is fundamentally the difference in "diaphragmatic," "chest," and "central" types of breathing. For generations people have been taught that there is but one correct way to breathe, but there has been much disagreement as to what this correct way is.

In normal speech, as in normal casual breathing, the abdominal and the thoracic movements occur approximately simultaneously; that is, expansion of the thorax occurs at about the same time as expansion of the abdominal region, although one may show a slight lag behind the other without being considered abnormal in any degree. Among stutterers, however, opposition is frequently found between the phases of the two regional cycles. In other words, while the thorax is expanding, the abdomen may be contracting, and vice versa. This particular abnormality in respiration is thought to be the result, rather than the cause, of stuttering.[17] In our present discussion we shall concern ourselves only with the phenomenon of breathing in normal speech.

Probably it makes little difference, in normal speech, whether one's breathing is predominantly thoracic ("with the chest," as it is called), measured as high under the armpits as possible, or predominantly medial, measured about the base of the sternum, or predominantly abdominal ("with the diaphragm"), measured just above the crest of the iliac, or with the movements of all three regions approximately equal. With most persons all three regions participate in the respiratory function, but it is undoubtedly true that the degree of "regional predominance" varies greatly. Records have been taken showing that the thoracic movement will vary from as little as 12 percent of the abdominal to as much as seven and one-half times as great, with no significant differences in the essential characteristics of the voice.[18]

It is sometimes urged that in inhalation the abdominal expansion should precede the thoracic, so that the lungs can fill "from the bottom." The

[17] W. E. Moore, "A conditioned reflex study of stuttering," *Journal of Speech Disorders* (1938), *3*: 163–183. See also M. D. Steer, "A qualitative study of breathing in young stutterers," *Speech Monographs* (1935), *2*: 152–156.

[18] Giles Wilkeson Gray, "Regional predominance in respiration in relation to certain aspects of voice," in *Studies in Experimental Phonetics, op. cit.*, pp. 59–78.

absurdity of such a theory becomes evident when one realizes that the air one breathes goes neither to the bottom nor to the top of the lungs, but fills them equally in all directions. In fact, assuming that the lungs at the beginning of the respiratory cycle are filled, or reasonably so, with carbon dioxide, one cannot conceive that a lighter gaseous mixture, air, as it is taken into the lungs, would sink "to the bottom." Furthermore, the multitude of branchings of the respiratory tubes in the lungs provides that the air shall reach all portions of both lungs at somewhere near the same time and, somewhat like the intake manifold of a multicylinder engine, in approximately equal amounts.

No investigations thus far reported have indicated that speakers are any more likely to have good or poor voices according to the particular type of breathing they use in either speaking or in casual respiration. In other words, a "diaphragmatic" or abdominal breather will not necessarily have any better voice than a "chest" or thoracic breather, nor will a person whose breathing is predominantly medial have any better voice than either of the other two types. It is true that the majority of people (about 65 percent, both men and women) breathe abdominally, so far as records indicate, with men showing a somewhat greater tendency in that direction than women. But there is much objective evidence that thoracic breathers, either men or women, average just as high as either abdominal or medial breathers in quality of tone, in strength of tone (audibility), and in ability to control the strength.[19]

On the other hand, Huyck and Allen,[20] employing an X-ray procedure in which maximum and minimum diaphragmatic excursions were measured for twenty good voices and twenty poor voices, found that greater excursions were shown for the good voices than for the poor, in normal speaking, loud speaking, and whispering. As observed subjectively, without objective evidence, the action of the diaphragm in good voices seemed to be steady, whereas that in the poor voices tended to be jerky.

The matter of controlling the strength of the tone is of great importance. A tone must be powerful or gentle at the speaker's will, and must be capable of all the gradations between strong and weak. Particularly, it must be steady, not wavering, at all degrees of strength. One of the main reasons for giving conscious attention to breathing, and for practicing some effective method of respiration, is to provide for steady, unwavering tones. Experience and research seem to show that steadiness during phonation may be obtained either by abdominal, by thoracic, or by medial breathing, or by a simultaneous

[19] *Ibid.*
[20] E. Mary Huyck and Kenneth D. A. Allen, M.D., "Diaphragmatic action of good and poor speaking voices," *Speech Monographs* (1937), 4: 101–109.

and approximately equal movement of all three regions. It has also been found that attempts to control specifically these types of breathing result in lowered effectiveness.[21] It seems not impossible that one's normal type of respiration may be the result of one's individual physical makeup.

Although no objective studies have been made of this type of respiration, clavicular (*extreme* upper chest) breathing appears to promote unsteadiness. If the expansion is predominantly in the extreme upper chest, so that the clavicles rise and the shoulders tend to hump up awkwardly and uncomfortably into a strained position, steady descent of the clavicles in exhalation is wellnigh impossible, and consequent fluctuations of control are practically inevitable. On the other hand, expansions of the abdomen and general thorax are not awkward or strained, and gradual decreases in diameter and altitude of the thoracic cone are natural and easy of control, so that the breath stream is forced upward steadily and evenly.

Clavicular breathing is to be avoided not only in the interest of steadiness, but also because it tends to interfere with the resonance of the voice. It is conducive to excessive tensions in the region of the neck and throat, which result in flatness and complete lack of richness. Furthermore, since an adequate supply of breath is impossible in this type of breathing, the tones of the voice are not likely to possess adequate strength. It becomes necessary for the speaker to breathe more frequently, thus interrupting the flow of phonation and leading to incorrect phrasing; that is, he is compelled to pause for breath at places where the sense does not demand pauses, and he is thereby unable to give proper expression to his meanings.

In clavicular and very deep breathing the *levator scapulae* (elevators of the shoulder blades) are probably active (Figure 21). They extend from the upper cervical vertebrae (in the neck) down to the upper surfaces of the scapulae.[22]

The chest should always be comfortably filled for phonation; one should never allow oneself to get completely out of breath. The sternum rises slightly with each inhalation, and the upper chest must not be allowed to cave in during exhalation. Vibrations of the sternum may be plainly palpable to the fingers at low pitches of the voice; the sternum and ribs should not be dead, flat, and inert to the touch, but lively and vibrant. But they probably contribute little or nothing, through forced vibration, to what is known as "chest resonance." "So long as the normal ratio between chest sound and oral sound

[21] Wesley A. Wiksell, "An experimental study of controlled and uncontrolled types of breathing," in *Studies in Experimental Phonetics*, *op. cit.*, pp. 99–164. See also Lindsley, *op. cit.*

[22] Charles M. Goss, M.D., Head of the Department of Anatomy, Louisiana State University Medical School, and Editor, *Gray's Anatomy*, Personal Conference, October 17, 1957.

was maintained, no evidence was found to verify the statements of those writers on voice training for singing and speech who say that the vibration of the thoracic walls plays an important part in the resonation of the voice." [23]

But the clavicles and shoulders should not rise and fall perceptibly with ordinary inhalation and exhalation. They should remain steady in their normal, comfortable position, leaving the respiratory movements to the thorax and abdomen. For violent shouting, or for extreme exertion, necessitating almost the maximum inhalation, the shoulders may be permitted to rise slightly, provided the thorax and abdomen have already expanded to capacity; but as the breath is used up, they must not fall below their customary point of reasonable elevation, lest flat, weak tones and unsteady control of the breath ensue. As a matter of observation, clavicular breathing, as a serious fault, is probably rather rare, and should, when it occurs, be corrected by individual attention.

Every person should find a manner of breathing conducive to good quality of tone, practical duration and strength of tone, and steady control of tone.

Exhalation.   Once the air has been drawn into the lungs, given up its oxygen and received the waste materials which are the product of bodily activity, the next problem is to get the air out. This may be accomplished, as has been said, in one of two ways: either by relaxing the muscles of inhalation and allowing the normal elasticity of the muscular and lung tissue to cause the structures to fall back to their condition of equilibrium, the gentle pressure being sufficient to expel the breath; or by positive contraction of certain other muscles of the torso so as to force the breath out with varying degrees of energy, depending on the vigor of the muscular contraction.

The former or passive type of exhalation is sufficient for normal, casual breathing and probably for quiet, relaxed conversation. It is the type we use when we are sitting quietly or sleeping or not engaging in any activity that calls for much exertion. But the breath stream, as it passes out in this fashion, is not strong enough to set the vocal bands into vigorous vibration. When we speak energetically, or sing, more pressure must be put back of the air, and this effect is achieved by the active functioning of certain muscles of the abdomen.

MUSCULAR ANTAGONISM.   Let us say that we have taken a deep breath. The diaphragm is drawn down as far as it will go, and the ribs have been

[23] Charles S. Mudd, Jr., "The effect of chest resonance upon the quality of the voice." Unpublished Master's Thesis, Louisiana State University, 1948. The "normal ratio" mentioned in the statement above was disturbed only by radical changes in the volume control which increased the intensity of the chest sound out of all proportion to that of the oral sound.

elevated as much as possible. The problem is to get the diaphragm back up and the ribs back down. Now there is a fixed principle in muscular action, the principle of *muscular antagonism*. Briefly stated, that principle may be formulated thus: for every muscle or group of muscles exerting force in one direction, another muscle or group of muscles exerts force in the opposite direction. The product in either case is likely to be a *resultant* of several forces.

This means, for example, that for one muscle or group of muscles that moves the arm to the right, another muscle or group of muscles moves it to the left; one for swinging the leg forward, another for swinging it backward; one for clenching the fist, another for extending the fingers, and so on. Similarly, if there is one muscle group active in inhalation, there must be another group active in exhalation. To put the principle in another way, a muscle can exert force in only one direction.

The diaphragm is a muscle of inhalation; its pull is downward. It cannot exert any force upward, any more than one can push effectively on a rope, or make a horse go faster by shoving on the reins. How, then, can the diaphragm be forced upward, once it has pulled the central tendon down as far as it will go? How can the ribs be pulled downward, on the other hand, when they have been elevated as far as they can be?

DECREASING THE THORAX. It will be recalled that when the diaphragm contracts and pulls the central tendon downward and forward, it may exert pressure on the abdominal viscera so that there is a lateral and forward expansion of the abdominal walls. Now if we push inward on these walls, the pressure on the viscera will force them to expand upward, since that is the only direction remaining for them to go. The action is like that of a partially inflated toy balloon: if we let it lie on the table and press gently downward, it will expand sidewise. If we press on the sides, it will expand upward.

A muscle or group of muscles having its fibers attached to the firm bones of the pelvis at one end, and extending upward and partially around the body to attach to the ribs, or to some inelastic tissue such as a thin membrane at the other end, will do one or both of two things: first, it will, on contraction, press inward on the abdomen, and second, it will pull the ribs down. And by pressing in on the abdomen it will force the viscera to expand upward, thus pushing the diaphragm up and, by decreasing the vertical dimensions of the thorax, expel the breath from the lungs. This vertical decrease, together with the lessening in the lateral dimensions caused by the downward movement of the ribs, is exactly what takes place in active exhalation.

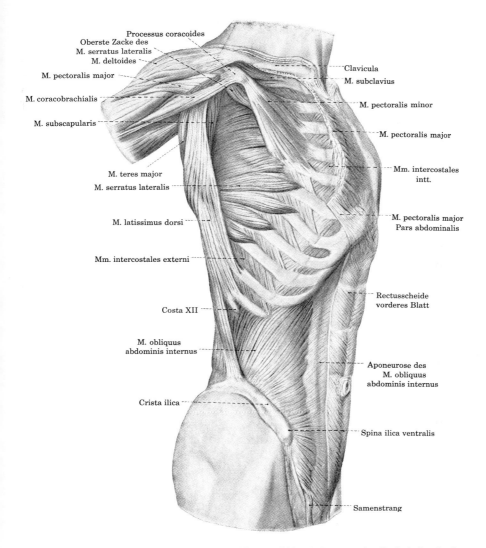

Figure 29. Muscles of the Abdomen. (From Alfred Benninghoff, *Lehrbuch der Anatomie des Menschen*, 4th ed., München-Berlin, Urban & Schwarzenberg, 1949, vol. I, p. 358.)

The principle stated above, that the muscles are responsible for the expulsion of the breath in active exhalation, is rejected by Carlson and Johnson,[24]

[24] Anton J. Carlson and Victor Johnson, *The Mechanism of the Body*, 4th ed., Chicago, University of Chicago Press, 1953, p. 223.

who maintain that "Expulsion of air from the lungs in the *expiratory phase* is done entirely by the elastic contraction of the lungs. . . ." In either the contraction of the abdominal walls, which pushes up the diaphragm, or in the downward movement of the ribs, "there is no actual compression of the lungs. The chest walls do not squeeze the lungs and forcibly expel the air. In expiration the diminishing size of the thorax simply makes possible the elastic contraction of the lungs themselves." Such a description would appear to be adequate for quiet, casual respiration, as has already been explained; but it does not seem adequate for a type of breathing that demands a more forcible expulsion of the breath, such as occurs in vigorous speaking.

Whether or not the lungs are actually squeezed by the diaphragm and the ribs the size of the thorax is unquestionably decreased in the process of exhalation, and this decrease is brought about by the action of certain muscle groups.

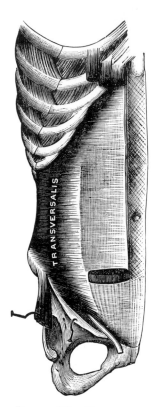

Figure 30. Transversus Abdominis (Transversalis). (From Gerrish in Wilbur P. Bowen and Henry A. Stone, *Applied Anatomy and Kinesiology*, 6th ed., Philadelphia, Lea & Febiger, 1949, p. 229. Courtesy of Lea & Febiger.)

THE MUSCLES OF EXHALATION. The most important muscles in exhalation are four in number. Together with a broad, thin, tendinous membrane which extends up the front of the abdomen and provides one attachment for these muscles, they form the lateral and anterior (side and front) walls of the abdomen. These muscles, like those of inhalation, are paired. They are (1) the *internal oblique* (*obliquus internus abdominis*), which extends upward and forward (Figure 29); (2) the *external oblique* (*obliquus externus abdominis*), extending upward and back (Figure 23); (3) the *rectus abdominis*, extending vertically up the front of the abdomen to the fifth, sixth, and seventh ribs (Figures 23, 29); and the *transverse abdominal* (*transversus abdominis*), which extends horizontally across the abdomen, and is attached on either side to the membrane mentioned above (Figure 30). In addition to these four, there is a fifth, the *transverse thoracic* (*transversus thoracis*) (Figure 31), which extends on either side from the lower portions of the sternum to the second to sixth ribs. This is the only muscle primarily for exhalation that is not abdominal;[25] it serves to pull the ribs downward and thus to constrict the chest. The *rectus abdominis* (Figure 23), extending from the pubis up to the fifth, sixth, and seventh ribs, pulls downward and thus assists somewhat in reducing the convexity of the abdomen.

Through the action of these muscles of inhalation and exhalation the means are provided for enlarging and reducing the thoracic cavity. The muscles of exhalation force the breath out with sufficient strength to set the vocal bands into vibration, and thus, with the action of the resonators to be discussed later in this chapter, to produce the sound. How that sound is modified into the sounds of speech will also be explained in later sections of this chapter.

The Problem of Effective Breathing

How shall we make the most effective use of this respiratory mechanism? It has already been pointed out that neither vital capacity, nor tidal air, nor the particular type of regional predominance has any significance in relation to the production of

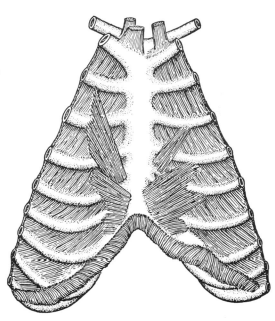

Figure 31. Transversus Thoracis.
(After Sobotta.)

voice. Does this mean that any method of breathing that we might want to use will be just as effective as any other? Probably not.

While the actual amount of air used in uttering a phrase is not large in any case, many people speak as if they were just about to exhaust their supply of breath; their voices are weak and give the effect of trailing off into nothingness. To avoid this fading, and to give sufficient strength to the tones, there must be a reasonable amount of breath in the lungs at all times. The lungs

[25] See reference to the function of the diaphragm and other musculature of inhalation in preventing too rapid exhalation, thus helping to regulate the outflow of breath (p. 162).

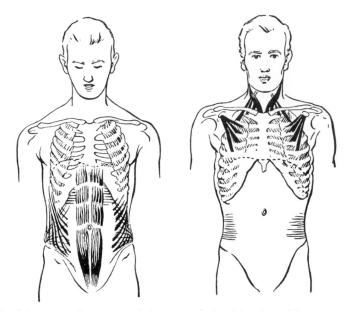

Figure 32. Schematic Drawing of Action of the Muscles of Respiration. (From Alfred Benninghoff, *Lehrbuch der Anatomie des Menschen*, 4th ed., München-Berlin, Urban & Schwarzenberg, 1949, vol. I, p. 200.)

should never be entirely inflated or entirely empty. There should be ample reserve, so that the vigor of the voice may be maintained and the speaker will not feel or sound out of breath.

The speaker's voice should be just as strong at the end of a phrase as at the beginning; if he is getting out of breath by the time he reaches the end of a phrase, it is difficult if not impossible for him to maintain this strength smoothly.

Careful attention to word-grouping and thought-grouping will enable one to avoid formulating phrases that are so long as to draw too much from the reserve supply of breath. A short, quick inhalation at the time of each short pause between convenient and logical word-groups, and a somewhat deeper inhalation as necessary during longer pauses, should provide sufficient breath for all speaking purposes.

As for exhalation, a few simple principles should be understood. As already stated, it is not important whether the maximum expansion in inhalation is abdominal or thoracic or medial, or a combination of all three. In any case, from the point of view of muscular action, active exhalation, whether the lungs are actually squeezed or not, is essentially a function of the abdominal

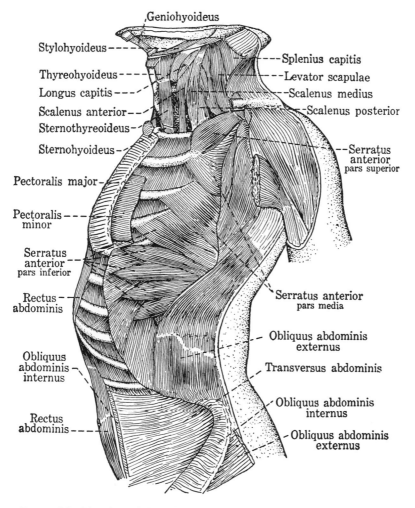

Figure 33. Muscles of the Thorax and Abdomen. (After Sobotta.)

musculature—a function which maintains whether the muscular force is exerted in pulling the ribs downward or in pressing in on the abdominal viscera and forcing the diaphragm upward. The following summary of these statements may help to fix them in mind:

1. Except for the *transversus thoracis*, there is no thoracic musculature of exhalation. This muscle is important, but it does not account for all thoracic movement in exhalation.

2. There is undoubtedly thoracic inhalation; most of the muscles of inhalation are thoracic. But the idea of thoracic exhalation is grossly exaggerated. Exhalation is essentially abdominal. Again except for the *transversus thoracis*, all the antangonists of the thoracic muscles of inhalation are abdominal.
3. The individual who uses thoracic breathing, employing the musculature of the thorax to elevate the ribs in inhalation, is also using his abdominal musculature most positively and most efficiently and most directly in exhalation. In other words, from a mechanical point of view, the direct downward pull on the ribs, thus creating a pressure on the lungs from the firm skeletal walls of the thorax, is more efficient than the indirect force exerted by the inward pressure on the abdomen, forcing the viscera and the diaphragm upward.

In order to provide sufficient breath to set the vocal bands into vibration, exhalation must be active, to a degree demanded by the necessary vigor of the utterance; the breath must be expelled by the positive contraction of the abdominal musculature. This action must be firm, comparatively steady, and free from any unnecessary tensions.

The outflow of the breath should be controlled not at the glottis, but primarily from the musculature of exhalation. Such control does not mean, however, that during exhalation all the muscles of inhalation are of necessity completely relaxed. If they were, the total control of the pressure of the outgoing breath would be on the muscles of exhalation. But it is a general experience that the regulation of delicate movements in one direction may be aided by gradually releasing the tensions in the antagonistic muscles. In a similar manner, it is probable that the gradual releasing of the muscles of inhalation, including the diaphragm, greatly assists in regulating the amount of breath exhaled, as well as the breath pressure itself.

There is some evidence that the articulatory apparatus is also operative in the control of the breath in speaking. In particularly vigorous utterance our articulation tends to be sharper and more positive than in more quiet talk; there is, characteristically, more pressure built up, and even though a considerable number of speakers actually use less volume of breath when speaking loudly than in speaking with normal intensity, the emissions of breath in varying degrees of force are easily possible by varying the sharpness of the articulatory movements.[26]

Undue tensions, often resulting from the attempt to control the outflow of breath at the glottis, should be entirely eliminated from the region of the neck and throat; they produce extreme weariness in the vocal mechanism, are

[26] See H. Philip Constans, "An objective analysis of the 'three forms of force' in speech," in *Studies in Experimental Phonetics, op. cit.*, pp. 7–36.

conducive to poor voice quality, and may even result in injury to the vocal apparatus itself.

Whatever exercises are practiced, they should be directed toward these three objectives: (1) firmness and smoothness of the action of the musculature of exhalation, namely, the abdominal muscles, together with a gradual release of the muscles of inhalation; (2) the providing of an ample supply of breath, with frequent, rather than extremely deep, inhalations, always allowing for adequate reserve; and (3) the relieving of all undue tensions in the muscles of the neck and throat.

Phonation

The Vibrators

This chapter has so far concerned itself with the source of the energy which actuates the voice-producing vibrators. We are now ready to take up the vibrators themselves, the housing in which they are mounted and the controls by which they are governed.

These vibrators, as has been previously said, are variously called vocal bands, vocal folds, vocal cords, and voice lips. This text uses *vocal folds* to designate the complete structure and *vocal bands* to designate the inner borders of it, as described below. As we have said of the lungs, and as we shall say of the organs of articulation and resonation, the vocal folds were not primarily designed by nature for purposes of speech. They still constitute biologically—that is, in relation to the preservation of the life of the species— a valve, capable on the one hand of excluding foreign matter from the trachea and lungs and on the other hand of shutting air up within the lungs. The necessity for excluding foreign matter from the lower respiratory tract is obvious, since the interruption for even three or four minutes of the air supply continuously needed for ventilation of the blood results in death by auto-intoxication. The necessity for impounding the air within the lungs arises whenever there is need for strenuous muscular effort on the part of the arms, such as lifting, or for the strong contraction known as "abdominal press," essential in elimination (urination, defecation) and in childbirth. It is only by "holding the breath" (i.e., closing the glottis) temporarily that the chest becomes rigid enough to make an effective attachment for the arms in heavy lifting; likewise, closing the glottis is necessary to effective abdominal pressure, for otherwise the only result of the pressure would be to force the air out of the lungs. It is the delicate adjustability of the glottis, permitting it to close

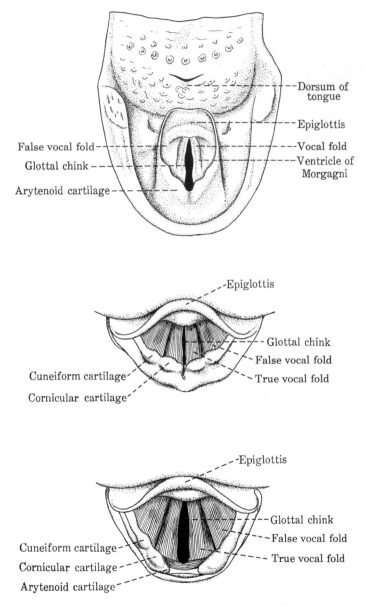

Figure 34. *Top*: The Glottis; *Center*: The Glottis in Speaking; *Bottom*: The Glottis in Breathing. (After Czermak, from Quain's *Anatomy*.)

lightly or firmly as desired in phonation, that makes it capable of being set into vibration by the breath stream and thus utilized for the production of voice.

The vocal folds are rather complex in structure, attachment, and control. They are as little as possible like the strings of musical instruments, despite the fact that the misleading common name, "vocal cords," suggests strings. They are not stringlike in any particular. Instead they are (1) rather thickish bits of striped (voluntary) muscle fiber (the thryo-arytenoid muscles) fastened at the ends and on the outer edges to the skeletal cartilages of the larynx in a complicated way presently to be described, and (2) bordered along the inner edges (the glottis or glottal chink) with thin white connective tissue (Figure 34, top). Each of these borders, one on either rim of the glottis, constitutes a vocal band (Ger. *Stimmband*, pl. *Stimmbänder*) as indicated earlier. Each band is 23 to 27 millimeters long in men and about five-sevenths as long in women. When the vocal fold (crico-arytenoid muscle) to which a vocal band is attached is relatively relaxed, as for the production of a low-pitched sound, the band appears to consist of two edges or lips, one above the other and some distance apart, and connected throughout their length by a flat strip of tissue, the whole considerably resembling in miniature a "thick shelf with upper and lower lips." When the vocal folds are relatively taut, as for a high-pitched sound, the effect of a thick edge diminishes, and so far as one can see from above (up to the present our only vantage point), only the upper of the two "lips" remains functional.[27]

One purpose of the vocal band seems to be to protect the muscular tissue behind it from wear during the contacts incident to the myriad closures of the glottis in its daily activities. Just as the cartilage in a joint protects the underlying bone from abrasion, so the vocal band protects the underlying thryo-arytenoid muscle. A second purpose is to contribute to the elasticity of the total structure. This elasticity is a matter of paramount importance in the functioning of the larynx for producing voice, as will be seen later.

Viewed from above, the vocal folds appear as two seemingly flat strips of muscle edged with connective tissue; viewed from below, they appear as two arched members approaching each other like the two sides of a Gothic window. This arched effect is the result of the relatively greater thickness of the muscles at their outer edges as compared with their inner edges.

[27] So described in *Larynx and Voice*, high-speed color film produced by Paul Moore and Hans von Lenen, at the Voice Research Laboratory of Northwestern University and the William and Harriet Gould Foundation, Evanston, Ill., 1956. Cf. also the Bell Telephone Company's high-speed film, Bell Laboratories, Summit, N.J., 1940.

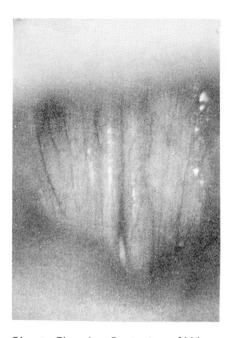 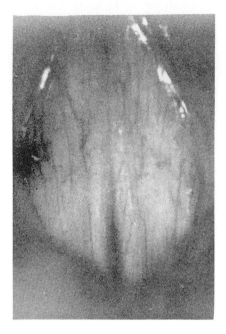

Glottis Closed at Beginning of Vibra-   Glottis Open Slightly at Anterior End.
tory Cycle.

Figure 35. From Svend Smith, "Remarks on the physiology of the vibrations of
the vocal cords," *Folia Phoniatrica* (Copenhagen, 1954), 6:166–178.

The Action of the Vibrators

Wide differences of opinion once existed regarding the nature of vocal band
vibration.[28] It is now clear that the bands, together with adjacent parts of the
vocal folds (crico-arytenoid muscles), vibrate synchronously.[29] High-speed
motion pictures of the bands in action permit a far more accurate study of such
movement than had earlier been possible.

In simplest terms, we may now say that the vocal bands open and close
rapidly in a horizontal plane at a frequency appropriate to the fundamental

[28] See Robert West, "The nature of vocal sounds," *Quarterly Journal of Speech Education*
(November, 1926), *12*: 244–295; and Wolfgang Metzger, "The mode of vibration of the vocal
cords," *Psychological Monographs* (1928), *38*: 82–159.

[29] Paul Moore, "Motion picture studies of the vocal folds and vocal attack," *Journal of
Speech Disorders* (1938), *3*: 235–238; D. W. Farnsworth, "High-speed motion pictures of the
human vocal cords," *Bell Laboratories Record* (March, 1940), *18*: 203–208. See also *Science
Supplement* (December 3, 1937), *86*: 12–13, and Moore and von Lenen, *op. cit.*

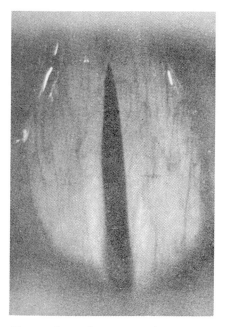 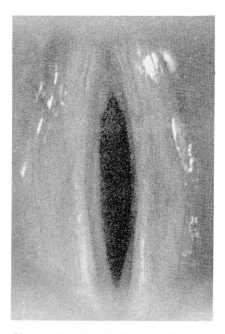

Glottis Partially Open Throughout
Most of Its Length.

Glottis Completely Open at Midpoint
of Vibratory Cycle. Note the thick
edges of the vocal muscles, each edge
being protected by a vocal band consisting of (a) inner border of connective tissues, (b) outer border, and (c)
connecting strip.

Figure 35 (*Continued*).

pitch of the tone being produced, alternately permitting the momentary outflow, then causing the momentary stoppage of the air stream which the
muscles of exhalation are forcing up from the lungs below. The interruptions
set the air stream into vibration to produce tone. (It is possible also to produce
tone during the inhalation of breath, but in practice this method is relatively
seldom employed.) The fact that the lower lips of the vocal bands open first,
followed by the upper lips, and that the lips close again in the same order,
accounts for the "rolling" motion of the glottic rims in vibration.

In slightly expanded form, we may describe the process of producing tone
as follows: The normal function of the larynx at low and optimum pitches,
i.e., at pitches which the dimensions and structure of the larynx best adapt it

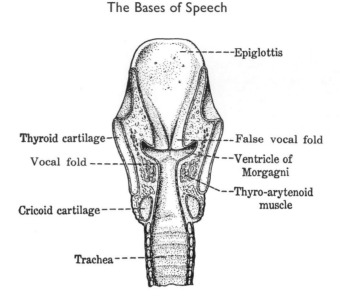

Figure 36. Section Showing Interior of Larynx. (After Sobotta.)

to produce, is ordinarily considered to involve a complete glottal closure with each successive vibration. During the closed phase of the movement, pressure develops beneath the vocal bands which in effect bursts them apart. When the vocal bands open thus, the breath stream momentarily passes through as an air puff, which constitutes an impulsive type of excitation to the vocal cavities above.

There appear to be two basic effects which cause the bands to return to the closed position. On the one hand, the natural elasticity of the system, actuated by the muscular tension which originally closed the glottis, tends to restore the vocal bands to the closed position. The other effect is caused by the air flow past the vocal lips, and may be explained by the Bernoulli principle of fluid dynamics. Bernoulli has stated a basic theorem of physics which describes the pressure and energy relationships in fluid flow under certain simple conditions. It follows from the Bernoulli equation that during the steady flow of a fluid, the pressure is less where the velocity is greater.[30] Such increased velocity will develop at the glottis, which is a narrow stricture in a passage wider both below and above. With the weakening of the internal

[30] Svend Smith states the principle thus: "A stream of air develops negative pressure (i.e., its internal pressure becomes less) on the sides of a narrow passage through (i.e., leading to) a broader tube." Svend Smith, "Remarks on the physiology of the vibrations of the vocal cords," *Folia Phoniatrica* (Copenhagen, 1954), *6*: 172. Arthur L. Foley, *College Physics*, 2nd ed. (Philadelphia, P. Blakiston's Son & Co., Inc., 1937), pp. 206–207.

pressure of the air stream at this point, there will be a tendency for the bands to be pushed together by the adjacent air of higher pressure, and there will be less resistance to the elasticity of the bands themselves. Accordingly, the bands will close, the pressure below will build up again, and the cycle will repeat itself.

The vibration of the vocal cords is thus supported both by a balance of the tension inherent in their own elasticity, as aided by the effects of the reduced air pressures between the vocal bands when air is flowing through the glottis, and opposed by sublaryngeal pressures. In this manner, the larynx operates as an oscillating valve; a similar principle of valve oscillation is to be found in many physical systems.

It is easily observed through direct laryngeal examinations or through high-speed motion picture photographs of the larynx, such as the Northwestern University film and the Bell film, that the vocal bands do not always execute a complete closure during their vibration. This is particularly the case when the fundamental frequency of the larynx is well above its optimum. The vocal bands may fail to approximate posteriorly, medially, or anteriorly; and sometimes they may not come together along the greater part of their edges during the oscillation. The partial puffs of air which escape through the glottis excite the vocal cavities above and produce tone. Along with these puffs, however, there is a relatively continuous, or d-c (see page 121), air flow, which in the extreme case results in what is commonly known as a breathy voice quality. The narrator with the Northwestern University film calls attention to the breathy quality at points in the film where the glottis is seen to be partially open during phonation.

One of the most curious effects is the initiation of vibration while the vocal bands are in a relatively open position. In this case it appears that the sublaryngeal pressure forces the cords still further open, whereupon their own tension and the Bernoulli effect of the increased air flow through the glottis tend to force them inward again. As before, the incomplete closure, at least when it is considerable, promotes breathy voice.

It should be pointed out that the process of phonation is likely to be somewhat more complicated than that indicated above. A complete theory has not yet been developed, and physical observations and data have not yet made the nature of laryngeal oscillation fully clear. For example, there is the problem raised by the observed fact in the Northwestern University film that the two sides of the glottis sometimes vibrate out of phase. As a tone diminishes, especially after the still vibrating bands have ceased to make contact with each other, the bands are sometimes seen to waver from their usual state of in-phase vibration, without, apparently, ever going so far as to get into opposite phase. Assuming that tone is still being produced, the as yet undetermined effect on the complete tonal output becomes a matter for study.

So far as can be determined from our only point of observation—viz., directly above the glottis—there is no vertical displacement of the folds, such as early theorists assumed.[31] It does appear that a change from making a tone

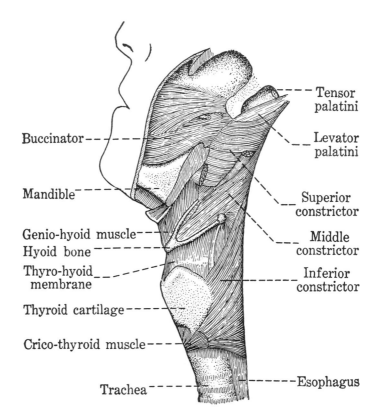

Buccinator

Mandible

Genio-hyoid muscle
Hyoid bone
Thyro-hyoid
  membrane

Thyroid cartilage

Crico-thyroid muscle

Trachea

Tensor
palatini

Levator
palatini

Superior
constrictor

Middle
constrictor

Inferior
constrictor

Esophagus

Figure 37. The Muscles of the Pharynx. (After Gray.)

on expired breath to making one on inspired breath is accompanied by a slight descent of the whole glottal structure. This would seem reasonable, since an upward-pushing breath stream is being exchanged for a downward-pressing one. But no vertical movement can be detected during usual phonation.

The matter of shape and position of the parts of the larynx can hardly be

[31] Robert Curry, *The Mechanism of the Human Voice*, New York, Longmans, Green & Company, 1940, p. 45.

grasped with any fidelity to facts without a study of diagrams and models. In this instance, as in all dealings with anatomy in this book, it is necessary for the reader to follow diagrams closely and to study models and films if available.

Housing and Musculature of the Vibrators

The phenomenon of the change of pitch, and the two general types of position taken by the bands (1) during the production of vocalized sounds (phonation) and (2) during breathing, cannot be explained without consideration of the housing of the bands and of their controlling muscles.

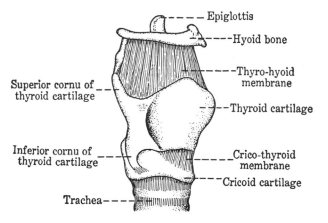

Figure 38. Lateral View of Cartilages and Ligaments of the Larynx. (After Cunningham.)

The vocal bands are housed in the larynx, a somewhat funnel-shaped structure of cartilage, muscle, and connective tissue, located at the top of the trachea (Figure 36, page 168). The larynx is suspended like the basket of an old-fashioned balloon by muscles and membranes which fasten to the hyoid bone just above (Figures 37, 38). The hyoid bone in turn, like the ring over the balloon basket, is suspended from above (1) by other muscles from the inner curve (Lat. *genu, knee*) of the lower jaw (inferior maxillary or mandible), and (2) by others to the styloid processes (styluslike or sticklike projections of bone just below and in front of the ears). In similar but inverted fashion the larynx is anchored from below by muscular attachment to the sternum (breastbone).

It will be of value at this point and later to note that a standard way of naming muscles in the body is by their points of attachment. It follows that

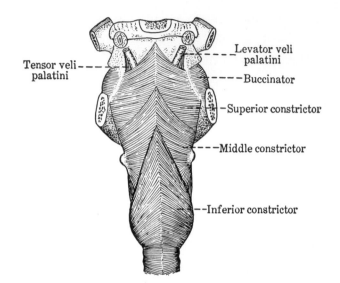

Tensor veli palatini

Levator veli palatini

Buccinator

Superior constrictor

Middle constrictor

Inferior constrictor

Figure 39. Posterior View of Pharynx and Constrictor Muscles. (After Cunningham.)

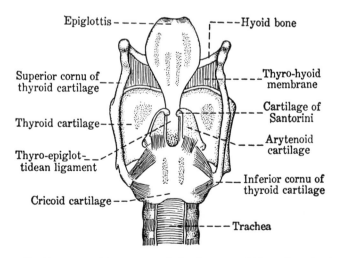

Epiglottis

Hyoid bone

Superior cornu of thyroid cartilage

Thyro-hyoid membrane

Cartilage of Santorini

Thyroid cartilage

Arytenoid cartilage

Thyro-epiglottidean ligament

Inferior cornu of thyroid cartilage

Cricoid cartilage

Trachea

Figure 40. Posterior Ligaments of the Larynx. (After Cunningham.)

a muscle attached to the curve of the mandible and to the tongue is the genioglossus; to the styloid process and the tongue, the styloglossus; to the sternum
and clavicle and to the mastoid process (blunt projection of bone behind the
ear), the sternocleidomastoideus. It will be seen in a moment that the intrinsic
(inner) muscles of the larynx are named in this way as well as the extrinsic
(outer) and neighboring muscles.

The larynx proper has a central skeletal structure and a fleshy enclosing
and articulating peripheral structure like the body as a whole (Figures 38, 41).
Its skeleton consists of nine cartilages, of which the largest are the cricoid and
the thyroid. To these two are added seven other highly specialized cartilages,

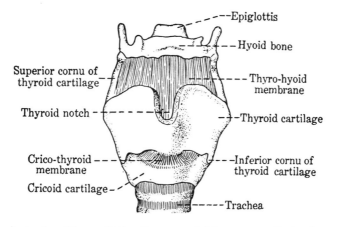

Figure 41. Anterior View of Cartilages and Ligaments of the Larynx. (After
Cunningham.)

viz., the two arytenoid cartilages, the two cornicular cartilages or cartilages
of Santorini, the two cuneiform cartilages or cartilages of Wrisberg, and the
epiglottis. The rings of the trachea are ordinarily thin, braceletlike circlets
of cartilage, rigid enough to keep the trachea open for the continuous free
passage of air, yet flexible enough to adjust themselves readily to bodily movements. They are open at the back, permitting ready expansion for the removal
of an intruding foreign body. But the ring which constitutes the first or lower
piece of the laryngeal skeleton is not very flexible and is not open at all.
Indeed, it is widened at the back where the opening would be expected, so
that it resembles a signet ring, from the Greek word for which it has taken
its name, cricoid cartilage (Gr. *krikos*, finger ring). This widening at the
posterior rim serves to make room for the attachment of muscles, as we shall

presently see, and, on the top of the posterior edge, for the location of two triangular lumps of cartilage mounted thereon, the arytenoid cartilages. The arytenoids sit on the top of the cricoid, forming there a pair of joints which permit a lateral sliding motion of the arytenoids, toward and from each other.

Each arytenoid has two processes, one projecting forward and the other upward and backward (Figure 40). The posterior processes are tipped with tiny points of cartilage called cornicular (Lat. *cornu*, horn; *ulus*, diminutive suffix) cartilages, fastened to the arytenoids with a fairly rigid joint. Near the arytenoids, on either side, are two "floating" cartilages, the cuneiform (Lat. *cuneus*, wedge), buried within the fleshy tissue of the aryepiglottic folds

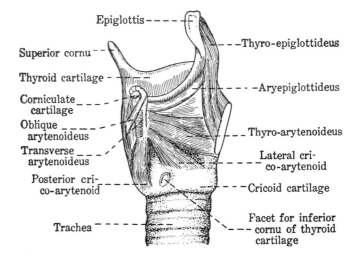

Figure 42. Intrinsic Muscles of the Larynx (Right Wing of Thyroid Removed).
(After Gray.)

(see page 177), and giving these folds a certain rigidity which aids them in preventing the entrance of foreign matter, both liquid and solid, into the larynx.

Nearly enclosing all seven of the cartilages just discussed is a relatively huge cartilage shaped like butterfly wings. This cartilage is easily palpable with the fingers and, in men, easily visible as the frontal projection of the larynx (Adam's apple). This is the thyroid (Gr. *thyreos*, oblong shield; and *eidos*, form) cartilage. It is the largest of all the laryngeal cartilages and, though somewhat ringlike, is, unlike the cricoid cartilage, open at the back. At the posterior top and bottom of each lateral wing of the thyroid is a prominent horn or cartilaginous projection. The two superior horns are jointed loosely to the two posterior tips of the horseshoe-shaped hyoid bone, which is otherwise a floating bone, being attached directly to no other bone of the body. The two inferior thyroid horns are fastened with sketchy-looking but effective joints at the sides of the cricoid cartilage.

Jointed against the inner surface of the superior-anterior wall of the thyroid cartilage is the epiglottis (Figures 36, 40, 43) (Gr. *epi*, upon; *glottis*, aperture of larynx), a leaf-shaped cartilage which ordinarily stands nearly upright over the glottal opening and just behind the tongue. It was once thought that the epiglottis served to cover the top of the larynx during swallowing, to exclude food and drink, but this theory is no longer accredited. Rather, the epiglottis appears to be a rudimentary organ. It was once much larger than now, and it overlapped the velum (soft palate; Lat. *velum*, veil) so as to guide the air

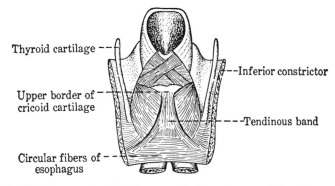

Figure 43. The Larynx in Relation to the Esophagus. (After Cunningham.)

into the nose, even though the mouth might be open, in order to facilitate olfaction (smelling). In keen-scented animals it still functions in this fashion, but in men it has fallen into disuse and grown short and ineffectual. In herb-eating animals the epiglottis has another function—to combine with the aryepiglottic folds of tissue (fastened at one end to the arytenoid cartilage, at the other to the epiglottis, and propped midway by the cartilages of Wrisberg) so as to exclude liquids from the larynx. In man the aryepiglottic folds are less important in this respect and this whole function has largely fallen into disuse. So unimportant has the epiglottis become that it may be removed without subsequent inconvenience or discomfort. Food and drink have to be excluded from the larynx, to be sure, but this is largely achieved by the rising of the larynx during deglutition (swallowing) so that the laryngeal opening is pressed against the back of the tongue and practically blocked. The fact that food and drink "cataract" over the dorsum of the tongue and pour directly into the esophagus also aids in protecting the larynx, hidden away as it is beneath the cataract. Any finishing touches to the exclusion process are effected by the closure of the vocal bands and of the false vocal bands, to be discussed later, so that the epiglottis is practically unnecessary as a valve.

It will aid greatly in understanding the muscular activities of the larynx, presently to be taken up, to refer to diagrams or, better still, to models, to observe the motions possible by reason of the joints of this cartilaginous laryngeal skeleton. It will be seen that the front of the cricoid and the front of the thyroid can approach and recede from each other by reason of the slightly movable joint effected by the inferior horns of the thyroid and the sides of the cricoid. Further, the front of the thyroid and the front of the hyoid bone can approach and recede from each other by reason of the junction of the superior horns of the thyroid with the posterior tips of the hyoid. Most important of all, the arytenoids can approach each other and recede from each other, and they can tilt backward. These motions will be seen to be of vast importance in the act of phonation and in the changing of vocal pitch.

Muscles of the Larynx. The muscles of the larynx are classified as extrinsic and intrinsic. The extrinsic muscles are those which are attached to the larynx at one end and extend from it to points of anchorage above, at the back, and below. The intrinsic muscles are those which are attached at either end to some point of the larynx itself. Contrary to the implication of "intrinsic," a number of these laryngeal muscles do not lie inside the larynx; they are intrinsic only in that they belong exclusively at all points of attachment to the laryngeal cartilages, in contrast with the extrinsic muscles, which extend from the larynx to external anchorages.

It is of no great importance for the present study to discuss by name the extrinsic muscles of the larynx. None are of major importance in phonation, except perhaps certain muscle fibers of the esophagus. It is important, however, to study diagrams and models and to observe the way in which the larynx is held in its place by muscles radiating to the sternum, to the hyoid bone, to the mandible, and to the styloid processes, as previously indicated.

The intrinsic muscles of the larynx, like the muscles of respiration and, indeed, muscles all over the body, are divided into agonists and antagonists. In these capacities they become the adductors and abductors, and the tensors and relaxers of the vocal bands. The adductors bring the bands into approximation for phonation and the abductors separate them for breathing. The tensors tighten the bands and the relaxers loosen them. Thus the individual changes at will from speech to breathing and, during speech, from high pitch to low pitch.

Central in this scheme of things are the vocal folds, composed except for their borders of connective tissue, of the thyro-arytenoid muscles (Figures 35, 36, 37). These muscles are attached anteriorly to the inner angle of the thyroid cartilage. Posteriorly they are attached to the forward horns or vocal processes of the arytenoid cartilages. This latter attachment is effected in such a way that the fibers are spread along the length of each vocal process so that some fibers are fastened at its base, others at its tip, and the remainder at evenly distributed points. This feature of the attachment is extremely important, for without fibers attached to the very tips of the vocal processes, the

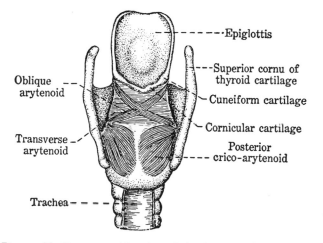

Figure 44. Posterior Muscles of the Larynx. (After Gray.)

vocal bands could not be brought together closely enough for effective phonation. Violations of this nicety of attachment account for the poor voices of many of the lower animals.

A reference to a diagram or model will show that the bands cannot approach each other for phonation except by the sliding of the arytenoid cartilages in their quasi-ball-and-socket joints on the superior-posterior edge of the cricoid.[32] This adduction is effected by contraction of the lateral crico-arytenoid muscles (Figure 42) and the arytenoid muscle. These crico-arytenoid

[32] Earlier diagrams, and especially jointed models of the larynx, showed the arytenoids pivoting at their joints of attachment on the cricoid. The Northwestern University film, referred to earlier on pages 165, 169, appears to disprove the theory of pivoting. The arytenoids are seen in the film to approach each other by a smooth lateral motion.

muscles are attached at their upper ends to the posterior horns of the arytenoid cartilages; thence they pass obliquely downward and forward inside the
inferior horns of the thyroid cartilage to points right and left on the sides
of the cricoid cartilage. The arytenoid muscle, consisting of one transverse
and two oblique parts, connects the arytenoid cartilages at the rear.

Because of the location of their respective points of attachment, these
three muscles exert a strong pull on the arytenoid cartilages, and readily
draw their vocal processes, and the vocal bands, into approximation.

Considering the lateral crico-arytenoid and the arytenoid muscles in
this function as agonists, we find them opposed by the posterior crico-
arytenoids as antagonists. These two muscles are likewise attached to the
posterior horns of the arytenoids, but they run immediately downward and
obliquely inward to their second points of attachment, side by side, at the
posterior vertical midline of the cricoid. When these muscles contract, they
draw the arytenoids far apart, producing between the vocal bands a wide
passage for breathing.

Laryngoscopic observation of the effect of these muscles in action shows the
bands swinging quickly together for phonation as the lateral crico-arytenoid
muscles and the arytenoid muscle contract. Immediately after phonation, the
bands flash apart by reason of the contraction of posterior crico-arytenoids,
with a motion much like that of the sudden opening of a photographic lens.
Such observation shows very surprisingly how loath the body is to lend its
life-sustaining mechanism for the foreign purpose of speech, and how, when
this function is for the moment completed, the body eagerly seizes the
mechanism for its own more vital purposes.

Pitch Changing Mechanism: Tensors and Relaxers[33]

The mechanism for changing pitch which we are about to discuss offers
numerous contradictions. It may be best to present the picture at first without
these contradictions, thus simplifying the problem, and later try to fit them
in. We may begin with the action of the thyro-arytenoid muscles themselves,
the muscles which constitute the main body of the vocal folds. Their contraction, considered for the moment as unopposed by that of any other muscles,
obviously shortens them. This shortening is accomplished by the tilting of
the cricoid forward and the pulling of the anterior portion of the arytenoid
forward, or, as the case may be, by the tilting of the thyroid upward and

[33] See Leon H. Strong, "The mechanism of laryngeal pitch," *Anatomical Record* (August 25,
1935), *63*: 13–18.

backward on its inferior horn connectives with the cricoid. Any or all of these motions tend to shorten the vocal bands and, so far as the shortening is permitted to control the situation, to raise the pitch. Concurrently, the thickening of the bands incident to their shortening would tend to lower the pitch.

The antagonists of the thyro-arytenoid muscles are several. Most obvious is the cricothyroid muscle (Figure 45), a paired group of muscle fibers arising on the outer anterior surface of the cricoid cartilage and spreading fanwise right and left to a second area of attachment on the inferior edge of the thyroid cartilage from a point near the front entirely along the margin to the inferior horns. When this muscle contracts, it pulls the anterior portions of the cricoid and thyroid cartilages together. This approximating motion may

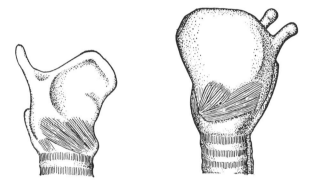

Figure 45. The Cricothyroid Muscle. (After Cunningham and Sobotta.)

be mutual on the part of both cartilages, or the anterior part of the thyroid may descend, or the anterior part of the cricoid may rise. Observation seems to show that the most notable motion is the lowering of the thyroid.

Reference to a diagram, or preferably a model, will show that if by any of these motions the front edges of the cricoid and thyroid approach, the vocal folds and bands will be tightened, lengthened, and made slenderer. So far as tightening and reducing of diameters are permitted to act unopposed, pitch will be raised.

It is clear that the tightening of the vocal folds and bands just described cannot take place unless the arytenoids are firmly held in fixation in their emplacements on the posterior cricoid rim. As a matter of fact, they are braced in their positions and even pulled backward on occasion. For this purpose, the antagonists to the cricothyroid muscle (and, for that matter, to the thryo-arytenoids themselves) are the posterior crico-arytenoids and certain superior esophageal tissues which are attached to the posterior horns of the arytenoids. As a measure of preventing the posterior crico-arytenoids, while serving thus as braces, from pulling the vocal bands apart, the lateral crico-arytenoids are doubtless obliged to contract to a degree appreciably stronger than would be required merely to bring the bands together in the optimum position for phonation. In this action of preventing the bands from being pulled apart by the contracting of the posterior crico-arytenoids in their bracing function, the arytenoid muscle aids considerably (Figures 44, 46).

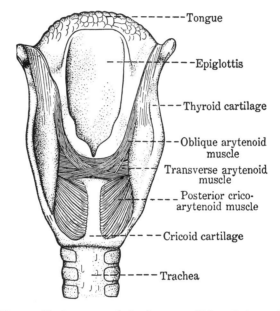

Figure 46. Interior of the Larynx. (After Sobotta.)

This muscle, running by both horizontal and oblique fibers from one arytenoid to the other, seems to slide the arytenoids toward each other.

Although the practice is regarded by many as bad because it diminishes the length and caliber of the laryngopharynx as a resonator, many individuals tend to raise their larynges during the phonation of very high pitches. The larynx rises toward, and almost inside the curve of, the hyoid bone, by reason of the contraction of the thyrohyoid muscle, the hyoid being held from sinking downward by the geniohyoid, hyoglossus, geniohyoglossus, mylohyoid, and middle constrictor. When this happens, the sternohyoid pulls downward, augmenting the already contracted cricothyroids in their band-tightening action. At the same time the esophagus, being attached to the diaphragm near the inferior end and to the cartilages of Santorini at the superior end, is pulled taut so that it anchors the arytenoids more firmly or even tilts them farther backward than before, thus tightening the bands still more.[34]

The Total Effect of Laryngeal Muscle Action. It is now pertinent to take up the contradictions which have for the time being been omitted in the artificial simplification of the preceding paragraphs. For one thing, when the thryo-arytenoids contract and so thicken themselves as a possible pitch-lowering device, they at the same time shorten and become tauter, and so tend to raise the pitch. Again, when by the various processes just described the diameter of the top of the larynx is increased and the vocal bands stretched as a possible pitch-raising device, the bands are at the same time lengthened, and so predisposed to produce tones of lower pitch.

It is evident that where muscular functions thus oppose each other, any actual change of pitch resulting from these functions must be gauged by the *algebraic sum* of their strengths, if one considers that these forces are directly opposing.[35] That is, if tightening the vocal bands raises pitch, it must do so first by overcoming the pitch-lowering effect of thickening the vocal folds.

Further to complicate the whole process of pitch raising and lowering come the experiments of Sir Victor Negus[36] and Professor Stephen Jones, which seem to show that any increase of tracheal air pressure raises the pitch. This would appear to mean that any time an individual wishes to increase the intensity or loudness of his tone, he must change the complete setup of muscular tensions in his larynx to prevent raising the pitch. If he wishes to decrease intensity, he must change in an opposite direction. It would seem, then, that to produce a smooth crescendo-decrescendo at constant pitch, a process perforce accompanied by an increase followed by a decrease of intra-tracheal pressure, the laryngeal muscular tensions, involving anywhere from twelve to two score neck muscles and an even larger number of thoracic and abdominal muscles, must change in such a way that while at no two successive moments will the adjustments be the same, their mutual ratios of contraction must be precisely the same mathematically, or the tone will waver off pitch. As a matter of fact, experiment has shown that neither singers nor speakers

[34] The nerve supply of the muscles of the larynx is as follows: Muscles of upper larynx (sphincter and dilator types), motor—Recurrent laryngeal nerve.

Transverse arytenoid, muscle—Superior laryngeal nerve.

Cricothyroid muscle—Superior laryngeal nerve.

[35] If these forces are composed of several pulls in a number of directions at once, as they probably are, then the net effect is the *resultant* of all of them.

[36] V. E. Negus, *The Mechanism of the Larynx*, London, William Heinemann, 1929, pp. 383–387.

are able to maintain constant pitch for more than two or three vibrations. But normally the variations are not great enough to offend the ear.

This is perhaps the appropriate place to say that no less notable authorities than those just referred to do not directly attribute vocal pitch changes to lengthening, shortening, thickening, thinning, tightening, and loosening of the folds. On the contrary, they attribute pitch changes to change of intra-tracheal air pressure, as just referred to, and to changes in the elasticity of the glottal margins. Perhaps it may be stated, in respect to their second contention, that to say the elasticity has changed is only another way of saying that tension, length, or mass, or all, have changed.

It must by now be evident that phonation, with its necessary characteristic of pitch change, is at best, a complicated process. Doubtless its complications come from the exigencies of the situation in which a mechanism not originally intended for vocal purposes in being used for those purposes. Obviously any apparatus designed specifically for speech could be much simpler. It is a marvel that an originally purely biological mechanism should have evolved into so effective a biosocial mechanism to make speech possible.

Until such time as the student has done much independent study of the action of the larynx, he is advised to think of each motion of cartilage and muscle groups separately. Only by so doing, and with diagrams and models ever before him, can he keep his thinking from becoming as complicated as the acts he is trying to picture. A synthesis of these acts can become meaningful only by following the suggestion made on page 181: to regard any final effect, as of pitch change, as resulting from the algebraic sum of directly opposing forces. Regarding these forces in this way, the student will presently find that he can contemplate their acts as a whole. (See p. 181, n. 35.)

Protection and Lubrication of the Bands.   Situated just above the vocal bands, but separated from them by narrow horizontal cavities, are two fleshy folds considerably like the vocal folds themselves in general appearance. These are the false vocal folds. Biologically they serve as helpers in the glottis-closing process. And their mucous membrane covering, together with the mucous membrane lining of the ventricles just below, serves as a source of supply for the mucus necessary to lubricate the vocal bands.

The ventricles just referred to are called the ventricles of Morgagni. They are sometimes thought of as possibly being the vestigial remnants of air sacs for storing air for rebreathing. In many mammals such air sacs are prominent parts of the laryngeal structure and are important for use in diving, etc. But while in man the ventricles of Morgagni now serve no such purpose, their service as lubricators is none the less valuable. The ventricles may, in addition, contribute to voice quality. Van den Berg has made X-ray pictures of the larynx of a singer, which lead him to believe that "the ventricle behaves as a low-pass filter for the components immediately above the vocal folds,"[37] thereby improving the voice by removing the higher harmonics. He cites as proof the mechanism of the harsh, metallic voice, caused, he believes, in certain cases by the withdrawing of the false vocal folds into the adjacent tissue until there is virtually no ventricle remaining, hence no low-pass filter.

Fundamental and Overtones in Phonation; Resonation

There have been many differences of opinion regarding the function of the larynx in the production of overtones. It now appears that the vocal bands serve merely as interrupters to the ascending breath stream, with the result that waves are established in the air columns and audible tone is produced, consisting of a fundamental and overtones. It follows that the vocal mechanism produces a set of overtones with each fundamental pitch phonated. As has been stated, it is the relative prominence or intensity of overtones in the tonal complex that gives distinguishable quality or timbre to any musical instrument, to any individual's voice, or to any vowel sound. In vocalizing, our capacity for varying the intensity of selected overtones becomes, then, exceedingly important. Without it, as simple a matter as pronouncing both *oh* and *ah* would be impossible. For the difference between *oh* and *ah*, pronounced at the same pitch, is a difference in the unconscious selection of a suitable combination of overtones for mingling with the fundamental. One set will produce a totality of effect on the sound wave conformation which will be interpreted by the brain through the ear as *oh*, the other, *ah*.

The process by which we choose a combination of overtones for relative emphasis or relative disregard, so as to produce a desired vowel sound or a desired quality of voice, is an attribute of the phenomenon of resonation. It is now necessary to discuss the structures concerned with resonation.

The important resonators of the human body are three tubes, the cavities of which contain columns of air. These tubes are the pharynx, the mouth, and the nose (a double tube), arranged roughly in the shape of a capital letter F. Besides these tubes, there are the larynx itself, the trachea, and the bronchi.

[37] J. W. Van den Berg (Groningen), "On the rôle of the laryngeal ventricle in voice production," *Folia Phoniatrica* (1955), 7: 57–69. The author notes that Felix Savart ("Mémoire sur la voix humaine," *Annales de Chimie et de Physique* (1825), *30*: 64–87) and A. Guillemin (*Sur le Génération de la Voix et de la Timbre*, Paris, 1897) believed that the ventricle of Morgagni formed the voice organ proper, while V. E. Negus (*op. cit.*) thought it had no function at all. He disputes both extreme views, as indicated above.

Still in addition to these are the various sinuses: the frontal behind the eyebrows, the maxillary beneath the projections of the cheek bones, and the ethmoid and sphenoid cells located near the lower inner orbits of the eyes, honeycombing the ethmoid and sphenoid bones. But the sinuses are by most authorities not now thought to serve as resonators. The ducts connecting

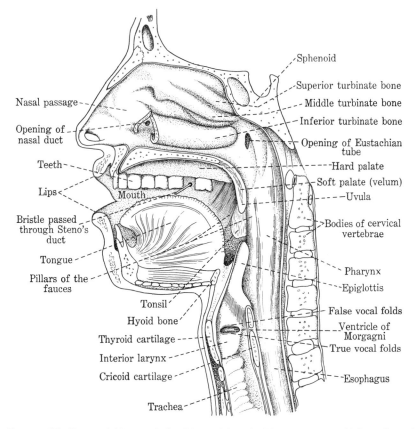

Figure 47. Sagittal View of the Nose, Mouth, Pharynx, etc. (After Gray.)

them with the nose are thought to be too small to permit the effective entrance of air waves for resonation. The sinuses are said to be vestigial remnants of supplementary nasal side chambers, serving to augment the surface supplied with the nerves of olfaction (smell). If they serve any purpose related to resonation, it is possibly to make the facial bones lighter and more vibrant as sounding boards.

As resonators, by all means the most significant of all these cavities are the mouth and the pharynx. Their importance lies in their extreme adjustability as to their own length and diameter and as to the diameter and length of their orifices or openings. This adjustability is possible because of the flexibility of the tissues bounding the cavities. The mouth is bounded frontally by the lips, which are capable of considerable forward distention and of producing an opening varying all the way from zero diameter, or entire closure, to two inches or more in diameter; it is bounded posteriorly at certain times by the velum and the palatal muscles (called the pillars of the fauces), and at other times by the velum and the oropharyngeal wall; only above is the boundary rigid, consisting of the hard palate.

The pharynx is almost equally adjustable in its boundaries, which consist of soft muscle at bottom, top, sides, and back, and of the velum and the body of the tongue in front. The pharynx extends from the tops of the larynx and esophagus, below, to the cushion of the Eustachian tube above, whence, in a curve of the superior constrictor muscle (*pharyngeus superioris*) the Eustachian tube leads upward and outward to the middle ear. The part of the pharynx opposite the posterior nares (nasal openings) is called the nasopharynx, that opposite the back of the mouth the oropharynx, and that in the neighborhood of the larynx the laryngopharynx. Not merely are the boundaries of these three pharynges adjustable for changing the diameter of the pharyngeal tube, but the length of the tube can be reduced superiorly by cutting off the nasopharynx entirely by the velum and its negligible (in English speech) pendular tip, the uvula. Inferiorly it can be reduced by raising the larynx, which tends to carry with it the attached mouth of the esophagus. Furthermore, when the upper opening of the pharynx is the mouth, a great change in its orifice is possible.

It is a well-known fact of physics that an open tube is adapted to resonate most perfectly a tone whose fundamental has a wave length twice the length of the tube. Such a tube will resonate all the overtones of that fundamental. It is known also that a closed tube is adapted to a wave length four times the length of the tube, together with its odd-numbered partials. It is further well known that the larger the cavity of a resonator, the lower the pitch to which it is adapted; the larger the aperture, the higher the pitch; and the longer the neck of the aperture, the lower the pitch. (See Chapter II, pp. 93–95.)

It will readily be seen that the mouth can operate as either a closed tube or an open tube by reason of the adjustability of the lips, and that the pharynx can have two outlets or only one because of the adjustability of the soft palate, which adds or cuts off at will the nasopharynx and the nose as extensions of the pharyngeal tube. When with these adjustments are compounded the many adjustments of length of tube, diameter of tube, diameter of aperture, and length of neck of aperture, it will be seen that by sheer application of the mathematical principles of permutation and combination, the number of different pitches (fundamental and partial) to which the pharynx is adapted for resonation is very large.

It becomes evident, then, that when the tone-complex, consisting of the fundamental and numerous overtones—sometimes as many as fifty or more, each one necessarily of a higher pitch than its predecessor—emanates from the glottis, the possibilities for the selection of overtones for emphasis and the possibilities for the change in the selection are almost innumerable. Thence arise the many shadings of each vowel sound, and the myriad delicate nuances that make voices different from each other and individual voices expressive of such a variety of meanings.

The nose shares in this resonating process, but in a less selective manner, because, unlike the mouth and pharynx, it can change its dimensions only little. It can, to be sure, be somewhat constricted at the anterior nares, and its posterior opening can be varied by adjustment of the velum. But these adjustments are small and relatively ineffective. Indeed, the slight differences among the principal English nasal sounds, *m* [m], *n* [n], and *ng* [ŋ] are caused by change in the length of the supplementing mouth cavity, and not by strictly nasal changes at all. Likewise in French and other languages with nasal vowels, the change from one vowel to another is an oral or oropharyngeal change, not a nasal change. Experiment consisting of completely eliminating the nasal cavities by plugging them both front and rear with gauze has proved that all so-called nasal consonants can be made perfectly without using the nasal passages as resonators; apparently what is commonly called nasal resonance is actually resonance in the nasopharynx.[38]

Besides being unadaptable to dimensional change, the nose is further incapacitated for versatility in resonance by being divided into two longitudinal tubes by a thin bone called the septum, and by the clogging of each tube by thin, scroll-shaped bones, called turbinates, attached to the cheek bones on the right and left. Both septum and the turbinates are covered with thick mucous membrane; the posterior nares are partially obstructed by short stiff hairs. All these structures tend to impair the effectiveness of the nose as a resonator. They serve admirably the vital purposes of cleaning, warming,

---

[38] Anyone wishing to repeat this experiment must learn to adjust his lips and tongue so as to permit the exit of a requisite amount of air through the mouth for the production of [m], [n], [ŋ], etc. Cf. C. M. Wise, [ɪz neɪzəl rɛzənənts æktʃuəlɪ neɪzo-fərɪŋgəl rɛzənənts. *Le Maître Phonétique*, Janvier-Juin, 1948.

and moistening the air, necessary for the proper protection of the delicate lung tissue and as a preliminary to the absorption of the oxygen by the body, but they are a hindrance rather than a help in resonation. Such structures point out once more the application of the so-called organs of speech to more elemental vital functions, and not primarily to speech. If we wish to use these organs in speech, we must temporarily borrow them, make what awkward use of them we can, and return them as quickly as possible to their primary uses.

A brief discussion is in order of the trachea as a resonator. Actually, the effects of any or all of the associated vocal cavities on laryngeal vibration need further definition. The trachea is essentially an open tube with conditions for fairly good sound absorption at its bifurcation. It may then be considered to function essentially as a tube open at the bronchial end and varying in cross section at the laryngeal end by reason of the variable glottal opening. The trachea obviously functions with characteristic properties of resonance and sound transmission. As a result, we may anticipate certain intereffects between the supralaryngeal cavities and the oscillations at the larynx. The tracheal effects probably reinforce and suppress the laryngeal oscillations according to specific conditions of size and opening as described on pages 185–187.

Additionally, the trachea functions as a pipe line for supplying the continuously necessary oxygen. It has, too, a lining of lively cilia, which intermittently lash upward to carry out any dust or germs that have escaped the vigilance of the nose and to eliminate any pus or other by-product of infection from the lungs or bronchi. And it has an ingenious device of cartilaginous rings for keeping itself open, thus moment by moment protecting the life of the individual.

We have spoken of the sounding-board uses of the facial skeleton. The sternum and ribs, particularly the posterior ends of the ribs, share in this sounding-board function. It is possible to feel all these structures vibrate by touching them with the fingers during phonation; by exploring with a stethoscope the strength of the vibration is easily confirmed. It has been shown that the vibrations which agitate the sternum and ribs reach these parts from the larynx by way of the sternolaryngeal muscles and tendons, by way of the air column in the trachea, by way of the spinal column, and by way of the soft tissues of the neck.[39]

It is known that a certain amount of sound emanates from the chest, but the exact amount has not been measured quantitatively and so it is as yet

[39] C. M. Wise, "Chest Resonance," *The Quarterly Journal of Speech* (June, 1932), *18*: 446–452.

unknown whether the effect of this sounding board is negligible or important.[40]

It appears that the sternum and adjacent structures would be most active as a sounding board at certain lower pitches; the skull bones (particularly the facial bones) appear to be most active as a sounding board at medium and higher pitches. These phenomena have given rise to the conception of registers, and to terms like head register, chest register—terms much used, much disputed, and probably little understood. Indeed, the concept of

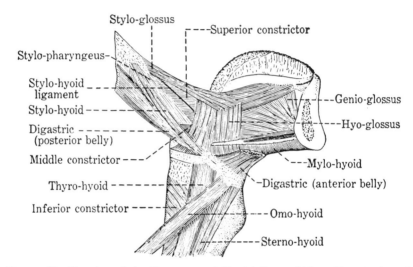

Figure 48. Muscles of the Tongue and Hyoid Bone. (After Cunningham.)

registers is probably useless, except perhaps in a subjective fashion, scarcely related to reality.

When all the factors involved in phonation are considered, it is little wonder that one can produce so many varieties of vocal quality, and that the sound of the human voice changes in such diverse ways, as the fundamental frequency of the voice is varied.

Articulation

The organs of articulation are those which can act as valves or valve contacts for the interruption of the breath stream by complete stoppage, or by constriction of its passage. Strictly speaking, articulation means joining, but

[40] Cf. C. S. Mudd, *op. cit.* See also p. 155.

these organs shape, join, and separate the sounds delivered to them by the vibrators and resonators. In the case of the vowels, such as [i], [u], [a],[41] etc., and the nonfricative consonants, [l], [r], [m], [n], and [ŋ], they simultaneously assist in delimiting resonance cavities while performing the duties of joining, shaping, and separating. The valvular organs are the lips, tongue tip, tongue blade, tongue dorsum, velum, and vocal bands. The valve contacts are the teeth, hard palate, and posterior pharyngeal wall.

These organs have already been described in other connections. If we limit the discussion to the strictly typical formation of English sounds only, we can name and define the action of the articulatory organs.

The Lips

By effecting complete stoppage of the breath stream through contact with each other and by following the stoppage with sudden separation from each other, the lips are the active agents in the articulation of [b] and [p]. In stopping the breath stream, the velum gives supplemental valvular aid by preventing the escape of air through the nose.

By stopping the breath stream at the lips while the open velum allows it to escape through the nose, the lips perform the major action of articulating [m].

By rounding, the lips articulate [w], and *wh* [ʍ]. The velum blocks the nares. The lips round also for the vowels [u], [ʊ], [o], [ɔ], and [ɒ]; they round partially for [ɝ], [ɜ], [ɚ], and [ə]; and they unround themselves for [i], [ɪ], [e], [ɛ], [æ], [a], and [ɑ].[42]

By pressing lightly against the upper teeth, the lower lip produces the requisite stricture or interference with the breath stream for the production of [f] and [v]. The velum blocks the nares.

Tongue Tip and Blade

By completely stopping the air through pressure of the tip of the tongue against the gum ridge back of the front teeth and by following the stoppage with sudden separation of the parts, the tongue is the active agent in articulating [t] and [d]. Here the velum again acts supplementally to block the posterior nares.

[41] See pp. 236–240 for phonetic chart and key-word list explaining the phonetic symbols used here and following.

[42] It is only by a broad definition of articulation that we can speak of articulating vowels. When we so speak we refer to the functions of the valvular organs of articulation (except the glottis) as they shape the resonating cavities and their orifices to adapt them for the resonation of the proper selection of overtones for a given vowel.

By identical stoppage without the supplemental velar action (that is, the velum having dropped to its neutral position, opening the nasal passages), the tongue is the active agent in articulating [n].

By pressure of the tongue tip against the center of the gum ridge without contact with the sides, so that air escapes freely bilaterally, the tongue articulates [l]. The velum blocks the nares supplementally.

By light, widely distributed pressure against the hard palate, the tongue constricts the breath stream so as to produce the requisite friction for *sh* [ʃ] and *zh* [ʒ]. The velum blocks the nares.

By elevating the tip or the blade toward the gum ridge so as to direct a constricted, compressed breath stream against the hard palate and thence down against the cutting edges of the lower teeth, the tongue becomes the most active member in articulating [s] and [z]. The velum blocks the nares.

By elevating the tip or blade toward the hard palate behind the gum ridge, the sides being in contact with the inner surface of the upper molars, the tongue interferes with the breath stream so as to constrict it in the manner requisite for [ɹ].

By pointing against the backs of the upper teeth so as to interfere with the breath stream and produce the requisite friction, the tongue articulates voiceless *th* [θ] and voiced *th* [ð]. The velum blocks the nares.

The Back of the Tongue

By making a complete stoppage of the breath through pressure against the velum, which in turn presses against the posterior pharyngeal wall so as to block the nares, and by sudden separation from the velum while the latter continues to block the nares, the back of the tongue becomes the most active member in articulating [k] and [g].

By similarly forming complete occlusion with the velum so as to block the mouth passage, the velum remaining down, the back of the tongue supplements the velum in producing *ng* [ŋ].

The Velum

By pressing down against the back of the tongue, the velum aids in blocking the mouth passage and permits the passage of the breath stream through the nose in the production of *ng* [ŋ].

By thus remaining down for [ŋ], likewise down but without touching the tongue for [m] and [n], and up for all the other consonants and for the vowels, the velum supplements the other organs of articulation, as previously described.

The Vocal Bands

By blocking the breath stream momentarily and then releasing the pent-up air, the vocal bands articulate the sound known as the glottal stop [ʔ].

By closing in such a fashion as to cause some glottic interference or friction with the breath stream, the vocal bands articulate [h].

Hearing

An understanding of how we are able to speak is hardly complete without an understanding of how we are able to hear. In Chapter II and in the preceding part of this chapter we learned the nature of sound waves, and how the human breathing and eating mechanisms have acquired the overlaid functions of producing sound waves and sending them forth through the air. Let us follow these waves and consider how they are received by the ear.

Sound Waves in the Air

It will be remembered that sound waves in the air are really traveling conditions of alternating condensation and rarefaction—molecules closely spaced and molecules thinly spaced. In a simple wave, such as is indicated in the graph of the sine curve (see Figure 49 and page 72), the transition from

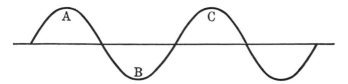

Figure 49. Graph of the Sine Curve.

condensation to rarefaction is perfectly gradual and even, so that if A is taken as a point where the air molecules are closest together there is an entirely gradual thinning out of the molecules toward B, where they are most widely spaced, then a corresponding reverse situation toward C, where they are again closely packed. But in a complex wave (and all waves occurring in speech are complex because of overtones) the transitions are irregular. In a wave like

the one in Figure 50 the rising curves represent periods of increasing condensation, and the falling curves periods of increasing rarefaction (or
decreasing condensation). The molecules are normally spaced at *A*, closest
together at *B*, more widely spaced at *C*, closer again at *D*, farther apart at *E*,
closer again at *F*, normally spaced at *G*, where one-half the cycle is completed.
The pattern is repeated in reverse order for the other half of the cycle, with

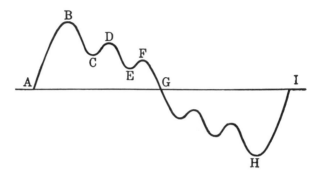

Figure 50. Graph of a Sound Wave.

the greatest rarefaction at *H* and normal spacing again at *I*. (It should be
pointed out, however, that the second half of the wave is not in every case
an exact reverse of the first.)

The Arrival of the Wave at the External Ear

The external ear of many animals is designed to collect these sound waves
and deliver them to the *tympanic membrane*, or eardrum, even having muscles
strong enough to point the ear in the direction of the sound. The human ear
is much less efficient in this regard, its pointing muscles being so weak as to
be of negligible service.

The air waves, then, must arrive at the *external meatus*, or ear canal,
unaided except by such acts as the turning of the head. The external meatus
is a tube about 22 millimeters long, small of caliber, crooked of passage,
studded with hairs to prevent the entrance of foreign bodies, and provided
with sebaceous glands that secrete a clean, bitter wax for antiseptic purposes.

The Effect of Air Waves on the Tympanic Membrane

This tortuous canal conducts to the tympanic membrane the complex air
waves of daily speech or song, and of the sounds of nature. The tympanic

membrane is a transducer of energy. It transforms the pressure patterns of the air-borne sound waves into mechanical vibrations of the bones of the middle ear. It is composed of annular (circular) and radial fibers arranged to form a convex membrane about 1 millimeter thick and 10 millimeters in diameter. It completely blocks the external meatus and so presents a wall beyond which the air waves, as such, cannot go.

The effect of the waves on the tympanic membrane is easily conceived if we bear in mind that wherever the molecules of the wave pattern are condensed, there is pressure also. This pressure is exerted against any object in the path of the advancing wave; and wherever there is rarefaction there is formed a partial vacuum, toward which any object will tend to sway, being pushed by the air on the other side. Accordingly, at A, a point of highest pressure in the graphed air wave (Figure 49), the tympanic membrane has been pushed inward; at B, the point of lowest pressure, it has sprung back, impelled by its own elasticity and by the air in the middle ear. At C, another point of highest pressure, the tympanic membrane has again been pushed in. This cycle of inward and outward movement is repeated once for each cycle of vibration, which is as often as the air waves arrive. The cycles follow one after another as rapidly as the tuning fork, piano string, vocal band, or other vibrator sets up the waves. If the vibrator is sounding the pitch of middle C, the tympanic membrane will move in and out 261.6 times per second, each "in-and-out" comprising one "double vibration," or cycle. (When $A = 440$, C has a frequency of approximately 261.6.)

This inward and outward motion just described is only the *general* motion of the tympanic membrane. It corresponds only to the *fundamental* of the tone being sounded by the vibrator. How are the *overtones* accounted for?

Let us recall again that the wave has the effect of a pressure pattern on any object in its path. If we follow the graph in Figure 50 (page 192) through in greater detail, we can easily see what happens to the tympanic membrane. It simply responds to the fluctuations in pressure: where the pressure increases (as indicated in the rising curves in the graph), the tympanic membrane is pressed inward to an extent corresponding to the height of the curve; where the pressure decreases (as indicated by the falling curves in the graph), the tympanic membrane moves outward again to an extent corresponding to the amount of the drop in the curve. And this response follows the minute fluctuations in a composite wave which may contain frequencies as high as 13,500 cycles per second, and components of such low intensity that only the most delicate instruments will measure them.

The sum of all this is a general inward and outward vibration of the tympanic membrane, during which there are simultaneously small inward and outward motions. If one moves the hand backward and forward slowly, at the same time causing it to quiver rapidly, he has a very good demonstration of the tympanic movement. The tympanic membrane, of course, moves much faster than the hand, taking whatever frequency of back and forward movement the originating vibrator has, from 16 to 20,000 or more vibrations or cycles per second, and repeating during each excursion the tiny subordinate inward-outward quiverings corresponding to the overtones.

Wave Motion in the Middle Ear

We have seen that the air waves cannot get past the tympanic membrane into the middle ear. But the effect of their motion can. The tympanic vibration is immediately communicated to the ossicular chain, or chain of tiny bones whose function is to transmit it to the inner ear. These bones, the *malleus* (hammer), *incus* (anvil), and *stapes* (stirrup), are contained in the cavity called the middle ear. The middle ear is a small, very irregularly shaped space, connected to the pharynx by the Eustachian tube and to the mastoid sinus back of the ear by a series of honeycomb cells. It is filled with air supplied from the pharynx through the Eustachian tube, whence arises the pressure from within, mentioned previously as aiding the tympanic membrane in its outward swing.[43] The ossicular chain constitutes the only contents of the middle ear, save for two small muscles: the *tensor tympani* (tightener of the tympanic membrane), which lies parallel to the Eustachian tube and attaches to the handle of the malleus, and the *stapedius*, which originates in the wall of the ear cavity and attaches to the neck of the stapes. The tensor tympani belongs phylogenetically to the masticatory muscle group, but practically it is an adjustor of the vibratory motion of the ossicles.

When the tympanic membrane vibrates, as previously described, its every motion—both the wide, general swing and the tiny subsidiary quiverings— is transmitted to the malleus, the handle of which is attached to the center of the tympanic membrane. The malleus carries the vibrations along its length to where its head is embedded by a ball-and-socket joint in the saddle of the incus; the incus carries them to the stapes; the stapes carries them to where its footplate sits upon the *fenestra ovalis*, or oval window of the *cochlea* or inner ear. Thus we have traced the motions which are the physical aspect of

---

[43] It may be noted in passing that the Eustachian tube is a frequent path of infection, through which germs from the throat often assail the middle ear, with resultant earaches and sometimes chronic septic conditions very damaging to the hearing. Such infections may find their way to the mastoid cells, with extremely dangerous possibilities.

sound to the place where they are to be translated into nerve impulses. Let us see what happens there.

The Inner Ear

The manner in which the vibratory motion delivered by the footplate of the stapes is translated into nerve impulses is dependent upon the peculiar

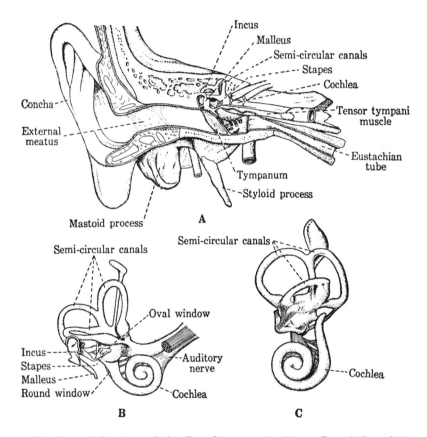

Figure 51. Sagittal Section of the Ear, Showing the Inner Ear. (After Sobotta.)

structure of the cochlea. The cochlea is a tiny spiral tube of bone very much resembling a small snail shell. Its coil is not limited to a single plane, but is conical, again like some snail shells. The tube is divided longitudinally into two passages, the *scala vestibuli*, or upper chamber, and the *scala tympani*, or lower chamber. The division is made partly by the *lamina spiralis*, a miniature shelf or ledge of bone on either wall, and partly by the *membrana spiralis*, or *basilar membrane*, a membrane bridging the distance not spanned by the laminae. This combination bone-and-membrane partition runs lengthwise of the tube from the large end, where the oval window is, to a point near the small end. Here it stops, leaving a connecting passage called the *helicotrema* between the scala vestibuli and the scala tympani.

The scala vestibuli is in turn divided lengthwise by the *membrane of Reissner*. The space between the basilar membrane and the membrane of Reissner is called the *ductus cochlearis*, or cochlear duct.

The cochlear duct is filled with a fluid called *endolymph*, and the scala vestibuli proper and the scala tympani with an identical fluid, which, by reason of its location, is called *perilymph*.

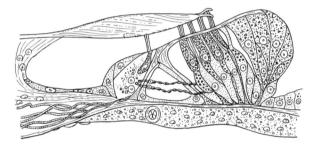

Figure 52. Partially Diagrammatic Representation of the Organ of Corti and the Tectorial Membrane. Nerve fibers are seen passing to Corti's organ through openings in the spiral lamina. (Adapted from Bailey.)

Upon the upper side of the basilar membrane is located the organ toward which all this description points, *the organ of Corti* (Figure 52). Its important parts are:

1. An intricate system of terminal fibers of the eighth cranial nerve, or auditory nerve, which enter by means of tiny openings through the bony wall of the cochlea at its junctures with the spiral laminae, and are embedded in the basilar membrane.
2. Rows of hair cells, in which these nerve fibers terminate.
3. Delicate stiff hairs, rooted in the hair cells and projecting upward into the endolymph.

A third membrane, the *tectorial membrane*, attached to the cochlear wall, floats in the endolymph in contact with the ends of the hair cells of the organ of Corti.[44] Its purpose is not definitely known, but it is thought to aid the endolymph in its stimulatory function, now to be described.

One other essential item remains, the *fenestra rotunda*, or round window. Like the oval window, it is a membrane, and is located at the large end of the scala tympani, not far from the footplate of the stapes.

We may now observe these complicated structures in action. When the stapes delivers its vibratory motion to the membrane of the oval window, these vibrations are communicated to the endolymph and the perilymph. The thrust of the stapes against the oval window probably pushes the whole lymph contents of the scala vestibuli and ductus cochlearis so that either the basilar membrane bulges toward the scala tympani, or a quantity of lymph is forced through the helicotrema and into the scala tympani, or both. As the pressure exerted through the lymph reaches the round window, the latter is bulged outward. When with the recoil of the stapes the oval window bulges outward in its turn, the whole direction of motion is reversed, and the round window bulges inward.[45] Thus it will be seen that the oval and round windows vibrate inward and outward in opposite phase, at whatever speed is set by the rate of vibratory motion delivered to the cochlea by the ossicular chain.[46] It will be seen, as a matter of fact, that the vibratory rate of the whole set of structures is set by the original vibrator, say the vocal bands.

Summarily, the bands create pressure patterns (waves) of given frequency in the air; these set the eardrum membrane to vibrating at the same frequency; the eardrum membrane transmits this rate to the malleus, incus, and stapes, and they in turn to the cochlear lymph and the oval and round windows. Even the subsidiary quiverings previously referred to as corresponding to the

---

[44] Stephen L. Polyak, *The Human Ear*, Elmsford, New York, The Sonotone Corporation, 1946, pp. 97, 102, 103. Also P. J. Kostelyik, *Theories of Hearing*, Leiden, Universitaire Presse, Leiden, 1950, p. 137.

[45] Many experiments have indicated that the round window does pulsate outward and inward. But paradoxically, experiments in attempting to immobilize the round window by blocking have yielded contradictory reports as to whether such blocking interferes with hearing. The "ultimate" function (of the round window) has not yet been fully elucidated." Kostelyik, *op. cit.*, p. 154.

[46] The interesting theory is advanced that the ossicular chain transmits the vibration of the tympanic membrane in such a way as to cause the oval window to be pulled outward when the tympanic membrane is pushed inward—or, in other words, the ossicles are thought to cause the oval window to vibrate in *opposite phase* with the tympanic membrane. If this is true, the tympanic membrane and the round window vibrate *in phase*. This may be an important factor during life after infancy, when the Eustachian tube is not freely open for the passage of air. For if the tympanic membrane and round window were in opposite phase, both would be hampered in their movements by fluctuation in air pressure in the middle ear; as the two membranes moved toward each other, pressure would be built up, and they receded from each other, a partial vacuum would be created. If, on the contrary, both membranes move in phase, the air pressure will remain practically constant.

overtones are also transmitted and set up their patterns as pressure variations in the lymph.

As these pressure patterns in the lymph pass over the hairs of the organ of of Corti, the hairs vibrate, perhaps additionally stimulated by the floating tectorial membrane. The vibrations communicate downward to the hair cells and to the nerve terminals where, as in the case of any stimulus to a nerve, they set up the electrochemical reactions which we call nerve current. This impulse follows the eighth cranial nerve to the brain, where it is interpreted as sound.

The Semicircular Canals

In all diagrams of the middle and inner ear, the organs of equilibrium, the semicircular canals, may be seen. These canals are structurally very closely connected to the inner ear and are supplied by fibers from the same nerve, the eighth cranial. There are also some interesting interrelations of function between the semicircular canals and the ear, and, in fact, between the canals and the eye. Further discussion of these functions is hardly in place in this book.

Pitch and Intensity

There now remains to mention how the ear is thought to distinguish between different frequencies, and so take cognizance of pitch; also, how it perceives the difference between strong vibrations and weak ones, so as to distinguish loud tones from soft ones. The famous German physicist Helmholtz (circa 1863) contributed greatly to our knowledge of pitch perception. He noted that when the basilar membrane was dissected out, it was, contrary to expectation, about twelve times wider at the small end of the cochlear spiral than at the large end. Measurements show it to be 0.041 millimeter wide at the large end of the cochlea, and 0.495 millimeter wide at the helicotrema.[47] Since the fibers of the basilar membrane are short at the oval window end and gradually longer toward the helicotrema end, Helmholtz maintained that the oval window end was the high-frequency end, and vice versa. In this he was right. Some fifty years later this theory of localized pitch perception was experimentally confirmed. It is now considered conclusive. "At the same time it has been demonstrated that the different responsive areas for the various

[47] John B. Watson, *Psychology from the Standpoint of a Behaviorist*, rev. ed., Philadelphia, J. B. Lippincott Company, 1924, p. 83.

tones of the auditory range are fairly regularly distributed along the basilar membrane."[48] Theorizing and experimentation relative to other aspects of cochlear function proceed continually. Explanations are offered—and often disputed—bearing on how degrees of loudness are perceived, on how the middle and inner ears protect themselves against damage from the shock pulses of very loud sounds, on whether the cochlear lymph moves as a mass or transmits wave movements, on whether such wave movements could be classified as traveling waves, and so on and on.

However, such refinements of the theory of hearing are hardly likely to disturb the basic concept long felt to be firmly established. What with the amazing modern efficiency in experimental techniques we may look forward to many such refinements.

[48] Kostelyik, *op. cit.*, p. 456.

Chapter IV

The Neurological Basis
of Speech

Functional Elements in Speech Control

In Chapter III attention is focused primarily on the basic biological functions of eating, drinking, hearing, and, most particularly, breathing, and on those organs concerned with these functions which are directly associated with the production of speech sounds. The chapter reveals that scores of muscles in the lips, tongue, pharynx, larynx, thorax, and abdomen are involved in the production of even a simple phrase. It also shows that since the muscle movements required for speech are extremely fine, they must be highly coördinated and synchronized. Each group of muscles must move in exact sequential order, neither a split second too soon nor too late. It is obvious that a muscular motor mechanism can meet such demands only through guidance from an exceedingly complex control system.

If we now take a broader view of the speech process, we shall see that the generation and modulation of speech sounds is but one link in the complete chain of speech communication. Other activities important to the final product have occurred prior to the moment in which contracting muscles actively fashion the sound elements of an utterance. These other activities are commonly referred to by such terms as *perception*, *memory*, and *abstract thinking*. It is important to keep in mind that the end product of the speech process (i.e., utterance) is dependent also upon control features stemming from these and similar activities. To understand more easily all that is involved, the student is advised to adopt, first, a macroscopic approach to the problem. This, in essence, implies finding out *what* effects the control of speech, *when* these controlling events occur, and finally, *how* and *where* they take place.

200

Time and Speech Control

The concept of time durations and sequences in the control of speech is introduced here for the primary purpose of encouraging questions such as these: Do such processes as *perception of stimuli*, *memory*, *thinking*, and *formulating speech responses* occur simultaneously, or do they follow definite sequential patterns?

Normally the processes to be studied are so completely integrated that they are not subjectively differentiable on a time basis. For example, it is impossible to establish a sequence for memory, abstract thinking, and creative thinking. On the other hand, it is possible to detect some common sequences in everyday speaking experiences. For example, we hear a familiar voice from an adjoining room; for some seconds we struggle to identify the speaker. Or an awkward social situation arises and we frantically search for the right word to alleviate the situation.

Experiences of this nature, where the time element seems attenuated or magnified, could promote a simple hypothesis, as follows: in a first moment a stimulus that will result eventually in speech is *received*; next occurs an interval of time during which the stimulus is *analyzed*; this is then followed by a period in which a suitable *speech response* is *formulated*; and, finally, muscles begin to contract as instructed, and *speech emerges*.

One value to be gained from considering speech in this way is that it induces us to cease considering it as an indivisible entity, for in some instances our major interest may center directly on time relationships or on total time consumed. For example, (1) the process of thinking requires more time for the aged than for the young, and more time than usual for the young if they are fatigued; (2) unusual and severe time distortions may be observed in some stuttering, cluttering, and spastic speech. At the moment we are interested in time as a device for focusing attention, but it may also have social and clinical implications.

Functional Relationships in Speech Control

Another effective approach to understanding speech control is to illustrate the relationship between functions by means of schematic diagrams. This approach is particularly useful for those who are not interested in specific neural pathways and sites, but in a larger overview of speech. There are reasons, however, why all such schemata must be viewed with caution. At one time it was hoped that neural processes could be localized as having their "homes" in specific, well-demarcated areas of the cerebral cortex. It now appears that while localization theories are supported in investigations of basic sensory and motor activities, pathways and sites, the more complex neural processes pertaining to language are diffuse, interwoven, and not well localized. This means, of course, that there is still confusion regarding both topographical and functional relationships. In referring now to Figure 53 this warning should be kept in mind.

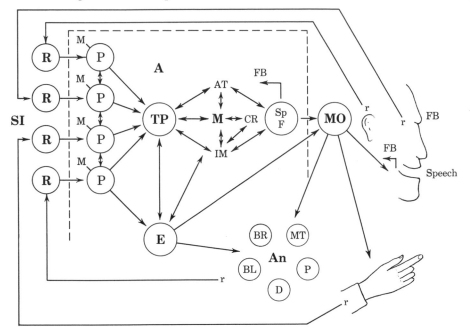

Functional Relationships in Speech Control

r	Receptors	IM	Imagination
R	Reception Centers	CR	Critical Reasoning
P	Perception Centers	AT	Abstract Thinking
TP	Total Perception	FB	Feedback
SI	Sensory Input	BR	Breathing
A	Association	BL	Blood
MO	Motor Output	MT	Muscle Tension
M	Memory (*small m represents memory element in perception of stimulus*)	D	Digestion
		P	Perspiration
		SpF	Speech Formulation
E	Emotion		
An	Autonomic		

Figure 53. Schema of Functional Relationships in Speech Control.

Reception and Perception of Stimuli

Speech is one of the behavioral devices by which man seeks to understand and manipulate things in his internal and external world. Typical influences to which he may respond with speech, such as a whistled melody, the sight of a familiar face, or running the finger tips lightly over a fabric, are detected by *receptors* (r). Reports from the receptors are transmitted over neural communication lines to *reception centers* (R) in the central nervous system. Here certain fundamental attributes of the stimuli may be recognized. For example, certain aspects of loudness, pitch, and quality are thought to be recognized in the reception centers for auditory stimuli. Comprehension of the significance of the stimuli, however, appears to take place in associated loci termed *perception centers* (P).

Some interesting observations may be made at this point. It is customary to regard the entire control process as containing three major networks: sensory input (SI), association (A), and motor output (MO). Note, now, that the perception centers are shown on the schema as lying within the association network. If we can hold in abeyance the question of whether perception is better described as an integral part of sensory input or of association, we can see that labeling perception as one of the association processes places emphasis upon several factors:

1. The difference between the detection and the perception of stimuli.
2. The relationship of memory and past experience to perception.
3. The integration of perceptions.

Most students have heard of individuals who, because of brain injury, can detect the presence of a stimulus but cannot "understand" it. This sensory disturbance is termed *agnosia* if fundamental recognitions are involved. An individual with *visual* agnosia or with *tactile* agnosia might see or feel a key without recognizing it as an instrument for opening a door; with *auditory* agnosia he might "hear" the sound of an automobile horn without relating it to possible danger from a moving car. If the disturbance is centered around the use of symbols, particularly the symbols found in language, it may be termed a form of *aphasia*. In this instance the word *toothbrush*, in spoken or written form, might be meaningless, while viewing or touching a toothbrush could still bring instant identification.

These are severe perceptual disorders, and the average person may encounter them rarely, if ever. But one often does encounter examples of personal disagreement in which neither party realizes that the stimulus being discussed is perceived quite differently by each discussant. It is sometimes wise to qualify statements by saying, e.g., "*It appears to me* that the colors blend well." The following account provides an illustration of the effect of past experience upon perception. A child of five, with normal hearing, looked up with delight from watching television and said, "Isn't that funny, 'Tit-tat-toe, tit-tat-toe.'" The program was a football game and the child was referring to the sound of spectators chanting "Get that ball!" When asked again what they were shouting, the child repeated with complete assurance, "Tit-tat-toe, tit-tat-toe."

Total Perception

The integration of perceptions far below the level of consciousness, and the summation of individual perceptions into a *total perception* (TP) are also indicated on our schema. For some perceptions, such as two-point tactile discrimination, a comparison of reports from the same family of receptors is apparently involved. When we make subjective judgments as to room temperature, we provide an instance where the reports take the form of an unconscious comparison between the temperature of the room and that of our own bodies. A room temperature may remain constant from hour to hour and day to day, and be judged warmer or cooler as our personal health, activity, and body temperature vary.

Summation of perceptions appears to occur at times far below the level of consciousness, and at other times just beneath conscious awareness of what is taking place. Most authorities believe that the perception of "hot" stems from the simultaneous reporting of the receptors for warmth and pain.

On the level just beneath consciousness is the summation of individual perceptions into total perception. For example, in recognizing that an approaching vehicle is an ambulance, we do not separately itemize the shape of the vehicle, the turning signal light on its roof, the fact that the light is flashing "red," and that we hear a siren. These individual perceptions fuse into a total perception, and we jam on our brakes and pull over to the side of the road.

If we return now to the question of whether perception is better thought of as an integral part of sensory input or of association, we can better appreciate the reasons why we chose to view it as predominantly an association phenomenon. The boundaries between sensory input and association are not, however, real and rigorous; the schema indicates that they are so only as an attempt to promote understanding of complex processes.

Speech Formulation

Many "mental" processes such as memory (M), imagination (IM), critical reasoning (CR), abstract thinking (AT), and speech formulation (SpF) take place in the association area. Exactly how they occur, and whether they occur entirely within the association area, are still largely matters of theorization. The consensus from all investigators, regardless of their research approach, is that they cannot be isolated. In considering the relationship of speech formulation to the other processes we can see that such formulation is often an end product of their activity; but they in turn may have required a form of subvocal speech. For while in some forms of thinking, such as in playing chess, we apparently employ no words at all, not even subvocally; at other times we do think with words. We can detect subvocal, or "covert," thinking by observing the minute impulses of energy in the muscles of articulation when thought is taking place. For example, we may observe twitchings of the lips of other people, or we may feel such movements in our own lips or tongues. In such instances we have paused after sensory perception to "talk to ourselves" about what we observed. We may make a tentative choice of verbal comment and mentally rehearse its likely consequence, and we may finally send our decision on through aloud.

There are certain levels of speech, such as identifying familiar objects or using the automatic "good morning" in response to a similar greeting, that seem close to the order of conditioned responses (page 230 f). Here some form of memory seems the dominant process. However, it is still possible for us to check such responses and substitute one seemingly more appropriate if the situation demands it.

Emotion and Speech

If we were called upon to relate personal experiences which would illustrate the relationship of *emotion* (E) to speech, we could quickly supply examples. It is possible to recall instances in which we believe we have talked with greater lucidity and effectiveness as a result of emotional stimulation. We can also recall instances in which our speaking patterns were radically and unhappily altered as a result of emotional stress. Emotions are keenly "felt" at times; and concomitant changes in behavior appear so obvious that it may come as surprising news that objective information about emotions is scant. Researchers in this area must rely heavily on introspection (asking a subject to analyze and describe his feelings) or on the measurement of certain changes in his behavior and the drawing of inferences as to their cause. Neither research method is considered fully reliable.

In formulating our schema, we have attempted to incorporate currently held theories about emotion. One emotion of particular interest to us is fear; we refer to one form of it as "stage fright." Here, the perception that we are being called upon to address a large audience is viewed as a threatening situation. A barrage of neural commands issues forth to prepare the body for "action." Muscles and brain may require more blood (BL); and so the heart rate is increased, the larger blood vessels are constricted, and blood is taken away from the viscera. Digestion (D) and alimentary processes are slowed down or stopped. Saliva, which is usually thin and watery, thickens. Our mouths feel dry. Perspiration (P) increases in preparation for the release of large amounts of heat from the body. We may notice trembling in our muscles; this arises from tension in antagonistic muscles as the general muscle tension (MT) increases. Our pupils may dilate. Breathing (BR) may change to effect a faster exchange of oxygen for carbon dioxide. At the same time, the *endocrine system* is engaged in parallel efforts to provide for the quickening expenditure of energy.

The neural integration of these activities is thought to occur in emotion centers on a subcortical level (to be specified later). It is assumed that one of the regular functions of the cerebral cortex is to inhibit the emotion centers from engaging in just this type of activity unless due cause exists. One of the currently held theories is that the cerebral cortex receives activity reports both from the emotion-integrating centers and, shortly after, from sensory receptors located primarily in the viscera. A decision is then made, through association processes, as to whether these actions are appropriate to the situation and should be facilitated (by removing inhibitory control) or suppressed. Apparently it is not always easy, if the decision is in favor of suppression, for the cortex to regain adequate control of the situation!

Speech without some emotional overlay is considered monotonous and undesirable. From the emotion centers there emanate patterns for speech refinements, such as alterations in voice quality, inflections, nuances, and bodily movements, which are incorporated into the final speech formulation. This is shown on the schema.

It appears also that other pathways exist between emotion centers and the facial and speech musculature which bypass the usual neural routing. Evidence for this is found in clinical cases. Persons who have sustained injury in certain motor areas of the cortex may have extreme difficulty in speaking; their vocabulary is limited and they repeat words they have no desire to utter;

but under emotional stress they will often speak fluently. Lesions in other areas have produced instances in which a person who is unable to smile at will can do so involuntarily if he regards an incident as humorous. The opposite situation is also found where the individual can show no change of facial expression with emotion, but can frown or smile if asked to do so.

Feedback in Speech

The general functional requirements of the motor output (MO) have been described (page 203). A closer study of the neural aspects of motor control requires greater detail and an expanded terminology. The term *feedback* (FB), which has already been encountered in Chapter I (pages 9–11), occurs at this time, and since the concept is applied in theorizing about several phases of speech, it merits particular attention.

The basic principle in feedback is that a sample of the end product of an activity is fed back through a loop arrangement to a point in the system where it may modify the ensuing activity. The returning information may be used to "trigger" successive steps in a series of events, to keep an activity functioning within some predetermined limits (through *negative* feedback), or to promote more of the same type of activity (through *positive* feedback).

It is thought that the motor area of the cortex does not emit at one time a "full set of instructions" for producing a word or phrase. The integrated movements of the speech organs may be governed in part by a continuous feeding back of progress reports from muscles already in action. Black and Moore have discussed this aspect of feedback.

After one has learned to say "top" he does not need to think, "Now my tongue has touched the tooth ridge. It is time to drop it, open my jaw, and say ah. Now I have said ah. It is time to close my lips quickly to get the p sound." The rapid sequence of movements is partly regulated by the reciprocal innervation from muscles in action. . . . Actually, this feedback mechanism is repeated in all the other nerves that serve the speech muscles. By this mechanism, centers about to be brought into action as well as those already in action receive messages that indicate the moment-to-moment state of muscular contraction in all speech structures.[1]

Feedback is most often employed to keep an activity functioning within some predetermined limits. One finds many applications of negative feedback in electronics, ranging from thermostatic control of household appliances to complex guidance systems for controlling the flight of missiles. When one considers a neurological or a communication process in these terms, one finds

[1] J. W. Black and W. E. Moore, *Speech*, New York, McGraw-Hill Book Company, 1955, p. 28.

similar range of complexity. In speech we may modify our persuasive arguments and explanations as we observe frowns, lifted eyebrows, or smiles on the faces of our listeners. The selection of words and phrases in formulating speech may possibly involve a feeding back of our tentative choices to other association areas for modification before final issuance. In muscle movement, there is not only the question of proper timing and coördination, but also the question of extent of movement and optimum tension. Questions such as these are often unconsciously resolved through some form of feedback, whether through proprioceptive, auditory, or visual channels.

Positive feedback produces a detrimental effect more often than a beneficial one. In this instance the returning impulse promotes a continuance, or ever-increasing output of the same activity, until the machine may finally "run wild." When the microphone and the loud-speaker of a public address system are brought into too close proximity, any sound picked up by the microphone is amplified, emerges from the speaker, feeds back into the microphone and emerges again in a recurrent cycle. The resultant noise, which will range from a low-pitched rumble to a high howl, is an example of unwanted positive feedback.

There are many examples to be found where this analogy has been applied to speech. In thinking processes it appears that once we make an initial selection of a response it is difficult to alter it. West has produced one illustration.

You are asked to introduce one of your friends to another. You look at each to recall his name. Your memory of the name of each is immediate, but you are dismayed to discover that only the first name of each "comes to your mind." The more you struggle to recall the last names, the more you are disconcerted, and the more loudly those first names ring out in your auditory memory. There is no use in struggling with the problem. To wrestle with a reverberating nerve net is futile.[2]

Some authorities have theorized that movements of the speech musculature produce a pleasant kinesthetic stimulus that tends to promote continued talking. Others have indicated the possibility that emotional crying spells, rages, tantrums, etc., that escape cerebral control, may be perpetuated because of feedback loops. While it should be noted that applying feedback analogies to speech involves a high order of speculation, it is also probably safe to assume that the control of the speech process is in part affected by countless interwoven feedback circuits.

    [2] Robert West, "The neurophysiology of speech," in L. E. Travis (ed.), *Handbook of Speech Pathology*, New York, Appleton-Century-Crofts, 1957, p. 89.

Neurological Elements in Speech Control

With some knowledge of the functions that are found in speech control, let us now consider their neurological bases. The components of the nervous system are diffusely spread throughout the body (see Figure 54) and serve a wide variety of functions. To simplify study and discussion, they have been divided into several categories, as when the *central nervous system* (CNS), composed of the brain and spinal cord, is distinguished from the *peripheral nervous system* (PNS), made up of the nerves and groups of cell bodies (ganglia) that lie outside of the brain and spinal cord. On a different basis of classification, we term that portion of the nervous system which must furnish responses to changes in the external environment the *somatic nervous system* (SNS), as distinguished from the *autonomic nervous system* (ANS; see Figure 55), which controls primarily the internal processes. As indicated above, these four categories are not mutually exclusive. Both the SNS and the ANS have components in the central and peripheral systems.

Differences Between the SNS and the ANS

1. The SNS is the motor system that stimulates the striped or voluntary muscles of the body. These muscles are sometimes called cross-striated, because of their striped appearance, and sometimes skeletal, because of their location and function. They are the muscles causing movements of the arm, jaw, tongue, diaphragm, etc. By contrast, the ANS serves to stimulate the smooth or involuntary muscles (plain muscles) of the viscera and blood vessels, the muscles of the heart, and the secretory tissues of the body.

2. The SNS as a stimulator of muscles is capable of rapid coördination, while the ANS produces only relatively slow movements. Even in intense contraction the plain muscles move slowly.

3. The SNS can produce finely differentiated muscular movements. One can move the muscles controlling a single finger, leaving the rest of the muscles of the hand and arm inactive. Movements produced by the ANS are far less discrete. If the walls of an artery are being constricted, most of the viscera of the body (the internal organs of the thorax and abdomen) will also be receiving neural commands.

4. The SNS is more directly and more definitely under voluntary control than is the ANS. This arrangement is fortunate, for the ANS is concerned with vital processes, e.g., digestion, the circulation of the blood, and

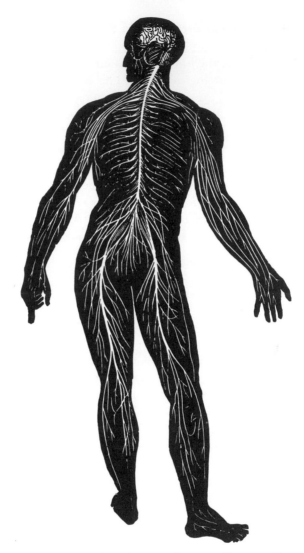

Figure 54. General View of the Nervous System, Showing Brain, Spinal Cord,
and Nerves. (After Martin.)

breathing. Some of the activities of the SNS overlap vital processes, as when
we modify breathing patterns for speaking, playing wind instruments, or
other special purposes; but the ANS stands ready to take over whenever, for
any reason, such as sleep, fainting, intoxication, or coma, the SNS fails. Were
it not for this arrangement, lapses of will would be fatal.

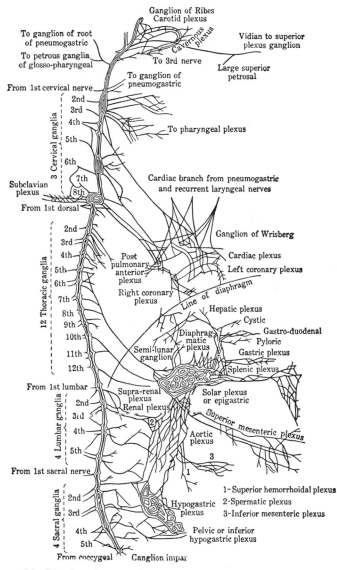

Figure 55. The Involuntary System of Nerves (ANS). (After Gould.)

5. The ANS is dominantly a motor system; i.e., it is an agency limited to *doing* things, whereas the SNS is an agency for *knowing* as well as doing things. It is because of its highly developed *afferent* system, which brings impulses to the centers, that the fine coördination of the SNS

over its *efferent* nerves, which convey impulses from centers to muscles, is possible.

After having noted the foregoing major differences between the SNS and the ANS, we should, to complete the picture, consider the interrelationship between the systems.

There is no real separation, however, between the somatic and visceral spheres. Visceral reactions are part of the organism's total adjustment to its environment, and probably every activity of skeletal muscle, even a slight shift in tonus [muscular tension], is accompanied by changes in the visceral field. The reverse is equally true. Increased visceral activity, which occurs during digestion, is accompanied by diminished circulation through the skin and voluntary muscles; and disorders in visceral activity may lead directly to somatic reactions, such as skeletal muscle spasm. Autonomic nerves, therefore, are in no way independent of somatic. The two are interdependent.[3]

Homeostasis; Sympathetic and Parasympathetic Systems

Our internal environment is in a constant state of flux. The requirements of the body vary from hour to hour and from situation to situation. More blood may be required in one area and less in another. Room temperatures may be cool, yet sweat may begin to appear on the surface of the body. Early attempts to consider each such variation as an isolated phenomenon produced a baffling picture. It was eventually discovered that much of the activity was serving to create a state of balanced conditions. Cannon used the term *homeostasis*[4] in describing this needed balance or equilibrium.

This balancing of activity within the visceral sphere is mediated by the *endocrine system* and by the *autonomic nervous system*. Up to this point the ANS has been considered as a unit. It may, however, be divided into two parts, the *sympathetic* and *parasympathetic systems*. Generally speaking, the sympathetic division exerts an exciting and stimulating influence on the glands and plain muscles of the body, whereas the parasympathetic system exerts a restraining and inhibiting influence. All tissues innervated by the ANS are supplied by both sympathetic and parasympathetic nerve fibers (see Figure 56). The tissues are thus provided with a potential means for the maintenance of homeostasis.

There are anatomical differences of great functional importance between

[3] John F. Fulton, *Physiology of the Nervous System*, rev. ed., New York, Oxford University Press, 1949, p. 204.
[4] W. B. Cannon, *The Wisdom of the Body*, New York, W. W. Norton & Company, 1932.

the two parts of the ANS. The sympathetic system has extensive interconnections between ganglia that produce a spread of activity throughout the
entire system (see Fig. 56). It functions as a complete unit. Activity in this
system will produce simultaneous dilation of the pupil, increase of heart rate,
constriction of large blood vessels, etc. Similar extensive interconnections do
not exist in the parasympathetic system, and so it can operate somewhat
selectively and furnish localized suppression.

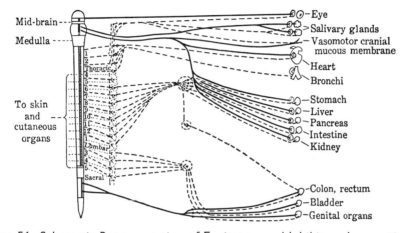

Figure 56. Schematic Representation of Excitatory and Inhibitory Innervation in
the Autonomic Nervous System. (Craniosacral innervation indicated by solid
lines; thoracicolumbar innervation, by dotted lines.) (After Berry.)

The Endocrine System

The glandular system contains two types of glands: exocrine (duct) glands
and endocrine (ductless) glands. Exocrine glands pour their secretions through
tubes into cavities of the body or out on its surface. Endocrine glands pour
their secretions directly into the blood stream for transmission throughout
the body. The secretions from the endocrine glands are called *hormones*.
Cortin, produced in the cortex of the adrenal glands, controls the sodium and
water content of the body. Thyroxin, produced in the thyroid gland, helps
regulate body metabolism. Insulin, produced in the pancreatic gland, helps
control the use of sugar in the body. The gonadal and pituitary glands also
play important parts in the control of body processes.

All of the above-named hormones contribute to homeostasis and thus
furnish a foundation for speech control. Of particular interest to us is the

hormone called *adrenalin*, produced in the medulla of the adrenal glands. It produces effects that closely parallel those from the sympathetic nervous system. It brings about relaxation of the visceral muscles, increases blood pressure, and alters the course of the blood supply as does the sympathetic system. In addition it brings about the release of red corpuscles and sugar into the blood stream, and it affects the coagulation rate of the blood.

The Central Nervous System

Authorities differ somewhat in the way in which they prefer to discuss the makeup of the CNS. They agree that a primary division of the system is between the *spinal cord* and the *brain*. In describing the sections of the brain, some choose to discuss it in terms of three main parts that can be traced from early stages of embryological development; *hindbrain, midbrain*, and *forebrain*.[5] Other authorities prefer a classification based on the five divisions found in the adult brain. As the embryo develops, the hindbrain divides into two parts, the *metencephalon* and *myelencephalon*; the forebrain also divides into two parts, the *telencephalon* and *diencephalon*; and the midbrain, which does not undergo division, is renamed the *mesencephalon*. To ease the path of students who may wish to consult other references, the latter classification is used here.

The Spinal Cord.   With the exception of increasing sensory reports from the head and outgoing motor impulses to the neck and face, all neural activity requiring integration in the brain must travel through the spinal cord. It is therefore possible to view the cord as a communication cable extending out from a central operating center, with circuits emerging at intervals from the main trunk line to serve various residential areas. The primary function of the cord is this long-line communication. In addition, the cord also serves as a means for directly connecting incoming sensory impulses to motor nerves. These short connections produce the automatic responses termed *spinal reflexes*.

The spinal cord is enclosed within the bones composing the spine, extending downward about two-thirds of the length of the vertebral column. It is somewhat like a fluted cylinder in shape, with two enlargements, the cervical enlargement at the level of the neck, and the lumbar enlargement at approxi-

---

[5] It is useful to know that cranial nerves V through XII have their cells of origin in the hindbrain. These are (V) trigeminal, (VI) abducens, (VII) facial, (VIII) auditory, (IX) glossopharyngeal, (X) vagus, (XI) spinal accessory, and (XII) hypoglossal.
  Cranial nerves (III) oculomotor, and (IV) troclear, have their cells of origin in the midbrain.
  Cranial nerves (I) olfactory, and (II) optic, have their cells of origin in the forebrain (see Figure 58).

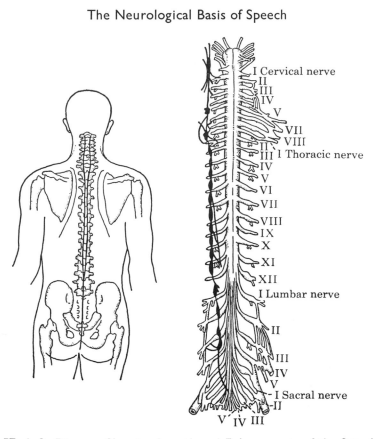

I Cervical nerve
II
III
IV
V
VII
VIII
1 Thoracic nerve
IV
V
VI
VII
VIII
IX
X
XI
XII
I Lumbar nerve

II

III
IV
V
I Sacral nerve
II
V IV III

Figure 57. *Left*: Diagram Showing Length and Enlargements of the Spinal Cord. (After Lickley.)

Figure 58. *Right*: Illustration Showing from Ventral Side Points of Emergence of Spinal Nerves from Spinal Cord, also Right Spinal Ganglia. (Note: The coccygeal nerve is not shown in this illustration.) (After Herrick.)

mately the level of the waist. Figures 57 and 58 illustrate its length and enlargements. The cord is hollow throughout, with the upper end of the hollow space widening to form the first, second and third ventricles in the forebrain, the fourth ventricle between the medulla and the cerebellum in the hindbrain, and the aqueduct of Sylvius, which passes through the midbrain to connect the third and fourth ventricles (see Figure 59).

Since the cell bodies and bare fibers of neurons are gray in appearance, transverse sections of the spinal cord show a gray columnar core, shaped much like the letter H (Figure 60). In general, the dorsal horns (so-called by reason of their appearance in cross section) are concerned with incoming

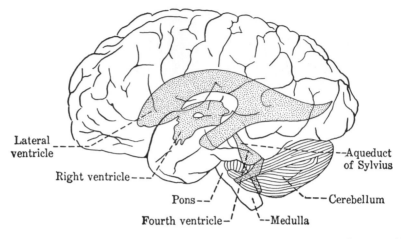

Lateral
ventricle

Right ventricle

Pons

Fourth ventricle

Aqueduct
of Sylvius

Cerebellum

Medulla

Figure 59. Schema Showing Relations of Ventricles to Surface of Brain. (After
Lickley.)

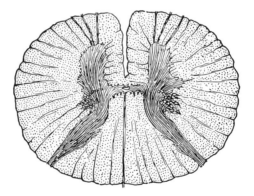

Figure 60. Transverse Section of the Spinal Cord Showing Gray Matter and
White Matter. (After Lickley.)

sensory fibers, and the ventral horns with outgoing motor fibers. The surrounding white matter is composed of ascending and descending fibers,
individually covered with a fatty substance called myelin. The apparent
purpose of this sheathing is to serve as insulation for preventing neural short
circuits.

The Myelencephalon.   The myelencephalon is the lowest division of the
brain and appears as a simple thickening of the spinal cord. It is commonly

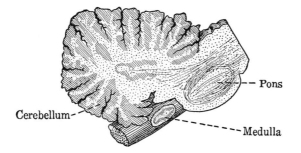

Figure 61. Vertical Antero-Posterior Section Through Hindbrain, Showing Medulla Oblongata, Pons, and Cerebellum. (After Lickley.)

called the *medulla* or *medulla oblongata* (see Figure 61). In it are located important autonomic centers that control heartbeat, blood pressure, and breathing. It is this part of the brain that is damaged in the most severe form of poliomyelitis, called bulbar poliomyelitis.

The Metencephalon. The *cerebellum* and *pons* (see Figures 61 and 62) are located in this division. Although the cerebellum does not originate muscle movements, it serves as locus for the interconnection of many motor fibers. The cerebellum also serves to coördinate the motor impulses into patterns that will produce smooth flowing movement. Its importance to speech control cannot be overemphasized. Slight damage here may result in indistinct speech. More extensive damage produces slow, slurred, and labored speech, since the coördination necessary for rapid muscular adjustments is lost.

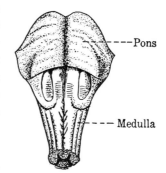

The pons lies anterior to and above the medulla and is continuous with it. It makes extensive connections with the cerebellum and contains a complex series of neural centers whose functions are not yet clearly understood. The centers

Figure 62. Anterior Surface of Medulla Oblongata and Pons. (After Lickley.)

apparently lie along neural loops that contribute to both speech coördination and the maintenance of respiratory rhythm.

The Mesencephalon. This division, as shown in Figure 63, lies above the pons. It is only three-fourths of an inch long, being the smallest and most constricted major division of the brain. It is sometimes called the *midbrain.* Much of its space is occupied by ascending sensory and descending motor fibers. Two important pairs of sensory centers are located here: the *superior*

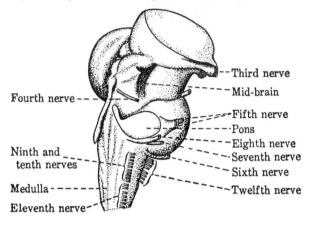

Figure 63. Metencephalon and Myelencephalon (Hindbrain) Together with Mesencephalon (Midbrain), Viewed from Side and Back, Showing Point of Emergence of Cranial Nerves. (After Lickley.)

colliculi, which are primitive visual centers, and the *inferior colliculi,* which are lower centers for hearing.

The Diencephalon. In current theorizing as to how complex neural activities are carried out, increasing attention is being devoted to three parts of the diencephalon. These parts are the *thalamus* (see Figure 64), *hypothalamus,* and the *pituitary gland.*

The *thalamus* is the great sensory relay station of the brain. It is known to contain connection centers for all general and special senses with the exception of the olfactory. It is now theorized that many concepts of size, form, quality, and intensity may gain basic formulation here rather than in the cerebral cortex. It is known that the thalamus has connections with the *striate bodies* (see Figure 64), located between this point and the cerebral cortex. Various loop arrangements between the cortex, striate bodies, and the thalamus are thought to mediate emotional responses such as smiling, crying, and laughing. It is further theorized that the emotional concomitants of speech (voice modulations, gestures, quality changes) may stem from similar loop arrangements, with the thalamus playing a dominating role in this type of activity.

The *hypothalamus* is the primary control center for autonomic functions.

Morgan and Stellar have commented on its importance.[6] All of the individual autonomic effects that can be produced by hypothalamic activity are controlled also by lower centers in the medulla and spinal cord. The distinctive importance of the hypothalamus is not in producing these autonomic effects, but in its *integration* of them into patterns of activity that adjust the internal environment of the organism.

In other words, the hypothalamus is the governing center for the maintenance of autonomic homeostasis. It is, accordingly, a center for emotional behavior. The visceral components of emotion are governed by the hypothalamus; the somatic components of emotion may be largely governed by the thalamus.

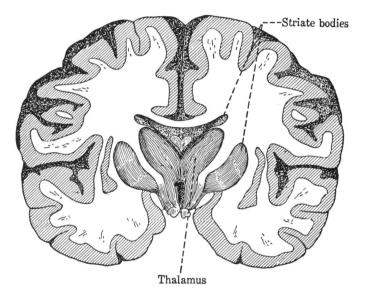

Figure 64. Vertical Transverse Section of the Cerebrum, Showing Thalamus and Striate Bodies. (After Lickley.)

The *pituitary gland*, which lies on the floor of the brain cavity in a round depression (diameter 1.2 to 1.5 cm) in the sphenoid bone, is sometimes compared with the hypothalamus as being the primary center for regulating glandular contributions to emotions. Although the hormones it secretes exercise some control over other glands, some glands receive direct neural innervation, or are stimulated into activity by the secretions of yet other

[6] C. T. Morgan and E. Stellar, *Physiological Psychology*, New York, McGraw-Hill Book Company, 1950, p. 45.

glands. Apparently the pituitary gland does not exercise the same degree of autonomy as does the hypothalamus.

The Telencephalon.   This division contains the cerebral hemispheres and the basal ganglia. The cerebrum is by far the largest and most complex portion of the nervous system (see Figure 65). Much of its total area is composed of a large core of white matter made up of myelinated nerve fibers ascending from or descending to the lower centers of the brain. Within the core, other bundles of fibers called the *corpus callosum*, run horizontally and provide cross-connection between the two cerebral hemispheres. Our primary

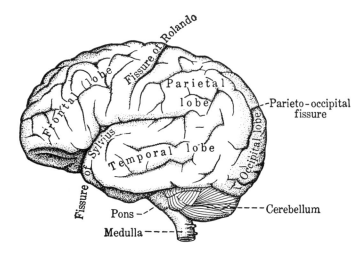

Figure 65. View of Left Side of Adult Human Brain. (After Watson.)

interest, however, is not to be centered on this core but on its thin outer covering.

Completely covering the core on all sides is the layer of gray matter, six cells deep, called the *cerebral cortex*. Its surface is wrinkled, being marked with many depressions and ridges. The deeper depressions are called *fissures*, the more shallow ones, *sulci*. The ridges between are called *gyri*. These topographical features are employed as landmarks in discussing cortical areas. The deepest fissure, the great *longitudinal fissure*, runs along the midline of the cerebrum from the back of the head to the front. This fissure divides the cerebrum into halves called the right and left cerebral hemispheres. Each hemisphere is then divided into four parts, called lobes, by the coursing of main fissures along its surface. These, as shown in Figure 65, are the fissure of Rolando, the fissure of Sylvius, and the parieto-occipital fissure. The lobes are frontal, temporal, parietal, and occipital, also shown in Figure 65. The right hemisphere is, with slight exception, concerned with the left half of the body and the left hemisphere with the right half.

The marking off of cortical areas is sometimes continued in a similar way through reference to the shallower sulci. Brodmann investigated the cell structures found in the cortex, and succeeded in identifying approximately fifty distinguishable cell types.[7] He then used this *cyto-architecture* as the basis of a numbering system which, though criticized, is still widely used in specifying cortical locations. His numbering system, with some revisions, is

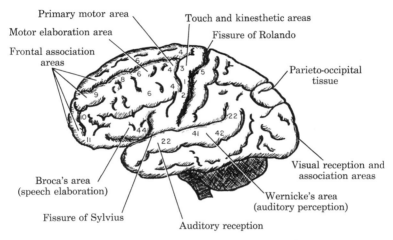

Figure 66. Brodmann's Numberings—Selected Illustrations.

employed in Figure 66. In considering concepts of cortical localization it should be emphasized again that while a given area may be thought to contribute to a given function, it rarely, if ever, is its sole governing agent.

1. Immediately in front of the fissure of Rolando is Brodmann's *area 4*. This is called the primary motor area. Movements of the toes, ankles, knees, hips, and on up to the brow have been produced by electrical stimulation along this area.[8]

2. *Area 6*, often referred to as the motor elaboration area, is located

---

[7] K. Brodmann, *Vergleichende Lokalisationslehre der Grosshirnrinde in ihren Prinzipien dargestellt auf Grund des Zellenbaues*, Leipzig, J. J. Barth, 1909.

[8] W. Penfield and T. Rassmussen, *The Cerebral Cortex of Man*, New York, The Macmillan Company, 1950, pp. 47–55.

anteriorially to area 4. It plays a part in establishing antagonistic and pro-
tagonistic muscle movements.

3. *Area 44* is concerned with the formulation of speech. Paul Broca, a
French surgeon, first discovered the function of this area; accordingly, it is
customarily called Broca's area. For the purpose of this book, Broca's area is
the most important of the association areas. It is part of the motor area,
located in the left hemisphere of the brain, in the third frontal convolution,
in the space above the place where the fissures of Rolando and Sylvius meet,
as is indicated in Figure 66. Broca's area is connected with the association
areas of the frontal and temporal lobes, fibers to the latter dipping beneath
the fissure of Sylvius by way of the island of Reil, a small lobe concealed
beneath the temporal lobe. Through these fibers leading to the various association areas, Broca's area is connected with every part of the cortical surface.
Every conscious experience of the individual thus becomes a fruitful matter
for speech. It is interesting to note that while speech, which requires complex
movement of the articulators, etc., has not been produced by electrical
stimulation of the cortex, cries (vowel sounds) have been produced by such
stimulation.[9]

4. *Areas 1, 2, 3, and 5* are sensory areas for touch and kinesthetic functions.

5. *Areas for auditory reception*, adjacent to area 22, and auditory *perception*
(Werniche's area) may also be noted.

6. *The frontal association areas* are also shown in this figure.

It has been assumed that elaboration of conscious thought (abstract thinking,
creative reasoning) may be carried out here. Some individuals with severe
neurotic or psychotic problems have had *prefrontal lobotomies*, in which the
neural connections to this area have been severed. Gardner has commented
as follows on results from this type of operation.

Emotional states may be so altered that the result has been somewhat inaccurately
termed a reversal of personality. The results are actually much more complex.
These patients often gain weight post-operatively, while their energy drive lessens.
They seem much more susceptible to external environmental changes; they have a
somewhat "happy-go-lucky" attitude. . . . It is as if they show emotional behavior
without experiencing emotion subjectively. . . . They are unable to visualize or
forecast the results which certain acts (planned acts) initiated by themselves will
have on them and their environment. Characteristically, once an act is performed,
they can see that what was done was wrong (or right).[10]

[9] *Ibid.*, p. 89.
[10] E. Gardner, *Fundamentals of Neurology*, Philadelphia, W. B. Saunders Co., 1947, p. 301.

The Receptors

The initial step in the process of the adjustment of the body to its environment and of the parts of the body to one another is the stimulation of nerves appertaining to one or more of the senses. Innumerable physical, chemical, and thermal forces are constantly coming in contact with the various human structures. It is the work of the CNS to analyze these many forces in order that adjustment may be made by the organism. The *receptors* are nerve endings found in the sense organs. Some senses, such as sight and hearing, have extremely complex organs, viz., the eye and ear. Other senses have very simple organs, the nerve endings being merely embedded in the skin or other tissue so that they are stimulated by a change of pressure or temperature. Each receptor is designed to respond to one form of energy; for example, the nerve endings in the eye respond to light, those in the ear to sound. It is true, however, that sounds above a certain intensity arouse the sensation of feeling and even of pain, and that the "cold" organs are set into function by moderately high temperatures. The receptors may be classified into three groups, according to the kind of stimuli they receive. These are the *exteroceptors*, the *enteroceptors*, and the *proprioceptors*.

The Exteroceptors. Exteroceptors are nerve endings which respond to external stimuli. Those in the eyes, the sense organs of sight, are sensitive to stimuli resulting from complex activities set up by the impact of certain light rays upon the rods and cones of the retina. The nerve endings in the organ of Corti in the inner ear, the sense organ of hearing, receive sensations resulting from complex action set up by the impact of molecules of air on the tympanic membrane (cf. Chapter III). Branches of the olfactory nerves, receptors for smell, embedded in the mucous membrane of the upper part of the nasal cavity, are stimulated if gases come in contact with their microscopic endings. Certain nerve endings in the skin, stimulated by heat radiation, are concerned with sensations of temperatures. Other nerve endings respond if the skin suffers mechanical distortion; i.e., if the sense of pressure is aroused.

The Enteroceptors. Enteroceptors receive sensations from the viscera, mainly the organs of the thorax and abdomen. They consist of nerve endings embedded in these organs, and hence are distributed through the heart, lungs, alimentary canal, liver, spleen, kidneys, sex organs, etc. They include the taste buds. They respond to mechanical, thermal, and chemical stimuli— most readily to the last.

The Proprioceptors. Proprioceptors receive kinesthetic sensations and sensations of equilibrium or balance, or of any muscular activity. The receptors for kinesthesia are nerve endings embedded in the tissues of the muscles, tendons, and joints. They are stimulated by the pressure and strain resulting from movement. The semicircular canals, adjacent to the inner ear and contiguous with it, also contribute to the sense of equilibrium (cf. Chapter III).

The Effectors

Corresponding to the receptors, or nerve endings which pick up stimuli, are the effectors or nerve endings which, after much relaying, deliver these stimuli to appropriate muscles or glands. The effector structures are much less complicated than the receptor structures. They consist merely of end plates on the nerve tips which attach themselves to muscle tissue and nerve endings adjacent to or within the glands. The conveyance of nerve impulses from receptor to effector is a matter of great importance and may well be a subject for our consideration.

The Nerve Impulses

When a stimulus has affected a particular receptor designed to respond to it, its energy is translated from the physical, chemical or thermal type to a form of energy called the nerve impulse. It was once believed that a gaseous substance, "animal spirits," or a fluid, "the nerve juice," flowed through the nerves, which were conceived to be hollow tubes. Soon after electricity was discovered, the nerve impulse was theoretically identified with it. Although the nerve impulse has not been demonstrated to be a current of electricity in the ordinary sense, it is possible, nevertheless, to measure a change in the electric potential in the nerve as the nerve impulse passes along the axon fiber. It is believed that each nerve cell, beginning with the one which receives the stimulus, undergoes electrochemical change, which in turn stimulates the next cell to undergo similar change, and so on. In contrast to ordinary electric current, which travels with the speed of light, nerve current travels much more slowly. On medullated fibers it is estimated to travel 100 to 125 meters per second; on nonmedulated fibers, 65 to 100 centimeters per second. This slow rate of speed sets a limit on the rapidity of muscular movements, especially repeated movements. One can tap a finger on the table about eight times per second. A speech sound, e.g., [t], can be repeated but little faster.

Were it not that the production of a tone at the glottis is effected by an elastic system, which is not dependent on a round trip of nerve current to the brain and back for each vibration, a human being could not produce a vocal tone, which requires a minimum of approximately 20 dv.

The Neuron

The nerve impulse travels from the sense organ to a muscle or gland by way of a chain of nerve cells or *neurons*. The neuron is the anatomical unit of

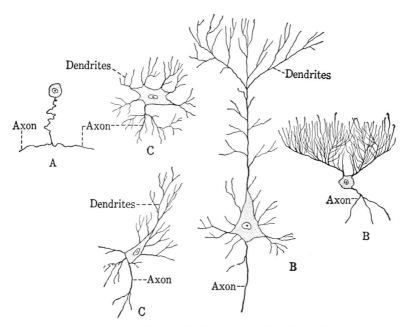

Figure 67. Types of Neurons. (After Berry.)

the nervous system and is defined as a nerve cell body with all its processes and all their coverings. All nervous tissue, including the brain, cord, ganglia, plexuses, and the nerve bundles, is composed of aggregations of neurons. Figure 67 shows some typical neurons greatly magnified. Although the cells are different in appearance, they have two features in common: a *cell body* and two or more projections, the *axons* and *dendrites*. Structurally, the axon and dendrites in Figure 67B and 67C are much alike, but they differ in function. Dendrites conduct the impulse *to* the cell body; axons conduct it *from* the cell body. As shown in Figure 68, the projections having few lateral arborizations (branches), straight, smooth outlines, and a terminal arborization are the axons. Only one is attached to a cell body. Sometimes the axons are more than a yard long, but they are always microscopic in diameter. The other projections are dendrites, which form a network of fine branchings that usually end near the cell body.

Neurons are classified into three groups according to their function and structure. One group consists of *sensory*, or *afferent*, neurons, which receive the various stimuli. They are the cells shown in Figure 67A. They have only two projections, with few arborizations.

Another group, illustrated in Figure 67B, is made up of the *motor*, or *efferent*, neurons, which are attached directly to the muscle cells for the control of contraction, and to the glands for the control of secretion. Cells of this type vary greatly in form; their identifying characteristic is the relatively greater length of their axons. They have many more arborizations than the sensory cells.

The third class of neurons, illustrated in Figure 67C, is composed of *internuncial*, or *intercalary*, cells. They make possible innumerable connections between afferent and efferent neurons within the nerve centers. Their projections are somewhat shorter than those of the other neurons.

Internal Structure of the Neuron.   Something is known about the composition of the cell body of the neuron. It consists principally of the variety of protoplasm called *cytoplasm*. As shown in Figure 67, it contains a *nucleus* which varies little from the nuclei of other kinds of cells. This nucleus is surrounded by *cytoplasm*, which contains *neurofibrils*, *perifibrillar* substance, and *Nissl bodies*. The neurofibrils are fine threadlike strands running through the cytoplasm in every direction and out into the axons and dendrites. The perifibrillar substance is a fluidlike material surrounding the neurofibrils and the granular Nissl bodies which are scattered through the cytoplasm. The Nissl bodies extend out into the larger dendrites but are not found in the axons. The neurofibrils, it must be conceded, have, for obvious reasons, not been viewed in living human nerves; but they have been demonstrated in nerves of certain living fish and amphibians, and so are assumed to be present in the living human body.[11]

They too extend into the dendrites, but not into the axons. The Nissl body granules become smaller when a neuron conducts a nerve impulse; hence it is thought that they contribute material necessary for generating and conducting it. In states of fatigue or in the presence of certain chemicals such as

[11] Henry Gray, *Anatomy of the Human Body*, 25th ed., Charles Mayo Goss (ed.), Philadelphia, Lea and Febiger, 1948, p. 756.

alcohol, the Nissl bodies tend to become smaller or to disappear. This change in the composition of the nerve cell body is called *chromotolysis*. When chromotolysis has occurred, the neuron does not function as well as before; it requires rest to restore the Nissl bodies. In some diseases the Nissl bodies completely disappear and the neurons that are thus affected will not function.

The axons of some neurons are, as noted earlier, covered with a substance known as the *medullary sheath*, or myelin, which probably provides insulation to prevent the overflow of the nervous impulse to adjacent cells. Some histologists believe that the medullary sheath contributes to the chemical processes necessary in nerve conduction. It seems desirable that in the ANS the nerve impulse spread very diffusely; the axons of the neurons of this system generally are not myelinated. In the ANS, therefore, an entire system responds to stimulation; in the CNS, where most fibers are myelinated, more specialized response is possible. If an axon is to be myelinated, it does not function until the process is complete. Many cells mature in this way after birth. Some of the senses in very young infants are not developed, and certain muscles are difficult to control as late as the tenth year. Many axons in the central nervous systems of people of low mentality have never been myelinated.

The Synapse

The arrangement of the neurons is such that the nerve impulse can go from one to several others, as shown in Figure 68. A dendrite conducts the impulse

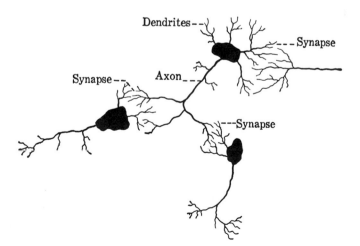

Figure 68. A Series of Neurons Showing Synaptic Connections. (After Gates.)

to its cell body, whence the axon conveys it to the dendrite of another neuron. The junction of the two neurons, the point at which the impulse passes from axon to dendrite, is a *synapse*. The structure of the synapse is fairly well known. The arborizations or branches of the axon usually terminate in microscopic knobs or buttons which, while resting against a dendrite or cell body, yet are separated from it so that neither the action of certain degenerative diseases nor the stain of methylene blue will cross over. The physical separation is effected by the interfaces of the parts in contact. This separation delays the passage of the nerve impulse, so that a reflex may occupy 2 to 4 msec, according to the number of synapses to be passed in a given reflex arc.[12]

An extremely important characteristic of the synapse is that it has the remarkable—and as yet unexplained—faculty of conducting the nerve impulse in only one direction, from axon to dendrite.[13] Without this faculty, the orderly routing of the messages carried by the nerves would be impossible, and such a delicately coördinated and sequential activity as speech could not be carried on.

The Reflex Arc

A nerve impulse travels from the receptor end of an afferent fiber, i.e., from a point of stimulus to a nerve center (the brain or cord or both). From there it transfers by way of a synapse to an internuncial neuron, possibly to one or more other internuncial neurons, and ultimately by another synapse to a motor neuron, through which it reaches the effector end of the journey in a muscle or gland. Here an appropriate response is produced, and we say that the nerve impulse has traversed a *reflex arc*. Figure 69 shows schematically nature of a reflex arc.

Three degrees of complexity of reflexes can be distinguished:

1. The simplest are very direct, involving, as we have seen, only one afferent and one efferent neuron, with possibly only one internuncial connection, in the spinal cord, medulla, or pons. Examples: The sensation of any chemical substance in the mouth causes the secretion of saliva; the sight of too bright a light brings a blink.

2. Perhaps a stimulus causing a reflex of this simple type may be prolonged or may be strong enough to cause an additional, more complicated response

---

[12] John Farquhar Fulton, *Physiology of the Nervous System*, 3rd ed., New York, Oxford Univeristy Press, 1949, pp. 54 ff. See also Frank Brink, Jr., "Synaptic mechanisms," in S. S. Stevens, *Handbook of Experimental Psychology*, New York, John Wiley & Sons, 1951, pp. 94 ff.
[13] Frank Brink, Jr., "Evolution and excitation of the neuron," in Stevens, *op. cit.*, p. 102.

involving some distant part of the body. Thus if an extremely bright light is flashed into the eyes, the simple blink is first evident. If the stimulus

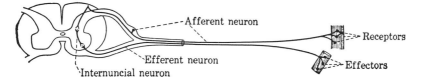

Figure 69. Schema of Cross Section Through Spinal Cord, Showing Elements of a Reflex Arc. (After Watson.)

continues, the whole body is adjusted to prevent sight of the light. In such reflexes, synaptic connections are made in the midbrain as well as in the lower centers, involving several motor neurons.

3. More complex responses may involve the cerebrum. To illustrate these, the story of the bright light may be completed. Its flash has evoked first the blink reflex and later the adjustment of the body to prevent further annoying sight. Now if the person who has been stimulated by the light wishes to do so, he may adjust his environment so that the light will be weakened or removed. He may lower a window shade, put on colored glasses, or go to another room.

The Memory Trace: Learning, Remembering, Forgetting. Much speculation and much experimentation have gone on in the effort to understand how we learn, how we remember, and how we forget; i.e., what happens along the length of a used reflex arc that may be called the physical evidence of learning something, that has the durability to permit us a shorter or longer period

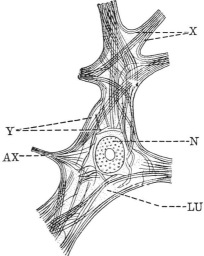

Figure 70. Diagram of Cell Body of a Neuron. AX, axon; LU, interfibrillar spaces occupied by chromophilic substances; N, nucleus; X, neurofibril passing from one dendrite to another; Y, similar fiber passing through body of cell. (After Herrick.)

of remembering that something, and that is subject to the probable impermanence that implies ultimately forgetting it. So-called *native* or *innate* or *inborn* reactions must be subtended by reflex arcs containing physical evidences already established in them at birth. And the nervous system must also contain at birth literally astronomical numbers of potential neural pathways which bear no evidence of the passage of nerve current. Little by little, great numbers of these pathways become beaten trails with the passage of neural impulses. These used pathways should contain evidence of having been used.

Names have been readied for application to the changes caused in a neural pathway by use, should these changes ever be identified. One such name is *neurogram*—a very apt term; another, the one used in this discussion, is *memory trace*.[14] This name applies well to the evidence of use in beaten paths established after birth, not so well to those established before birth.

Inborn reactions subtended by prenatal memory traces are much alike in all normal people. They appear to be concerned on the one hand with such vegetative processes as taking food, digesting, eliminating, etc., and on the other hand with the basic emotions of love, fear, and rage. After birth more memory traces are acquired through experience. Individual characteristics are subtended by these acquired traces; on them are based the ideas, beliefs, thinking, actions, memories, hopes, and—important for the communicating of all these things—the speech of each person. All education, whether it is gained in schools or through other experience, consists in acquiring additional memory traces. This is the process ordinarily called learning. The neural focus of learning[15] is wherever neural impulses travel a pathway repeatedly and leave a memory trace.

Forgetting is the fading of these memory traces, by reason of the disuse of particular pathways. Repetition, which had originally fixed a trace for a considerable time, may later be used to revive a fading one. Learning, originally measured by the number of repetitions necessary to fix the trace, may later be measured by the time necessary to revive it after it has faded.

The Law of the Conditioned Reflex.   Some of the laws governing the formation of acquired memory traces, i.e., of learning, have been discovered. Among these, and basic to many of them, is the law of the conditioned reflex. For years (ante 1926) the Russian scientist Pavlov conducted experiments to determine these laws. The principle that he gradually evolved is known as Pavlov's Law of the Conditioned Reflex. In order to understand Pavlov's Law, certain terms must be defined and illustrated. An *adequate stimulus* is

[14] Clifford T. Morgan, "The psychophysiology of learning," in *ibid.*, p. 781.
[15] *Ibid.*, p. 789.

one which will evoke a native reaction; any other is an *inadequate stimulus* for that particular response. For example, the introduction of a chemical substance into the mouth is a stimulus adequate to produce a flow of saliva; all other stimuli are relatively inadequate for this purpose. (A great many kinds of stimuli are totally inadequate.) However, an inadequate stimulus may become effective through the process of *conditioning*, which is defined as follows in the statement of the law: Whenever an adequate and an inadequate stimulus are repeatedly presented simultaneously, calling forth a certain response, there is a tendency, after repeated trials, for the inadequate stimulus alone to become a substitute stimulus capable of calling forth the desired response. A reflex established in this way is a *conditioned reflex*.

Pavlov experimented with the salivary secretion of dogs. He devised an operation by which the ducts connecting the salivary glands with the mouth could be diverted and the saliva collected for measurement. The environment was such that all stimuli could be carefully controlled. The experiments consisted in the simultaneous presentation of a substitute stimulus such as a light, a noise, or an electric shock, and the original stimulus, i.e., the introduction of some chemical substance into the mouth. After a sufficient number of presentations, a conditioned reflex always resulted; that is, the substitute stimulus alone would cause the flow of saliva. The number of presentations necessary to establish the conditioned reflex varied. Some dogs "learned" very quickly, others only after long, patient experimentation. In all cases, unless the substitute stimulus was occasionally reinforced by the original, the conditioned response became progressively weaker, until the substitute stimulus was entirely ineffective.

Pavlov found that substitute stimuli, when well established, could be used as the basis for another process of conditioning. For example, when a dog had been conditioned to secrete saliva in response to a given sound, another substitute stimulus, perhaps a certain light, was simultaneously presented without the introduction of any substance into the dog's mouth. After several repetitions, the light was sufficient to evoke the secretion. In the dog, it was not possible to establish further conditioned reflexes with the second substitute stimulus as the basis. No one knows how far this process can be carried in the process of human learning.

Inhibition and Excitation.   Pavlov found that after the flow of saliva had begun in response to either the original or the substitute stimulus, it could be inhibited by the presentation of another stimulus. Thus, the dog's salivary secretion would become less or cease altogether if, *after* the secretion had begun, the animal was stimulated by new sounds, sights, or pains. Pavlov concluded that there are two types of response to stimuli: *excitation* and *inhibition* of reflexes (see Figure 56). Any inadequate stimulus can be made a substitute stimulus for either excitation or inhibition, depending on the time it is presented during the process of conditioning. If it is presented simultaneously with the adequate stimulus, an excitatory reflex will be formed; if it is presented after the response is in progress, an inhibitory reflex will result.

The Conditioned Reflex in Speech.   Speech, along with its secondary aspect, written language, is a continuing series of conditioned reflexes marking successive stages of learning, somewhat as follows: A young child sees, let us say, a kitten. The act of seeing is a native reaction to a light stimulus; or at least, since new-born infants see poorly, very nearly a native reaction. If now along with the adequate stimulus, the sight of the kitten, the child's mother presents repeatedly an inadequate stimulus, the spoken word, kitten, the child will in time react to the word as if it were the animal itself. That is, either at the sight of the kitten or the mention of the word, he may himself utter the word kitten. He now possesses a conditioned reflex, which can be set off by the substitute stimulus. A few years later, the child's teacher presents a new inadequate stimulus, the written word kitten, and presently a new level of conditioning is established for the child.

For the rest of his normal life, through childhood and adulthood, the individual will conduct his intellectual activities at one or another level of conditioning, continually learning, continually using, continually forgetting, and frequently relearning. As a single example, he will for a number of years acquire a vocabulary at the rate of about three words per day or perhaps 1000 per year, will lose from his vocabulary a considerably smaller number of words per year,[16] and will often relearn some lost words.

Selectivity of Learning.   When we consider that at some period in learning the individual appears to check his theretofore random acquiring of synaptic linkages and, as Sperry comments,[17] to adopt "a selective reinforcement of the adaptive linkages with atrophy and degeneration (fading) of the maladaptive linkages. In the learning process in the mature animal, some kind of selective retention on the basis of functional effects does take place. . . . The self-

---

[16] H. A. Gleason, *Introduction to Descriptive Linguistics*, New York, Henry Holt and Company, 1955, p. 7.
[17] R. W. Sperry, "Mechanisms of neural maturation," in Stevens, *op cit.*, pp. 236–280.

regulative, operational organization of the nervous system, not just the character of its protoplasm, is what enables it to utilize its experience selectively to improve its own structure."

Here we very nearly go beyond neurology, at least as we know it up to this date. For here we approach the need of *knowing* about memory traces instead of postulating about them, and of knowing what consciousness is. These needs are scarcely answered by Descartes' *Cogito, ergo sum*, because now we want to know also *how* we overtly set about thinking, and how we select the subjects of thought. Neurology is hardly ready to tell us all these things—but in the meantime some knowledge of neurology certainly aids us in dealing with the problems of speech.

The Hegemony of the CNS

The carrying out of a muscular movement of any complexity involves the contraction of certain muscles and the relaxation of certain others, which, because of their attachments, would prevent the intended movement if they were not relaxed. Thus the muscles that close the jaw must be relaxed when the jaw is to be opened. Hence rapid movements of the parts of the body equipped with striped muscles involve in the CNS a rapid shift of inhibition and excitation from one muscle group to another. A muscle fiber contracts if the impulses coming to it over the nerve fiber innervating it are sufficiently strong to set off the processes of muscle metabolism. Whether the impulses are strong enough to accomplish this result depends upon the activity of the fibers that synapse with the fiber serving the muscle. Each of these fibers innervating the muscle may synapse with many fibers higher in the nervous system. Some of them serve to excite the lower nerve and some to inhibit it. What the lower fiber will do will depend upon the final or total resultant of the nerve impulses acting upon it. If the resultant is excitatory, the muscle will contract; if it is inhibitory, the muscle will relax. In general, in any synapse involving several upper neurons terminating around the cell body of a lower motor neuron, those neurons that originate in the cerebrum are more inhibitory than those arising from a lower level. Thus a strong stimulation of the cerebrum by a blow on the skull causes a relaxation of the skeletal muscles; the destruction of the motor parts of the cerebrum brings abnormally tense muscle contractions; and a strong stimulation of the centers in the cord causes a muscle contraction in spite of the inhibitory influence of the higher centers.

Summary

Students who are interested primarily in understanding the relationship between neurological processes and "normal" speech may be advised to reëxamine the schema on functional relationships in speech control (Figure 53, page 202). The relationships shown in that schema are by no means exhaustive. With further reflection, the student should be able to note other examples of feedback, such as in hearing, and from proprioceptive stimulation during gesturing. Other association processes may be added to the picture. The relationships of emotion and homeostasis to speech are illustrated both by speakers who purposefully pace back and forth to engender a feeling of excitement before addressing audiences and by those of various cults that strive for inner tranquility or the "control of mind over body." The difference between detection and perception of stimuli is worthy of considerable thought. In any study of the psychology of speech, mention is made of the difference between *listening* and *hearing*. Some of these differences may profitably be traced back to their neurological origin.

The ability to speak is based upon incredibly nice adjustments of the nervous system. With such close tolerances, any sort of neural disturbance may throw them out of order. Too much excitation may produce a degree of muscular tension called spasticity; too much inhibition may produce ungovernable muscular laxness or flaccidity. After injury to the lower motor neuron, as from poliomyelitis (infantile paralysis) or from diphtheria, the lack of excitation to the muscles may result in complete muscular flaccidity. After cortical injury, such as from a brain concussion or infection, unopposed excitation of muscles may produce a spastic paralysis of these muscles. If the emotions are abnormally stirred, the lower brain may compete with the cerebrum for control of the vocal musculature so as to produce an impedance to speech! Indeed, the opportunities for maladjustment of so many reflex arcs governing so many muscles performing so intricate a process, are so infinitely numerous that the marvel is not that we sometimes speak faultily but that we speak at all. The vital, life-sustaining functions of breathing and taking food are more comprehensible, because the reflex arcs connected with them are natively established; but the function of speech, being in a sense overlaid or superimposed upon the musculature of these primitive functions and being forced to use borrowed mechanisms, represent acquired or learned adjustments, adaptations, and coördinations nothing short of miraculous.

Chapter V

The Phonetic Basis
of Speech

The Relation of Phonetics to General Linguistics

Phonetics is a branch of the subject of general linguistics. Linguistics is a very broad term including, as will be seen in Chapter VI, almost every aspect of language study. Phonetics is limited to one aspect only—the sounds of speech. The present chapter takes up such phases of the study of speech sounds as seem necessary to the scope and intention of this book. The chapter is by no means intended to serve as a complete textbook in phonetics.

The Inconsistencies of Spelling

Except in the rarest of instances, speech begins with sound. It is primarily audible rather than visible or touchable. Written symbolization is a secondary development.

Such symbolization is almost never thoroughly efficient. Its chief failure is its lack of consistency. The sounds of speech, that is, the phonemes, or contrasting, mutually exclusive sound classes, ought to be represented by one symbol each and one only; conversely, each symbol should represent only one phoneme.

These conditions are almost never completely observed in a written language. In English the lack of observance is flagrant to the point of perversity. The letter *o* has a different sound in each one of the following words: *go, do, dove, woman, women, not*. The vowel sound [ɪ] as in *bit* is represented in many different ways, some of which occur in the following list: *a* in *courage*, *ay* in *Monday*, *e* in *pretty*, *ea* in *fear*, *ee* in *been*, *i* in *bit*, *ie* in *sieve*, *o* in *women*, *u* in *busy*, *y* in *cyst*. These examples are not exceptional. Hardly one of the sounds of English is represented by one symbol only.[1]

The Need for a Phonetic Alphabet

For this reason if for no other, a phonetic alphabet, which is not subject to vagaries and inconsistencies, is essential to any basic study of speech. There have been many such alphabets. The one now most frequently used is that of the International Phonetic Association, known as the IPA alphabet. The IPA alphabet, containing not only the sounds of English, but also those of many other languages, is shown on page 237. The two symbols [ɝ] and [ɚ], commonly used by American phoneticians and accepted by the IPA, have been added to the IPA list of vowel symbols.

An added value in the inclusion of a study of the phonetic basis of speech lies in making the student speech conscious. Nothing sensitizes him to speech problems, principles, and phenomena—standard speech, substandard speech, beauties of speech, dialects, language relationships, etc.—so much as a sound-by-sound analysis of speech. With phonetic study he begins for the first time really to hear speech sounds accurately.

Phonetic study, then, frees the student from the contradictions and inefficiencies of ordinary alphabets and orthography and sharpens his perception of the intricate and fascinating problems of his subject matter.

Making English Sounds

Everyone has some notion, and usually thinks he knows accurately, how to make the several vowel and consonant sounds. But this knowledge is often inaccurate. Many who think they are making [g] and [k] in *glass* [glæs] and *class* [klæs] in reality always make [d] and [t], so that they pronounce instead *dlass* [dlæs] and *tlass* [tlæs]. Others substitute [ɪ] for [ɛ] and say *min* [mɪn] and *tin* [tɪn] for *men* and *ten*; or by a related principle say *age* [eɪdʒ] for *edge* [ɛdʒ]. It is therefore continually necessary to aid students in pronunciation by explaining how the sounds are really made.

Key Words

The common way of explaining the values of phonetic symbols by the use of key words may be helpful or misleading, according to whether the

---

[1] Vera Yeteva Johnson, *The Comparative Frequency of the Spellings of the Phonetic Elements*, unpublished Master's Thesis, Louisiana State University, 1936.

THE INTERNATIONAL PHONETIC ALPHABET.
(Revised to 1951.)

CONSONANTS

	Bi-labial	Labio-dental	Dental and Alveolar	Retroflex	Palato-alveolar	Alveolo-palatal	Palatal	Velar	Uvular	Pharyngal	Glottal
Plosive	p b		t d	ʈ ɖ			c ɟ	k g	q ɢ		ʔ
Nasal	m	ɱ	n	ɳ			ɲ	ŋ	ɴ		
Lateral Fricative			ɬ ɮ								
Lateral Non-fricative			l	ɭ			ʎ				
Rolled			r						ʀ		
Flapped			ɾ	ɽ					ʀ		
Fricative	ɸ β	f v	θ ð s z ɹ	ʂ ʐ	ʃ ʒ	ɕ ʑ	ç ʝ	x ɣ	χ ʁ	ħ ʕ	h ɦ
Frictionless Continuants and Semi-vowels	w ɥ	ʋ	ɹ				j (ɥ)	(w)	ʁ		

VOWELS

	Front	Central	Back
	i y	ɨ ʉ	ɯ u
	ɪ ʏ		ɤ ʊ
Close			ɣ* o
	e ø		
		ə	
Half-close	ε œ	ɜ	ʌ ɔ
	æ		
		ɐ	
Half-open	a		ɑ ɒ
Open			

Secondary articulations are shown by symbols in brackets.   * The symbol ɣ is used in this book for unrounded u.

OTHER SOUNDS.—Palatalized consonants: ṭ, ḍ, etc.; palatalized ʃ, ʒ : ɕ, ʑ. Velarized or pharyngalized consonants: ɫ, d̶, s̶, etc. Ejective consonants (with simultaneous glottal stop): p', t', etc. Implosive voiced consonants: ɓ, ɗ, etc. ɼ fricative trill. σ, ʚ (labialized θ, ð, or s, z). ʗ, ʒ (labialized ʃ, ʒ). ʇ, ʗ, ʖ (clicks, Zulu c, q, x). ɺ (a sound between r and l). ŋ Japanese syllabic nasal. ʓ (combination of x and ʃ). ʍ (voiceless w). ɩ, ʏ, ɵ (lowered varieties of i, y, u). з (a variety of ə). ɵ (a vowel between ø and o).

Affricates are normally represented by groups of two consonants (ts, tʃ, dʒ, etc.), but, when necessary, ligatures are used (ʦ, ʧ, ʤ, etc.), or the marks ⌢ or ⌣ (t͡s or t͜s, etc.). ⌢ also denote synchronic articulation (m͡ŋ = simultaneous m and ŋ). c, ɟ may occasionally be used in place of tʃ, dʒ, and ʒ for ts, dz. Aspirated plosives: ph, th, etc. r-coloured vowels: ɛɹ, aɹ, ɔɹ, etc., or eʴ, aʴ, ɔʴ, etc., or ɚ, ɑ, ɔ, etc.; r-coloured ə : əɹ or əʴ or ɹ or ɚ, or ɹ.

LENGTH, STRESS, PITCH.— ː (full length). · (half length). ˈ (stress, placed at beginning of the stressed syllable). ˌ (secondary stress). ˉ (high level pitch); ˗ (low level); ˊ (high rising); ˏ (low rising); ˋ (high falling); ˎ (low falling); ˆ (rise-fall); ˇ (fall-rise).

MODIFIERS.— ˜ nasality. ̥ breath (l̥ = breathed l). ̬ voice (s̬ = z). ʻ slight aspiration following p, t, etc. ̫ labialization (n̫ = labialized n). ̪ dental articulation (t̪ = dental t). ˔ palatalization (z̧ = ʑ). ̣ specially close vowel (ẹ = a very close e). ̨ specially open vowel (ę = a rather open e). ˔ tongue raised (e˔ or e̝ = ẹ). ˕ tongue lowered (e˕ or e̞ = ę). ˖ tongue advanced (u˖ or u̟ = an advanced u, t̟ = t̪). ˗ or ̠ tongue retracted (i̠ or ɩ̠ = ɨ, t̠ = alveolar t). ˎ lips more rounded. ˏ lips more spread. Central vowels: ï (= ɨ), ü (= ʉ), ë (= ə̈), ë (= ə), ö (= ɵ), ö̈. ɛ̈, ö̈. ˌ (e.g. n̩) syllabic consonant. ˰ consonantal vowel. ʃ variety of ʃ resembling s, etc.

individual reading the key words pronounces the sounds contained in them with values approaching those given to the symbols by phoneticians on the basis of average standard pronunciation. Many people use other values, according to regional custom or individual idiosyncrasy. For example, during World War I the Boston *Transcript* answered in its columns an inquiry about the pronunciation of *Neuve Chapelle*, stating that the first word was pronounced like the English word *nerve*. This explanation did very well for Boston, where the educated pronunciation of *nerve* as [nɜv] approximates passably the correct French [nœv]; but it was a very bad explanation in the General American area, where it is pronounced [nɝv], with a distinct sense of [r]; it was equally bad for parts of the South, where many people pronounce it as [nɜɪv]; and in New York's East Side the occasional rendering of the word as [nɔɪv] is far indeed from the French rendering of *Neuve*. Even more common sounds cannot always be safely explained by key words. Nothing seems more simple and direct than to say that the so-called Italian *a*, usually marked diacritically as ä and represented phonetically by [ɑ], is equal to the *a* in *farm* [fɑ(r)m]; yet many people in the South pronounce the word as *form* [fɔm], and many in New England say [fam]. Key words are very untrustworthy.

Nevertheless, key words have been used in Chapters I, II, and III, and will be used here for whatever help they may give. But the reader is warned not to depend upon them unless he can determine positively that the positions his vocal organs assume in pronouncing each sound agree with those described with the aid of the vowel and consonant tabulation chart of the IPA alphabet, and that the significant sounds themselves correspond to those intended in presenting the key words.

Pending more accurate study, the phonetic symbols, English and foreign, used herein may be interpreted as follows:

`	sign of aspiration
˒	sign of unaspiration
⊥	sign of raising the tongue
⊤	sign of lowering the tongue
⊣	sign of fronting the tongue
⊢	sign of retracting the tongue
ˌ	beneath a consonant makes it a syllable
ˈ	above and to left of a syllable, primary stress
ˌ	below and to left of a syllable, secondary stress
ʔ	glottal stop
ˇ	trill

⊓	sign of dentality
ː	lengthening sign
~	sign of nasalization
[a]	*a* in eastern *farm* [fam]; first sound of diphthong [aɪ] in *dine* [daɪn] or of the diphthong [aʊ] in *cow* [kaʊ]
[aɪ]	*i* in *dine* [daɪn]
[aʊ]	*ow* in *cow* [kaʊ]
[ɑ]	*a* in *calm* [kɑm]
[ɒ]	*o* in British *not* [nɒt]
[æ]	*a* in *hat* [hæt]
[b]	*b* in *bit* [bɪt]
[β]	*b* and *v* as in Spanish *abreviar* [aβreˈβjar]; voiced bilabial fricative
[ç]	*ch* as in German *ich* [ɪç]; like *h* as in *huge* pronounced breathily. Used after a front vowel or [r]
[d]	*d* in *done* [dʌn]
[ʤ]	*j* in *Jumbo* [ˈʤʌmbo]
[e]	lightly stressed *a* in first syllable of *vacation* [veˈkeɪʃən]; first sound of diphthong [eɪ] in *late* [leɪt]
[eɪ]	strongly stressed *a* in *late* [leɪt]
[ə]	*a* in *cobra* [ˈkoʊbrə]—always unstressed
[ɛ]	*e* in *yes* [jɛs]
[ɜ]	Eastern, Southern, British *ur* in *burn* [bɜn] (stressed)
[ɝ]	General American *ur* in *burn* [bɝn] (syllabic [r] stressed)
[ɚ]	General American *er* in *mother* [ˈmʌðɚ] (syllabic [r] unstressed)
[f]	*f* in *foul* [faʊl]
[g]	*g* in *go* [goʊ]
[ɟ]	symbol for front [g]
[ɣ]	*g* in dialectal German *Wagen* [ˈvaɣən]; *g* in Spanish *Aragón* [araˈɣɔn]. A voiced spirant made with the back of the tongue nearly touching the soft palate.
[h]	*h* in *him* [hɪm]
[i]	*ee* in *seem* [sim]
[ɪ]	*i* in *hit* [hɪt]
[ɨ]	*i* as in dialectal [ˈsɨstə] for *sister*; a centralized [ɪ]
[j]	*y* in *yet* [jɛt]
[k]	*k* in *kind* [kaɪnd]
[c]	symbol for front [k]
[l]	*l* in (S., E., Br.) *lily* [ˈlɪlɪ]
[ɫ]	*l* in *ball* [bɔɫ]
[l̩]	syllabic [l] as in *brittle* [ˈbrɪtl̩]
[ʎ]	*ll* in Castilian *calle* [ˈkaʎe] much like *l*+*y* in *impel you*, but with the tongue-tip down
[m]	*m* in *beam* [bim]

[m̩]　syllabic [m̩] as in *stop 'em* [stɑp m̩]
[n]　*n* in *dine* [daɪn]
[n̩]　syllabic [n̩] as in *kitten* ['kɪtn̩]
[ŋ]　*ng* in *ring* [rɪŋ]
[ŋ̩]　syllabic [ŋ̩] as in *I can go* [ai kŋ̩ goʊ]
[o]　lightly stressed *o* in *oration* [o'reɪʃən]; first sound of diphthong [oʊ] in *note* [noʊt]
[oʊ]　strongly stressed *o* in *note* [noʊt]
[ɵ]　in dialectal New England *home* [hɵm]; unround [o], a sound suggesting [ʌ]
[œ]　in Fr. *coeur* [kœr], Ger. *Köpfe* ['kœpfə]; rounded [ɛ]
[ɔ]　*aw* in *jaw* [ʤɔ]
[ɔɪ]　*oi* in *boil* [bɔɪl]
[p]　*p* in *pit* [pɪt]
[r]　*r* in *ring* [rɪŋ]
[ɾ]　the one-tap trill in Eastern, British *merry* ['mɛɾɪ]
[ʀ]　uvular trill as in Parisian French *rue* [ʀy]
[s]　*s* in *song* [sɔŋ]
[ʃ]　*sh* in *she* [ʃi]
[t]　*t* in *too* [tu]
[t̚]　[t] unexploded in [bɪt̚]
[ʧ]　*ch* in *child* [ʧaɪld]
[θ]　*th* in *thin* [θɪn]
[ð]　*th* in *that* [ðæt]
[u]　*oo* in *cool* [kul]
[ju]　*u* in *imbue* [ɪm'bju]
[ʊ]　*oo* in *cook* [kʊk]
[ɤ]　as in dialectal [gɤd] for *good*; an unrounded [ʊ]
[ʌ]　*u* in *cup* [kʌp]
[v]　*v* in *vile* [vail]
[w]　*w* in *witch* [wɪʧ]
[ʍ]　*wh* in *which* [ʍɪʧ]
[x]　*ch* in German *Nacht* [nɑxt]; akin to [ç], but used after a back vowel
[y]　French *u* in *une* [yn], or German *u* in *müde* ['mydə]; rounded [i]
[z]　*z* in *buzz* [bʌz]
[ʒ]　*s* in *casual* ['kæʒuəl]

The Vowel Diagram

The best scheme yet devised for explaining graphically the position of the lower jaw and tongue in producing vowels is the vowel diagram, shown in Figure 71, which is drawn to show only the English vowel system as indicated on page 241. The diagram is to be interpreted thus: the position of [i] indicates that it is pronounced with the tongue high and front in the mouth; [a], with the tongue low and front; [ɑ], with the tongue low and back; and [u], with the tongue high and back.

The sounds [ɪ], [e], [ɛ], and [æ] are all made with the tongue front, and with the jaw and tongue dropping progressively by approximately equal distances (doubled between [e] and [ɛ]) from [i] through [ɪ], [e], [ɛ], and [æ] to [a]. The sounds [ɒ], [ɔ], [o], and [ʊ] are made with the tongue back, and with the jaw and tongue rising progressively by approximately equal distances

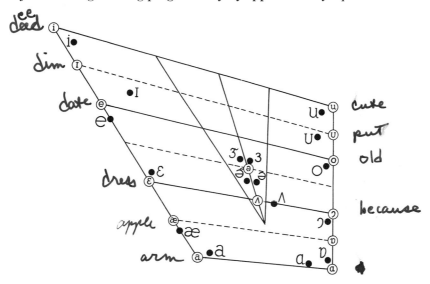

Figure 71. Vowel Diagram. (Theoretic pronunciations, small symbols; author's pronunciations, large symbols.)

(doubled between [ɔ] and [o]) from [ɑ] through [ɒ], [ɔ], [o], and [ʊ] to [u]. The sounds [ɜ], [ə], [ɝ] and [ɚ] are central, made with the tongue about halfway from the front toward the back, and about halfway from low toward high. The sound [ʌ] in American speech is somewhat centralized but is lower and farther back than the central vowels.

Articulation-Enunciation

Consonants

The word lists here are calculated to afford practice specifically with all the English consonants and concomitantly with most of the English vowels.

Emphasis is on the articulation of the consonants. The word lists may be used (1) simply for pronunciation, or (2) for transcription and pronunciation. The actions of the organs used in forming speech sounds, as categorized on pages 188–191, are detailed here as applied to the sounds individually. Here, and throughout this exercise, there is no attempt to give more than an elementary consideration to the ways of forming sounds. This is not thought to be the place to distinguish, for example, between the degrees of aspiration in *peak* and *speak*.

Lips

[p]

The sound [p] is a voiceless, bilabial, aspirated plosive. The term voiceless means that a sound to which it is applied is pronounced without vibration of the vocal bands. It is pronounced (typically) with a sharply exploded aspiration or puff of air immediately at the end of the sound, or preceding any following vowel or consonant. Some foreigners—south Germans, Spaniards, Frenchmen, and Italians—omit the aspiration, especially initially, with the result that the sound seems like [b] to English-speaking hearers.

Peal, pill, pail, pelican, pan, pass, partner, Paul, pole, pull, poodle, pearl, poignant, pile, pound.

Apple, dapple, ripple, cripple, pippin, ripping, tripping, slipping, sleeping, creeping, chopping, cheeping; heap, hip, nape, step, cap, gasp, hop, hope, hoop, cup.

[b]

The sound [b] is a voiced, bilabial, unaspirated plosive. The term voiced means (except in whispered speech) that a sound to which it is applied is pronounced with the vocal bands vibrating. The sound [b] is pronounced without clearly audible explosion or aspiration, especially in initial positions. Spanish-speaking people will need to be taught to speak the sound with firm lip closure when it is not initial after a pause and especially when it occurs intervocalically (between vowels); they will tend to substitute for this [b] the bilabial spirant [β], which, though made with the two lips instead of the lower lip and upper teeth, will sound like [v] to English-speaking hearers. Germans and Russians will need to take care to voice final [b]; their tendency will be to pronounce it as [p] in final positions.

Beat, peat; bit, pit; bate, pate; bet, pet; bat, pat; bard, pard; bottle, pot; bought, paw; bole, pole; bull, pull; boodle, poodle; budge, pudgy; burly, pearly; bind, bound, boy.

Feeble, dribble, gable, pebble, rabble, abominate, sober, tuber, rubber, herbaceous.

Glebe, peep; jib, jip; Abe, ape; ebb, Epstein; cab, cap; knob, drop; robe, rope; tube, dupe; herb, curb; bind, boil.

[w], *wh* [ʍ]

The sound [w] is a voiced bilabial glide; [ʍ] is a voiceless bilabial glide. The term glide refers to the fact that the tongue moves rapidly from the position of [u] to that of whatever vowel follows in the syllable. Germans, Russians, and Scandinavians must be on guard not to substitute [v].

Weal, veal; wine, vine; which, witch, Vichy; where, wear; whether, weather; why, Wye, vie; while, wile, vile; when, wen,. vent; whim, women, vim; white, wight, vital.

[m]

The sound [m] is a voiced bilabial nasal. The term nasal refers to the fact that the air escapes through the nose, the lips being closed.

Mean, mill, Amy, Emma, cam, command, calm, Maude, mope, simoom, mother, murder, mile, moil.

[f]

The sound [f] is a voiceless labiodental fricative. The term fricative refers to the fact that the air makes an audible friction as it escapes through its narrow stricture—in this case between the upper teeth and lower lip.

Feel, fill, fail, effort, Africa, famine, fast, fodder, fall, foal, foot, fool, fudge, furl, foil, file, foul, beef, tough, cliff, Ralph.

[v]

The sound [v] is a voiced labiodental fricative. German students will need to be taught not to pronounce initial *v* as [f]. Spanish students must not follow the Spanish pattern of pronouncing *v* as [b] when it is in the absolute initial position, i.e., initial in a word group after a pause, and when it is preceded by *n*; also, they must not pronounce *v* as [β] *at any time.*

Venal, bean, Fenian; village, bill, fill; veil, bail, fail; velvet, bell, fell; vat, bat, fat; advantage; volume; vault, fault, Baltic; volt, foal, bole; voodoo, fool, boost; vulture, bulge, fun; virtue, birth, firm; voile, vile, vow; invite, invitation, environment, inveigh, invariable, give, have.

[tʃ] in combination, though it has both [t] and [ʃ]. Speakers of French will have to learn to put the sounds together to make the affricate [tʃ].

Chide, rich, chicken, convention, suspension, hitching, chance, fracture, actually, church.

j [ʤ]

The sound [ʤ] is a voiced affricate, composed of a [d] which is exploded through the aperture of [ʒ]. Because the letter *j* has other values in foreign languages, Germans and Scandinavians will need to guard against substituting *y* [j] for this sound; Frenchmen, *zh* [ʒ]; Spaniards, [x], the voiceless velar fricative. In other words, Germans and Scandinavians must not pronounce *joke* as *yoke* [jok]; Frenchmen must not say *zhoke* [ʒok]; or Spaniards [xok]. All must learn *joke* [ʤouk]. The sound [ʤ] does not occur in combination in French or Russian, and German and Spanish lack [ʒ]. Students to whom these languages are native will have to give special attention to [ʤ]. Teutonic and Slavic speakers must not unvoice [ʤ] to [tʃ]; they will have a special tendency to do so when the sound is final.

Jump, George, gem, genial, jest, just, gist, gibe, gyrate, gyroscope, jail, gaol, James, judge.

[s]

The sound [s] is a voiceless alveolar fricative. It is a sharply hissing sound in English. Spanish students will need to place the tongue a little farther forward than they are accustomed to do.

Sing, seem, vice, thus, hissing, mists, insists, wrists, posts, ghosts, asks, tasks, asked, flasks.

[z]

This sound [z] is a voiced alveolar fricative. Spanish students should place the tongue farther front than for the infrequently occurring Spanish [z]; they must not substitute [s] or [θ] (the sound of the *th* in *thing*). Germans and Russians must not unvoice [z] to [s] when it occurs finally.

Zeal, please, easy, busy, reason, bids, cogs, example, exact, exaggeration, freeze, breeze, dizzy, his, hers, theirs, prize.

[r]

The sound [r] is a voiced retroflex (tongue-tip or blade directed toward center of hard palate). No general exercises can be devised for [r] except as used initially in a syllable, or initially with one or two consonants. Foreign students must take care not to trill English [r].

Ring, bring, string, abridge, wry, cry, Friday, playwright, wring, Christmas, spray, drove, adroit, drowsy.

y [j]

The sound [j] is a voiced palatal glide. The tongue moves rapidly from the position of [i] to that of whatever vowel follows in the syllable. Scandinavians sometimes substitute [ʤ] for [j] as a reaction against their natural tendency to use [j] for [ʤ]. *Junion* [ˈʤunjən] for *union* may result, but the correction is easy, because the speakers have the [j] sound in their native languages.

Yes, yield, yesterday, ewe, your, peculiar, pew, putrid, puma, fugitive, futile, few, feud, fuse, fume, tune, dew, due, student, constitution, new, knew, duty.

NOTE: From the word *tune* onward, i.e., after *t*, *d*, and *n*, many General American speakers will pronounce the examples without [j], thus: [tun] instead of [tjun]. [tun], etc., are regarded as standard alongside [tjun]. Southerners are more nearly uniform in the use of [tjun], etc.

th [θ]

The sound [θ] is a voiceless dental fricative. The tongue lightly touches the rear surfaces of the upper front teeth. This sound presents great difficulty to nearly all foreigners. The Spanish (even though they have the sound [θ] in words like Castilian *cinco*) and French (but not the Canadian and Louisiana French) usually substitute [s] for [θ], and other foreigners usually substitute [t]. Less educated Negroes, many less educated city dwellers, especially in the East, some less educated Southerners, and the Canadian and Louisiana French also substitute [t]. All these speakers need much practice, followed by continual vigilance.

Thin, thing, thistle, forth, fourth, firth, withe, goeth, cometh, heareth, thalamus, thong, Thwing, thwack, thole, Thorstein, throttle, throstle, thrash, three, fifth, sixth, seventh, eighth, ninth, tenth, eleventh, twelfth, heath, breadth, width, length, strength, froth, bath, lath, aftermath.

th [ð]

The sound [ð] is a voiced dental fricative. Like [θ], this sound is very difficult for many foreigners. Spaniards alone find it easy, since they have a sound nearly like it in Castilian, and exactly like it in American Spanish, in such words as *nada*. Less educated Negroes, less educated city dwellers, some less educated Southerners, and the Canadian and Louisiana French substitute [d] for [ð], especially in the commoner words such as the definite article, pronouns, etc. All these need much practice and great subsequent vigilance.

The, this, that, these, those, them, their, theirs, themselves, other, father, mother, brother, whether, weather, rather, gather, either, neither, breathe, heather, feather, lather, lathe, bathe, scathe, wither.

The Back of the Tongue and the Velum

[k]

The sound [k] is a voiceless, aspirated, velar plosive. Initially, it is sharply aspirated. Germans, Spaniards, Frenchmen, and Italians must take care not to omit the aspiration, lest the sound seem like [g] to English-speaking hearers. Americans must avoid the insertion of a *y* sound [j] between [k] and a following vowel, especially the vowel [æ] and the diphthong [aʊ]. That is, *cask* [kæsk] and *cow* [kaʊ] must not become *kyask* [kjæˑsk] and *kyow* [kjæˑʊ].

Cask, care, cattle, can, can't, cant, cab, cabbage, camshaft, cat, camera, castle; cow, count, county, cowl, account, couch, cowry.

[g]

The sound [g] is a voiced, unaspirated, velar plosive. Spaniards and some Germans will have a tendency to substitute the velar spirant [ɣ] in intervocalic positions. This must be avoided and a firm, crisp [g] used intervocalically, exactly as in initial positions. Germans must avoid substituting [x] and [k] finally.

Eager, intrigue; gill, kill, figure; gale, kale, negate; get, kettle, keg; gad, cad, drag; gar, car, Lafargue; gall, call, augment; goat, coat, roguish, rogue; ghoul, cool, rugal; guzzle, cuddle, rug, rugged, girl, curl, regurgitate, iceberg.

The Glottis

[ʔ]

The sound [ʔ] is a voiceless glottal plosive. Germans, who use the glottal stop frequently before stressed initial syllables beginning with vowels, should refrain from carrying their native pattern into English. Scots, Cockneys, and New Yorkers should avoid substituting the glottal stop for [t] and other stops, as they often do in their everyday speech. In standard English, glottal stop is useful to prevent ambiguity, as may be observed below.

Some mice, some ice; beater, bee eater; heats, he eats; freeze, free ease; Grover, grow over; seals, see eels.

[h]

The sound [h] is a voiceless glottal fricative. The French, Spanish, and Italians do not pronounce *h*, though it occurs in the spelling of their languages. Russian has no *h*. The French and Italians simply omit [h] in English. Russians and speakers of Spanish tend to substitute [x]. Cockneys and a few other Englishmen, commonly of lesser education, omit initial [h] frequently. These should pronounce their [h]'s except as indicated in the next sentence. It is entirely acceptable to drop *h* from *has, have, had, he, his, him*, and *her*, when these words occur in unstressed positions. See examples in sentences below.

Have, how, home, hope, Harry, hiss, hold, holy, wholly, hand, heel, hill, hailed, hello, help, has, hod, haul, hone, hoop, hum, heard, Hoyle, howl, hide.

Is HE [hi] here? Is he [ɪ] HERE? Here's HIS [hɪz] hat. Here's his [ɪz] HAT. I see HIM [hɪm]. I SEE him [ɪm]. Where's her [ə,ɚ] MOTHER? Where's HER [hɜ] (or [hɝ]) mother?

Vowels
Tongue, Hard Palate, Velum, and Lips

All vowels (except in whispered speech) are voiced. They are made with the lips either rounded or unrounded, and with the tongue arched either in the front, center or back of the mouth. The elevation of the tongue varies in the degrees indicated by the terms high, low high, high mid, low mid, high low, and low. When these terms are combined in the description of vowels, the results are as follows:

Front Unround		*Central* Partly Round	*Back Round*	
High	i		High	u
Low high	ɪ		Low high	ʊ
High mid	e		High mid	o
		Mid ɝ, ɚ, ə, ɜ		
Low mid	ɛ	Low mid, backed, unround ʌ	Low mid	ɔ
High low	æ		High low	ɒ
Low	a		Low, unround	ɑ

Read as follows: [i] is a high front, unround vowel; schwa [ə] is a mid central, partly round vowel; [ɔ] is a low mid back, round vowel; etc.

See the vowel positions illustrated by tabulation on page 249 and the vowel diagram on page 241. There are no standard nasal vowels in English.

The pronunciation of vowels in English is a twofold proposition: (1) pronunciation in stressed syllables, (2) pronunciation in unstressed syllables. It is pertinent to illustrate both briefly at this juncture.

Any vowel in an unstressed syllable in English tends to lose its identity to a greater or lesser degree, and to become one of three things:

1. In the case of the diphthongs [eɪ] and [oʊ], a light, pure (undiphthongized) form of the first elements respectively, i.e., [e] and [o]. Examples: *orate* ['oʊret], *oration* [o'reɪʃən], *coeval* [ko'ivəl], *donation* [do'neɪʃən], *donate* ['doʊnet]. Note that *orate* and *donate* illustrate stressed [oʊ] and unstressed [e], while *oration* and *donation* illustrate unstressed [o] and stressed [eɪ].
2. The vowel [ɪ]. Examples: *character* [kærɪktə, kɛrɪktə] or [kærɪktɚ, kɛrɪktɚ], *example* [ɪg'zæmpl̩] or [ɪg'zɑmpl̩].
3. The vowel schwa [ə]. Examples: *attar* ['ætə] or ['ætɚ], *eater* ['itə] or ['itɚ], *tapir* ['teɪpə] or ['teɪpɚ], *labor* ['leɪbə] or ['leɪbɚ], *future* ['fjuʧə] or ['fjuʧɚ], *martyr* ['mɑtə] or ['mɑrtɚ], abet [əbɛt]. (Note alternate use of ɚ.)

Foreigners learning English should learn the English manner of unstressing as soon as possible. Erroneous stressing of unstressed syllables is an outstanding feature of most foreign accents.

The Phoneme

It is often said that the notion of one sound per symbol and one symbol per sound, although convenient to beginners, is inaccurate. The more accurate statement is one symbol per phoneme. A phoneme consists of from one to several constituent members called allophones. One phoneme, the /t/ phoneme, may be noted in the following series of allophones: *rate, eighth, cattle, mutton*. Each of these [t]'s is made in a different way. We have alveolar [t] in [reɪt], dental [t] in [eɪtθ], laterally exploded [t] in ['kætl̩], and nasally exploded [t] in ['mʌtn̩]. Yet each is recognizable as a [t] and so belongs as an allophone to the /t/ phoneme. (Phonemes are indicated by diagonals.)

If however, we should substitute, say, [k] for [t] in *rate*, the resultant word, *rake*, would have a different meaning, thus proving that [t] and [k] belong to different phonemes. Phonemes differ for different languages. Thus in Italian the [n] in *hanno* ['anːo] and the [ŋ] in *cinque* ['ʧiŋkwe] belong to the same phoneme, the /n/ phoneme, whereas in English they belong to two phonemes, the /n/ phoneme and the /ŋ/ phoneme. In English, the [h] in *hand* [hænd] and the [ç][2] in *human* ['çumən] both belong to the /h/ phoneme, whereas in German they belong to two separate phonemes, the /h/ phoneme and the /ç/ phoneme.

The beginning student may well bear in mind that many common mispronunciations consist in using an allophone that is not in good standing. A good example is the high nasal [æ̆¹], which is often used for [æ] in words like *man* [mæn].

Phonetic Transcription

Throughout this and many other texts, and especially in this chapter, considerable proficiency in reading phonetic symbols is necessary. The best way to achieve this proficiency is to practice transcription. The following exercises offer practice with all the symbols used in English. It is to be understood that, this book not being a text in phonetics, these exercises are only to aid in acquiring the minimum knowledge necessary for the most elementary uses.

Transcribe. peach, deeper, peep; pigeon, dipper, drip; paid, draping, ape; petting, inept, step.

bat, babble, Ahab; bath, brand, band; ball, strawberry, daub.

toper, rotation, note; took, put-in, foot; tool, looted, shoot.

cuckoo, dukedom, duckling, dirk-edge.

geese, gizzard, gale, get, Gatling, garden, Gordon, ghosts, good, goose, gudgeon, girder.

dream, grim, blame, gem, amnesty, alarm, warm, quarter, airdrome, doom, dumb, crumb, worm, term, germ.

spring, Englewood, jangle, strength, strong, clung, clink, bank, junk, string, thing, inglenook.

meal, kill, jail, shell, amalgamate, doll, Carl, call, cajole, full, fool, gull, curl; coil, spoil, oil, foil, file, foul, fowl, flower, floor.

ring, bring, drink, green, Reno, rain, brain, render, Brent, ran, brand, grand, rock, crock, raw, crawl, roll, troll, root, ride, brood, rough, brush, truck, grudge.

are, car, char, jar, art, cart, chard, jarred, Arthur, Martin, hour, our, fowler, flour, cower, order, ardor, four, door, oar, o'er, over, Dover, cover, more, course, coarse, horse, hoarse, corps, corpse, chore, care, hair, pair, pear, rare, roar, number, slumber, roarer, pourer, fourteen.

feature, fixture, fake case, fender, factual, fan, gnats, farther, father, foxglove, folk carols, Fuller's.

verdure, virginal, vermiform appendix; eventide, Ivry, Avery Island, everyone, avocation, Chauvinism, movement.

---

[2] *Ch* as in German *ich* [ıç].

thesis, thin, thane, Themistocles, thankful, thong-like, thule, thumb, third.

these, this, they, them, that, these, thus, either, feather, clothes; breathe, with, scathe, clothe, loathe.

Æsop, hyssop, ace-high, esoteric, asparagus, periosteum, Austerlitz, boastful, trustworthy, rooster, brutish, bursting, thirsty, oyster, Christ, ouster.

breeze, fizz, blaze, jazz, ah's, jaws, rose, dews, dues, ruse, cruise, buzz, furs.

specie, wishful, gracious, Gresham, ashes, cautious, cushion, usher, worship.

heedless, hysteria, heinous, hen, handicraft, hockey, hardihood, hawk, hall, whole, hooded, who, whoop, huddle, herd.

when, wen; Whig, wig; where, were, wear; which, witch; whither, wither; wheel, weal; whoa, woe; what, Watt; whacker, Wacker; wheat, why, whistle, whim.

weep, willow, Wales, welkin, wall, wold, wool, Worcester, worst.

yield, yesterday, yap, yawp, yodel, use, union, united, euphonious, humor, human, tune, duke, constitution, knew, student, new, yowl.

chicken, riches, checkers, wretches, chance, thatches, chop, botch, chalk, choke, broach, chew, chuckle, clutch, church, birch, choice, chowder, chide.

Jesus, gist, James, Jimmy, Jack, jog, jaw bone, joke, jewelry, June, just, judge, Jergens, dungeon, pigeon, bludgeon, fudge, trudge, smudge, Scrooge, gyrate, gyroscope, John, general.

serious, she, shear, leisurely, ye, weed, wheats, be easy, re-emerge; mint, meant; since, sense, scents, cents; bin, Ben, ban; tin, ten, tan; fin, fen, fan; Jim, gem, jam; wrench, rinse.

yes, shake, whale, wail, chain, jail, goal.

pet, bet, Thames, temporal, fence, dense, dents, lest, reparations, February, vexations, separate, blessing, resent, azure, hand-hold, asks, asked, tasks.

talk, balk, walk, ought, awful, caught, bought, brought, sought, thought, fought, taught, hawk, chalk.

Cuba, appear, awake, upper, over, apple, procrastinate, wanted, hunted, telephone, telegraph, churches, idiot, command, applaud, expect, example.

Phonetic Reading

The following paragraph contains few words which would be pronounced differently in the different major American dialects. This paragraph will furnish an approach to reading in phonetic transcription.

sou ʤan gru tə sɪmpəl bɔɪhud ænd tə strɔŋ mænhud. wɪð ðə kʌmɪŋ əv ədʌlt streŋ(k)θ, keɪm ðə raɪpənɪŋ əv grounʌp ʤʌʤmənt. ɛmə rɪʤɔɪst ɪn hɪz grouθ, ænd preɪd ðæt æz ðə taɪm ʃud kʌm ʍɛn hi ʃəd du ðə θɪŋ ɔn ʍɪtʃ ɪz ɪgzɪstən(t)s hɪnʤd, hɪ wud bi ʔeɪbəl tə teɪk ʌp pɔlz loud wɪð ə sʌnz ʤʌst praɪd ɪn peɪɪŋ ə rɛkəgnaɪzd dɛt.

How to Pronounce a Word

"Is there a single standard of English pronunciation?" Or "Is there some one accepted way to pronounce each word?" These are perennial questions in English, and there are corresponding questions relative to all other important languages. Shall we say *grass* [græs] or *grass* [grɑs]? *Again* [əˈgeɪn] or *again* [əˈgɛn]? *Neither* [ˈniðə] or *neither* [ˈnaɪðə] or *neither* [ˈniðɚ] or *neither* [ˈnaɪðɚ]? *Advertisement* [ædˈvɜtɪzmənt] or *advertisement* [ædˈvɜtəzmənt] or *advertisement* [ˌædvɚˈtaɪzmənt]? All persons linguistically inclined take a scholarly interest in pronunciation problems; and nearly all persons, including those not at all linguistic or pedantic, find delight in the consideration of, and even in controversy over, the pronunciation of all sorts of words, from the more or less academic *dirigible* [ˈdɪrɪdʒəbl] to the plain, everyday *film* [fɪlm]. We may very well consider how to pronounce a word.

Words Having Only One Standard Pronunciation. Most words in English have only one standard pronunciation. Normal variations in the use of the members of a phoneme being granted, there is only one standard way to pronounce *hush* [hʌʃ], *being* [ˈbiɪŋ], *district* [ˈdɪstrɪkt]. Such pronunciations will be found in the dictionary and can be depended upon. Words like these are pronounced in the same way (with such allophonic variations as might be seen, for example, in British [hʌ˞ʃ] and American [hʌʃ]) all over the English-speaking world. Any deviation from the dictionary pronunciation of these words, such as [hɛʃ] for [hʌʃ] or [ˈdɪstrɪk] for [ˈdɪstrɪkt], can indicate only carelessness or ignorance.

Words Having More Than One Standard Pronunciation. But there is another type of word in respect to which opinions as to variant pronunciation cannot be ascribed to ignorance and cannot be reconciled by the dictionary. This is the type of word whose pronunciation varies from country to country or from region to region. In many instances of this type, the dictionary, instead of being an ever-present help, as with the first type, becomes a potential hindrance in that it seems to substantiate equally well two diametrically opposite opinions. The *Thorndike Century Dictionary*, for example, spells out a sort of phonetic pronunciation of the word *secular*, thus: sekˈū lər. Southerners, Easterners, and Englishmen (if we may presume on their willingness not to question the use of [ju] rather than [jʊ] or [jə] in an unstressed syllable) would instantly interpret this explanatory spelling as [ˈsɛkjulə]; but speakers from the General American speech area would as instantly and positively interpret it as [ˈsɛkjulɘ]. In addition to the controversy thus set up between sections, there would be the contention by the English, the Easterners, and many educated Southerners that, whereas in the expression *secular laws* the pronunciation would properly be [ˈsɛkjulɘ lɔz], in the expression *secular acts*, where the *r* is followed by a vowel, it would be [ˈsɛkjulɘr ækts] or [ˈsɛkjulɘr ækts]. Another reference, the *Standard Dictionary*, indicates by its quasi-phonetic symbols that the pronunciation of *grass* is [gras]— a pronunciation that would be summarily discarded in favor of [græs] almost everywhere in the United States except in parts of New England, and as summarily dismissed in favor of [grɑs] in other parts of New England, and in Great Britain. It thus becomes evident that in respect to both these words, where locality figures in producing variants, the question as to how to pronounce a word is not easy to answer at once.

The Dialects of English.[3]   Before we undertake to offer a practicable answer to the question propounded, it will be well to consider further the many dialects of English containing pronunciations varying with country or region.

When a language is spread throughout the world, as English is, variations of pronunciation are unavoidable and resultant dialects inevitable. These dialects will differ in rhythm, intonation, and idiom, matters intensely fascinating and important, but mainly outside the province of this chapter. They will also differ radically as to the values assigned to the vowels and consonants of a given word, a matter which is specifically the province of this chapter. It follows, therefore, that an Australian poet landing in San Francisco and ordering his first American restaurant meal may quite naturally be puzzled when the waitress tells him, "There's bean [bin] soup," and may be excused for replying in bewilderment, "But I don't want to know what there's been [bin]; I want to know what there is."

Thus there is a dialect of Australia (with several subordinate dialects within it), a dialect of America (with important subsidiaries likewise, as we shall see), one for South Africa, for British Guiana, for Jamaica, for India, for Ireland, for Scotland, for Wales, for Cornwall, for northern England, and for southern England. Each dialect has its subdialects. England proper, despite her relatively small size, is particularly rich in them. Every English county

----

[3] "Dialect" is used arbitrarily in this chapter to designate any form of English, homogeneous in itself, spoken by a considerable number of people and differing appreciably from analogous forms of English. Relative literacy of speakers is disregarded; all English, polished or illiterate, widely used or provincial, is considered as belonging to one or another of the several dialects. "Dialect: any given mode of speech or language."—*Standard Dictionary*.

shows at least small differences from the rest, and some counties, like Lanca-shire and Northumberland, differ from others to the point of partial unintel-ligibility to outsiders. Some of these many dialects—as for example the major American dialects, the South-of-England dialect, etc.—are spoken by so many educated people that they are regarded as highly cultured forms of speech. Others, such as the Cockney dialect of London, the dialect of the less educated residents of New York, called New Yorkese, and the mountain dialect of the Appalachians and Ozarks, are regarded as local or provincial.

Is There a Single Standard of English?

In some countries there is an authority, or quasi-authority, which designates one or another of the several dialects of the mother tongue as standard. The French Academy, by its rulings as to the pronunciations entered in its dictionary, so designates the speech of the Île de France, a dialect much influenced by Paris; The Spanish Academy designates the Castilian dialect; the German stage, the High German dialect; the Norwegian government, a composite Norse, or *Landsmaal* (also called *Nynorsk*) derived synthetically from various dialects; [4] and the British preparatory school authorities, the dialect of the upper and upper-middle classes of southern England. These fiat standards, even with social, scholarly, or governmental authority back of them, commonly prove difficult to establish and maintain. The inhabitants of Tours resist the dominance of the speech of northern France, and the Catalonians prize the Catalan (which, though of semi-independent Romance origin, has much the semblance of a Spanish dialect) above the standard Castilian.

But there is much to say in favor of a single standard dialect for such small countries as France, Spain, Norway, and England. With the onward sweep of modern transportation and communication, such wide variations of dialect as these countries all exhibit within such narrow borders become a distinct handicap. The very integrity of government is sometimes threatened, as when the Catalonians at various times have contemplated separation from Spain and the establishment of a Catalan-speaking state; and as when the Irish, just before the setting up of the Irish Free State, later called Eire, sought a revival of Gaelic for use as a national language as one means of stirring themselves toward separation from the British.

In the case of languages which are widely distributed, no fiat or decree to

[4] See Einar Haugen, "The linguistic development of Ivar Aasen's New Norse," *PMLA* (June, 1933), *48*: 2.

regard a given dialect as standard is ever seriously heeded. Central and South American Spanish is apparently permanently divergent from Castilian, especially in respect to *c*, *z*, and *ll*, so that Castilian *calle* [ˈkaλe], *vez* [beθ] and *cinco* [ˈθiŋko] yield to colonial [ˈkaje], [bes], and [ˈsiŋko].

The situation as to English is analogous to that of Spanish; as we have seen in the enumeration of the major English dialects, an even wider spread of territory is covered. Singularly enough, except in the British Isles themselves, the differences are not great enough to occasion inconvenience in communication. With communication assured, there remains only social pressure (social in the sense of fashionable) to induce the far-flung English-speaking area to try to conform to a single standard pronunciation. The result is little conscious conformity.

The United States, with its vast area and relatively slight differences in pronunciation (considering ease of communication as the basis of judgment), represents a situation much like that of the English-speaking world as a whole outside the British Isles. Except occasionally in cities, there is no condition of crowding radically different dialects into small areas in such a fashion as to produce social friction, governmental disturbance, or practical communicative inconvenience. Moreover, there is no academy, governmental body, or other agency in the United States with power to designate, much less to try to enforce, the use of any given dialect as standard American English.

There is in the United States, therefore, no such thing as a single standard English. Nonetheless, there was for a number of years an attempt to designate and popularize one. The attempt still persists, though now very feebly. The favored dialect is the same South-of-England form previously referred to, together with the Eastern American dialect, which strongly resembles South-of-England speech. Sponsors of the project were usually occasional phoneticians who derived their attitudes directly from England, a considerable number of speech or "elocution" teachers of New England antecedents, and, most insistent of all—sometimes to the point of what may fairly be called fanaticism—a number of "convert" teachers, i.e., persons whose native dialects were other than Southern British or Eastern American, but who adopted one of these, or a combination of the two, as a standard, and were anxious that all speakers follow their example.

These adherents to the standard English idea were earnest and diligent, and at one time seemed to be gaining ground. If their idea could have been sufficiently motivated, they might not have lost ground. But, as we have said, there being no difference among the major American dialects sufficient to hinder communication, adequate motivation was hard to find. In their search some of these enthusiasts hit upon a motive which added to their ranks a considerable contingent, the army of social climbers, but which alienated many others who might otherwise have been converted. This was the social preferment motive. American society is not definitely, or at least not permanently, stratified, and the dictum that one must speak a certain dialect to be socially acceptable has always been disagreeable to large majorities of educated people. The *nouveaux riches* often tried anxiously to conform, but lacking educational and especially linguistic background for consistent conformity, they often succeeded only in achieving an amusing agglomeration of misplaced broad *a's* and slain *r* sounds.

Those who might have joined most properly in the standard English aggressive, the actors, mainly took no part. Reasons why they might have been interested are not lacking and will presently be discussed, but the actors themselves were doubtless too busy with the more strongly motivated problem of making a living. The great body of the teachers of speech stood aloof.

Orderly Procedure Necessary in Pronunciation

And yet teachers of speech, of all people, ought to have some policy in relation to standard English. Their apparent indifference probably means in effect that each teacher is disregarding the suggestions of the advocates of a single standard and is continuing to use and teach the speech of the section to which he is native. Such a practice would not agree badly with that which is presently to be suggested by this chapter, were it not for the fact that indifference toward other dialects of English is too often likely to indicate imperfect and unorganized knowledge of one's own. In addition, the teacher who is merely a drifter as to his own opinions on pronunciation, and who lacks a conscious overt policy on the subject, is likely to find himself in serious professional difficulty. It is by all odds the best practice to think the pronunciation problem through in a definite manner and to arrive at a well-fortified decision regarding personal practice.

Standards Commonly Accepted in America

An examination of the contemporary scene shows that most teachers of speech now accept the idea of regional standards of pronunciation in America. This is the view this book supports. From this standpoint the answer to the original question as to the correct pronunciation of a word is then as follows: The correct pronunciation of a word in America is that used by the majority of educated speakers in a given American major speech area.

The Major American Dialects. There are three major dialects in the United States, each including a number of subsidiary dialects: (1) the Eastern dialect, spoken by about 19 millions of people; (2) the Southern dialect, spoken by about 49 millions; and (3) the General American dialect, spoken by about 112 millions. The Eastern dialect predominates in New England, in the City of New York[5] with some deviations, and in that part of Canada east of the Province of Quebec. In some ways, particularly in word selection,[6] its influence affects the speech of upstate New York and the northern third of Pennsylvania. The Southern dialect is spoken in those states which formed the Confederacy, with certain additions (Kentucky, southern Delaware, and southeastern Maryland), and with certain subtractions (the southern Appalachian highlands, the highlands of Arkansas and Louisiana, and all of Texas except a relatively small southeastern portion). The General American dialect prevails in the rest of the nation —and, with some variations, in the part of Canada west of the Province of Quebec.

It must be understood that the exact boundaries of the various areas are not at all well defined. All along the borders the speech is mixed. Many General American characteristics can be observed mingling with Eastern speech in Vermont and western New England generally, and with Southern speech in northern Kentucky, Arkansas, and northern Louisiana, west of the Mississippi River lowlands. Stating the case another way, we may say that the boundaries between speech regions in America are never sharp enough to be lines; rather, they are strips or bands of varying width within which the speech of two regions overlaps. Perhaps the band is narrowest along the Ohio River, which may almost be called a boundary "line"; probably it is widest in east

---

[5] It is sometimes debated whether to regard New York City as belonging dialectally to the East, the South, or alone as a separate region; some of its pronunciations parallel those of the East, some those of the South, and some neither.

[6] Hans Kurath, *A Word Geography of the Eastern United States*, Ann Arbor, University of Michigan Press, 1949, Figs. 3–8. Cf. also Albert H. Marckwardt, "Principal and subsidiary dialect areas in the North-Central States," *Publication of the American Dialect Society*, April, 1957, pp. 2–15.

NOTE: Kurath, disregarding pronunciation altogether, and mapping word-choices only, such as *Dutch cheese*, *stoop* (porch), *stone boat*, traces isoglosses defining regional boundaries separating what he calls the North, the Midland, and the South. The northern boundary of the Midland extends west from central New Jersey to a point near where the Pennsylvania–Ohio line intersects Lake Erie. The southern boundary of the Midland extends southwest from central Delaware to a point near the southern extremity of the Appalachians. Marckwardt, also mapping only word-choice (except for *greasy* ['grisɪ,'grizɪ]), continues the northern boundary of the Midland to the Mississippi River. Marckwardt also uses Kurath's terms North, Midland, and South. *Bases of Speech*, disregarding word-choice and considering only pronunciation, includes the Midland and that part of the North from the Pennsylvania line westward as a part of the General American area.

and central Texas, where some Southern characteristics extend for hundreds of miles into essentially General American territory.

It goes without saying that these three major dialect areas contain groups of people speaking many subsidiary dialects. Outstanding among these dialects are New Yorkese, Pennsylvania German, Milwaukee German, the Negro dialect, the mountain dialect, the Mexican dialect of the Southwest, the French-Canadian dialects, and the Louisiana French or "Cajan" dialect. Besides these there are forms of broken English spoken by foreigners, which are dialects in a different sense. Of these there are French, German, Spanish, Norwegian, Swedish, Yiddish, Polish, and many others; and there are at least two European English dialects fairly common, namely, Irish and Scots. These nonmajor dialects are never thought of as candidates for use as any sort of "standard" speech and so are given no consideration in this chapter. There remain, then, the Eastern, Southern, and General American dialects, each of which is spoken by large numbers of educated and cultured people.

To recapitulate, this text advises each teacher and student of speech to regard as standard for general teaching purposes the speech of the majority of educated people in whichever one of the three great dialect regions he happens to be working. As a corollary, it naturally advises that each inhabitant of a given major speech area undertake to improve his personal speech until it approximates that used by the majority of the educated people of his area.

The authors offer this advice in no particularly controversial vein. They ask of anyone who disagrees only that he have for his personal practice a plan as well thought out as the one offered here. The ideal of a regional standard rather than a single standard is suggested, partly because it is evident that the overall habit of language practice is to adhere substantially to regional standards, and such situations cannot, practically speaking, be changed by the action of any minority group. Moreover, it is obvious that should a teacher of speech undertake to change the pronunciation of his pupils in the Southern and General American areas to that of New England or London he would have to spend all his time in petty correction of pronunciation, to the exclusion of other matters of greater significance in speech improvement. Still further, it is the belief of the authors that though the three major American dialects do not differ from one another sufficiently to hinder communication in the least, still each one has a peculiar beauty of its own if spoken with reference to all the characteristics of good speech outlined and discussed in Chapter I.[7]

[7] For an extended discussion of the relative uniformity of pronunciation in America, see Giles Wilkeson Gray, "American modes of speech," in *Opinions and Attitudes*, Stewart Morgan (ed.), New York, Thomas Nelson & Sons, 1938, pp. 202–232.

Necessity and Function of Stage Diction.   Despite any seeming contradiction of the ideal of regional standards just set forth, there is one situation in the English-speaking world where a standard English dialect is not merely desirable but quite necessary. This is for certain classes of plays, upon the professional and semiprofessional stage. The reason for this is very simple. The actors in any professional or semiprofessional [8] company come not merely from the various speech areas of the United States, but from England and other foreign-speaking parts of the world. Often they are cast to represent families or neighbors who in real life would have an entirely homogeneous speech. If each actor used his native speech, the composite result would be misleading and often ridiculous. It is obvious that actors must agree upon some common dialect. The question of course naturally arises, "What dialect?" Fortunately the answer is simple. It has been decided not by any fiat but, as such questions are, by the course of events. The American stage derives from the British stage. Its first actors were English actors. Through all its history, even to the present day, large numbers of its actors have continued to be Englishmen. American actors have customarily imitated the speech of their English co-workers, and American dramatics schools have taught British speech as correct stage diction.

This text therefore suggests that the same South-of-England speech which we have advised against as a standard for universal use be frankly and conscientiously adopted for stage use. The difficulties that would present themselves in teaching this speech to the whole population largely disappear in the teaching of prospective actors. Their numbers are small and they are usually taught in special classes or schools. Because of their professional ambitions, their learning will be amply motivated, and if they possess the linguistic proficiency really essential to acting they will master the dialect easily.

South-of-England diction must be understood not to be applicable indiscriminately to all speech on the stage but rather only to classic plays, translated plays, British plays, and most plays with a locale in eastern United States. Even so, stage diction applies only to parts written in grammatically correct English, representative of the speech of literate people. Actors representing characters who in life would use a provincial dialect such as broad Scots, or a broken English dialect such as might be spoken by a Greek immigrant, should use the dialect indicated by the situation without reference to stage speech. It is, indeed, an error rather than a virtue to mix in any one acting role the pronunciations of provincial or broken English with those of stage

[8] The term "semiprofessional" is used here to include the actors in the better college and university theaters and the more important civic theaters.

speech, except as called for by the play, as in Shaw's *Pygmalion* and its musical counterpart, *My Fair Lady*. These principles apply equally to stage, motion pictures, and radio and TV drama.

Plays presented by students of most high schools and elementary schools would better be given in the standard regional speech of the area where the school is located, with variations for broad dialectal parts as indicated by the playwright. Interpretative readers, if professional, may well use stage diction as a basic speech; if nonprofessional, the speech of the region where each reader lives. Both professional and nonprofessional readers must, of course, use characterizing dialect as indicated by the author of the material read.

It may be asked in passing whether South-of-England speech will always remain the accepted dialect for dramatic speech. Of course it is impossible to predict certainly. For that matter, it is impossible to predict whether the major American dialects will maintain their separate integrity. It is evident that, with the spread of education and the improvement of transportation and communication, the provincial and broken English dialects of America are losing their identity and blending with the major dialects which geographically enclose them. It remains to be seen whether one of these major dialects will then ultimately engulf the others, or whether a homogeneous blend of the three will someday prevail.

The fact that many radio and TV announcers use General American dialect, and that hundreds of moving picture, radio, and TV actors use it, tends to suggest that the dominant speech of America will be not Eastern or Southern but General American. It is significant, too, that there is no longer a western frontier toward which emigrants can move; instead the new agricultural frontier is in the South, which is attracting thousands of immigrants from the East and Middle West. In many instances the tide of migration has been not merely deflected toward the South but actually turned back upon itself, so that the drift of western and midwestern migration is toward the industrial cities of the East.

These facts might seem to point toward the final predominance of General American speech. Of course, the fact that about 112 millions of people speak it, against a total of about 68 millions speaking the other two dialects, may be expected to have some weight in these days of continuous linguistic inter-mingling through travel, radio, and TV, and sound pictures. But whatever the ultimate outcome, for many years and certainly for the lifetime of this book, the three great regional dialects will maintain their essential separate-ness. Therefore for the present it seems wisest to adhere to regional standards for daily use, and to South-of-England speech for professional and semi-professional dramatic use.

Beauty in Language

We sometimes see or hear discussions purporting to compare the relative beauty of the major American dialects. Such discussions are futile and reveal their futility through their inconsistency. Any statement, for example, that the [æ] sound in the Southern and General American pronunciation of *grass* is unbeautiful falls down immediately before the fact that even in those dialects where *grass* is pronounced [grɑs], the [æ] sound nonetheless occurs in *lass* [læs], *package* ['pækɪʤ], *sadly* ['sædlɪ], *attitude* ['ætɪtjud], and many other words, without arousing any criticism of its alleged unmusical quality. It is safe to say that any comparison of the various dialects intended to disparage one or more of them can be shown to be similarly inconsistent. It is reasonably certain, too, that such criticisms are usually made in an attempt to rationalize or justify adherence to a so-called "standard English," without real knowledge of any way, if indeed there is any, to compare the relative esthetic values of dialects. Without venturing formally into the realm of esthetics, the present authors are willing to risk the statement that beauty of utterance consists not so much in the selection of values to be assigned to vowels and consonants as in the manner of uttering these sound values.

Thus the sound [æ] can be uttered with lower jaw up and tongue arched into occlusion with the inner surfaces of the upper molars so that the resulting tone is flat and pinched; on the other hand, it can be uttered with the jaw dropped and the tongue detached from contact with the upper molars, so that the sound is musical and beautiful. In other words, the /æ/ phoneme or sound class contains allophones which are unacceptable and others which are entirely acceptable. Of course our ideas of acceptability are conditioned, and rightly so, by the customary practice of educated people. For this reason, [sæs], however musically pronounced, could never be accepted as a well-sounding pronunciation of *sauce* so long as educated people pronounce it [sɔs]. But we reject [sæs] not because of any inherent lack of beauty, but because of its lack of currency among educated people. It is safe to say that if all prejudice can be eliminated from an individual's judgment he will admit that any of our major dialects, when well spoken, is beautiful.

It must be evident from the foregoing that adherence to regional standards does not give one *carte blanche* to lull oneself into security and to feel that one's own speech is acceptable without careful thought and attention. The regional speech of many if not most students requires careful improvement in order to put it at its best.

Inadequacy of English Spelling and Ordinary Dictionaries

It has been shown earlier in this chapter that ordinary spelling and ordinary dictionaries are inadequate to cope with the speech problem. They are particularly inadequate to help in the perfecting of regional speech.

There is nothing about the spelling of the word *only*, for example, or about the average dictionary's semiphonetic respelling of it, to prevent the Vermonter, whose native inclination is to call it [ənlɪ], from continuing this pronunciation even after looking it up. In other words, it is impossible to talk intelligently or otherwise to communicate accurately regarding pronunciation without some more accurate medium than ordinary spelling or the customary dictionary respelling.

English spellings often have little or no relation to pronunciation, having been established long ago and having failed to change as the pronunciation has changed. The famous *ough*-group—*ought* [ɔt], *dough* [doʊ], *bough* [baʊ], *enough* [ɪˈnʌf], *through* [θru], *cough* [kɔf], etc.—are sufficient illustrations of the discrepancy. The average dictionary's respellings are based upon key words. We have already seen that this basis breaks down of its own weight if the reader does not pronounce the words as the dictionary maker pronounced them. For example, it is of little avail to put into a dictionary a statement that the *a* in *Thames* is pronounced like the *e* in *men* if the reader pronounces *men* [mɪn], as many Southerners do.

Phonetics as an Instrument for Speech Improvement

Earlier in this chapter we recommended the International Phonetic Alphabet as an adequate instrument for use in the improvement of speech. This phonetic alphabet is based not upon key words but upon positions of the vocal organs which may be described and pictured, and which, when correctly assumed by given speakers, will invariably produce the correct sound. With such a phonetic alphabet it is possible to indicate the following variant pronunciations of a perverse word like *first*, thus: [fɝst], [fɜst], [fɒɪst], [fɔɪst], [fɜɪst]. With ordinary spelling it would be possible to indicate only one of these pronunciations accurately, namely, *foist* [fɔɪst].

Phonetics *per se* does not have anything to do with the advocacy of a given dialect or a language as standard. It is a science—the science of the sounds of speech—employing for the sake of consistency in designating those sounds a system of symbols, wherein each symbol stands for a phoneme or group of sounds so closely related as to be regarded as only slightly variant forms (allophones) of the phoneme. By means of these symbols any language or dialect can be accurately represented. For the purposes of the beginner, one may disregard the phoneme and say with reasonable accuracy that phonetics employs a system of symbols wherein each symbol represents a single sound and each sound is represented by a separate symbol. This conception will serve the beginner very well until he is prepared for more scientific analysis.

Application of Phonetics to Speech Improvement

The value of phonetics consists, as we have stated, in increasing the student's sensitivity to language phenomena, especially to speech sounds as individual entities, and in providing a scientific approach to language accuracy. Assuming that the reader is by this time speech conscious to a high degree, we shall now consider some simple applications of phonetics to the knowledge, and improvement in speaking, of the three great regional dialects of America, and to acquiring the stage dialect.

In setting down the standard sound systems of these various dialects, only those characteristics are recorded for a given dialect which contrast with corresponding characteristics of the other dialects. Features common to all are omitted. Matters of intonation and rhythm are also omitted, and variation of vowel length as well, except in a limited number of cases.

General American English

Standard General American

[i]   is used in *either* and *neither*. Thus [ˈiðɚ], [ˈniðɚ].

[ɪ]   or [ə] is used in unstressed initial syllables spelled with *e* or *i* followed by a consonant. Examples: *remote* [rɪˈmoʊt, rəˈmoʊt], *divert* [dɪˈvɜt, dəˈvɜt].

[ə]   is used for unstressed medial *e, i, y*, and for the *i* of the pronoun *it* when unstressed. Examples: servility [səˈvɪlətɪ], *intimate* (adj.) [ˈɪntəmət], *telephone* [ˈtɛləfoʊn], *I see it* [aɪ ˈsi ət].

> *Transcribe.*   agitate, alimony, allegation, alligator, application, impossible, intimate (verb), pacify, paralysis, telegraph, telegram.

If the sound following unstressed *e* or *i* is a vowel, [ɪ] is used. Examples: *vitiate* [ˈvɪʃɪˌeɪt], *permeable* [ˈpɜmɪəb̩].

[ə]   is used in the suffixes *ace, ad, ain, as, ase, ate, ed, en, es, ess, et, ice, id, in, ip, is, ist, it, ite, op, ous, uce, up, us, ute.* Examples: *palace* ['pæləs], *salad* ['sæləd], *villain* ['vɪlən], *Dallas* ['dæləs], *purchase* ['pɜtʃəs], *palate* ['pælət], *hunted* ['hʌntəd], *chicken* ['tʃɪkən], *birches* ['bɜtʃəz], *fearless* ['fɪrləs], *bucket* ['bʌkət], *Alice* ['æləs], *pallid* ['pæləd], *coffin* ['kɔfən] *Philip* ['fɪləp], *appendicitis* [əˌpɛndə'saɪtəs], *tourist* ['tʊrəst], *limit* ['lɪmət] *requisite* ['rɛkwəzət], *gallop* ['gæləp], *furious* ['fjʊrɪəs], *lettuce* ['lɛtəs], *syrup* ['sɪrəp], *circus* ['sɜkəs], *minute* ['mɪnət].

     [ɪ] is also used in words of this class by a limited number of individuals and communities.

[æ]   is used in all so-called "broad *a*" words. Examples: *half* [hæf], *halves* [hævz], *class* [klæs], *path* [pæθ], *baths* [bæðz], *can't* [kænt]. (See definition of "broad *a*," page 300.)

[ɑ]   is used in monosyllables and stressed syllables spelled with *ar* final or before a consonant, and not preceded by the sound of [w]. Examples: *bar* [bɑr], *card* [kɑrd], *target* ['tɑrgət].

     Transcribe. argument, barn, farm, hard, harm, jar, Margaret, dark, yard, yarn. See also word lists, pages 295, 296.

[æ]   or [ɛ] is used in words in *air* and *are* and in certain words in *ear*. Examples: *pair* [pær, pɛr], *pare* [pær, pɛr], *pear* [pær, pɛr].

     Transcribe. bare, bear, fair, fare, glare, hair, hairy, mare, share, tare, tear, wear. See also word list, page 315.

     Most speakers use [æ] with words in *arr*, but some use [ɛ]. Examples: *barrow* ['hæro, 'bɛro], *carry* ['kæri, 'kɛri].

     Transcribe: arrow, marrow, marry, parry, sparrow, tarry.

[ɑ]   is used for the so-called "short *o*." Examples: *hot* [hɑt], *positive* ['pɑzətɪv], *not* [nɑt].

     Transcribe. abominable, cot, lot, obsolete, obstacle, ominous, opposite, top. See word list, page 283.

[ɑ]   is used in *was* [wɑz], *water* ['wɑtɚ], *watch* [wɑtʃ], *what* [ʌɑt].

[ɔ]   is used as a high low-back sound, the tongue being depressed somewhat more than half the distance between [o] and [ɑ]. The sound does not suggest [oʊ], in words spelled with *all, au, all, ough*, as does the corresponding sound in British and some Eastern speech. Examples: *thought* [θɔt], *all* [ɔl], *law* [lɔ].

     Transcribe. ball, call, Claude, fall, Maude, ought, saw, taught.

[ɔ]   or [ɑ] is used in *wash* [wɔʃ, wɑʃ]; *wasp* [wɔsp, wɑsp]. [ɔ] predominates.

[ɔ] is used predominantly in stressed syllables spelled with *o* followed by *r* plus a vowel. Examples: *Florida*[9] [ˈflɔrədə], *forest*[9] [ˈfɔrəst], *horrid*[9] [ˈhɔrəd], *orange*[9, 10] [ˈɔrɪndʒ], *torrent*[9] [ˈtɔrənt].

[ɑ] is used occasionally in these words, particularly in those parts of the General American area which border the Eastern and Southern areas.

[ɔ] is used predominantly in stressed syllables spelled with *a* preceded by [w] and followed by *r* plus vowel. Example: *quarry* [ˈkwɔrɪ].[11]

[ɑ] is also used, especially in the Far West and in those parts of the General American area bordering the Eastern and Southern areas.

Transcribe. quarrel, quarantine.

[ɔ] is used predominantly in the *og* words except in Utah, Wyoming, Idaho, and some adjacent parts of the Rocky Mountain area. Examples: *catalog* [ˈkætəˌlɔg], *foggy* [ˈfɔgɪ], *frog* [frɔg], *log* [lɔg].[12]

Transcribe. bog, fog, hog.

Foggy is pronounced with [ɑ] oftener than the others listed.[12] Other words frequently pronounced with [ɑ] are *cog, jog, eggnog, clog, togs, toggle.*

[ɔ] is used nearly universally in the single word *dog* [dɔg].[13]

[oʊ] is used with various spellings in monosyllables and stressed syllables. Examples: *open* [ˈoʊpən], *road* [roʊd], *below* [bɪˈloʊ, bəˈloʊ], *ford* [foʊrd], *more* [moʊr], *four* [foʊr].

[oʊ] is also used in syllables of secondary stress, as in *canto* [ˈkænˌtoʊ], *solo* [ˈsoʊˌloʊ], and *territory* [ˈtɛrəˌtoʊrɪ].

Transcribe. amatory, bore, crematory, door, laboratory, lavatory, mold, mould, polo, soar, told, tore, bolo, polo.

[oʊ] is used in *coarse* [koʊrs—kɔrs], *course* [koʊrs], *hoarse*[14] [hoʊrs], *mourning*[14] [ˈmoʊrnɪŋ].

[ɔ] is also used, but less frequently.

---

[9] C. K. Thomas, "The dialectal significance of the non-phonemic low-back vowel variants before r," *Studies in Speech and Drama in Honor of Alexander M. Drummond*, Ithaca, N.Y., Cornell University Press, 1944, pp. 244 ff. Referred to hereafter as Thomas, "Dialectal Significance."

[10] C. K. Thomas, "American dictionaries and variant pronunciations," *American Speech* (October, 1939), *14*: 175 f. Referred to hereafter as Thomas, "American Dictionaries."

[11] Thomas, "Dialectal significance," pp. 244 ff.

[12] C. K. Thomas, letter to C. M. Wise.

[13] *Ibid.*

[14] Hans Kurath, "Mourning and morning," *Studies for William A. Read* (Nathaniel M. Caffee and Thomas A. Kirby), Baton Rouge, Louisiana State University Press, 1940, pp. 166–173.

[o]   is used in unstressed syllables, as in *opinion* [oˈpɪnjən], *Roberta* [roˈbɝtə].

  Transcribe. oration, potato, tomato, window.

  Collect other examples. Distinguish words of this class from words such as *alto* [ˈælˌtoʊ]. In words ending in unstressed *o* and *ow*, [o] is regular, but [ə] is often used colloquially. Example: *window* [ˈwɪndo, ˈwɪndə]. Sometimes [ʊ] is heard, as in [ˈwɪndʊ].

[e]   is used in certain relatively unstressed syllables. Example: *Baconian* [beˈkounɪən]. Collect other examples.

[u], [ju], and [ɪu] are used for the spellings *eu, ew, u* after *d, t,* and *n,* as in *due* [du, dju, dɪu]; *knew* [nu, nju, nɪu]; *neutral* [ˈnutrəl, ˈnjutrəl, ˈnɪutrəl]. [u] is the most frequently heard; [ju] appears to be the most highly regarded in educational circles.

  Transcribe. constitution, dew, during, duty, neural, newspaper, numerous, pneumatic, stew, tube, tune.

[u]   is used for *u* after [l, θ, s, z] as in *resolute* [ˈrɛzəˈlut], *enthusiasm* [ɪnˈθuzɪˌæzm], *suit* [sut], *resume* [rɪˈzum].

[ʌ]   is used as a very nearly central vowel, strongly resembling [ə] except in duration. Actually the tongue is slightly lower and slightly farther back than for [ə]. The sound does not suggest [ɑ] as in British and some Eastern speech. Examples: *up* [ʌp], *just* [ʤʌst].

  Transcribe. above, but, dove, governor, judge, love, mud, such, tongue. See word list, page 304.

The use of r *in general American speech.* All *r*'s that appear in the spelling are pronounced, whether of vowel or consonantal characteristics.

[ɝ]   is used in most stressed syllables containing *ear, er, ir, or, our, ur,* and *yr.* Examples: *heard* [hɝd], *fern* [fɝn], *bird* [bɝd], *work* [wɝk], *journey* [ˈʤɝnɪ], *absurd* [æbˈsɝd], *myrtle* [ˈmɝtl̩].
  See word lists, page 295.

[ɝ]   assimilates, in General American speech, what might otherwise appear as a medial [r] attached to the succeeding syllable. Words illustrating this point are usually spelled with *o* or *u* plus *r* or *rr* plus vowel. Examples: *furry* [ˈfɝɪ], *hurry* [ˈhɝɪ], *thoroughly* [ˈθɝəlɪ], *worry* [ˈwɝɪ].

  Transcribe. burrowing, burry, flurry, purring, surrey, turret.

[ɚ]   is used in unstressed syllables spelled with *ar, er, ir, or, our, ur, ure, yr.* Examples: *mortar* [ˈmɔrtɚ], *butter* [ˈbʌtɚ], *tapir* [ˈteɪpɚ], *flavor* [ˈfleɪvɚ] *flavour* (Canadian and British spelling) [ˈfleɪvɚ], *murmur* [mɝmɚ], *nature* [ˈneɪtʃɚ], *satyr* [ˈseɪtɚ].

[ḷ]   or [əl] is used in most words ending in *ile*. Examples: *fertile* [ˈfɝtl̩], *reptile* [ˈrɛptl̩], *fragile* [ˈfrædʒəl], *futile* [ˈfjutl̩].

NOTE: *Juvenile* and *senile* are pronounced with both [l̩] and [aɪl].

[ł]   that is, dark [l], made toward the back of the mouth, is used wherever *l* is pronounced in General American speech. Obviously it is farther back before back vowels and finally than before front vowels; but even before front vowels it is too far back to be classified as clear [l].

[ʍ]   is used in most words spelled with *wh* except *who*, *whole*, and their derivatives. Examples: *when* [ʍɛn], *which* [ʍɪtʃ], *why* [ʍaɪ].

Transcribe. whack, what, wheat, wheel, where, whether, whey, while, whim, whip, whistle, whither, whiz. See list, page 318.

[w] is used by a limited number of individuals.

Both primary and secondary stresses are used in numerous polysyllables, particularly those ending in *ary, ery, ory*. Examples: *dictionary* [ˈdɪkʃənˌɛrɪ], *confectionery* [kənˈfɛkʃənˌɛrɪ], *territory* [ˈtɛrəˌtoʊrɪ].

Transcribe. cemetery, ceremony, circumstance, conservatory, contributory, declamatory, dormitory, extraordinary, imaginative, itinerary, laboratory, library, melancholy, military, necessary, nominative, oratory, ordinary, preparatory, remunerative, secretary, solitary, stationary, stationery, tributary, voluntary.[15]

Substandard Deviations from Standard General American

Substitution of [ɔ] *for* [ɑ].   Use [ɑ], not [ɔ], in monosyllables and stressed syllables containing *ar* final or preconsonantal and not preceded by [w]. Examples: *car* [kɑr], not [kɔr]; *garden* [ˈgɑrdn̩], not [ˈgɔrdn̩]. This use of [ɔ] is ordinarily found only in some cities (e.g., St. Louis and Philadelphia) and in those parts of the General American area bordering the Southern area. See pages 294 and 295 for lists for drill.

Substitution of [ɑ] *for* [ɔ].   Use [ɔ], not [ɑ], in words spelled with *al, au, augh, aw,* and *ough*. Examples: *talk* [tɔk], not [tak]; *Maude* [mɔd], not [mad]; *hawk* [hɔk], not [hak]; *naughty* [ˈnɔtɪ], not [ˈnatɪ]; *bought* [bɔt], not [bat].

Transcribe. audience, awful, balk, cough, chalk, gawk, haughty, laudable, mawkish, nautical, ought, trough, walk. Collect other examples.

---

[15] For list, see John Samuel Kenyon, *American Pronunciation*, 8th ed., Ann Arbor, Mich., George Wahr, 1940, pp. 83–86. For longer list, see 4th ed., 1924, pp. 160–164.

Substitution of [a] *for* [aɪ].   Use [aɪ], not [a].   Examples: *by* [baɪ], not [ba]; *high* [haɪ], not [ha]; *island* ['aɪlənd], not ['alənd]. This pronunciation occurs most frequently in that part of the General American area bordering the Southern area. See list, page 295. Collect other examples.

Substitution of [ɔr] *for* [ɔɪ].   Use [ɔɪ], not [ɔr], for words spelled with *oil*. Examples: *boil* [bɔɪl], not [bɔrl]; *oil* [ɔɪl], not [ɔrl].

   Exercise.   coil, soil, spoil, toil. Collect other examples.

Anticipatory Raising of Vowels Before [t], [d], *and* [n].   Use *can* [kæn], not [kɪn]; *catch* [kætʃ], not [kɛtʃ]; *get* [gɛt], not [gɪt]; *radish* ['rædɪʃ], not ['rɛdɪʃ]; *itch* [ɪtʃ], not [itʃ]; *drain* [dreɪn], not [drin]; etc. The raising of [ɛ] to [ɪ], as seen below, is a common illustration of the principle involved here.

Substitution of [ɪ] *for* [ɛ].   Use [ɛ], not [ɪ], preceding nasals in words like the following: *fence* [fɛnts], not [fɪnts]; *any* ['ɛnɪ], not [ɪnɪ]. This pronunciation is found particularly in those parts of the General American area bordering the Southern area, but it appears to be spreading. For word lists, see page 296. List other words of this class.

Substitution of [ɛ] *for* [ɪ].   Use [ɪ], not [ɛ], in such words as *been* [bɪn], not [bɛn]; *since* [sɪnts], not [sɛnts].

Dissimilation of [r].   (See definition of dissimilation, page 361.) Pronounce *r* wherever it occurs in the spelling. Actually there is no tendency to omit *r* in General American speech except where the sound appears two or more times in the same word. In such cases the phonetic tendency for dissimilation sometimes takes effect. Use *surprise* [sɚ'praɪz], not [sə'praɪz]; *particular* [pɚ'tɪkjʊlɚ], not [pə'tɪklɚ]; *February* ['fɛbrʊˌɛrɪ], not ['fɛbjuˌɛrɪ].

   NOTE: Dissimilation is, of course, not limited to *r*; cf. the case of *n* in the substandard pronunciation of *government* ['gʌvənmənt] as ['gʌvəmənt]. Collect other instances of dissimilation.

Intrusive [r].   Use [a], not [ur], in words like the following: *Chicago* [ʃə'kago], not [ʃə'kargo].

   NOTE: This is a border pronunciation. If Southern *car* [ka] corresponds to General American [kar], then Southern *Chicago* [ʃə'kago] would seem to call for General American [ʃə'kargo].

Use [ɔ], not [ɔr], in words like the following: *ought* [ɔt], not [ɔrt]; *thought* [θɔt], not [θɔrt]; *August* ['ɔgəst], not ['ɔrgəst].

Use [ɔ], not [ɔr] or [ɔɪ], in words spelled with *osh* or containing [w] plus *ash*. Examples: *wash* [wɔʃ], not [wɔrʃ] or [wɔɪʃ]; *bosh* [bɔʃ], not [bɔrʃ], or [bɔɪʃ].

> *Transcribe.* gosh, squash, Washington.

> NOTE: [ɑ] is also regarded as standard in most words of this class.

Use [ʊ], not [ʊr] or [ʊɪ], in words like the following: *bush* [bʊʃ], not [bʊrʃ] or [bʊɪʃ]; *cushion* [ˈkʊʃən], not [ˈkʊrʃən] or [ˈkʊɪʃən]; *push* [pʊʃ], not [pʊrʃ] or [pʊɪʃ].

Collect other examples of each of the four classes above.

Substitution of [ɜ] *or* [ʌɪ] *for* [ʌ]. Use [ʌ], not [ɜ] or [ʌɪ] in words like the following: *hush* [hʌʃ], not [hɜʃ] or [hʌɪʃ]; *mush* [mʌʃ], not [mɜʃ] or [mʌɪʃ]; *punish* [ˈpʌnɪʃ], not [ˈpɜnɪʃ].

Collect other examples.

Substitution of [ɚ] *for* [o]. Use [o], not [ɚ], in the final syllable of words ending in *o* and *ow*. Examples: *tomato* [təˈmeɪto], not [təˈmeɪtɚ]; *window* [ˈwɪndo], not [ˈwɪndɚ].

> *Transcribe.* bellow, fellow, follow, following, marshmallow, mellow, piano, potato, shallow, yellow.

> [ə] is often used in rapid utterance instead of [o] as above, and in informal speech is regarded as acceptable. This statement applies also to a number of loan words used as names, such as *Puerto Rico*, *San Jacinto*, *Rio Grande*, etc.

List other words of the classes above.

Substitution of [ɤ] [16] *or* [ɤə] *for* [ʊ]. Use [ʊ], not [ɤ] or [ɤə]. Examples: *good* [gʊd], not [gɤd] or [gɤəd].

> *Transcribe.* could, hood, should, soot, wood, would. Collect other examples.

Dissyllabication of monosyllables ending in [l]. Use [l], not [əl], in monosyllables spelled with *ool, eel, ule*. In other words, do not exaggerate the [l] so as to expand it into a separate syllable.

> NOTE: This is one of the features of what is designated the Western drawl. Examples: *school* [skul], not [ˈskuəl]; *mule* [mjul], not [ˈmjuəl]; *feel* [fil], not [ˈfiəl].

> *Transcribe.* cool, drool, fool, pool, rule, tool, meal, seal, heel, peel. Collect other examples.

[16] This symbol represents the unrounded [ʊ].

"*Burred*" [r]. Use any [r] sound, i.e., [r], [ɜ], and [ɚ] without giving it undue or unnecessary length and prominence or allowing it to absorb adjacent sounds. That is, do not "burr" the [r]. Examples: *very* ['vɛrɪ], not ['vɜɪ]; *where* [ʌɛr], not [ʌɜ]; *American* [ə'mɛrɪkən] or [ə'mɛrəkən], not [ə'mɜəkən]; *terrible* ['tɛrəbl̩], not [tɜəbl̩]; *mother* ['mʌðɚ], not ['mʌðˌɜ]; *barn* [bɑrn], not [bɑr:n] or ['bɑən]. The last instance illustrates a form of the Western drawl, where a mono-syllable becomes a dissyllable.

Collect other examples.

Substandard Deviations Common to General American, Southern, and Eastern

There are many pronunciations common to the substandard speech of all three dialect areas. A discussion of these is inserted at this point as a continuation of the deviations from standard General American speech. This section should be considered likewise an addition to the sections on deviations from standard Southern and standard Eastern speech.

Substandard city speech. All large cities, no matter whether they are in the Eastern, Southern, or General American areas, have certain common speech features. These are partly derived from the languages of foreign immigrants, and appear principally in under-world and street gamin speech. Not all of the following appear in every city, but most of them do.

[t] for [θ]. Use *thing* [θɪŋ], not [tɪŋ]; *nothing* ['nʌθɪŋ], not ['nʌtn̩]; *with* [wɪθ], not [wɪt].

[d] for [ð]. Use *this* [ðɪs], not [dɪs]; *that* [ðæt], not [dæt]; *there* [ðɛr, ðɛə], not [dɛr, deə]; *other* ['ʌðɚ, 'ʌðə], not ['ʌdə, 'ʌdə]; *with* [wɪð], not [wɪd].

[ɔ] for [ɑ]. Use *car* [kɑr, kɑ:], not [kɔr, kɔ:]; *hard* [hɑrd, hɑ:d], not [hɔrd, hɔ:d]. (Cf. longer discussion, pages 309–314.)

Archaic or relic pronunciation. The following are old pronunciations, some of which were at one time regarded as standard. They are now replaced in educated speech by modern forms, but they are still used by individuals in some communities. Use *afraid*, not *afeared*; *are*, not *air*; *ate*, not *et*; *boil*, not *bile*; *burst*, not *bust*; *calm*, not [kæm]; *care*, not [kɪr, 'kɪə]; *learn*, not *larn*; *certain*, not *sartain*; *chair*, not [tʃɪr, 'tʃɪə]; *climbed*, not *clumb* [klʌm]; *curse*, not *cuss*; *dare*, not *dast*; *dare(d) not*, not *dastn't*; *deaf*, not [dif]; *far* [fɑr, fɑ], not [fɜ, fɔ]; *farther*, not [ˈfɜdɚ, ˈfɜdə]; *further*, not [ˈfɜdɚ, ˈfɜdə]; *gaunt*, not [gænt]; *haunt*, not [hænt]; *heard*, not [hɪrd]; *herbs*, not [jɑrbz]; *hers*, not *her'n*; *his*, not *his'n*; *jaunt*, not [dʒænt]; *join*, not [dʒaɪn]; *joint*, not [dʒaɪnt]; *nearer*, not [ˈnɪrdɚ, ˈnɪədə]; *oil*, not *ile*; *ours*, not *our'n*; *palm*, not [pæm]; *point*, not [paɪnt]; *poison*, not [ˈpaɪzən]; *psalm*, not [sæm]; *real*, not [reɪl]; *roiled*, not [raɪld]; *saucy*, not [ˈsæsɪ]; *scare*, not [skɪr, ˈskɪə]; *spoil*, not *spile*; *theirs*, not *their'n*; *yours*, not *your'n*; *ewe* [ju], not [joʊ].

Collect other examples.

Centralization.   Centralization here refers to the fact that the front vowels in the stressed syllables of the following words are made central vowels by the withdrawal of the highest part of the tongue arch to the central part of the mouth. Use *cemetery* [ˈsɛmɪˌtɛrɪ, ˈsɛməˌtɛrɪ], not [ˈsʌməˌtɛrɪ]; *leather* [ˈlɛðɚ, ˈlɛðə],[17] not [ˈlʌðɚ, ˈlʌðə]; *minister* [ˈmɪnəstɚ, ˈmɪnəstə], not [ˈmɪnəstɚ,[18] ˈmɪnəstə]; *president* [ˈprɛzə-dənt], not [ˈprʌsədənt]; *rather*, not *ruther*; *Senator*, not *sunnator*; *sinister*, not *sunnister*; *simple*, not [ˈsɪmpəl]; *trestle*, not *trustle*; *whip* [ʍɪp, wɪp], not [ʍɪp, ʍʌp, ʍʊp][19]; *wish*, not [wʊʃ][19]; *syrup* [ˈsɪrəp], not [ˈsɜrəp]; *America* [əˈmɛrəkə, əˈmɛrɪkə], not [əˈmɜəkə].

Collect other examples.

Substandard voicing.   (See discussion, page 360.) Use *absorb*, not *abzorb*; *attic*, not *addic*; *absurd*, not *abzurd*; *Baptist*, not *Babtist*; *baptize*, not *babtize*; *hospital*, not *hozbital*; *little*, not *liddle*; *notice*, not [ˈnoʊdəs, ˈnoʊdɪs]; *protestant*, not *prodestant*; *satisfy*, not *sadisfy*; *significant*, not *signifigant*; *water*, not [ˈwɑdɚ, ˈwɔdə].

Collect other examples.

Lowering.   Use spirit [ˈspɪrət, ˈspɪrɪt], not [ˈspɛrət]; *been* [bɪn], not [bɛn]. Use [ɪ] in *hinder*, *miracle*, *stint*, *pith*, *rid*, *rinse*, *since*. Use [eɪ] in *nape*, *ague*.

Substandard unvoicing.   Use *second*, not *secont*; *killed*, not *kilt*; *held*, not *helt*; *hold*, not *holt*, or *a-holt*.

False analogy.   Do not confuse part of the pronunciation of *burst* [bɜst, bɜst] with that of *rust*; *cemetery* [ˈsɛməˌtɛrɪ, ˈsɛmɪˌtɛrɪ] with *symmetry*;

---

[17] In American English the sound [ʌ] is very nearly a central vowel, and the symbol [ʌ] serves for the centralized [ɛ]. (The British [ʌ] is lower and farther back.)

[18] The sound [ɪ] is the centralized [ɪ].

[19] Here the arch of the tongue has passed the central part of the mouth and has gone on to the back. The preceding [w] has probably by progressive assimilation effected a rounding of the vowel.

column [ˈkɑləm] with *volume*; *February* [ˈfɛbruˌɛrɪ] with *January*; *genealogy* [ˌdʒinɪˈæləʤɪ] with *biology* (though [ˌdʒinɪˈɑləʤɪ] is often heard); *hearth* [hɑrθ] with *earth*; *licorice* [ˈlɪkərəs, ˈlɪkərɪs] with *thickish*; *percolate* [ˈpɝkəˌleɪt, ˈpɝkəˌleɪt] with *formulate*; *put* [pʊt] with *but*; *rather* with *further*; *root* [rut] with *foot*; *sacrilegious* (though [—ˈlɪʤəs] is known) [ˌsækrəˈlɪʤəs, ˌsækrɪˈlɪʤəs] with *religious*; *similar* [ˈsɪmələ˞, ˈsɪmɪlə] with *simulate*; *substantiate* [səbˈstænʧɪˌeɪt] with *formulate*; *together* with *gather*; *zoology* [ˌzouˈɑləʤɪ, ˌzouˈɒləʤɪ] with *zoom*, *punish* [ˈpʌnɪʃ] with *burnish*.

Collect other examples.

False analogical verb forms.   The following represent false irregular forms constructed by analogy, or pseudo-regular forms devised to make irregular verbs regular.   Use *blew*, not *blowed*; *born*, not *borned*; *brought*, not *brang* or *brung*; *climbed*, not *clumb*; *dived*, not *dove* [douv] (sometimes accepted); *drove*, not *druv*; *fought*, not *fit*; *heard* [hɝd, hɜd], not *heared*; *knew*, not *knowed*; *saw*, not *seed*; *stung*, not *stang*; *swam* (pret.), not *swum*; *threw*, not *throwed*; *winked*, not *wunk* (humorous).

Collect other examples.

Substandard unstressing.   (See page 368 for discussion.) Use [jʊ], not [ə], for *u* in most unstressed syllables. Example: [ˈrɛgjʊˌleɪt], not [ˈrɛgəˌleɪt].

Transcribe. accumulate, accurate, ague, calculate, contribute, education, figure, reputation, strangulate.

Use [ə], not [ɪ], in words spelled with final *a*. Example: *soda* [ˈsoudə], not *sody* [ˈsoudɪ].

Transcribe: Alabama, America, Asia, California, China, Columbia, Florida, Oklahoma, opera, Russia, sofa.

Collect other examples of the two classes above.

Folk etymology. (See definition, page 378.) Do not use [braunˈkitɪs] for *bronchitis* [branˈkaɪtɪs]; *cartoon* for *carton*; *cow buckle* for *carbuncle*; *diptheria* for *diphtheria* [ˌdɪfˈθɪrɪə]; *dipthong* for *diphthong* [ˈdɪfθɒŋ]; *drugs* for *dregs*; *empire* for *umpire*; *loom* for *loam*; *mad axe* for *mattock*; *mushmelon* for *muskmelon*; *mushrat* for *muskrat*; *overhauls* for *overalls*; *pinchers* for *pincers*; *plowsheer* for *plowshare*; *reddish* for *radish*; *scullion* for *scallion*; *selphur* for *sulphur*; *serious* for *series*; *steeple* for *staple*; *study* for *steady*; *Westminister* for *Westminster*; *wrench* for *rinse*; *east* for *yeast*.

Collect other examples.

Hyperurbanism (overcorrection).   (See definition, page 378.) Use *Cincinnati,* not *Cincinnata; confetti,* not *confetta; linen,* not *linning; Miami,* not *Miama; Missouri,* not *Missoura; mountain,* not *mounting; often,* not *offing.*
> Collect other examples.

Substandard assimilation.   (See definition of assimilation, page 357.) Use *clothes,* not *clo'es; give me,* not *gimme; going to go,* not *gonna go; isn't,* not *idn't; let me,* not *lemme; months,* not *mont's; unless,* not [ən'ɛs]; *wasn't,* not *wadn't; winter,* not *winner.*
> Collect other examples.

Intrusive sounds.   Use *chimney,* not *chimley*[20] or *chimbley*[21]; *family,* not *fambly.*
> Collect other examples.

Loss of [t] *and* [d] *after consonants.*   Use *crept,* not *crep'; hand* not *han'; hind,* not [haɪn]; *kept,* not *kep'; land,* not *lan', slept,* not *slep'; sounds,* not *soun's; directly,* not *direk'ly; didn't,* not *didn'; mostly,* not *mos'ly; bankrupt,* not *bankrup'.*
> See list, page 297. Find other words of this class.

Metathesis.   (See definition, page 372.) Use *ask* [æsk], not *ax; asked,* not *axed; asks,* not *axes; bronchial,* not *bronichal; children* ['tʃɪdrən], not *childern; hundred,* not *hunderd; larynx* ['lærɪŋks, 'lɛrɪŋks], not *larnyx; modern,* not *modren; nuclear,* not *nucular; pattern,* not *patren; perspiration,* not *prespiration; pharynx* ['færɪŋks, 'fɛrɪŋks], not *pharnyx; precaution,* not *percaution; predicament,* not *perdicament; pretty* ['prɪtɪ], not *purty; unless,* not ['lɛsən]; *worsted* ['wʊstəd, 'wʊstɪd], not ['wʊstəd] (distant metathesis; *r* in first syllable migrates to second). Do not confuse *cavalry, Calvary.*
> Collect other examples.

Retracted stress.   Most of the following words are regarded as unacceptable when stressed on the first syllable. However, the pronunciations of some of them with the stress on the first syllable are recognized by some recent dictionaries as second choices. Use *address',* not *ad'dress; adult',* not *ad'ult; allies',* not *al'lies; defect',* not *de'fect; research',* not *re'search.*
> The following are regarded as definitely substandard when the stress is on the first syllable: Use *cement',* not *ce'ment; Detroit',* not

---

[20] In this word the [n] has been completely assimilated to the [m] and has vanished; its tongue position, slightly modified, has contributed to the intrusion of the glide [l].

[21] Here the bilabial characteristic of the [m] has induced the bilabial plosive [b].

De'troit; *Supreme' Court*, not *Su'preme Court*; *Unit'ed States*, not *U'nited States*; *Uni'ted Nations*, not *Un'ited Nations*.

Collect other examples.

Omission from the cluster [sks]. Use [sks], not [sk] or [s:], in words spelled with *sks* or *sques*. Examples: *masks* [mæsks], not [mæs:] or [mæsk]; *bisques* [bɪsks], not [bɪs:] or [bɪsk].

> *Transcribe.* basks, casks, casques, Fisk's, flasks, masques, musks, risks, rusks.

List other words of this class.

Omission from the cluster [skt]. Use [skt], not [sk] or [st], in words ending in *sked*. Examples: *asked* [æskt], not [æsk] or [æst].

> *Transcribe.* basked, masked, risked, tasked.

List other words of this class.

Omissions from the cluster [sps]. Use [sps], not [sp] or [s:], in words spelled with *sps*. Example: *clasps* [klæsps], not [klæsp] or [klæs:].

> *Transcribe.* crisps, hasps, rasps, grasps.

List other words of this class.

Omission from the cluster [spt]. Use [spt], not [sp], in words spelled with *sped*. Example: *clasped* [klæspt], not [klæsp].

> *Transcribe.* crisped, grasped, rasped.

List other words of this class.

Omissions from the cluster [sts]. Use [sts], not [st] or [s:] or [stəz], in words spelled with *sts*. Examples: *ghosts* [goʊsts], not [goʊs:], [goʊst], or ['goʊstəz]; *nests* [nɛsts], not [nɛs:], [nɛst], or ['nɛstəz].

> *Transcribe.* blasts, costs, Christ's, coasts, costs, dusts, interests, lists, roasts, wastes.

List other words of this class.

Omission of l from [lj], [lr], *or* [l] *plus vowel.* Use *all right*, not [ˌɔ'raɪt]; *already*, not [ˌɔ'rɛdɪ]; *million*, not ['mɪjən]; *tolerable*, not ['tɑrəbl̩]; *William*, not ['wɪjəm].

Collect other examples.

Spelling pronunciation. Use *almond* ['amənd], not ['almənd]; *garage* [gə'rɑʒ], not [gə'rɑdʒ] or ['gærɪdʒ]; *Greenwich*, Br. ['grɪnɪdʒ, 'grɛnɪdʒ], Am. ['grɛnɪtʃ], not ['grin͵wɪtʃ]; *often* ['ɔfən], not ['ɔftən]; *towards* [tɔrdz, toʊrdz, tɔdz, 'toədz], not [tə'wɔrdz, tə'wɔdz]; *victuals* ['vɪtəlz], not ['vɪktʃuelz]; *Worcester* ['wustɚ, 'wustə], not ['wɔˌsɛstɚ, 'wɔrˌsɛstə]; *worsted* ['wustəd, 'wustɪd], not ['wɝstəd, 'wɝstɪd].

Collect other examples.

Raising and nasalization of [aʊ]. Use [aʊ], not [æʊ], [æ̃ʊ], [jæʊ], or [jæ̃ʊ]. Examples: *out* [aʊt], not [æʊt]; *town* [taʊn], not [tæ̃ʊn]; *gouge* [gaʊʤ], not [gjæʊʤ]; *count* [kaʊnt], not [kjæ̃ʊnt].

Note that nasalization is most likely to occur before a nasal consonant, and that the insertion of the superfluous sound [j] is induced by a preceding [k] or [g].

List other words of the classes above.

Raising and nasalization of [æ]. Use [æ], not [æ˕], [æ̃˕], [jæ˕], or [jæ̃˕]. Examples: *at* [æt], not [æ˕t]; *ant* [ænt], not [æ̃˕nt]; *cat* [kæt], not [kjæ˕t]; *cant* [kænt], not [kjæ̃˕nt].

Note as before that the nasalization of [æ] is most likely to occur before a nasal consonant and that the insertion of the superfluous sound [j] is induced by a preceding front [k] or [g].

List other words of these classes.

Restressing. In many unstressed words the vowel values are normally reduced to [ə], but the meaning of the sentence sometimes restores stress to them. In such instances, a vowel thus restressed should resume its original value. Thus *to*, in *run to me* [rʌn tə mi] is unstressed; but in *run TO me, not FROM me* [rʌn tu mi, nɑt frɑm mi] it is restressed, and the stressed vowel [u] replaces the unstressed [ə]. In some cases, however, a vowel (oftenest [ʌ], [ɜ], or [ɝ]) phonetically nearer [ə] than the original vowel, is placed in the word. Note the instances below.

In stressed positions use *for* [fɔr, fɔ], not [fɝ, fɜ]; *of* [ɑv], not [ʌv]; *what* [ʍɑt, wɒt], not [ʍʌt, wʌt]; *was* [wɑz, wɒz], not [wʌz], though some dictionaries allow [ʌv] and [wʌz]. Remember, that the unstressed forms of these and similar words are [fɝ, fə], [əv], [ʍət, wət], and [wəz]. These forms are all entirely proper so long as the words are only lightly stressed. It is when the stress is heavy that the original vowel value of the word must be restored; but some other vowel values must not be substituted. In illiterate writing instances occur of the confusion which unstressing and restressing bring about. For example, both *have* and *of* may be unstressed to [əv] as in *it might have been* [ɪt maɪt əv bɪn], *three of a size* [θri əv ə saɪz]. An illiterate writer, slowly and laboriously pronouncing each word as he writes, may choose the wrong referent for [əv] and set

down *"He ought to of come."* In the same way, out of the unstress-
ings of *and* and *than* in *he 'n' I* and *better 'n' his* may come the
writing of such expressions as *bigger and you* for *bigger than you.*

Substitution of [eɪ] *or* [æ] *for* [ɛ].   Use *beg* [bɛg], not [beɪg] or *bag*; *edge* [ɛdʒ],
not *age*; *egg* [ɛg], not [eɪg] or [æg]; *keg*, not [keɪg] or *kag*; *leg*, not
[leɪg] or *lag*; *measure* ['mɛʒɚ, 'mɛʒə], not ['meɪʒɚ, 'meɪʒə]; *pleasure*,
not ['pleɪʒɚ, 'pleɪʒə].

Substitution of [ə] *for* [ɪ] *in him, etc.*   Use [ɪ], not [ə], in the unstressed form
of *him*; thus, *I met him* [aɪ mɛt ɪm], not [aɪ mɛt əm]. This latter
pronunciation is found principally in cities. Instances are known
where *I met her* and even *I met it* have been rendered also as [aɪ mɛt
əm]. The only defensible use of [əm] is as the colloquial unstressed
form of *them.* Example: *I met 'em* [aɪ mɛt əm].

Substitution of [ɔ] *for* [æ].   Use *champ* [tʃæmp], not [tʃɔmp]; *stamp* [stæmp],
not [stɔmp]; *tramp* [træmp], not [trɔmp]; *tassel* ['tæsəl], not
['tɔsəl]. Collect additional examples.

Substitution of [ʊ] *for* [u].   Some words containing *oo* are indubitably acceptably pronounced with [u]; examples, *moon, boot, cool, boon, boost.*
Some are definitely pronounced with [ʊ]; examples, *book, look,
cook, hook, wool, wood.* Some words are in dispute; examples,
broom, room, coop. In case of divided practice, [u] seems usually to
stand in higher regard. Following this principle, we may, then, use
room [rum], not [rʊm]; *broom* [brum], not [brʊm]; *root* [rut], not
[rʊt]; *hoof* [huf], not [hʊf]; *soon* [sun], not [sʊn].[22]

Substitution of [n] *for* [ŋ].   This substitution occurs most frequently in words
spelled with *ing.* A typical example is *askin'* for *asking.* The sound
shift is often called the dropping of the *g.* Actually it is impossible
for *g* to be dropped, since from a phonetic point of view there is no
g in *asking* ['æskɪŋ]. It is therefore dangerous to speak of *g*-dropping,
lest students undertake to replace the allegedly lost sound and
produce ['æskɪŋg].

   Use *morning*, not *mornin'*; *reading*, not *readin'*; *singing*, not
singin'; *talking*, not *talkin'*; *writing*, not *writin'*.

   List and practice the pronunciation of other words of this
class.

Substitution of [n] *for* [ŋ] (*special instances*).   Use [ŋ], not [n], in these two
words: *length* [lɛŋkθ], not [lɛnθ]; *strength* [strɛŋkθ], not [strɛnθ].

---

[22] See C. H. Grandgent, "English in America," *Die Neueren Sprachen*, New York, Stechert,
1895, *2*, p. 257.

Substitution of [tl] *and* [dl] *for* [kl] *and* [gl].   Use *class*, not *tlass*; *climb*, not *tlimb*.

Substitution of [j] *for* [hj].   Use *hew, hue, Hugh* [hju], not [ju]; *Hubert* [ˈhjubət, ˈhjubət], not [ˈjubət, ˈjubət]; *huge* [hjuʤ], not [juʤ]; *human* [ˈhjumən], not [ˈjumən]; *humanity* [hjuˈmænətɪ], not [juˈmænətɪ], *Huron* [ˈhjurən], not [ˈjurən].

List other words of this class.

Substitution of [w] *for* [ʍ]. In General American and Southern areas it is usually conceded that [ʍ] should be used in most words beginning with *wh*, excepting *who, whole,* and their derivatives; in the East opinion is divided as to whether [w] or [ʍ] should be used. The following list is for those who prefer [ʍ]. Use *what*, not *watt*; *when*, not *wen*; *whether*, not *weather*; *which* [ʍɪtʃ], not *witch*; *while*, not *wile*; *whisper*, not [ˈwɪspɚ, ˈwɪspə]; *whistle*, not [ˈwɪsəl]; *white*, not *wight*; *whither*, not *wither*; *why*, not *Wye*.

Collect other words suitable for drill.

Substitution of [n̩] *for a preposition.*   Use *out of*, not [ˈɑut n̩]; *off of* or *off from*, not [ˈɔf n̩].

Substitution of [s] *for* [ʃ] *before* [r].   Since the cluster [sr] does not occur in standard English, it encounters no opposition when, in substandard speech, it displaces [ʃr]. Use *shrub* [ʃrʌb], not [srʌb]; *shrimp*, not [srɪmp]; *shrivel*, not [ˈsrɪvl̩].

Collect other examples.

Substitution of [ɔ] *for* [ʌ] *in prefix un.*   Use *uneasy* not *oneasy*; *untie*, not *ontie*.

Collect other examples.

Prefixing of superfluous [s] *before* [k] *and* [p].   Use *cringe*, not [skrɪnʤ]; *crouch*, not [skrautʃ]; *plunge*, not [splʌnʤ].

Excrescent final [s].   Use *anywhere*, not *anywheres*; *nowhere*, not *nowheres*; *somewhere*, not *somewheres*.

Anaptyxis.   (See definition, page 363.) Use *athletic*, not *athaletic*; *athlete*, not *athalete*; *elm*, not [ˈɛləm]; *film*, not [ˈfɪləm]; *series* [ˈsɪriz], not *serious* [ˈsɪrɪəs]; *grievous* [ˈgrivəs], not [ˈgrivɪəs]; *mischievous* [ˈmɪstʃɪvəs], not [mɪsˈtʃivɪəs].

Collect other examples.

Superfluous [t], [d], *and* [əd].   Use *across*, not *acrost*; *attacked*, not *attackted*; *close* (adj.), not [kloust]; *closer*, not *closter*; *dose*, not [doust]; *drowned*, not *drownded*; *once*, not [wʌnst]; *twice*, not [twaɪst]; *stole*, not *stoled*.

Syncope. (See definition, page 371.) Use *accurate*, not *acc'rate*; *adjective*, not *adje'tive*; *company*, not *comp'ny*; *family*, not *fam'ly*; *geography*, not *jog'aphy*; *regular*, not *reg'lar*; *tolerable*, not *tol'able*; *Louisiana*, not *Looziana*; *memorial, not memor'al*; *curiously*, not *cur'ously*.

Collect other examples.

Vowels fronted or fronted and raised before front consonants. The words *fronted* and *raised* here refer to the position of the highest part of the tongue arch. Use *brush*, not *bresh*; *cover*, not *kiver*; *hush*, not *hesh*; *judge*, not *jedge*; *just*, not *jest* or *jist* (one pronunciation of *just* [dʒɪst], uses the centralized vowel [ɨ], which some linguists regard as one of the vowel phonemes of English); *shut*, not *shet*; *such*, not *sech* or *sich*; *touch*, not *tetch*.

Collect other examples.

Vowels raised before front consonants. The word *raised* here refers to the position of the highest part of the tongue arch. Use *addition*, not [əˈdiʃən]; *again*, not [əˈgɪn]; *against*, not [əˈgɪnst]; *bedstead*, not *bedstid*; *can*, not [kɪn]; *catch*, not [kɛtʃ]; *drain*, not [drin]; *fish*, not [fiʃ]; *gather*, not *gether*; *get*, not *git*; *had*, not [hɛd]; *has*, not [hɛz]; *have*, not [hɛv]; *instead*, not *instid*; *itch*, not [itʃ]; *kettle*, not *kittle*; *radish*, not [ˈrɛdɪʃ]; *rather*, not [ˈrɛðɚ, ˈrɛðə]; *steady*, not *stiddy*; *superstition*, not [ˌsupɚˈstiʃən, ˌsupəˈstiʃən]; *sufficient*, not [səˈfiʃənt]; *wish*, not [wiʃ]; *yesterday*, not *yisterday*.

Miscellaneous substandard pronunciations. Use *arrow* [ˈæro, ˈɛro, ˈæɾo, ˈɛɾo], not [ˈɑro, ˈæɪɪ, ɑɾɪ]; *audacious* [ɔˈdeɪʃəs], not [auˈdeɪʃəs]; *barrow* [ˈbæro, ˈbɛro, ˈbæɾo, ˈbɛɾo], not [ˈbɑro]; *because, not becuz*; *been* [bɪn], not [bɛn]; *borrow*, not *borry*; *bulge* [bʌldʒ], not [bʊldʒ]; *bulk* [bʌlk], not [bʊlk]; *bundle*, not [bʌnɭ]; *chest*, not *chist*; *chew*, not *chaw*; *cud* [kʌd], not [kʊd]; *desk*, not *dest*; *ear*, not [ˈjɪə, jɪr]; *every*, not *ever'*; *forward* [ˈfɔrwɚd, ˈfɔwed], not [ˈfauwɚd, ˈfauwəd]; *guarantee* [ˌgærənˈti], not [ˌgɑrənˈti]; *guardian*, not *gardeen*; *handle*, not [ˈhænɭ]; *harrow* [ˈhæro, ˈhɛro, ˈhæɾo, hɛɾo], not [ˈhɑro, ˈhæɾɪ, ˈhɑɾɪ]; *narrow* [ˈnæɾo, ˈnɛro, ˈnæɾo, ˈnɛɾo], not [ˈnɑɾʊ, ˈnæɾɪ, ˈnɑɾɪ]; *parents* [ˈpærənts, ˈpɛrənts], not [ˈpeɪrənts]; *partner*, not *pardner*; *quarry* [ˈkwɔrɪ, ˈkwɑrɪ], not [ˈkweɪrɪ]; *rather* not *ruther*; *seven, eleven*, not [ˈsɛbm̩, ˈlɛbm̩]; *shook*, not *shuck*; *soot* [sʊt], not *sut* [sʌt]; *statistics*, not *stastistics*; *sure*, not *shore*; *took*, not *tuck*; *yellow*, not *yaller*; *yonder*, not *yander* or *yender*.

Be careful to use [ə], not [ɪ] in the last syllable: soda, sofa, Eva,

Laura, Juanita, Anna, Rita, Rhoda, Ora, Nora, Flora, banana, Melba, Thelma, opera, camera, extra, Martha, Noah, America.

Be careful to use [ɪ], not [ə] in the last syllable: Missouri, Cincinnati, confetti.

Read slowly, avoiding unstressing, then rapidly, so as to pronounce the third personal pronouns in unstressed form:

I see them [aɪ si ðɛm, aɪ si ðm̩, (colloq.) aɪ si əm].
I see him [aɪ si hɪm, aɪ si ɪm].
I see her [aɪ si hɝ, aɪ si ɚ]; [aɪ si hɜ, aɪ si ə].
I see it [aɪ si ɪt, aɪ si ət].
He saw them [hi sɔ ðɛm, hi sɔ ðm̩, (colloq.) hi sɔ əm].
He saw him [hi sɔ hɪm, hi sɔ ɪm].
He saw her [hi sɔ hɝ, hi sɔ ɚ]; [hi sɔ hɜ, hi sɔ ə].
He saw it [hi sɔ ɪt, hi sɔ ət].

The following tabulation illustrates the application of the principle of unstressing to various "particles"—articles, conjunctions, prepositions, pronouns, auxiliary verbs, etc. This unstressing is a progressive process, increasing with the speed of utterance. It applies equally to all dialects. Foreigners, particularly, need to master its intricacies. Not to unstress in the English fashion is to speak English with a decided foreign accent.

Word	*Pronunciation*	
	Stressed	Unstressed [23]
a	eɪ	ə
an	æn	ən, n̩
the	ði	ðɪ, ðə
and	ænd	ənd, nd, ən, n̩
but	bʌt	bət
that	ðæt	ðət
to	tu	tʊ, tə
for	fɔ (r)	fɚ, fə
from	frɑm, frʌm	frəm
by	baɪ	bə
of	ɑv	əv
he	hi	hɪ, ɪ
his	hɪz	ɪz
him	hɪm	ɪm, əm (provincial)

[23] Cf. Lee S. Hultzén, "The pronunciation of monosyllabic form-words in American English," *Studies in Speech and Drama in Honor of Alexander M. Drummond*, Ithaca, N.Y., Cornell University Press, 1944, pp. 255–284.

Word	*Pronunciation*	
	Stressed	Unstressed
her	hɝ, hɝ	ə, ɚ
them	ðɛm	ðəm, əm (colloquial)
it	ɪt	ət
its	ɪts	əts
has	hæz	əz, z
had	hæd	əd, d
have	hæv	əv, v
shall	ʃæl	ʃəl
will	wɪl	wəl, l [24]

Southern American English

As with all dialects, the identifying characteristics of Southern speech are as much in matters of placement, lengthening and shortening of vowel duration, pitch, tempo, and rhythm, as in sound system. These subtler factors have to be heard to be appreciated. As simple a thing as a peculiar stress on *so* in *that's not so good* [ðæts nɑt soʊ gʊəd], contrasted with the General American [ðæts nɑt sə gʊd] may give a distinctly Southern flavor to a whole sentence. The actual Southern sound (i.e., phoneme) system itself hardly differs from the General American, except as to *r*, as will be seen below.

Standard Southern

[i]   is used in *either* and *neither*. Thus [ˈiðə, ˈniðə].

[eɪ]   is used alternately with [ɛ] in *again* and *against*. Thus [əˈgeɪn, əˈgɛn].

[eɪ]   is used in *holiday* [ˈhɑləˌdeɪ] and *yesterday* [ˈjɛstəˌdeɪ]. It sometimes appears in *Monday, Tuesday*, etc.

---

[24] See C. M. Wise, *Applied Phonetics*, Englewood Cliffs, N.J., Prentice-Hall, Inc., 1957, for exercises on special substandard forms:

Chapter 14. Speech of New York City, p. 281.
Chapter 15. Substandard Southern Negro Speech, p. 293.
Chapter 16. Mountain Speech, p. 303.
Chapter 17. French dialect (general), p. 349; Canadian, p. 352; Louisiana French-English, p. 254.
Chapter 19. Pennsylvania German, p. 403.
Chapter 20. Yiddish, p. 411.
Chapter 21. Norwegian, p. 427.
Chapter 22. Italian, p. 447.
Chapter 23. Spanish (including Mexican), p. 467.
Chapter 24. Russian, p. 504.
Chapter 25. Brazilian Portuguese, p. 537.

[ɪ]   is used in most unstressed initial syllables spelled with *e* or *i* followed
        by a consonant. Examples: *respect* [rɪˈspɛkt]; *preclude* [prɪˈklud]; *dispose*
        [dɪsˈpouz].
            Occasionally [ə] is used, as in *response* [rəˈspɑnts].

[ə]   is used for unstressed medial *e*, *i*, and *y*. Examples: *telegram*
        [ˈtɛləˌgræm]; *agitate* [ˈædʒəˌteɪt]; *analysis* [əˈnæləsɪs]; *appetite*
        [ˈæpəˌtaɪt].
            If the sound following *e* or *i* is a vowel, [ɪ] is used. Examples:
        initiate [ɪˈnɪʃɪˌeɪt]; *permeate* [ˈpɜmɪˌeɪt]. The vowel of the pronoun *it*,
        when unstressed, is [ɪ]. Thus, *I see it*, [aɪ ˈsi ɪt].

        Transcribe.   create, react, vitiate, reality.   List other words in this class.

[ɪ]   is used in the suffixes *ace, ad, as, ase, ate, ed, eit, en* (when the stem
        contains a front vowel), *eon, es, ess, et, ice, id, in, ip, is, ist, it, ite, uce,
        ute,* etc. Examples: *solace* [ˈsɑlɪs]; *salad* [ˈsælɪd]; *Pallas* [ˈpælɪs]; *pur-
        chase* [ˈpɜtʃɪs]; *palate* [ˈpælɪt]; *wanted* [ˈwɔntɪd]; *forfeit* [ˈfɔfɪt];
        kitchen [ˈkɪtʃɪn]; *pigeon* [ˈpɪdʒɪn]; *searches* [ˈsɜtʃɪz]; *peerless* [ˈpɪəlɪs];
        bracket [ˈbrækɪt]; *Alice* [ˈælɪs]; *limpid* [ˈlɪmpɪd]; *coffin* [ˈkɔfɪn]; *Philip*
        [ˈfɪlɪp]; *crisis* [ˈkraɪsɪs]; *tourist* [ˈtUrɪst]; *vomit* [ˈvɑmɪt]; *opposite*
        [ˈɑpəzɪt]; *lettuce* [ˈlɛtɪs]; *minute* [ˈmɪnɪt]. [ə] is also used in words of
        this class by a limited number of individuals.

[eɪ]   as well as [ɛ] is used in certain words where *a* or *ai* in stressed syllables
        precedes [r]. Examples: *dairy* [ˈdɛrɪ, ˈdeɪrɪ]; *gregarious* [griˈgɛrɪəs,
        griˈgeɪrɪəs]; *Mary* [ˈmɛrɪ, ˈmeɪrɪ]; *various* [ˈvɛrɪəs, ˈveɪrɪəs]; etc.

[æ]   is used in all so-called "broad *a*" words. Examples: *calf* [kæf]; *calves*
        [kævz]; *pass* [pæs]; *bath* [bæθ]; *baths* [bæðz]; *plant* [plænt]. See page 315
        for definition of "broad *a*." Exception is made in tidewater Virginia
        and occasionally elsewhere on the south Atlantic coast by some
        speakers who use [ɑ] as in British and some Eastern speech. Thus, *calf*
        [kɑf], etc.

[ɑ]   is used in monosyllables and stressed syllables containing *ar* final or
        followed by a consonant and not preceded by the sound of [w].
        Examples: *article* [ˈɑtɪkəl]; *bar* [bɑ]; *barter* [ˈbɑtə]; *Carter* [ˈkɑtə];
        dart [dɑːt] [25] *garment* [ˈgɑmənt]; *heart* [hɑːt].

        Transcribe.   are, arbor, army, arsenal, art, artistic, far, gar, hearty, harsh,
        lark, mar, marble, margin, marsh. (See word lists, pages 294, 295.)

---

[25] Though length is, as a general rule, nonphonemic in English, it is occasionally necessary
in standard Southern to recognize the phonemic function of length and to use the lengthening
sign to prevent ambiguity. Thus without the lengthening sign, *card* [kɑːd] would be indis-
tinguishable from *cod* [kɑd]; *dart* [dɑːt] from *dot* [dɑt]; *hard* [hɑːd] from *hod* [hɑd], etc.

[æ] is most often used ([ɛ] occasionally) in words in *air* and *are* and in certain words in *ear*. Examples: *pair* ['pæə]; *pare* ['pæə]; *pear* ['pæə]. (See word lists, pages 265, 301.)

[æ] is practically universal with words in *arr*. Examples: *carry* ['kærɪ]; *marry* ['mærɪ]. (See word lists, pages 265, 301.)

[ɑ] is used for the so-called "short *o*." Examples: *hopped* [hɑpt]; *object* (noun) ['ɑbʤɪkt].

Transcribe. copper, dot, hobble, mobbing, mopped, obsolete, opportunity, opposite, rot, sot.

List other words of this class.

[ɑ] is used prevailingly in *watch* [wɑtʃ], *was* [wɑz]; *what* [ʍɑt]; *squat* [skwɑt]; *quadrangle* ['kwɑdˌræŋɡəl]; *wash* [wɑʃ]; *wasp* [wɑsp]. [ɔ] is used by some individuals.

[ɑ] is used predominantly in stressed syllables containing *o* followed by *r* or *rr* plus a vowel. Examples: *Florida* ['flɑrədə]; *forest* ['fɑrɪst]; *horrid* ['hɑrɪd]; *orange*[26] ['ɑrɪnʤ]; *torrent* ['tɑrənt]. [ɔ] is used occasionally in these words.

See page 302 for a list of additional words of this class.

[ɑ] is used predominantly in stressed syllables spelled with *a* preceded by [w] and followed by *r* or *rr* plus a vowel. Example: *quarry* ['kwɑrɪ].[26] [ɔ] is also used in these words by some individuals.

Transcribe. quarrel, quarantine, warrant, warren.

[ɔ] is used as a low-mid back sound, the tongue taking a position somewhat below the halfway point between [o] and [ɑ]. The sound does not suggest [oʊ] in certain stressed syllables with *all, aul,* or *aw* final, or with *all, augh, aul, aw,* or *ough* plus one or more consonants, as does the corresponding sound in British and some Eastern speech. Examples: *brought* [brɔt]; *call* [kɔl]; *saw* [sɔ].

Transcribe. bought, daughter, fought, gone, hawk, long, on, raw, Saul, talk, walk, want. (See lists, pages 302 and 315.)

[ɔ] is used in *water* ['wɔtə].

[ɑ] is occasionally used.

[ɔ] is used predominantly in the *og* words. Example: *catalog* ['kætəˌlɔg]; *log* [lɔg]; *foggy* ['fɔgɪ]; *frog* [frɔg].[27]

---

[26] Thomas, "American Dictionaries," pp. 175–176.

[27] *Ibid.* See also Albert Donald George, *Some Louisiana Isoglosses,* Unpublished Master's Thesis, Louisiana State University, 1951. George found that of 380 instances in Louisiana, 316 were pronounced with [ɔ], 64 with [ɑ]. [ɑ] was used most often in *fog,* least often in *log* and *dog.*

Transcribe. bog, dog, fog, hog.

[o]   is used in unstressed syllables, as in *obey* [oˈbeɪ].

Transcribe. egoism, poetic. Collect other examples.

Do not confuse words of this class with words with secondary stress such as *polo* [ˈpoʊˌloʊ], or with words in final unstressed *o* and *ow*, which use both [o] and [ə], as in *tomato* [təˈmeɪto, təˈmeɪtə] and *follow* [ˈfalo, ˈfalə].

[e]   is used in certain relatively unstressed syllables: Example: *gyrate* [ˈʤaɪret]. Collect other examples.

[oʊ]   is used with various spellings in monosyllables and in the stressed syllables of words of more than one syllable, including syllables of secondary stress. Examples of monosyllables: *course* [ˈkoəs];[28] *rope* [roʊp]; *ford* [ˈfoəd]; *door* [doə]; *floor* [ˈfloə]. Examples of syllables of secondary stress: *alto* [ˈælˌtoʊ]; *bolo* [ˈboʊˌloʊ]; *Negro* [ˈniˌgroʊ], *fourteen* [ˌfoətˈtin]; *dormitory* [ˈdɔməˌtoʊrɪ].

Transcribe. allegory, bone, coarse, coed, cone, hoarse, indoors, oval, score, solo.

[ɜʊ]   is used in tidewater Virginia[29] for [au] spelled *ou* and followed by a voiceless consonant.
Examples: *out* [ɜʊt]; *doubt* [dɜʊt]; *mouse* [mɜʊs]. If an inflected form of a word containing [ɜʊ] introduces a voiced consonant after the diphthong, the diphthong changes to [aʊ]. Thus: sing. *house* [hɜʊs], plu. *houses* [ˈhaʊzɪz].
ow final and *ou* and *ow* followed by a voiced consonant are [aʊ] in this area, as in *cow* [kaʊ]; *how* [haʊ]; *cloud* [klaʊd]; *plowed* [plaʊd].

[ju]   is used for the spellings *eu*, *ew* and *u* after *d*, *t*, and *n*, as in *dupe* [djup] *neutral* [ˈnjutrəl]; *new* [nju].
[u] is occasionally heard.

Transcribe. contusion, ducal, duke, innumerable, newsprint, pneumonia, tubular.

[u]   is used after [l], [θ], [s], [z], as in *lute* [lut]; *enthusiastic* [ɪnˌθuzɪˈæstɪk]; *pursuit* [pəˈsut]; *presume* [prɪˈzum].

---

[28] Where *r* (pronounced [ə]) follows the stressed vowel, the second element of the diphthong is assimilated, so that [oʊə] becomes [oə].

[29] E. W. Shewmake, "Laws of pronunciation in Virginia," *Modern Language Notes* (December, 1925), *40*: 489–492. Also in *English Pronunciation in Virginia*. Davidson, N.C., Davidson College, 1927, pp. 23–24. Referred to hereafter as Shewmake, *English Pronunciation*.

[ʌ]   is used as very nearly a central vowel, closely resembling [ə] except in duration. Actually the tongue is a little lower and a little farther back than for [ə]. The sound does not suggest [ɑ] as in British and some eastern speech. Examples: *but* [bʌt]; *love* [lʌv]. See word list, page 267.

The Use of [r] in Southern Speech

With the exception of final and preconsonantal *r* (also called postvocalic *r*), as in *ear* and *carting*, all the *r*'s which appear in the spelling are pronounced as [r] in standard Southern speech. The various other ways of rendering the orthographic *r* will appear in the succeeding paragraphs.

It should be added that in many parts of the South, even final and preconsonantal *r*'s are pronounced in the General American fashion, sometimes irregularly, and sometimes consistently, even though other pronunciation characteristics, including intonation characteristics, are definitely Southern. This practice is most noticeable in all parts of the Southern States bordering the General American area. This border area is at its widest as it crosses Texas. In parts of the South there is large-scale intermingling of people from all parts of the United States, as in Florida and all the larger cities.

Particularly as a result of the interchange of populations, but also partly as a result of the influence of the predominantly General American speech on the radio and in the motion pictures (see page 261), the use of final and postvocalic *r* appears by nonstatistical observation to be increasing in the South. In the nature of the case, this implies an increase also in the use of [ɝ] and [ɚ], as in *burner* [ˈbɝnɚ].

Notwithstanding the tendencies toward the wider use of these *r*-sounds, it appears that for the present it will be best to regard such sounds as not yet acclimated in the most typical standard Southern speech. Accordingly, all the entries regarding Southern speech herein are made on the assumption that final and preconsonantal *r*'s are not pronounced with *r*-quality in standard Southern.

[ɜ]   is used in most stressed syllables containing *ear, er, ir, or, our, ur,* and *yr*. Examples: *earth* [ɜθ], *eternal* [iˈtɜnl̩], *dirge* [dɜdʒ], *word* [wɜd], *journal* [ˈdʒɜnl̩], *curd* [kɜd], *myrrh* [mɜ]. (See word list, page 295.)
        List other words belonging to this class.

[ʌ]   is used in a number of words spelled with *o* plus *r* or *rr* plus vowel, and *u* plus *rr* plus vowel. Examples: *thoroughly* [ˈθʌrəlɪ], *furry* [ˈfʌrɪ], *hurry* [ˈhʌrɪ], *worry* [ˈwʌrɪ]. (See word list, page 297.)

Find other words of this class.

[ə]   is used in unstressed syllables spelled with *ar, er, ir, or, our, ur, ure, yr*. Examples: *tartar* [ˈtatə], *sister* [ˈsɪstə], *fakir* [ˈfeɪkə], *humor* [ˈhjumə], *humour* (Canadian and British spelling) [ˈhjumə], *sulphur* [ˈsʌlfə], *nature* [ˈneɪtʃə], *martyr* [ˈmatə].

[ə]   is used in monosyllables and stressed syllables where *r* is preceded by [ɪ], [ɛ], [æ], [o], [ʊ], or the diphthongs [aɪ] and [aʊ]. Examples:

1. After [ɪ]: *fear* [ˈfɪə], *mere* [ˈmɪə], *peer* [ˈpɪə], *pier* [ˈpɪə].
2. After [ɛ]: *there* [ˈðɛə], *where* [ˈʍɛə].
3. After [æ]: *air* [ˈæə], *care* [ˈkæə], *fair* [ˈfæə].
4. After: [o]: *door* [ˈdoə], *more* [ˈmoə], *soar* [ˈsoə].

(See footnote 28, page 284, on the reduction of [oʊə] to [oə].)

5. After [ʊ]: *moor* [ˈmʊə], *poor* [ˈpʊə], *pure* [ˈpjʊə], *sure* [ˈʃʊə].
6. After [aɪ]: *fire* [ˈfaɪə], *hire* [ˈhaɪə], *lyre* [ˈlaɪə], *pyre* [ˈpaɪə], *sire* [ˈsaɪə], *tire* [ˈtaɪə], *wire* [ˈwaɪə].
7. After [aʊ]: *flour* [ˈflaʊə], *hour* [ˈaʊə], *our* [ˈaʊə], *sour* [ˈsaʊə].

[ə]   or omission of [r] occurs in monosyllables and stressed syllables where *r* is preceded by [ɔ]. Examples: *cord* [ˈkɔəd, kɔd], *for* [ˈfɔə, fɔ], *horse* [ˈhɔəs, hɔs].

r   following [ɑ] in the same syllable is not pronounced. Examples: *car* [kɑ], *card* [kɑːd],[30] *cart* [kɑːt],[30] *dark* [dɑːk],[30] *darling* [ˈdɑlɪŋ], *garden* [ˈgɑdn̩].

r   is not preceded by [i], [eɪ], or [u] in the same syllable. In spelling combinations where [i] might be anticipated, the vowel is pronounced [ɪ]. Thus, *deer* [ˈdɪə], not [ˈdiə]. In an analogous fashion we have [ɛə], not [eɪə] in *they're gone* [ˈðɛə gɔn], not [ˈðeɪə gɔn]; [ʊə], not [uə] in *tour* [ˈtʊə}, not [ˈtuə].

r   is pronounced as [r] between vowels both in the interior of a word and at the end of a word followed by another word beginning with a vowel. Examples: *far away* [ˌfɑrəˈweɪ], *very* [ˈvɛrɪ], *library* [ˈlaɪˌbrɛrɪ], *marry* [ˈmærɪ].

NOTE: This is the "linking [r]." All good speakers use it in the interior of words like those above. Although only a minority of good

---

[30] The lengthening sign is used here to prevent the ambiguity of transcribing *card* and *cod*, *cart* and *cot*, *dark* and *dock* in the same way. See footnote, p. 282.

speakers use it between words as in the example of *far away* above, it is regarded as better practice to do so.

List and pronounce other examples of words containing medial [r]. Form combinations of words each containing a word ending in *r* and followed by another beginning with a vowel. Pronounce, retaining the [r].

[l̩]   or [əl] is used in most words ending in *ile*. Examples: *agile* [ˈæʤəl], *fertile* [ˈfɜtl̩].

(See word list, page 268, and note, page 317.)

Find other words of this class.

Clear [l], i.e., [l] made in the front of the mouth, is used before and between front vowels. Examples: *lean* [lin], *feeling* [ˈfilɪŋ], *steely* [ˈsti̇lɪ], *hilly* [ˈhɪlɪ].

Transcribe. Billy, chilly, Lillian, lily, peeling, valley.

[ɫ], i.e., dark [l], is used everywhere else.[31]

[ʍ]   is used in nearly all words spelled with *wh*, except *who*, *whole*, and their derivatives. Examples: *where* [ˈʍɛə], *while* [ʍaɪl], *whistle* [ˈʍɪsl̩]. Numerous speakers in cities, especially New Orleans, use [w] as in [ˈwɪsl̩].

(See lists, pages 268, 318.) List other words of this class.

Both primary and secondary stress are used in numerous polysyllables, particularly those ending in *ary*, *ery*, *ory*. Examples: *dictionary* [ˈdɪkʃənˌɛrɪ], *stationery* [ˈsteɪʃənˌɛrɪ], *laboratory* [ˈlæbərəˌtoʊrɪ].

For word list, see page 268.[32]

Deviations from Standard Southern

Substitution of [ɔ] *for* [ɑ]. Use [ɑ], not [ɔ], in monosyllables and stressed syllables containing *ar* final or followed by a consonant and not preceded by the sound of [w]. Examples: *car* [kɑ], not [kɔ]; *card* [kɑːd],[33] not [kɔd]; *park* [pɑk], not [pɔk].

---

[31] In this text no special symbol is used for clear [l]; likewise no special symbol is used for dark [l], except when it is a matter of specific discussion.

[32] See also John Samuel Kenyon, *American Pronunciation.* Ann Arbor, Mich.: George Wahr, 8th ed., 1940, pp. 83–86; for longer list see 4th ed., 1924, pp. 160–164.

[33] The lengthening sign is used here to prevent ambiguity between *card* and *cod*. See footnote, p. 282.

Through mispronunciation of words of this class homonyms are often produced from such pairs as *hark-hawk, stark-stalk, ardor-order*. See list, pages 294 and 295, for drill in distinguishing between these pairs.

Substitution of [eɪ] *for* [æ] *and* [ɛ].   Use [æ], not [eɪ], in the following: *can't* [kænt], not [keɪnt]; *aunt* [ænt], not [eɪnt].

Collect other examples.

Use [ɛ], not [eɪ], in the following: *head* [hɛd], not [heɪd]; *red* [rɛd], not [reɪd]; *bed* [bɛd], not [beɪd]; *yes* [jɛs], not [jeɪs].

Collect other examples.

Substitution of [ɑ] *for* [ɪ] *and* [ɛ].   In the transcriptions following, an alternate use of [r] is indicated for the speech of parts of the South, such as the areas bordering the General American area, where final and preconsonantal [r] are used. (See page 285.) Use *here* [ˌhɪə, hɪr], not [hjɑ, hjɑr]; *there* [ˈðɛə, ðɛr], not [ðɑ, ðɑr]; *where* [ˈʍɛə, ʍɛr], not [ʍɑ, ʍɑr].

Substitution of [a] *and* [ɑ] *for* [aɪ].   Use [aɪ], not [a] or [ɑ], in words like the following: *I* [aɪ], not [a] or [ɑ]; *my* [maɪ], not [ma] or [mɑ]; *high* [haɪ], not [hɑ].[34]

The substitution of [a] for [aɪ] is much more common than the substitution of [ɑ]. Some individuals who use [a] never use [ɑ], and some individual words seem never to be pronounced with [ɑ].[35] In tidewater Virginia and occasionally elsewhere on the south Atlantic coast, "long" *i* before voiceless consonants is often pronounced with a sound approaching [ɜɪ]. Examples: [bɜɪt] for *bite* [baɪt], [wɜɪf] for *wife* [waɪf].

(See page 295 for list of words for drill.)

Diphthongization of [æ] *to* [æɪ].   Use [æ], not [æɪ] in the following: *dance* [dænts], not [dæɪnts]; *class* [klæs], not [klæɪs]; *ask* [æsk], not [æɪsk].

Collect other examples.

Substitution of [ɑ] *for* [aɪ] *before* [r].   This is a special case of the modification of the diphthong [aɪ], in that [ɑ] is generally used, not [a]. In the following, as above, an alternate use of [r] is indicated for the speech of parts of the South, such as the areas bordering the General American area, where final and precor onantal [r] are used. (See page 285.) Use *fire* [ˈfaɪə, faɪr], not [fɑ, fɑr]; *hired* [ˈhaɪəd, haɪrd], not

---

[34] Shewmake, *English Pronunciation*, pp. 24–25.

[35] See C. M. Wise, W. Scott Nobles, and Herbert Metz, "The Southern American diphthong [aɪ]," *The Southern Speech Journal*, May, 1954, pp. 304–312.

[hɑːd, hard]; *iron* ['aɪən, aɪrn], not [ɑn, ɑrn]; *tire* ['taɪə, taɪr], not [tɑ, tɑr]; *tired* ['taɪəd, taɪrd], not [tɑd, tɑrd]; *wire* ['waɪə, waɪr], not [wɑ, wɑr]; etc.

Collect other examples.

Substitution of [ɛ] for [eɪ]. Use *afraid* [ə'freɪd], not [ə'frɛd]; *make* [meɪk], not [mɛk]; *naked* ['neɪkɪd], not ['nɛkɪd]; *take* [teɪk], not [tɛk]; *snake* [sneɪk], not [snɛk]; etc.

Collect other examples.

Substitution of [æ] for [ɛ]. Use [ɛ], not [æ], in *where* and *there*. Thus: ['ʍɛə], not ['ʍæə]; ['ðɛə], not ['ðæə].

Substitution of [ɔo], [ɔʊ], and [aʊ] for [ɔ]. Use [ɔ], not [ɔo] or [ɔʊ] or [aʊ], in words like the following: *walk* [wɔk], not [wɔok, wɔʊk, waʊk]; *long* [lɔŋ], not [lɔoŋ, lɔʊŋ, laʊŋ].

> *Transcribe.* all, auction, audible, audit, ball, cloth, coffee, gaunt, haunt, long, moss, nautical, Paul, strong, talk.

(See additional list, page 315.) List other words of this class.

Substitution of [ɜɪ] and [ɔɪ] for [ɜ]. Use [ɜ], not [ɜɪ], in monosyllables and stressed syllables containing *ear, er, ir, or, our, ur,* and *yr,* plus consonant, as illustrated by words such as the following: *heard* [hɜd], not [hɜɪd]; *term* [tɜm], not [tɜɪm]; *bird* [bɜd], not [bɜɪd]; *work* [wɜk], not [wɜɪk]; *journal* ['ʤɜnl̩], not ['ʤɜɪnl̩]; *urn* [ɜn], not [ɜɪn].

Instead of [ɜɪ], [ɔɪ] is occasionally heard in cities, e.g., New Orleans. Thus, [bɔɪn] for *burn* [bɜn], etc.

(See drill list, page 295.) List other words of this class.

Omission of [ə] from [oə]. Use [oə], not [o], in words like the following: *door* ['doə], not [do]; *four* ['foə], not [fo]; *fourteen* [ˌfoət'tin], not [ˌfot'tin]; *floor* ['floə], not [flo]; *more* ['moə], not [mo]; *store* ['stoə], not [sto].

> *Transcribe.* coarse, course, force, ford, hoarse, tore, wore.

(See list, page 295.) Collect other examples.

Substitution of [o] for [ʊə]. Use [ʊə], not [o], in the following: *poor* ['pʊə], not [po]; *sure* ['ʃʊə], not [ʃo]; *your* ['jʊə], not [jo]. Resembling these words, but probably originating in a spelling pronunciation, is ['woʊmən] for *woman* ['wʊmən].

Omission of [ɪ] from diphthong [ɔɪ]. Use [ɔɪ], not [ɔ], in words like the following: boil [bɔɪl], not [bɔl]; spoil [spɔɪl], not [spɔl]; etc.

(See list, page 313.) Collect other examples.

Substitution of [ɜ] *for* [ɔɪ].   Use [ɔɪ], not [ɜ] for the following: *spoil* [spɔɪl], not [spɜl]; *oil* [ɔɪl], not [ɜl]; *boil* [bɔɪl], not [bɜl]. This pronunciation is found in cities, particularly New Orleans.

Substitution of [ɪu] *for* [u].   Use [u], not [ɪu], in words spelled with *o* and *oo*, such as the following: *too* [tu], not [tɪu]; *do* [du], not [dɪu].

> *Transcribe.*   approve, move, moon, noon, soon, spoon, two.

(See word list, page 314.) Collect other examples.

Substitution of [æ] *for* [ɪ] *before* [ŋ].   Use [ɪ], not [æ], in monosyllables and stressed syllables spelled with *ing*. Examples: *bring* [brɪŋ], not [bræŋ]; *thing* [θɪŋ], not [θæŋ]; *think* [θɪŋk], not [θæŋk].

Collect other examples.

Substitution of [ɪ] *for* [ɛ].   Use [ɛ], not [ɪ], in words spelled with [ɛ] plus nasal, especially [n], such as the following: *ten* [tɛn], not [tɪn]; *any* [ˈɛnɪ], not [ˈɪnɪ]; *attempt* [əˈtɛmpt], not [əˈtɪmpt]; *length* [lɛŋkθ], not [lɪŋkθ].

(See lists on page 296.)

This is a particularly persistent substandardism in the South. Intensive practice is required to change it.

Substitution of [ɛ] *for* [ɪ].   Use [ɪ], not [ɛ], in words containing vowel plus nasal, especially [n], such as the following: *interest* [ˈɪntərəst], not [ˈɛntərəst]; *Minden* [ˈmɪndən], not [ˈmɛndən]; *since* [sɪnts], not [sɛnts]; *simple* [ˈsɪmpl̩], not [ˈsɛmpl̩]; *thing* [θɪŋ], not [θɛŋ]; *import* [ˈɪmˌpoət], not [ˈɛmˌpoət]; *been* [bɪn], not [bɛn].

> *Transcribe.*   fin, in, mint, sing, tin.

(See also list on page 297.)

This pronunciation is the converse of the one discussed under the preceding heading.

Collect other examples.

Substitution of [ɚ] *or* [ɜ] *for* [ə] *and* [uə].   Use [ə], not [ɚ] or [ɜ] in the following: *ruin* [ˈruən], not [ˈruɚn] or [rɜn]; *woman* [ˈwumən], not [ˈwumɚn]; women [ˈwɪmən], not [ˈwɪmɚn].

Substitution of [ou] *for* [ɔ].   Use [ɔ], not [ou], in the following: *gone* [gɔn], not [goun]; *on* [ɔn], not [oun]; *want* [wɔnt], not [wount].

This deviation is ordinarily limited to the foregoing three words and their derivatives, such as *foregone, upon, whereon,* etc.

Intrusive [j].   [j] must not intrude between [k] or [g] and a following vowel.

Thus: *car* [kɑ], not [kjɑ]; *garden* [ˈgɑdn̩], not [ˈgjɑdn̩]; *calf* [kæf], not [kjæf]; *county* [ˈkaʊntɪ], not [ˈkjæʊntɪ].

List other words of this class.

Omission of l.   Use [l] in the pronoun *self* and all its compounds and in certain analogous words. Examples: *self* [sɛlf], not [sɛf]; *film* [fɪlm], not [fɪm]; *help* [hɛlp], not [hɛp]; *twelve* [twɛlv], not [twɛv]; *college* [ˈkɑlɪdʒ], not [ˈkɑːɪdʒ], *William* [ˈwɪljəm], not [ˈwɪjəm].

> *Transcribe.* elm, helm, herself, himself, itself, myself, ourselves, realm, themselves, yourself, yourselves, million, billion, stallion.

Substitution of [ə], [ʊ], *and* [o] *for* [l].   Use [l] in each of the following: *milk* [mɪlk], not [mɪək, mɪʊk, mɪok]; *felt* [fɛlt], not [fɛot].

> *Transcribe.* false, fell, fill, mill, silk, tell, till.

Collect other examples.

Substitution of [n] *for* [ŋ].   Use *length* [lɛŋkθ], not [lɛnθ]; *strength* [strɛŋkθ], not [strɛnθ]; *coming* [kʌmɪŋ], not [kʌmɪn, kʌmən]; *nothing* [ˈnʌθɪŋ], not [ˈnʌθɪn, nʌθən].

Omission of final [t].   Use [t] always in the final combinations [ft], [kt], and [st]. Examples: *best* [bɛst], not [bɛs]; *first* [fɜst], not [fɜɪs]; *left* [lɛft], not [lɛf]; *next* [nɛkst], not [nɛks]; *expect* [ɪkˈspɛkt], not [ɪkˈspɛk].

> *Transcribe.* collect, east, ghost, host, last, least, most, must, past, post, reflect, reject, select, west, worst.

List other words of this class.

Omission of final [d].   Use [d] always in the final combinations [ld], [lds], [nd], [nds]. Examples: *field* [fild], not [fil]; *sand* [sænd], not [sæn].

> *Transcribe.* band, cold, fold, gold, hands, mold, old, shields.

Exception, *and* [ænd], which may when unstressed be pronounced [ənd, ən, n̩].

Syllabic syncope.   (See definition, page 371.) Use *Louisiana* [ˌluəzɪˈænə], not [ˌluzɪˈænə]; [36] *pronunciation* [prəˌnʌnsɪˈeɪʃən], not [prəˌnʌnˈseɪʃən]; *pictorial* [ˌpɪkˈtoʊrɪəl], not [ˌpɪkˈtoʊrəl].

> *Transcribe.* association, curiosity, experience, memorial, miserable, Pierrette, Pierrot, positive, quarreled, realize, territorial, tonsorial.

---

[36] Also not [ləˌwizɪˈænə], since the name is a derivative of *Louis*, not *Louise*.

Dissimilation. (See definition, page 361.)   Use *government* ['gʌvənmənt], not ['gʌvmənt]; *recognize* ['rɛkəgˌnaɪz], not ['rɛkəˌnaɪz]; *library* ['laɪbrɛrɪ], not ['laɪbɛrɪ], *candidate*, ['kændəˌdeɪt], not ['kænəˌdeɪt]. Collect other examples.

Substitution of [t] *and* [f] *for* [θ], *and* [d] *for* [ð].   Use *with* [wɪð] or [wɪθ], not [wɪt, wɪd, wɪf], *both* [bouθ], not [bout, bouf]; *this* [ðɪs], not [dɪs]; *that* [ðæt], not [dæt]; *they* [ðeɪ], not [deɪ]; *then* [ðɛm], not [dɛm]; *the* [ðə], not [də]; *other*, ['ʌðə], not ['ʌdə]. (See list, page 311.)

This pronunciation is usually limited to frequently used words, such as those above. The speakers can pronounce [θ] and [ð] without difficulty, and do so regularly in less frequently used words.

Omission of linking [r].   1. Use linking [r] between vowels in the interior of a word. Examples: *very* ['vɛrɪ], not ['vɛɪ]; *carry* ['kærɪ], not ['kæɪ].

Transcribe.   berry, cherry, fairy, ferry, hairy, Harry, library, marry, Mary, merry.

List other words of this class.

2. Use linking final [r] when the following word begins with a vowel. Example: *our own* [aʊr oun], not [aʊ ʔoun, aʊ(w)oun]; *clear and sunny* [klɪr ən ˈsʌnɪ], not [klɪə ʔn̩ ˈsʌnɪ].

List other examples like these.

Intrusive linking [r].   Although the linking [r] between words ending with *r* and followed by another word beginning with a vowel is by no means universal, yet its influence suffices to induce a false link between a word ending in a vowel and a following word beginning with a vowel. Thus *odor of sanctity* [oudər əv ˈsæŋktətɪ] is paralleled by *sodar is cheap* [soudər ɪz ˈtʃip]. Use *sofa and table*, not *sofar and table*, *Louisiana* [ˌluəzɪˈænə] *and Texas*, not *Louisianar and Texas*, *Ada is oldest*, not *Adar is oldest*.

Retraction of stress.   The stress on final syllables of dissyllables and medial or final syllables of trisyllables must not be transferred to the initial syllables. Examples: *police* [pəˈlis], not [ˈpouˌlis]; *Monroe* [mənˈro], not [ˈmʌnˌro]; *event* [ɪˈvɛnt], not [ˈiˌvɛnt] *pecan* [pəˈkɑn, pɪˈkɑn], not [ˈpʌˌkɔn] or [ˈpiˌkɑn]; *idea* [aɪˈdɪə], not [ˈaɪdɪə, ˈaɪdɪ]; *insurance* [ɪnˈʃurənts], not [ˈɪnˌʃurənts]; *afternoon* [ˌæftəˈnun], not [ˈæftənun].

Transcribe.   escape, express, increase (verb), select.

Collect other examples.

Advance of stress. This is the reverse of the retraction illustrated above. Example: [lo ˈkeɪt] for [ˈloʊˌkeɪt].

>   *Transcribe.* rotate, gyrate.

Miscellaneous substandardisms. Use *children* [ˈtʃɪldrən], not [ˈtʃʊən, tʃɜn]; *drop* [drɑp], not [dræp]; *going* [ˈgoʊɪŋ], not [gwaɪn]; *hungry* [ˈhʌŋgrɪ], not [ˈhaŋgrɪ, ˈhɔŋgrɪ]; *Negro* [ˈnigroʊ], not [ˈnɪgrə]; *to* [tu, tʊ, tə], not [toʊ]; *whip* [ʍɪp], not [ʍʊp, ʌʊp, ʌʌp]; *wrap* [ræp], not [rɑp].

To complete the study of this section, it will be necessary to refer back to pages 268 to 280, where substandardisms common to all sections of the country are discussed.

The Southern drawl requires separate consideration. There is a certain wrongness about listing it as a substandardism, for in moderation it is an engaging characteristic. Moreover, not all Southerners use it— probably much fewer than half do. But in excess it becomes a fault by reason of its conspicuousness. This drawl is not merely slowness, as is often supposed; it is the proliferation of sounds from one vowel *resulting* from slowness. English has few pure vowels at best: *a* = [eɪ]; *i* = [aɪ]; *o* = [oʊ]. Off-glides with many vowels are more nearly the rule than the exception, as may be noted by examining the syllabics of English as set up by modern phonemicists. The Southern drawl makes of any stressed vowel as many as two, three, or four sounds. In the course of this attenuating, front vowels may develop [j] medially, and back vowels [w]. The possible results follow:

[æ]   becomes [ˈæjə, ˈæɪjə], as in *bass* [ˈbæjəs, ˈbæɪjəs].
[ɛ]   becomes [ˈɛjə, ˈɛɪjə], as in *yes* [ˈjɛjəs, ˈjɛɪjəs]. The [ɛ] may even be raised and diphthongized to [eɪ], so that [ˈjeɪjəs] results.
[ɪ]   becomes [ˈɪjə], as in *bit* [bˈɪjət].
[i]   becomes [ˈijə], as in *field* [ˈfijəld].
[ɑ]   becomes [ˈɑwə], as in *car* [ˈkɑwə].
[ɔ]   becomes [ˈɔwə], as in *cord* [ˈkɔwəd].
[ʊ]   becomes [ˈʊwə], as in *good* [ˈgʊwəd].
[u]   becomes [ˈuwə], as in *cute* [ˈkjuwət].
[ɜ]   being central, cannot develop [j] or [w], and becomes [ɜɪ], as in *burn* [bɜɪn].

Exercise to Separate the [ɔ — ɑ] Phonemes

This exercise and the one following it are principally for use in parts of the South where the indicated sounds are confused.

ought [ɔt]	art [ɑt]
maw [mɔ]	mar [mɑ]
auk [ɔk]	ark [ɑk]
maul [mɔl]	marl [mɑl]
balk [bɔk]	bark [bɑk]
sawed [sɔd]	sard [sɑːd] [37]
taw [tɔ]	tar [tɑ]
author ['ɔθə]	Arthur ['ɑθə]
paw [pɔ]	par [pɑ]
stalk [stɔk]	stark [stɑːk]
dawn [dɔn]	darn [dɑːn]
hawk [hɔk]	hark [hɑːk]
caw [kɔ]	car [kɑ]
yawn [jɔn]	yarn [jɑːn]
jaw [dʒɔ]	jar [dʒɑ]
caught [kɔt]	cart [kɑːt]
bawd [bɔd]	bard [bɑd]
awe [ɔ]	are [ɑ]
haughty ['hɔtɪ]	hearty ['hɑtɪ]
gauze [gɔz]	gars [gɑz]
cawed [kɔd]	card [kɑːd]
mawk [mɔk]	mark [mɑːk]
call [kɔl]	Carl [kɑl]
Lord [lɔd]	lard [lɑd]
cord [kɔd]	card [kɑːd]
for [fɔ]	far [fɑ]
form [fɔm]	farm [fɑm]
tort [tɔt]	tart [tɑːt]
former ['fɔmə]	farmer ['fɑmə]
cork [kɔk]	cark [kɑːk]
corpse [kɔps]	carps [kɑːps]
stork [stɔk]	stark [stɑːk]
mortar ['mɔtə]	martyr [mɑtə]

---

[37] The lengthening sign [ː] is used occasionally throughout these lists to prevent ambiguity —in this instance of *sard* with *sod*.

Pronounce with [ɑ], not [ɔ]:

char	tarn
Margaret	guarded
starve	barn
arms	carbon
heart	carbine
part	cart
farce	Martin
park	star
depart	bar
gar	mart

Pronounce the following words with the single vowel [ɜ], not the diphthong [ɜɪ]. Example, *bird* [bɜd]. If the student has difficulty, let him pronounce *were* [wɜ], and then carefully add [k] for *work* [wɜk], [d] for *word* [wɜd] without permitting the intrusion of [ɪ] after [ɜ].

birth	absurd	myrtle	spur	burst
word	turn	Perkins	hurt	first
worth	earn	burly	shirt	worst
yearn	urn	term	Bert	urge
herd	worm	girl	alert	colonel
third	curdle	Turner	curtain	girdle
learn	Hearn	Burton	turtle	journey
tern	quern	flirt	spurt	spurn
pearl	earl	nerve	purse	splurge

Pronounce with the diphthongs [oə] or [ʊə], not [o].

sore ['soə]	core ['koə]
wore ['woə]	boar ['boə]
pure ['pjʊə]	insure [in'ʃʊə]
cure ['kjʊə]	two-by-fours ['tu bə ,foəz]
fourth ['foəθ]	yourself [jʊə'sɛlf]

Pronounce with [aɪ], not [ɑ] or [a].

I'd	ride	bridal	mile	tight
might	bride	quietly	mileage	life
mine	bridle	smile	tie	knife
try	dry	file	fry	cry
lie	fly	rye	height	fright
side	chide	delight	night	bright
bide	cried	mind	sigh	why

Pronounce without [j]. Example, *car* [kɑ], not [kjɑ]; *care* [kæə], not[kjæə].

carbon	card	Garner	cam
cart	Carver	care	camera
Carter	carve	calf	callow
Cartersville	guard	cad	gallop
gasp	codger	Casper	cast
can	can't	carrot	Carroll

Exercise to Separate the [ɛ-ɪ] Phonemes

ten [tɛn]	tin [tɪn]
cents [sɛnts]	since [sɪnts]
Ben [bɛn]	bin [bɪn]
men [mɛn]	Min [mɪn]
meant [mɛnt]	mint [mɪnt]
gem [dʒɛm]	Jim [dʒɪm]
tent [tɛnt]	tint [tɪnt]
hem [hɛm]	him [hɪm]
tender ['tɛndə]	tinder ['tɪndə]
fender ['fɛndə]	hinder ['hɪndə]
gentlemen ['dʒɛntǀmən]	ginger ['dʒɪndʒə]
attention [ə'tɛntʃən]	cinder ['sɪndə]
when [ʍɛn]	whinny ['ʍɪnɪ]
pen [pɛn]	pin [pɪn]
send [sɛnd]	sinned [sɪnd]

Pronounce with [ɛ], not [ɪ].

many	anyone	condemned	anything
any	general	again	lengthened
anybody	went	friend	twenty
torments	rent	end	enemy
avenge	send	splendid	adventure
attempt	sensible	comprehension	attend
comprehend	amend	contend	extend
trenches	drenched	fence	tense
envious	invention	spent	mend
amen	appendix	apprehend	plenty

Pronounce with [ɪ], not [ɛ]. Example, *since* [sɪnts], not [sɛnts]

inch	Indian	evince	intake
tinge	bring	convince	impact
mince	think	imminent	individual
mints	interest	instinct	inset

Pronounce without omitting final [d] or [t].

invest	wept	first	soft	next	arrest
sold	swept	kept	loft	second	attempt
shield	lost	burst	rest	last	contempt
hold	host	child	best	slept	least

Pronounce every syllable of the following words fully. Do not omit medial syllables or parts of syllables. Example, *association* [ə,soʊsɪ'eɪʃən], not *assoc'ation* [ə,soʊ'seɪʃən].

appropriation	government
enunciation	positive
carried	really
seriously	misery
quarreling	experimentally
recognizable	Louisiana
curious	variously

Pronounce without omitting the medial [r]

cemetery ['sɛmə,tɛrɪ]	environment [ɪn'vaɪrənmənt]
bury ['bɛrɪ]	voluntary ['vɑlən,tɛrɪ]
hurry ['hʌrɪ]	Surrey ['sʌrɪ]
worry ['wʌrɪ]	tarry ['tærɪ]
Larry ['lærɪ]	Jerry ['ʤɛrɪ]
Perry ['pɛrɪ]	flurry ['flʌrɪ]
parry ['pærɪ]	carry ['kærɪ]
furry ['fʌrɪ]	Derry ['dɛrɪ]

Pronounce, comparing the ordinary pronunciation of the words ending in *r* with their pronunciation when the linking [r] is used with a following word beginning with a vowel.

(NOTE: When this exercise is used by Eastern speakers, some will prefer to use [ɾ] instead of [r] for the link.)

our ['auə]	our own [ˌaur'oun]
hour ['auə]	hour of trial [ˌaurəv'traɪəl]
here ['hɪə]	here it is ['hɪrɪtˌɪz]
car [kɑ]	the car in the road [ðə'kɑrɪn ðə ˌroud]
where ['ʍɛə]	where is it? [ʍɛr 'ɪz ɪt]
over ['ouvə]	over and over [ˌouvərænd 'ouvə]
more ['moə]	more and more [ˌmourænd 'moə]

Pronounce without an excrescent linking [r] (or, for some Easterners, [ɾ]).

Maria and Hannah	sofa and chair
Hannah and Maria	following
soda and sugar	hollowing
raw oysters	Emma and Jane
India Office	Thelma and Melba
America and China	law and order
China and America	he is here
Theta Alpha	Florida and Louisiana
The idea of it!	Louisiana and Georgia

Exercise to Separate the [ɔ-ou] Phonemes

on [ɔn]	own [oun]
upon [ə 'pɔn]	a pone [ə poun]
want [wɔnt]	won't [wount]

Pronounce with [ɔ], not [ou].

whereupon	gone
thereupon	foregone
whereon	bygone

Pronounce with the stress on the last syllable.

ally	Detroit	return
Monroe	erect	cigarette
recess	report	cigar
defect	research	resource
magazine	adult	address

NOTE: ['riˌsɛs] is also used, especially by children.

Pronounce with [θ] or [ð], not with [t] or [d].

with	the	feather	throw
this	other	thumb	further
that	mother	thing	whether
they	father	either	weather
them	brother	neither	rather

Eastern American English

New England does not possess a dialect as homogeneous as that of the General American area. Like the South, which has the older Virginia and Carolina variant local forms, New England has many local variants. The following study is, then, at best a generalization, and sometimes an arbitrary one. It includes what scholars usually regard as the so-called typical New England pronunciations.

Standard Eastern

[aɪ]   and [i] are both used in *either* [ˈaɪðə, ˈiðə], and *neither* [ˈnaɪðə, niðə].

[ɪ]   or [ə] is used in unstressed initial syllables that are spelled with *e* or *i* preceded by a consonant. [ə] in this use is found principally in western and south central New England. Examples: *reflect* [rɪˈflɛkt, rəˈflɛkt], *refused* [38] [rɪˈfjuzd, rəˈfjuzd].

[ə]   and [ɪ] are used for unstressed medial *e, i* and *y*. [ɪ] is used for the vowel of *it* when the pronoun is unstressed, as in *I see it*. Examples: *American* [əˈmɛrɪkən, əˈmɛrəkən],[39] *analysis* [əˈnæləsɪs, əˈnælɪsɪs], *cemetery* [ˈsɛməˌtɛrɪ, ˈsɛmɪˌtɛrɪ][40], *imitate* [ˈɪmɪˌteɪt, ˈɪməˌteɪt], *telephone* [ˈtɛlɪˌfoʊn, ˈtɛləˌfoʊn], *tenement* [ˈtɛnəmənt, ˈtɛnɪmənt],[41] *I see it* [aɪ ˈsi ɪt].

If the sound following *e* or *i* is a vowel, [ɪ] is used. Examples: *palliate* [ˈpælɪˌeɪt], *roseate* [ˈrouzɪˌeɪt].

---

[38] Hans Kurath, *The Linguistic Atlas of New England*. Providence, R. I., Brown University, 1939, *2*, p. 407a. NOTE: Hereafter this publication will be referred to as *Atlas*. As of this date three volumes of the *Atlas* are available, each in two parts: *1*, 1939; *2*, 1941; *3*, 1943.

Those familiar with the *Atlas* will observe that the *Atlas* data have of necessity often been highly simplified for the purposes of this book. Sometimes this simplification takes the form of the grouping of several variants of a phoneme under one symbol; sometimes of disregarding scattering variants; sometimes of using a more familiar symbolization than that employed by the *Atlas*; sometimes by making generalizations on very few inductions, where the *Atlas* furnishes only a few, etc. Certain additions for nonrustic New England speech are based on observations made by the undersigned during residence and travel in New England.—C. M. W.

[39] *Atlas*, *2*, p. 451.   [40] *3*, p. 525.   [41] *2*, p. 535.

[ɪ]   and [ə] are used in the suffixes *ace, ad, ain, as, ase, ate, ed, eit, en* (when the stem contains a front vowel), *eon, es, ess, et, ice, id, in, ip, is, ist, it, ite, uce, ute.* [ɪ] predominates in the generality of words of this class, but in every case it is possible to find some speakers who use [ə]. Occasionally, as in *salad*, [ə] predominates. When a given word is pronounced with [ə] by only a limited number of speakers, these are likely to be found in the southwest of New England, in the northwest, and in the neighborhood of Boston. Examples: *palace* [ˈpælɪs, ˈpæləs]; *salad* [42] [ˈsæləd, ˈsælɪd]; *mountain* [43] [ˈmaʊntɪn, ˈmaʊntn̩]; *Dallas* [ˈdælɪs, ˈdæləs]; *purchase* [ˈpɜtʃɪs, ˈpɜtʃəs]; *obstinate* [44] [ˈɒbstɪnɪt, ˈɑbstənət]; *exhausted* [45] [ɪgˈzɔstɪd, ɪgˈzɔstəd]; *forfeit* [ˈfɔfɪt, ˈfɔfət]; *chicken* [46] [ˈtʃɪkɪn, ˈtʃɪkən]; *pigeon* [pɪdʒɪn, ˈpɪdʒən], *foxes* [47] [ˈfɒksɪz, ˈfɑksəz]; *actress* [48] [ˈæktrɪs, ˈæktrəs]; *basket* [49] [ˈbæskɪt, ˈbæskət]; *jaundice* [50] [ˈdʒɒndɪs, ˈdʒɑndəs]; *solid* [ˈsɒlɪd, ˈsɑləd]; *coffin* [51] [ˈkɒfɪn, ˈkɒfən]; *Philip* [ˈfɪlɪp, ˈfɪləp]; *appendicitis* [52] [əˌpɛndɪˈsaɪtɪs, əˌpɛndəˈsaɪtəs]; *tourist* [53] [ˈtʊrɪst, ˈtʊrəst]; *vomit* [54] [ˈvɒmɪt, ˈvɑmət]; *opposite* [ˈɒpəzɪt, ˈɑpəzət]; *lettuce* [55] [ˈlɛtɪs, ˈlɛtəs]; *minute* [56] [ˈmɪnɪt, ˈmɪnət].

[æ], [a], and [ɑ] are used in the words commonly called "broad *a*" words. Most of these words are spelled with *a* before [f] (with [v] for plurals), [s], [θ] (with [ð] for plurals), and *n* plus consonant. Examples: *half* [hæf, haf, hɑf]; *halves* [hævz, havz, hɑvz], *pass* [pæs, pas, pɑs], *path* [pæθ, paðz, pɑðz], *dance* [dænts, dants, dɑnts].[57]

See pages 318, 319 and 320 for list for practice.

It should be borne in mind that not all words spelled as indicated above are "broad *a*" words. The spelling can at best serve only as a rough guide. For example, words ending in *and* are not "broad *a*" words except for the derivatives of Latin *mandare*, such as *command* [kəˈmænd, kəˈmand, kəˈmɑnd], and even here one derivative, *mandate* [ˈmænˌdeɪt] is pronounced only with [æ]. Some "broad *a*" words do not lend themselves to orthographical classification, e.g., *aunt* [ænt, ant, ɑnt]; *rather* [ˈræðə, ˈraðə, ˈrɑðə]; and *example* [ɪgˈzæmpl̩, ɪgˈzampl̩, ɪgˈzɑmpl̩].

Many words containing the sound [ɑ] are not included under the arbitrary term "broad *a*." Examples: *father, harm, art*, etc., and *hot*,

[42] *Atlas, 2*, p. 449. [43] *2*, p. 39. [44] *2*, p. 471. [45] *2*, p. 482. [46] *1*, p. 112. [47] *1*, p. 228. [48] *2*, p. 448. [49] *2*, p. 360. [50] *3*, p. 511. [51] *3*, p. 524. [52] *3*, p. 509. [53] *2*, p. 449. [54] *3*, p. 504. [55] *2*, p. 241. [56] *1*, p. 86. See also *1*, p. 115 (picket); *1*, p. 216 (giblets); *1*, pp. 240–241 (hornet); *2*, p. 406 (mitten); *2*, p. 356 (rented); *2*, pp. 476–477 (excited); *2*, p. 343 (kitchen); *2*, p. 467 (careless); *3*, p. 510 (tuberculosis).
[57] The standard reference for identifying and pronouncing these words is Daniel Jones, *An English Pronouncing Dictionary*, New York, E. P. Dutton & Co., 1937.

got, etc., where "short *o*" is not pronounced [ɒ]. (See discussion below.)

The pronunciation [ɑ] in recognized "broad ɑ" words is mainly an urban and coastal pronunciation. It "appears with some regularity around Boston (within thirty-five miles of the city) and again in Maine from Portland eastward. Elsewhere its occurrence is haphazard, sometimes as a survival, sometimes as a recent fashionable pronunciation. In western New England it is exceedingly rare."[58] It is used by a minority of the population in both New England and New York City. [ɑ] is widely used in eastern and central New England and scatteringly elsewhere. [æ] predominates in west central and western New England but is known in eastern New England. [æ] predominates also in New York City, [ɑ] being limited mainly to the stage and to acquired pedantic or "fashionable" use.

[ɑ]   or [a] is used in words spelled with *ar* final or plus consonant and not preceded by the sound of [w]. Examples: *Harvard* ['hɑvəd, 'havəd], *farthest* ['fɑðɪst, 'faðəst, 'faðɪst, 'faðəst].

   Transcribe. barn,[59] barbed wire,[60] car,[61] cartridge,[62] far,[63] far off,[64] garbage,[65] guardian,[66] harmonica,[67] harness,[68] hearth,[69] largest,[70] marsh,[71] park.[72]

[æ]   and [ɛ] are used in many words spelled with *air, are, arr, ear*. [æ] predominates. Examples: *harrow*[73] ['hæro, 'hɛro] ([ɛ] very seldom); *wheelbarrow*[74] ['ʍilbæro, 'ʍilbɛro] ([ɛ] very seldom); *repair*[75] [rɪ'pæə, rɪ'pɛɔ]; *parents*[76] ['pærənts, 'pɛɹənts] ([æ] 15 times, [ɛ] 17 times in 32 instances).

   Transcribe. bear, care,[77] chair,[78], marry,[79] square.[80]

[ɒ]   and [ɑ] are used for words spelled with the so-called "short *o*." Examples: *college*[81] ['kɒlɪʤ, 'kalɪʤ]; *cottage*[82] ['kɒtɪʤ, 'katɪʤ]; *crop*[83] [krɒp, krap]; *foxes*[84] ['fɒksɪz, 'faksəz]; *not*[85] [nɒt, nat]; *rods*[86] [rɒʤ, raʤ]; *tot*[87] [tɒt, tat].

   (See word lists, pages 265 and 283.)

   [58] Hans Kurath, *Hamdbook of the Linguistic Geography of New England*, Providence, R. I., Brown University, 1939, Chart 15, p. 34. NOTE: Hereafter this publication will be referred to as *Handbook*.
   [59] *Atlas, 1*, p. 101. [60] *1*, p. 116. [61] *1*, p. 184. [62] *1*, p. 161. [63] *1*, p. 47. [64] *1*, p. 48. [65] *1*, p. 135. [66] *2*, p. 391. [67] *2*, p. 391. [68] *1*, p. 176. [69] *2*, p. 329. [70] *2*, p. 27. [71] *1*, p. 31. [72] *3*, p. 546. [73] *1*, p. 167. [74] *1*, p. 163. [75] *1*, p. 152. [76] *2*, p. 373. [77] *2*, p. 396. [78] *2*, p. 325. [79] *2*, p. 408. [80] *3*, p. 546. [81] *3*, p. 537. [82] *2*, p. 299. [83] *1*, p. 124. [84] *1*, p. 128. [85] *3*, p. 674. [86] *1*, p. 45. [87] *2*, p. 379.

[ɒ]   and [ɑ] are used in *watch*[88] [wɒtʃ, watʃ], *was*[89] [wɒz, waz], *what*[90] [ʍɒt, ʍat, wɒt, wat].

[ɑ]   and [ɔ, ɒ] are used in stressed syllables containing *o* followed by [r] plus a vowel. Examples: *Florida*[91] [ˈflɑrɪdə, ˈflɔrɪdə, ˈflɒrɪdə]; *forest* [ˈfɑrɪst, ˈfɔrɪst, ˈfɒrɪst]; *orange*[92] [ˈɑrɪndʒ, ˈɔrɪndʒ, ˈɒrɪndʒ]. [ɑ] predominates in eastern and central New England; [ɔ, ɒ] in western New England.[93]

> *Transcribe.* authority, borrow ([ɑ] infrequently), corridor, foreign, horrible, horrid, sorry, tomorrow[94] ([ɑ] infrequently), torrent.

[ɑ] and [ɔ, ɒ] are used in stressed syllables spelled with *a* preceded by [w] and followed by [r] plus a vowel. Examples: *quarry* [ˈkwɑrɪ, ˈkwɔrɪ, ˈkwɒrɪ]; *warrant* [ˈwɑrənt, ˈwɔrənt, ˈwɒrənt]. [ɑ] predominates in eastern and central New England; [ɔ] in western New England.[95]
(See word list, page 283.)

[ɔ]   is very unstable in New England, showing variations from high to low, thus: [ɔˈ, ɔ, ɔ̞]. The vowel of a word like *frost* may be found at all these levels; in addition vowels outside the [ɔ] phoneme, such as [o] above it, and [ɒ] and [ɑ] below it, are substituted. The average level seems to be at about [ɔ], or perhaps toward [ɔ̞]. Examples: *cork*[96] [kɔk], *cough*[97] [kɔf], *frost*[98] [frɔst], *hornet*[99] [ˈhɔnɪt], *loft*[100] [lɔft], *saw*[101] [sɔ].
(See list, page 294.)

In New York City [ɔ] not followed by *r* is pronounced with the tongue higher than for the usual American [ɔ], so as to give to hearers from other areas an acoustic effect approaching that of [o]. Examples: *all* [ɔl, oˈl], *saw* [sɔˈ], *thought* [θɔˈt], *daughter* [ˈdɔˈtə].

[ɔ]   and [ɒ] are used in *water*[102] [ˈwɔtə, ˈwɒtə]. [ɑ] appears occasionally in this word in western New England.

[ɔ]   [ɒ], and [ɑ] are used in words spelled with *og*, with [ɑ] predominant. Example: *frog* [frɔg, frɒg, frɑg].

> *Transcribe.* bog,[103] catalog, cog,[104] fog,[105] foggy, hog,[106] log.[107]

[ɑ] is found principally in the south, west and west central parts of New England.

[88] John Samuel Kenyon and Thomas A. Knott, *A Pronouncing Dictionary of American English*, Springfield, Mass., G. & C. Merriam Company, 1944, p. 470.
[89] *Atlas, 3*, p. 604. [90] *2*, p. 329. [91] *1*, p. 15. [92] *1*, p. 273.
[93] Thomas, "Dialectal Significance," pp. 244–254.
[94] *Atlas, 1*, p. 72.
[95] Thomas, "Dialectal Significance," p. 249.
[96] *Atlas, 1*, p. 144. [97] *3*, p. 500. [98] *1*, p. 98. [99] *1*, pp. 240–241. [100] *1*, p. 102. [101] *3*, p. 659. [102] *2*, p. 311. [103] *1*, p. 130. [104] *1*, p. 158. [105] *1*, p. 96. [106] *1*, p. 204. [107] *2*, p. 330.

In the single word *dog*[108] [ɔ] predominates, with [ɒ] second and [ɑ] very little used.

[oʊ] is used in monosyllables and syllables with either primary or secondary stress. Examples: *coal* [koʊl], *ratio* [ˈreɪˌʃoʊ], *know* [noʊ], *odor* [ˈoʊdə].

Occasionally, though rarely, [ɜʊ], as in British English, is heard in words of this class.

[o] is used in certain unstressed syllables, typically spelled with *o* and preceding stressed syllables. Examples: *rotation* [roˈteɪʃən], *rotunda* [roˈtʌndə].

Collect other examples. Distinguish words of this class from words of secondary stress, such as *alto* [ˈælˌtoʊ], which use [oʊ]. Distinguish also from words in final unstressed *o* and *ow*, which are pronounced both with [o] and colloquial [ə], as in *potato* [pəˈteɪto, pəˈteɪtə]; *window* [ˈwɪndo, ˈwɪndə].

[e] is used in certain relatively unstressed syllables. Example: *chaotic* [keˈɒtɪk, keˈɑtɪk].

[oə] and [ɔə] are used with the spellings *oar, or, oor, ore,* and *our* in many words. Examples: *oar* [ˈoə, ˈɔə], *ford* [ˈfoəd, ˈfɔəd], *boar* [ˈboə, ˈbɔə], *four*[109] [ˈfoə, ˈfɔə]. [oə] predominates; [ɔ] is occasionally heard, especially in urban speech.

Transcribe. border, chore,[110] clapboards,[111] cord, core,[112] door,[113] gourd, hoard.

[ɔ] and [ˈoə] are used with words spelled with *or* final or preconsonantal in a word or syllable. Examples: *corn*[114] [kɔn, ˈkɔən] *horse*[115] [ˈhoəs, hɔs], *orchard*[116] [ˈɔtʃəd, ˈoətʃəd].

[ɒ] appears as a frequent variant. When this spelling is preceded by a bilabial or alveolar consonant, the vowel is most frequently rendered [ˈoə]. Examples: *porch*[117] [ˈpoətʃ, ˈpɔətʃ, pɔtʃ], *torn*[118] [ˈtoən, ˈtɔən, tɔn].

[u] and [ʊ] are both used for words spelled with *oo* plus consonant, as in all American dialects; but New England favors [ʊ] more than regions elsewhere. *Boot* is probably always [but]; and *hook, cook* and *look* are always [bʊk, kʊk, lʊk]; but both [u] and [ʊ] are used with the following[119] *broom, coop, Cooper, hoof, hoop, nook, proof, roof,*[120] *rook,*

---

[108] *Atlas, 1,* p. 211,   [109] *1,* p. 54.   [110] *1,* p. 217.   [111] *2,* p. 350.   [112] *2,* p. 271.
[113] *2,* p. 347.   [114] *1,* p. 106.   [115] *1,* p. 196; *1,* p. 199 (horseshoes); *1,* p. 109 (horsestable).
[116] *2,* p. 246.   [117] *2,* p. 397.   [118] *3,* p. 665.
[119] C. H. Grandgent, "English in America," *Die Neueren Sprachen.* New York, G. E. Stechert & Company, 1895, *2,* p. 457. This reference contains a list of words of this class.
[120] *Atlas, 2,* p. 348.

room,[121] *rooster, root, spook, woof.* In case of controversy [u] is usually regarded as preferable.

[u]   and [ju] are used with the spellings *eu, ew* and *u* after [d], [t], and [n].[122] Examples: *pneumatic* [nuˈmætɪk, njuˈmætɪk], *dew* [du, dju], *tune* [tun, tjun], *dues*[123] [duz, djuz], *new*[124] [nu, nju], *student*[125] [ˈstudn̩t ˈstjudn̩t], *Tuesday*[126] [ˈtuzdɪ, ˈtjuzdɪ].

   After [l], [s], [z], and [θ], [u] prevails. Examples: *lute* [lut], *assume* [æˈsum], *presume* [prɪˈzum], *enthusiasm* [ɪnˈθuzɪˌæzəm], *suit* [sut].[127] [ju] is used occasionally in these words.

[ʌ],   which is very nearly a central vowel in most American speech, is lowered or lowered and backed in the speech of some New Englanders, especially in eastern and north central New England. Thus, *much* may be pronounced [mʌ˔˕ʧ], which sounds a little like [mɑʧ]. In the word *pluck*[128] a sound as low as [ɑ˔] is fairly frequent; thus [plɑ˔k]. But [plʌk] is by far the most common, with a scattering of [plʌ˕k] and [plʌ˔˕k].

   Transcribe. bulk,[129] bulge,[130] cup,[131] gulley,[132] lugged,[133] mumps,[134] shut,[135] tucked.[136]

   (See word lists, pages 267 and 285.)

The Use of [r] in Eastern Speech

   Except for final and preconsonantal *r* as in *ear* and *remark*, all *r*'s which appear in the spelling are pronounced as *r* (occasionally [ɾ] in linking positions) in standard Eastern speech. The various other ways of rendering orthographic *r* appear in the succeeding paragraphs. "In western New England and in New Brunswick the [preconsonantal and final] *r* is regularly pronounced, in most of eastern New England it is dropped, while the Connecticut valley is mixed and unstable in practice. . . . *r* is gaining ground in the Connecticut valley."[137]

   These pages arbitrarily select as typical the speech of eastern New England, where final and preconsonantal *r* are pronounced [ə] or omitted.

[121] *Atlas, 2,* p. 323 (parlor, sitting room) and p. 337 (bedroom). See also *2,* p. 335 (soot).
[122] *Handbook,* Chart 17, p. 35. "For eastern New England, the simple vowel [u, ʊu] predominates in words of this [*tube, new*] type."
[123] *Atlas, 3,* p. 563. [124] *2,* p. 361 a. [125] *2,* p. 445. [126] *1,* p. 67. [127] *2,* p. 361 a. [128] *1,* p. 209. [129] *3,* p. 55. [130] *2,* p. 362. [131] *1,* p. 133. [132] *1,* p. 37. [133] *1,* p. 165. [134] *3,* p. 507. [135] *2,* p. 347. [136] *2,* p. 481.
[137] Quoted from *Handbook,* Chart 16, p. 34.

[ɜ]   is used as the vowel of monosyllables and the stressed syllables of many words containing *ear, er, ir, or, our, ur,* and *yr.* Examples: *heard* [hɜd], *fern* [fɜn], *kirk* [kɜk], *worth* [wɜθ], *journey* [ˈdʒɜnɪ], *turn* [tɜn], *myrrh* [mɜ].

(See word list, page 295.)

[ʌ]   and [ɜ] are used in a number of words spelled with *o* or *u* plus *rr* plus vowel. Examples: *furrow* [138] [ˈfʌro, ˈfɜro], *curry* [ˈkʌrɪ, ˈkɜrɪ], *worry* [139] [ˈwʌrɪ, ˈwɜrɪ]. Similarly pronounced is *o* plus *r* plus vowel as in *thorough* [ˈθʌro, ˈθɜro].

[ə]   is used for unstressed syllables containing *ar, er, ir, or, our, ur, ure, yr.* Examples: *attar* [ˈætə], *worker* [ˈwɜkə], *tapir* [ˈteɪpə], *color* [ˈkʌlə], *colour* (Canadian spelling) [ˈkʌlə], *sulphur* [ˈsʌlfə], *nature* [ˈneɪtʃə], *satyr* [ˈseɪtə].

[ə]   is used in monosyllables and stressed syllables where *r* is preceded by [ɪ], [ɛ], [æ], [o], [ʊ], or the diphthongs [aɪ] and [aʊ]. Examples:

    1. After [ɪ]:   *tear* [ˈtɪə], *here* [ˈhɪə], *sheer* [ˈʃɪə], *pier* [ˈpɪə].
    2. After [ɛ]:   *there* [ðɛə], *where* [ˈʍɛə].
    3. After [æ]:   *pair* [ˈpæə], *pare* [ˈpæə], *pear* [ˈpæə]. (But these are often [ˈpɛə].)
    4. After [o]:   *ford* [ˈfoəd], *lore* [ˈloə], *board* [ˈboəd]. (But see page 303 for the pronunciation of [ɔə, ɔ] in these words. See also footnote 28, page 284, on the reduction of [oʊə] to [oə].)
    5. After [ʊ]:   *impure* [ɪmˈpjʊə], *assure* [əˈʃʊə].
    6. After [aɪ]:   *require* [rɪˈkwaɪə].
    7. After [aʊ]:   *flour* [ˈflaʊə], *our* [ˈaʊə].

[ə]   or silence is used in monosyllables and stressed syllables where *r* is preceded by [ɔ]. Examples: *chord* [ˈkɔəd, kɔd], *for* [ˈfɔə, fɔ], *remorse* [rɪˈmɔəs, rɪˈmɔs].[140]

[r]   following [ɑ], [a], and [ɜ] is not pronounced. Examples: *tar* [tɑ, ta], *tart* [tɑːt,[141] tat], *dearth* [dɜθ].

(See pages 286 and 317 for additional words in these classes for drill lists.)

---

[138] *Atlas, 1,* p. 123.   [139] *3,* p. 498.
[140] See p. 294 for word list.
[141] The lengthening sign is used here to prevent the ambiguity of transcribing *tart* and *tot* the same way. Of course, the ambiguity would arise only with people who pronounce *tot* as [tat]. For those who pronounce it [tɒt], there would be no ambiguity.

[i], [eɪ], [u], or [ʌ] do not appear before [r] in the same syllable. In combinations where [ɪə] might be expected, the vowel is pronounced [ɪ]. Thus, *near*[142] [ˈnɪə], not [ˈniə]. In an analogous fashion, we have [ɛə], not [eɪə] in *they're here* [ˌðɛə ˈhɪə], not [ˌðeɪə ˈhɪə]; [ʊə], not [uə] in *yours*[143] [ˈjʊəz], not [ˈjuəz]; [ɜ], not [ʌ] in *fur* [fɜ], not [fʌ].

r   is pronounced as [r] between vowels, both in the interior of a word and at the end of a word followed by another word beginning with a vowel. Examples: *far away* [ˌfɑrəˈweɪ], *very* [ˈvɛrɪ], *cherry* [ˈʧɛrɪ].

       NOTE: This is the "linking r." Some speakers, especially in urban centers, pronounce it as the one-tap trill [ɾ].

[ļ]   is used in most words ending in *ile*. Examples: *fertile*[144] [ˈfɜtļ], *futile*[145] [ˈfjutļ]. However, some words, such as *juvenile* and *senile*, are pronounced with both [ļ] and [aɪl].

Clear [l]—that is, [l] made in the front of the mouth—is used with considerable consistency, before and between front vowels. Examples: *lane*[146] [leɪn], *feeling*[147] [fiˈlɪŋ], *Nelly*[148] [ˈnɛlɪ], *Billy*[148] [ˈbɪlɪ]. [ɫ]—that is, dark [l]— is used everywhere else. (See note, page 268, for comment on [ɫ] and note, page 287.)

[ʍ] and [w] are both used in most words spelled with *wh*, except *who*, *whole*, and their derivatives. Examples: *when* [ʍɛn, wɛn], *while*[149] [ʍaɪl, waɪl]; *wheel* [ʍil, wil]; *whet* [ʍɛt, wɛt].

       Transcribe.   what,[150] wheat,[151] wheelbarrow,[152] whip, whinny.[153]

(See lists, pages 268 and 318.)

There is widespread practice of using only primary stress in numerous polysyllabic words, particularly those ending in *ary*, *ery*, *ory*. Examples: *dictionary* [ˈdɪkʃənərɪ], *cemetery*[154] [ˈsɛmətərɪ, ˈsɛmətrɪ], *confectionery* [kənˈfɛkʃənərɪ, kənˈfɛkʃənrɪ], *library*[155] [ˈlaɪbrərɪ, ˈlaɪbrɪ], *territory* [ˈtɛrɪtrɪ, ˈtɛrɪtərɪ]. However, a considerable number of speakers use both primary and secondary stress.

       For a list of words see page 268. See also John Samuel Kenyon, *op. cit.*, pp. 83–86; for a longer list, see 4th ed., 1924, pp. 160–164.

---

[142] *Atlas, 1*, p. 175.   [143] *3*, p. 498.
[144] Kenyon and Knott, *op. cit.*, p. 118.
[145] *Ibid.*, p. 178.
[146] *Atlas, 1*, p. 44.   [147] *3*, p. 493.   [148] *2*, p. 433.   [149] *3*, p. 727.   [150] *3*, p. 561.   [151] *2*, p. 281.   [152] *1*, p. 163.   [153] *1*, p. 179.   [154] *3*, p. 525.   [155] *3*, p. 540.

Deviations from Standard Eastern

Substitution of [æ] *for* [a] *or* [ɑ].   In monosyllables and stressed syllables spelled with *ar* final or followed by a consonant but not preceded by [w], the normal [ɑ] or [a] sometimes is replaced by [æ], so that *cartridge* [156] [ˈkɑtrɪʤ, ˈkatrɪʤ] is pronounced [ˈkætrɪʤ]; *tart* [taːt, tɑːt] is pronounced [tæt]; etc. Obviously, the change is not merely in phoneme but also in the length of the vowels; the duration of [ɑ] and [a], especially the former, has to be shortened considerably when the vowel shifts to the customarily briefer sound [æ].

See page 314 for list of words designed to clarify the ambiguities produced by this pronounciation.

Substitution of [ɜɪ] *for* [aɪ].   Use [aɪ], not [ɜɪ], in words like the following: *flies* [flaɪz], not [flɜɪz]; *mice* [maɪs], not [mɜɪs]; *wife* [157] [waɪf], not [wɜɪf]. This is an archaic survival of British speech brought to America by the colonists. Franklin, who was a Bostonian, used [ɜɪ] for [aɪ].[158]

Transcribe. file, fine, find, grind, hind, kind, line, mile, mine, Nile, pile, pine, ride, rind, sign, wide.

Collect other examples.

Substitution of [oə] *and* [aɪ] *for* [ɔɪ].   Use [ɔɪ], not [oə], in words like the following: *boil* [bɔɪl], not [boəl]; *oil* [159] [ɔɪl], not [oəl].

This pronunciation is found mainly in the extreme south of New England.

[aɪ] is also used rustically in these words, as well as in *point, enjoy*, etc.

Collect other examples.

Transcribe. coil, foil, roil, soil, spoil, toil, joint, loin, enjoyment. See page 271 for discussion of the pronunciation of [aɪ] in such instances.

Substitution of [ʊ] *for* [u].   Use [u], not [ʊ], in words like the following: *spoon* [spun], not [spʊn]; *school* [160] [skul], not [skʊl]; *soon* [sun], not [sʊn]; *Tuesday* [161] [ˈtuzdɪ, ˈtjuzdɪ], not [ˈtʊzdɪ]; *tube* [162] [tub, tjub], not [tʊb].

[156] *Atlas, 1,* p. 161. See also *1,* p. 135 (garbage); *1,* p. 31 (marsh); *2,* p. 413 (harmonica).
[157] *2,* p. 375.
[158] Jared Sparks, ed., *The Works of Benjamin Franklin,* Boston; Tappan and Whittemore, 1838, *6,* pp. 293–303. See also C. M. Wise "Franklin as a Phonetician," *Speech Monographs,* 1948.
[159] *Atlas, 1,* p. 167.   [160] *2,* 444.   [161] *1,* p. 67.   [162] *2,* p. 186.

Substitution of [ʌ] *for* [ɜ]. Use worth [wɜθ], not [wʌθ]; nurse [nɜs], not [nʌs].

Substitution of [ɛ] *for* [æ]. Use have, has, had [hæv, hæs, hæd], not [hɛv, hɛz, hɛd].

Insertion of intrusive linking [r]. The almost invariable use of the linking [r] where a word ends in [r] and is followed by a word beginning with a vowel, induces the insertion of a supernumerary [r] after a word ending in a vowel and followed by another word beginning with a vowel. Thus the correct *far away* [ˌfɑrəˈweɪ, ˌfɑrəˈweɪ] lays the foundation for *the idear of it* instead of the correct form, *the idea of it.* Use *raw oysters*, not *rawr oysters*; *law and order*, not *lawr and order*; *Augusta and Bangor*, not *Augustar and Bangor.* Often the intrusive [r] becomes so associated with the word that it remains attached to it even when no word beginning with a vowel follows. Use *Maria*, not *Mariar*; *Hannah*, not *Hannar*; *sofa*, not *sofar.*

Collect other examples.

Substitution of [tə] *for* [tu] *in final positions.* Use [tu], not [tə] in expressions like the following: *I don't want to* [aɪ doʊnt wɒnt ːu], not [aɪ doʊnt wɒntə]. (Of course, it is perfectly right to unstress *to* in positions other than final, as in *go to town* [goʊ tə taʊn]).

Substitution of [ɵ] *for* [oʊ]. Use [oʊ], not [ɵ], particularly in the following four words: *home* [hoʊm], not [hɵm]; *only* [oʊnlɪ], not [ɵnlɪ]; *stone* [stoʊn], not [stɵn]; *whole* [hoʊl], not [hɵl]. The sound [ɵ] is often called the "New England short *o.*" [163] It is exceedingly prevalent— less so in western Vermont and central and western Massachusetts and Connecticut. It is usually an undiphthongized [o], unrounded and centralized. [ɵ] itself sometimes expands to [ɵə]. See page 313 for list of words for drill.

Collect other examples.

Labialization. There is a fairly widespread tendency toward excessive labialization or lip rounding, appearing as an on-glide or an off-glide [w] attached to a back vowel. The presence of the superfluous sounds often affects the vowel itself, causing it to be more rounded than is normal. Examples: *ague* [164] [ˈeɪgjuw]; *boil* [165] [bwɔəl, bwɔɪl]; *Boston* [ˈbwɒstən]; *boys* [bwɔɪz]; *crib* [166] [kwɪb] (exception); *goal* [167] [guwl]; *down* [168] [dawn]; *humor* [169] [ˈjuˀwmə]; *loose* [170] [luˤws];

---

[163] C. H. Grandgent, "From Franklin to Lowell," *PMLA* (1899), 7: 217. This reference contains a list of words of this class. See also *Handbook*, Chart 1, p. 26.

[164] *Atlas, 3,* p. 505.   [165] *3,* p. 512.   [166] *1,* p. 106.   [167] *3,* p. 585.   [168] *3,* p. 494.   [169] *2,* p. 469.   [170] *3,* p. 555.

music [171] [ˈmjuᵀwzɪk]; *new* [172] [nuw]; *oats* [173] [oᴸwts]; *school* [174] [skʊwl].

Palatalization with vowels. Corresponding to the tendency toward labialization with back vowels is a tendency toward palatalization with front vowels. That is, there appears an off-glide [j] attached to the vowel. The off-glide often palatalizes the vowel itself to an appreciable degree. Examples: *deaf* [175] [dijf], *lay me* [176] [lej mɪj], *lie* [177] [laj], *peeved* [178] [piᵀjvd], *piece* [179] [pijs], *t.b.* [180] [ˈtij ˈbij], *Tennessee* [181] [ˌtɛnɪˈsɪj].

Miscellaneous. *gums*, not [gumz]; *well*, not [wæl, wal]; *faucet*, not [ˈfæsɪt]; *how are you*, not *how be you*; *colonel* [ˈkɜnəl], not [ˈkʌnəl]; *wasn't*, not [want]; *trough* [trɔf], not [trɔθ]; .pasture [ˈpæstʃə], not [ˈpæstə].

To complete the study of this section, it will be necessary to include pages 271 to 281, where substandardisms common to all sections of the country are discussed.

Urban Substandardisms

The section following is based on the speech of New York City.

Parts apply to the speech of other cities, both in the East and elsewhere. Some of the pronunciations originate in foreign accent.

Substitution of [ɪ] *for* [i]. Use [i], not [ɪ], in monosyllables and stressed syllables ending in a consonant in words like the following: *keep* [kip], not [kɪp]; *asleep* [əˈslip], not [əˈslɪp].

Transcribe. beat, creep, deep, feed, heap, keen, keel, leap, meat, need, peel, reel, seed, weed.

Substitution of [ɛ] *or* [ɛə] *for* [æ]. Use [æ], not [ɛ] or [ɛə], in monosyllables and stressed syllables, as in the following: *bat* [bæt], not [bɛt, ˈbɛət]; *passing* [ˈpæsɪŋ], not [ˈpɛsɪŋ, ˈpɛəsɪŋ].

Transcribe. bass, class, dash, fad, fashion, gallon, hack, Jack, lack, mad, nab, pack, sad.

Substitution of [ɛi] *or* [ei] *for* [i]. Use [i], not [ɛi] or [ei], in monosyllables and stressed final syllables ending in [i], as in the following: *agree* [əˈgri], not [əˈgrɛi, əˈgrei]; *me* [mi], not [mɛi, mei].

Transcribe. bee, debris, degree, fee, he, key, knee, Lee, pea, plea, quay, sea, tea, we.

[171] *Atlas, 2*, p. 412.   [172] *1*, p. 111.   [173] *1*, p. 128.   [174] *2*, p. 444.   [175] *3*, p. 502.   [176] *3*, p. 494.   [177] *3*, p. 494.   [178] *2*, p. 472.   [179] *1*, p. 120.   [180] *3*, p. 510.   [181] *1*, p. 16.

Substitution of [ɔ] *for* [ɑ]. Use [ɑ], not [ɔ], in monosyllables and stressed syllables spelled with *ar* final or followed by a consonant but not preceded by [w]. Thus: *car* [kɑ], not [kɔ]; *farmer* [ˈfɑmə], not [ˈfɔmə]. Such words are often pronounced with [r].

Transcribe. art, arbor, bark, cart, card, dark, hark, lard, lark, mar, marble, mark, martyr, park, star.

(See additional list, pages 294 and 295.)

Substitution of [oə] *and* [ɔə] *for* [ɔ]. Use [ɔ], not [oə] or [ɔə], in monosyllables and stressed syllables spelled with *all*, *aul*, or *aw* final, and *all*, *augh*, *aul*, *aw*, or *ough* plus one or more consonants (but not *r*), in words like the following: *call* [kɔl], not [ˈkoəl, ˈkɔəl]; *appall* [əˈpɔl], not [əˈpoəl, əˈpɔəl].

Transcribe. all, bought, caught, daughter, fault, fought, haughty, law, naughty, ought, Paul, raw, saw, taught, thought, wall, walled, wrought.

Substitution of [ɑ] *for* [ʌ]. Use *some* [sʌm], not [sɑm]; *up* [ʌp], not [ɑp].

Transcribe. bun, done, fun, gum, jump, just, love, run, son, sun, won.

Substitution of [ɒɪ, ɑɪ] *for* [aɪ]. Use [aɪ], not [ɒɪ, ɑɪ], in words such as the following: *I* [aɪ], not [ɒɪ, ɑɪ]; *my* [maɪ], not [mɒɪ, mɑɪ].

Transcribe. buy, die, dye, dyke, fight, fly, guide, hide, high, cider, kind, lie, live, mine, night, pike, pine, quiet, ripe, rise, side, sigh, size, tie, tide, tile, time, vine, wide.

Substitution of [ɜɪ, ɔɪ] *for* [ɜ]. Use [ɜ], not [ɜɪ, ɔɪ], in words spelled with *ear*, *er*, *ir*, *or*, *our*, *ur*, *yr*, plus consonant, in words such as the following: *bird* [bɜd], not [bɜɪd, bɔɪd]; *certain* [ˈsɜtn̩], not [ˈsɜɪtn̩, ˈsɔɪtn̩].

Transcribe. burn, burst, burly, circle, curl, dermis, dirt, fern, firm, flirt, further, germ, Germany, girl, girder, girdle, heard, herd, hurl, Herkimer, jerk, journal, journey, Kirk, kirtle, learn, Lerner, mirth, murder, myrtle, pearl, serve, serge, sermon, skirt, turn, urn, verge, Virgil, word, work, worth.

Substitution of [ɜɪ], [ɝ] *for* [ɔɪ]. Use [ɔɪ], not [ɜɪ] or [ɝ], in words spelled with *oi* or *oy* plus consonant. Examples: *boil* [bɔɪl], not [bɜɪl, bɝl]; *poison* [ˈpɔɪzn̩], not [ˈpɜɪzn̩, ˈpɝzn̩].

Transcribe. coil, Coit, Doyle, foil, goiter, hoist, hoyden, join, joint, joist, loin, moist, oil, ointment, oyster, point, soil, spoil, toil, void.

Substitution of [ɪu, ɛu] *for* [u].   Use [u], not [ɪu, ɛu], in words or stressed syllables ending in [u], such as the following: *do* [du], not [dɪu, dɛu]; *true* [tru], not [trɪu, trɛu].

   Transcribe.   clue, crew, flue, too, two, shrew.

Substitution of [əm] *for* [ɪm], *etc.*   Use only [ɪm], not [əm], for the unstressed form of the word *him.* Use only [ə] for the unstressed *her,* and [ɪt] for *it.* Thus, *I caught him* [aɪ kɔt ɪm], not [aɪ kɔt əm]. (See discussion of [əm] for *her* and *it,* page 277).

Unvoicing final voiced consonants.   Use [d], not [t], in words like the following: *bad* [bæd], not [bæt] or [ˈbɛət]; *side* [saɪd], not [saɪt].

   Transcribe.   bed, bid, cede, died, goad, head, hide, hoed, killed, lad, led, mowed, neighed, paid, piled, posed, stayed, wade.

   Use [v], not [f], in words like the following: *have* [hæv], not [hæf] or [ˈhɛəf]; *live* (v.) [lɪv], not [lɪf].

   Transcribe.   brave, cave, drove, eve, gave, give, heave, hive, live (adj.), love, move, prove, strive, strove, verve, weave, wove.

   Use [z], not [s], in words like the following: *goes* [gouz], not [gous]; *is* [ɪz], not [ɪs].

   Transcribe.   bays, bees, boys, days, dies, doze, flays, flees, flies, froze, gaze, goes, haze, hose, jays, Joe's, Jews, keys, knows, lies, mows, news, nose, pays, peas, peruse, pose, rose, says, sews, ways.

   Use [b], not [p], in words like the following: *robe* [roub], not [roup]; *rib* [rɪb], not [rɪp].

   Transcribe.   cab, daub, ebb, gab, hub, job, lobe, Mab, nab, probe, rub, stab.

Substitution of [t] *for* [θ], *and* [d] *for* [ð].   These are aspects of foreign accent or of street-gamin talk. An immigrant may make the substitutions in any words spelled with *th,* but the street gamin will do so only with a limited number of frequently used words, such as the following: Use *the* [ðə, ðɪ][182] not [də, dɪ]; *this* [ðɪs], not [dɪs]; *that* [ðæt], not [dæt], [ˈdɛət]; *these* [ðiz], not [diz]; *those* [ðouz], not [douz]; *thing* [θɪŋ], not [tɪŋ]; *nothing* [ˈnʌθɪŋ], not [ˈnʌtn̩].

   Transcribe.   bath, bathroom, both, bother, brother, death, father, mother, other, than, thick, thin, think, thumb, tooth, whether.

[182] [ə] before consonants, [ɪ] before vowels.

Affrication.[183]   Use [t] and [d] only, not [ts] and [dz], for initial [t] and [d]. Thus *tool* [tul], not [tsul]; *dome* [doʊm], not [dzoʊm].

>*Transcribe.*   tale, tame, teal, tide, told, dame, deal, dime, door, doom.

Intrusive [g] *or* [k] *after* [ŋ].   Use [ŋ] only, not [ŋg] or [ŋk] in most words spelled with *ng*. Thus, *Long Island* [ˈlɔŋ ˈaɪlənd], not [ˈlɔŋ ˈgaɪlənd]; *nothing* [ˈnʌθɪŋ], not [ˈnɑθɪŋk].

>*Transcribe.*   bringing, calling, coming, darling, evening, flinging, going, hoisting, imagining, jumping, longing, morning, nursing, opening, playing, ringing, singing, thronging, working.

>Exceptions: *linger* [ˈlɪŋgə], and words such as those in the following paragraph.

Omission of [g].   Use [ŋg], not [ŋ] alone, in words like the following: *English* [ˈɪŋglɪʃ], not [ˈɪŋlɪʃ]; *finger* [ˈfɪŋgə], not [ˈfɪŋə].

>*Transcribe.*   bangle, Bangor, dangle, jangle, jingle, jungle, languor, linger, longer, longest, mangle, mingle, monger, single, singlet, stronger, strongest, tangle, tingle, wrangle.

The glottal stop.   The glottal stop is not phonemic in English. Do not substitute it for any plosive. Thus, *cattle* [ˈkætl̩], not [ˈkæ ʔl̩]; *little* [ˈlɪtl̩], not [ˈlɪ ʔl̩].

>*Transcribe.*   bacon, battle, bottle, chatter, doctor, fattest, fiddle, fittest, gentle, hottest, latter, middle, patter, sitter, tattle, water, written.

Substitution of [v] *for* [r].   Use plosive plus [r], not [v], in words such as the following: *precede* [priˈsid], not [pviˈsid].

>*Transcribe.*   pretend, prevent, privacy, protect, prudent.

>Use [r, ɾ] not [v], between vowels in words like the following: *very* [ˈvɛrɪ, ˈvɛɾɪ], not [ˈvɛvɪ].

>*Transcribe.*   berry, bury, fairy, ferry, furry, merry, Perry, parry, weary.

Voicing of final [s].   Use [s], not [z], in words like the following, where the word or syllable following [s] begins with a vowel or a voiced consonant: *baseball* [ˈbeɪsˌbɔl], not [ˈbeɪzˌbɔl]; *gas mask* [ˈgæsˌmæsk], not [ˈgæzˌmæsk], [ˈgɛəzˌmɛəsk].

>*Transcribe.*   bass voice, case of samples, face down, lace gloves, loose ends, nice baby, piece goods, this man.

---

[183] An affricate is a sound composed of a plosive plus a fricative. The most common examples in English are [ʧ] as in *catch* [kæʧ] and [ʤ] as in *July* [ʤulaɪ].

Substitution of [ʃ] *for* [stʃ].   Use [stʃ], not [ʃ], in words spelled with *stion*. Thus, *question* [ˈkwɛstʃ ən], not [ˈkwɛʃən].

   Transcribe. bastion, digestion, indigestion, ingestion, questionable, suggestion.

Omission of [h] *in* [hj].[184]   Do not omit [h] in the pronunciation of words spelled with *h* plus *ew, u, ue*, such as the following: *Hugh* [hju], not [ju].

   Transcribe. Hume, humid, hue, hew, Hudibras, Huguenot. (See additional words of this class, page 278.)

Substitution of [ʧ] *for* [ʤ].   Use [ʤ], not [ʧ], in words such as the following: *Coolidge* [ˈkulɪʤ], not [ˈkulɪʧ]; *James* [ʤeɪmz], not [ʧeɪms].

   Transcribe. age, bridge, budge, cabbage, cottage, college, courage, dirge, edge, gem, gist, Hodges, jail, jelly, Jim, joke, Jukes, Madge, passage, porridge, rate, ridge, sage, sedge, sludge, wedge.

Exercises

Pronounce with [oʊ], not [ɵ] or [ɵə].[185]

boat	Polk
both	polka
coat	post
colt	road
Holmes	spoke

Pronounce with [ɔɪ], not [aɪ], [ɜɪ] or [ɝ]

boil	roil	goiter	oysters
oil	soil	point	joist
buoyant	spoil	moil	moist
buoy	foil	toil	hoist
join	coin	coil	joy
enjoy	employ	choice	rejoice

Pronounce with [u], not [ʊ].[186]

spoon	groom	rooster	food
soon	proof	root	bloom

[184] It will be recognized, of course, that many of the words of this class are pronounced in English with [ç] as well as with [hj]. Thus, *huge* [hjuʤ, çuʤ].

[185] See C. H. Grandgent, "From Franklin to Lowell," p. 217.

[186] See C. H. Grandgent, *Die Neueren Sprachen, 2,* p. 457.

Distinguish between [ɪ] and [i]:

dill	deal	dim	deem
fill	feel	Glynn	glean
grid	greed	grit	greet
hip	heap	lid	lead
list	leased	live	leave
mit	meet, meat	rid	read, reed
rill	reel	sick	seek
sin	seen	sip	seep
sit	seat	slit	sleet
tick	teak (wood)	till	teal
tin	'teen	did	deed
dip	deep	fill	feel
flit	fleet	pitch	peach
rich	reach	still	steal

Distinguish between [ɑ—a] and [æ]:

bard	bad	heart	hat
card	cad	lark	lack
cart	cat	marred	mad
pard	pad	part	pat

Pronounce with [u], not [ɪu] or [ɛu].

to	noon	true
too	soon	through
two	rune	moon
do	blue	root

Stage Speech

It has already been explained that the accepted model for stage speech is the South-of-England or educated London speech. This dialect has many points in common with General American speech, more with Southern speech, and most of all with Eastern speech.

Standard Southern British, or Stage Speech[187]

[ɪ]   is generally used in the suffixes *ace, ain, ate, ed, eit, eon, en* (if the stem contains a front vowel), *es, ess, et, ice, id, ip, is, ist, it, ite, uce, ute.*

[187] Use Daniel Jones, *op. cit.*, and the word lists in this book. Disregard ordinary dictionaries entirely as guides for stage speech.

Examples: *palace* ['pælɪs], *plantain* ['plæntɪn], *prelate* ['prɛlɪt], *stinted* ['stɪntɪd], *forfeit* ['fɔfɪt], *chicken* ['tʃɪkɪn], *pigeon* ['pɪdʒɪn, 'pɪdʒən], *boxes* ['bɒksɪz], *careless* ['kɛəlɪs], *pocket* ['pɒkɪt], *Alice* ['ælɪs], *stolid* ['stɒlɪd], *coffin* ['kɒfɪn], *Philip* ['fɪlɪp], *crisis* ['kraɪsɪs], *tourist* ['tʊrɪst], *vomit* ['vɒmɪt], *definite* ['dɛfɪnɪt], *lettuce* ['lɛtɪs], *minute* ['mɪnɪt].

Transcribe. necklace, curtain, palate, wanted, kitchen, ashes, ruthless, bracket, chalice, pallid, puffin, fillip, basis, purist, limit, infinite.

[ɪ] is generally used for *e, i,* and *y* in medial syllables. Examples: *telephone* ['tɛlɪˌfoʊn, 'tɛlɪˌfɜʊn], *ability* [ə'bɪlɪtɪ], *paralysis* [pə'rælɪsɪs].

Transcribe. agility, analysis, calibrate, dominate, telegram, telegraph, telepath, telescope, televise.

[ə] is also used in words spelled with *y.* Example: *paralysis* [pə'ræləsɪs].

[ɛ] is used in a large number of words spelled with *air, are, ear.* Examples: *fairy* ['fɛrɪ], *hare* ['hɛə], *bear* ['bɛə]. But analogous words in *ar* and *arr* plus a vowel are pronounced with [æ], as in *paradox* ['pærəˌdɒks], *marry* ['mærɪ].

Transcribe. air, bare, care, carry, dare, fair, fare, hair, lair, mare, pair, parallel, pare, pear, tare, tarry, tear, wear.

[ɑ] is used in "broad *a*" words, i.e., in certain words most of which are spelled with *a* plus [f] ([v] in plurals), [s], [θ] ([ð] in plurals), and *n* plus consonant. Examples: *calf* [kɑf], *calves* [kɑvz], *pass* [pɑs], *path* [pɑθ], *paths* [pɑðz], *dance* [dɑns]. (Note: British phoneticians do not use [t] in transcribing *dance, fence, sense,* etc.) Some spellings do not fall exactly under these categories, like *aunt* [ɑnt], *banana* [bə'nɑnə], *example* [ɪg'zɑmpl̩,] *rather* ['rɑðə]. (See previous references to broad *a,* pages 265, 282, 301.) (See pages 318, 319, 320 for a long list of words.)

[ɑ] is used in most monosyllables and stressed syllables for *ar* final or preconsonantal but not preceded by [w]. Examples: *far* [fɑ], *farm* [fɑm].

Transcribe. arm, barn, carter, darn, farther, garden, hard, hearth, jar, large, marker, part, tarpon, varnish.

[ɔ] when spelled with *all, aul,* or *aw* final in the syllable and with *al, augh, aul, aw,* or *ough,* plus one or more consonants, is pronounced with the tongue higher in the mouth than for the American [ɔ]. It suggests [o] to American ears. Thus, all [ɔ˕l] suggests [oːl].

Transcribe. ought, ball, bought, call, caught, dawn, daughter, fall, fought, hall, haul, haughty, law, naught, saw, Saul, sought, tall, taught, wall, walled, wrought.

[ɔ] is used in a large number of words spelled with *oar, oor, ore, our.* Examples: *board* [bɔd], *door* [dɔ], *more* [mɔ], *four* [fɔ].

> *Transcribe.* boar, coarse, core, course, deplore, fourteen, gore, hoard, lore, pore, pour, roar, soar, sore, tore, wore.

[ɒ] is used for "short *o*," and in many instances where *a* in *wa, wha,* and *qua* represents a vowel of briefer duration. Examples: *hot* [hɒt], *not* [nɒt], *common* ['kɒmən], *wad* [wɒd], *what* [wɒt], *squalid* ['skwɒlɪd].

> *Transcribe.* bottle, cottage, gobble, hod, homonym, job, jot, knot, lot, mottle, pot, rob, rod, stop, squat, totter, waddle, wallop, whatever.

[ɔ] is used in *wash* [wɔʃ], *watch* [wɔtʃ], and *water* ['wɔtə].

[oʊ] and [ɜʊ] are used in monosyllables and stressed syllables where only [oʊ] would be used in nearly all American English. [oʊ] is used exclusively by Jones,[188] but [ɜʊ] probably actually predominates in southern British and stage speech. Examples: *coast* [koʊst, kɜʊst], *no* [noʊ, nɜʊ], *smoke* [smoʊk, smɜʊk].

> *Transcribe.* boast, code, dole, foal, ghost, home, joke, load, most, mould, note, oath, post, rode, sold, told, though, vote, won't.

[ʌ] is lower and farther back than the usual American [ʌ]. It suggests [ɑ] to American ears. Thus, *much* [mʌᵀʳtʃ] suggests [mɑtʃ].

> *Transcribe.* above, bud, bunch, buck, come, cup, cut, dove, dust, funnel, govern, hut, jungle, just, jut, love, lust, must, nut, one, pun, puppy, rust, tub, up, won.

[ɜ] is used in many monosyllables and stressed syllables containing *ear, er, ir, or, our, ur, yr.* Examples: *heard* [hɜd], *herd* [hɜd], *whirl* [wɜl, ʍɜl], *worthy* ['wɜðɪ], *adjourn* [ə'dʒɜn], *furl* [fɜl], *Myrtle* ['mɜtl].

> *Transcribe.* bird, bur, burn, burst, curd, curl, dearth, dermal, dirty, durst, earth, early, err, fern, fir, firm, German, gird, her, hermit, irk, jerk, journey, Kirk, learn, murky, murmur, nerve, pearls, service, term, turkey, vernal, were, world.

[ə] is used for unstressed syllables ending in *ar, er, ir, or, our, ur, ure, yr.* Examples: *tartar* ['tɑtə], *worker* ['wɜkə], *fakir* ['feɪkə], *rector* ['rɛktə], *flavour* (British and Canadian spelling) ['fleɪvə], *murmur* ['mɜmə], *feature* ['fitʃə], *martyr* ['mɑtə].

> *Transcribe.* attar, barter, copper, debtor, earlier, firmer, girder, humor, joker, kicker, liquor, murmur, neighbor, odor, pastor, starter, tapir, vapor, warder.

---

[188] *An English Pronouncing Dictionary, q.v.*

[ə] is used for *r* when orthographic *r* appears in a monosyllable or stressed syllable following [ɪ], [ɛ], [ʊ], [aɪ], [aʊ]. Examples: *hear* [ˈhɪə], *there* [ˈðɛə], *poor* [ˈpʊə], *ire* [ˈaɪə], *our* [ˈaʊə].

Transcribe. appear, bier, dear, dour, dire, fire, flour, hire, hour, leer, Lear, lyre, mere, mire, near, peer, pyre, rear, sear, sire, sour, tear, their, tour, tire, veer, where.

[ə] or omission of *r* occurs after [ɔ] in monosyllables and stressed syllables. Omission predominates. Examples: *bore* [bɔ, ˈbɔə], *course* [kɔs, ˈkɔəs], *court* [kɔt, ˈkɔət]. (For a list of words for drill, see page 295.)

Silence is used for *r* final or plus consonant in monosyllables and stressed syllables after [ɑ], [ɜ]. Examples: *bar* [bɑ], *stir* [stɜ]. (See pages 294, 295, 296 for drill lists.)

NOTE: [r] does not appear in the same syllable after [i], [eɪ], [u], [ʌ]. For discussion see page 286.

[ɾ] is used for *r* intervocalically within a word, and at the end of a word followed by another word beginning with a vowel. Examples: *berry* [ˈbɛɾɪ], *far away* [ˌfɑɾəˈweɪ].

Transcribe. bury, carry, courage, dairy, erring, furry [fʌɾɪ], fury, garnish, hoary, hurry, Jerry, Kerry, lorry, merry, nearing, oration, pouring, quarry, rearing, sparing, tarry, very, weary, where are you, there are four, her aunt.

[aɪl] is used for the suffix *ile*, as in *reptile* [ˈrɛpˌtaɪl].

Transcribe. fertile, futile, juvenile, prehensile, senile, versatile.

[l] is clear (front, dental) before front vowels, as in *lean* [lin] and *lily* [ˈlɪlɪ]. Clear [l] may be practiced by saying [li]. This syllable brings the tongue into the correct position. (Except before front vowels, [l] is dark, i.e., [ɫ].)

Transcribe. believe, deliver, labor, lady, blade, leave, let, little, lift, live.

[ju] is used in a large number of words where the spellings *eu*, *ew*, and *u* follow [d], [t], [n], [θ], [s], [z] and (less frequently) [l].[189] Examples: *dew* [dju], *duke* [djuk], *tune* [tjun], *neutral* [ˈnjutrəl], *new* [nju], *thews* [θjuz], *enthusiasm* [ɪnˈθjuzɪˌæzəm], *assume* [əˈsjum], *presume* [prɪˈzjum], *absolute* [ˌæbsəˈljutlɪ].

Transcribe. absolution, constitution, due, duty, endure, lute, neural, newspaper, pursue, pneumatic, enthusiastic, suit, resume.

---

[189] [u] is predominant after [l].

[w]   and [ʍ] are used for most words spelled with *wh* (except *who, whole* and their derivatives). [w] predominates. Examples: *what* [wɒt, ʍɒt]; *when* [wɛn, ʍɛn], *which* [wɪtʃ, ʍɪtʃ], *whopper* [ˈwɒpə, ˈʍɒpə].

> *Transcribe.* whack, whale, wharf, Wharton, wheat, wheedle, wheel, wheeze, whelk, overwhelm, where, whet, whether, whiff, whig, while, whim, whip, whir, whirl, whisker, whiskey, whisper, whit, white.

Medial [t] is aspirate, as in *city* [ˈsɪtˈɪ]. It does not weaken to [d] or [ɾ] as in the common American pronunciations [ˈsɪdɪ, sɪɾɪ].

> *Transcribe.* attitude, bitter, ditty, fettle, getting, hotter, jotting, kettle, kitten, natty, patty, ratty, settle, witty.

The assimilation of [s] to [ʃ], as in American *issue* [ˈɪʃu], *tissue* [ˈtɪʃu], while sometimes used, is avoided, [ˈɪsju], [ˈtɪsju] being preferred.

Several words retain an archaic pronunciation of *e* before *r* which is known in American English in the word *sergeant* [ˈsadʒənt, ˈsɑrdʒənt]. Some of these are *clerk* [klɑːk], *derby* [ˈdabɪ], *Berkeley* [ˈbaklɪ], *Hertfordshire* [ˈhɑfədʃə].

> Collect other examples.

Certain pronunciations do not readily fall into categories. Some of these are *ate* [ɛt], *been* [bin], *either* [ˈaɪðə], *neither* [ˈnaɪðə], *nephew* [ˈnɛvju], *again* [əˈgeɪn], *against* [əˈgeɪnst], *tomato* [təˈmato], *record* (n.) [ˈrɛkˌɔd], *lieutenant* (army) [lɛfˈtɛnənt], *schedule* [ˈʃɛdˌjul].

> Collect other examples.

Polysyllables have secondary stress less often than in American English. In comparison, this is especially noticeable in words in *ary, ery, ory*. The vowels in parentheses below tend often to drop out, whereupon, [ɾ] becomes [r]. Examples: *extraordinary* [ɪkˈstrɔdən(ə)rɪ], *territory* [ˈtɛrɪt(ə)rɪ], *stationery* [ˈsteɪʃən(ə)rɪ].

> *Transcribe.* advertisement, apiary, aviary, circumstances, confectionery, dormitory, lavatory, library, necessary, ordinary, statutory.[190]

> Collect other examples.

The following lists of words will give specific practice in stage diction as compared with the other forms of speech prevalent in America.

[ɑ] *and* [æ]	*General American*	*Southern, Eastern*	*Eastern, British, Stage*
behalf	bɪhæf	bɪhæf	bɪhaf
telegraph	tɛləgræf	tɛləgræf	tɛlɪgraf

[190] See Kenyon, *op. cit.*, pp. 83–86; for longer list, see 4th ed., 1924, pp. 160–164.

[a] *and* [æ]	*General American*	*Southern, Eastern*	*Eastern, British, Stage*
staff	stæf	stæf	staf
after	æftɚ	æftə	aftə
laughter	læftɚ	læftə	laftə
bath	bæθ	bæθ	baθ
path	pæθ	pæθ	paθ
hath	hæθ	hæθ	hæθ
wrath	ræθ	ræθ	raθ
craft	kræft	kræft	kraft
shaft	ʃæft	ʃæft	ʃaft
waft	wæft	wæft	waft
rather	ræðɚ	ræðə	raðə
brass	bræs	bræs	bras
glass	glæs	glæs	glas
grass	græs	græs	gras
pass	pæs	pæs	pas
class	klæs	klæs	klas
classic	klæsɪk	klæsɪk	klæsɪk
ask	æsk	æsk	ask
cask	kæsk	kæsk	kask
task	tæsk	tæsk	task
flask	flæsk	flæsk	flask
mask	mæsk	mæsk	mask
clasp	klæsp	klæsp	klasp
grasp	græsp	græsp	grasp
blast	blæst	blæst	blast
cast(e)	kæst	kæst	kast
(re)past	pæst	pæst	past
shan't	ʃænt	ʃænt	ʃant
fast	fæst	fæst	fast
last	læst	læst	last
mast	mæst	mæst	mast
vast	væst	væst	vast
castle	kæsl̩	kæsl̩	kasl̩
master	mæstɚ	mæstə	mastə
nasty	næstɪ	næstɪ	nastɪ
pastor	pæstɚ	pæstə	pastə
example	ɪgzæmpl̩	ɪgzæmpl̩	ɪgzampl̩
command	kəmænd	kəmænd	kəmand
demand	dɪmænd	dɪmænd	dɪmand

[ɑ] *and* [æ]	*General American*	*Southern, Eastern*	*Eastern, British, Stage*
hand	hænd	hænd	hænd
and	ænd	ænd	ænd
remand	rɪmænd	rɪmænd	rɪmɑnd
reprimand	rɛprəmænd	rɛprəmænd	rɛprɪmɑnd
advance	ədvænts	ədvænts	ədvɑns
chance	tʃænts	tʃænts	tʃɑns
dance	dænts	dænts	dɑns
fancy	fæntsɪ	fæntsɪ	fænsɪ
France	frænts	frænts	frɑns
glance	glænts	glænts	glɑns
lance	lænts	lænts	lɑns
answer	æntsɚ	æntsə	ɑnsə
aunt	ænt	ænt	ɑnt
can	kæn	kæn	kæn
can't	kænt	kænt	kɑnt
cant	kænt	kænt	kænt
chant	tʃænt	tʃænt	tʃɑnt
grant	grænt	grænt	grɑnt
branch	bræntʃ	bræntʃ	brɑntʃ
body	bɑdɪ	bɑdɪ	bɒdɪ
common	kɑmən	kɑmən	kɒmen
concrete	kɑnkrit	kɑnkrit	kɒn(ŋ)krit
copy	kɑpɪ	kɑpɪ	kɒpɪ
fond	fɑnd	fɑnd	fɒnd
fox	fɑks	fɑks	fɒks
honest	ɑnəst	ɑnɪst	ɒnɪst
John	dʒɑn	dʒɑn	dʒɒn
lot	lɑt	lɑt	lɒt
not	nɑt	nɑt	nɒt
pocket	pɑkət	pɑkɪt	pɒkɪt
pond	pɑnd	pɑnd	pɒnd
possible	pɑsəbl̩	pɑsəbl̩	pɒsɪbl̩
Robert	rɑbət	rɑbət	rɒbət
stop	stɑp	stɑp	stɒp
swallow	swɑlo	swɑlo	swɒlo

Chapter VI

The Linguistic Basis
of Speech

Introduction

There is, in the usual understanding of the term, a certain redundancy in speaking of the linguistic basis of speech. But in the sense of this discussion there is none, for the reference here is to certain selected linguistic facts, chosen to serve as one of the bases for college speech study.

As stated in Chapter V, linguistics is a very inclusive term, capable of embracing almost any phase of language study. Accordingly, it is customarily limited or qualified. Thus we have *comparative linguistics*, a comparison of the various languages of the earth; *historical linguistics*, a "diachronic" or chronological study of a language or languages; and *descriptive linguistics*, also more technically called *structural linguistics*, a "synchronic" study of a language, now usually as of current date. A brief introductory account of descriptive linguistics constitutes a portion of this chapter.

Any of these varieties of linguistic study may include sections on phonetics, phonemics, and morphology, as will be seen presently in the account of descriptive linguistics. Some may take up etymology, the "laws" of sound change, linguistic geography, semantics, syntax, inflection, graphemics, speech science, or information theory. There are yet other fields of study which are either linguistic or related to linguistics. And there are certainly many metalinguistic terms[1] clustering about the foregoing terms, as when What-mough[2] equates the whole field of the mechanics of language with glosso-

---

[1] Metalinguistics as used here is "a language used to make assertions about another language." Cf. Einar Haugen, "New directions in linguistics," *Language* (July–September, 1951) *27*: 211–212.

[2] Joshua Whatmough, *Language*, New York, St. Martin's Press, 1956, p. 199.

dynamics and glossostatics, and a part of the field with information theory. Obviously the divisions of linguistics overlap; it is difficult to prevent the parts of so large a subject from encroaching upon one another.

Out of the many aspects of linguistics named or implied here, departments of speech have, during the last quarter-century or more, adopted into their curricula several important segments of the subject. These have included speech science (cf. Chapters II, III, and IV), phonetics (cf. Chapter V), semantics and general semantics (cf. Chapter IX), descriptive linguistics, linguistic geography, languages of the world, and language change, the last four of which are taken up in this chapter.

Descriptive Linguistics

Historical Background

Linguistic thought is as old as the Rosetta stone, Pānini's Sanskrit grammar, Aristotle's discussions of number and case, the library at Alexandria, and the translation of the Old Testament into the Greek Septuagint. But linguistics as we think of it began to take unique form in the first half of the nineteenth century, through the comparative studies of Rasmus Rask, Jacob Grimm, Franz Bopp, August Friedrich Pott, and August Schleicher; later of Herman Paul and the Junggrammatiker, who debated the existence of invariable laws governing sound change under the cryptic question: "Giebt es Lautgesetze?" and of Wilhelm Wundt and the psychologists, who groped for the ultimate origins of speech. These and the many other nineteenth-century writers were mainly historical linguists. Structural linguists were yet to come. The historical linguists were preoccupied with the study of the well-known European languages. Their work had great merit, but its approach was bound by the strait jacket of traditional Latin and Greek grammar.[3]

More Recent History

Late in the second half of the nineteenth century, Franz Boas (1850–1942), Arctic explorer, tropical archaeologist, Indianologist, and for thirty-seven years after 1899 a professor of anthropology at Columbia University, "turned toward language as a primary source of insight into ethnology. Boas . . . concentrated on accurate language description. Since from the point of view of

[3] C. M. Wise and Ruth Hirsch, "Directions in linguistics," *The Quarterly Journal of Speech* (April, 1953), *39*: 225–226.

another language, any language is arbitrary in its classification, it reflects its speakers' culture, which then may be studied from the language point of view." [4]

During the first half of the twentieth century, Edward Sapir (1884–1939), anthropologist and Indianologist, taught at the Universities of California and Pennsylvania, worked in the Canadian National Museum, taught again at the University of Chicago, and finally became a professor of anthropology and linguistics at Yale.

Sapir also viewed language in its cultural context. . . . He went further, however, by prefiguring phonemic principles. Sapir realized that the sounds of language are not a haphazard agglomeration, but that they are "structured"; that every language has only a relatively small number of these structured sound features, i.e., phonemes; and that these structured units appear in patterns characteristically different in every language. This concept of structure is Sapir's great contribution to modern linguistic science. [5]

It remained for Benjamin Lee Whorf (1897–1941) to put the capstone, as it were, on the thinking of Boas and Sapir on the interrelation of language and culture. If Whorf had not been an insurance man investigating fire damage, scores of today's linguists could never have told their classes of his inspired observation that people behave toward empty gasoline drums as if the drums were really empty, and not, instead, full of explosive vapor, ready to be ignited by the first match or cigarette. And if he had not been a student of Sapir, he never would have studied Hopi, and so never would have reported on how unique a Hopi's thought processes on plurals have to be. For him

. . . plurals and cardinals are only for entities that form or can form an objective group. There are no imaginary plurals, but instead ordinals used with singulars. Such an expression as "ten days" is not used. The equivalent statement is an operational one that reaches one day by a suitable count. "They stayed ten days" becomes "they stayed until the eleventh day" or "they left after the tenth day." "Ten days is greater than nine days" becomes "the tenth day is later than the ninth." Our "length of time" is not regarded as a length but as a relation between two events in lateness. Instead of our linguistically promoted objectification of that datum of consciousness we call "time," the Hopi language has not laid down any pattern that would cloak the subjective "becoming later" that is the essence of time. [6]

[4] *Ibid.*
[5] *Ibid.*
[6] Benjamin Lee Whorf, "The relation of thought and behavior to language," *Language, Culture, and Personality*, p. 31. Reprinted in *Four Articles on Metalinguistics*, Washington, D.C., Foreign Service Institute, Department of State, 1950.

Overlapping Boas, Sapir, and Whorf is the life of Leonard Bloomfield (1887–1949), famous teacher at the University of Chicago (1927–1940) and at Yale (1940–1949). By reason of the excellence and the timeliness of his great book, *Language* (1933), he became the true founder of modern American linguistics. "From Sapir came the notion of patterning, yet to Bloomfield belongs the real credit for formulating the American approach to phonemics . . ."[7] If with Boas, Sapir, and Whorf the necessity of linguistics in anthropology became axiomatic, with Bloomfield the foundations of what nowadays has come to be called "rigorous methodology" in linguistic work were either demonstrated or foreshadowed.

Modern Linguistic Writings

Recent years have seen a steady stream of books and articles by American linguists. A restricted chronological list follows:

W. Freeman Twaddell, *On Defining the Phoneme*: Language Monographs No. 16, Baltimore, Linguistic Society of America, 1942, 62 pp.

Bernard Bloch and George L. Trager, *Outline of Linguistic Analysis*, Baltimore, Linguistic Society of America, 1942, 82 pp.

Kenneth L. Pike, *Phonetics*, Ann Arbor, University of Michigan Press, 1943, 182 pp.

Kenneth L. Pike, *Phonemics*: *A Technique of Reducing Languages to Writing*, Ann Arbor, University of Michigan Press, 1947, 254 pp.

Martin Joos, *Acoustic Phonetics*: Language Monograph No. 23, Baltimore, Linguistic Society of America, 1948, 136 pp.

George L. Trager, *The Field of Linguistics*, Studies in Linguistics: Occasional Papers, No. 1, Norman, Okla., The Battenberg Press, 1949.

Eugene A. Nida, *Morphology*, 2nd ed., Ann Arbor, University of Michigan Press, 1949, 342 pp.

George L. Trager and Henry Lee Smith, Jr., *An Outline of English Structure*, Studies in Linguistics: Occasional Papers, No. 3, Norman, Okla., Battenberg Press, 1951, 92 pp.

Zellig H. Harris, *Methods in Structural Linguistics*, Chicago, University of Chicago Press, 1951, 384 pp.

H. A. Gleason, *Introduction to Structural Linguistics*, New York, Henry Holt and Company, 1955, 389 pp.

Joshua Whatmough, *Language*, New York, St. Martin's Press, 1956.

Archibald A. Hill, *Introduction to Linguistic Structures*, New York, Harcourt, Brace and Company, 1958, 496 pp.

[7] Archibald A. Hill, "Linguistics since Bloomfield," *Quarterly Journal of Speech* (October, 1955), *41*: 253.

Charles F. Hockett, *A Course in Modern Linguistics*, New York, The Macmillan Company, 1958, 621 pp.

Harold B. Allen, *Readings in Applied English Linguistics*, New York, Appleton-Century-Crofts, Inc., 1958, 428 pp.

W. Nelson Francis, *The Structure of American English*, New York, The Ronald Press Company, 1958, 614 pp.

Most of the recent articles on linguistics will be found in the following magazines: *Acta Linguistica, American Speech, Archivum Linguisticum, Folia Phoniatrica, International Journal of American Linguistics, Journal of the Acoustical Society of America, Language, Lingua, Maître Phonétique, Publications of the American Dialect Society, PMLA, The Quarterly Journal of Speech, Studies in Linguistics, Word.*

Phonetics

Phonetics is an orderly study of significant speech sounds. It uses an alphabet, usually the International Phonetic Alphabet (IPA), which avoids the ambiguities of ordinary spelling, where one letter may represent several sounds, and one sound may be represented by several spellings. It not only uses symbols for phonemes, but also uses freely many symbols for allophones.

Phonetics is an indispensable tool in linguistic work, e.g., in collecting the *corpus* or body of preliminary data necessary for determining the structure of any language, known or unknown, about to be analyzed. The corpus consists of phonetic transcriptions of the sounds of the language as heard, both as isolated sounds and as sequences of sounds.

Later, phonetics is again necessary for supplying the symbols for such sounds as are submembers (allophones) of unique, contrasting sound-units (phonemes). This chapter assumes a previous study of phonetics, entailing at least as much practice in transcription as is called for in Chapter V. Accordingly, no further discussion of phonetics is pursued here.

Criteria and Materials for Language Structure.   Harris names two criteria for language structure:

Linguists use two choices of criteria, leading to two different sets of elements, the phonologic and the morphologic. Each of these two sets of elements by itself covers the whole duration of all utterances: every utterance can be completely identified as a complex of phonemic elements, and every utterance can be identified as a complex of morphemic elements. The elements in each set are grouped into various classes, and statements are made about the distribution of each element relative to the others in its set.[8]

[8] Zellig H. Harris, *Methods in Structural Linguistics*, Chicago, University of Chicago Press, 1947, p. 21.

More simply, Gleason states that to comprehend language structure we must note that language operates with two kinds of material, *sound* (called *expression*), and *ideas* or *meanings* (called *content*). Speech sounds can be arranged according to their kinds and sequences. Patterns will emerge, and will repeat themselves. This patterning is the structure of expression, and the most fundamental sound elements in expression are called *phonemes*. Ideas or meanings are likewise capable of being arranged in patterns which repeat themselves. This patterning is the structure of content, and its units, composed of one or more phonemes each, are called *morphemes*. Since morphemes are made up of phonemes, thus making morphemic structure and phonemic structure interacting, we may say that the total structure of expression is the sum of the patterns of its phonemes and morphemes.[9]

Definitions.   The segmental or vowel and consonant phonemes have been given many definitions. One of the oldest and simplest is Daniel Jones' "a phoneme is a family of sounds,"[10] which was closely followed by Bloomfield's "a minimum unit of distinctive sound feature."[11]

Perhaps the most complete definition is Trager's which, though many-featured, is quite easily followed when each feature is understood: "A phoneme is a selectional class of complementarily distributed, phonetically similar, and congruently patterned sound-types; it contrasts and is mutually exclusive with every other similar class in the language, with some or all of which it enters into juxtapositional classes."[12]

Class as used here refers to the several sounds, i.e., allophones, which compose the phoneme. The phoneme /t/,[13] as a prolific example, includes the aspirated alveolar [tʻ], as in *tale* [tʻeɪl]; the unaspirated alveolar [t'], as in *stale* [st'eɪl]; the unreleased alveolar [t̚], as in *bat* [bæt̚], spoken without plosion; the nasally exploded [t̃], as in *kitten* ['kit̃n̩]; the laterally exploded [t], as in *rattle* ['ræt̩l]; the dental [t̪] as in *eighth* [eɪt̪θ]; and several others.

Complementarily distributed refers here to the fact that, e.g., the English aspirated [tʻ] will always occur initially in a stressed syllable, as in [tʻeɪl], while the unaspirated [t'] will always occur after [s]. Thus each serves as a

----

[9] H. A. Gleason, *Introduction to Descriptive Linguistics*, New York, Henry Holt and Company, 1955, pp. 2–3, 11.

[10] Daniel Jones, *Proceedings of the International Congress of Phonetic Sciences*, Amsterdam, 1942.

[11] Leonard Bloomfield, *Language*, New York, Henry Holt and Company, 1933, p. 79.

[12] G. L. Trager, "The phoneme 'T': A study in theory and method," *American Speech*, October, 1942, p. 145.

[13] Symbols enclosed in diagonals, as with this /t/, are phonemic symbols; those enclosed in brackets, such as [tʻ], are phonetic symbols.

complement to the other, and the two never occur in the same environment in contrast.

Phonetically similar in Trager's definition is a very nearly self-explanatory term. All the [t]'s designated above as allophones of the phoneme /t/ have at least two phonetic features in common, viz., voicelessness, and closure with the tip of the tongue. There should always be at least one common phonetic feature.

Congruently patterned means that the allophones of different phonemes often occur in parallel environment, thus forming congruent patterns, as for example:

	Aspirated	*Unaspirated*	*Nasally Exploded*
p	p'eɪt	sp'eɪt	stap m̩
t	t'eɪk	st'eɪk	'fætn̩
k	k'eɪn	sk'eɪn	'teɪkŋ̍ kould

Contrasts means that two or more phonemes set in contrast will distinguish meaning. Compare /t, s, r, b/ in *team, seam, ream, beam.*

Mutually exclusive means that no sound may belong to more than one phoneme.

Minimal Pairs.   Phonemes are usually separated out from the corpus of phonetic features of a language by means of a device called the minimal pair. A minimal pair is a pair of words alike in all their sounds except at one point in each. If the use of one different sound in the second word of the pair gives to the second word a different meaning from that of the first, the two different sounds are thus proved to be phonemes.

The tabulation below, if extended to its limit, will provide minimal pairs contrasting each possible phoneme with every other possible phoneme, and will thus demonstrate which are true phonemes of English.

Phonemicists customarily use an alphabet based on IPA, but varying from it at various points. Here follow the phonemic symbols not found in IPA which are required for reading the tabulation. Paired with them are their IPA equivalents. (Phonemic symbols are used as needed throughout this chapter.)

Phonemic	iy	i	ey	e	a	ow
IPA	i	ɪ	eɪ	ɛ	ɑ	oʊ

Most works on descriptive linguistics recognize in English some twenty-four consonants, twelve vowels and seven principal diphthongs.

Partial Tabulation of Phonemes Arranged in Minimal Pairs

Vowels (rows) × *Consonants* (columns)

Vowels	p	b	t	d	k	g	l	r	m	n
p	p	bat / pat	tat / pat	day / pay	Kate / pate	gate / pate	late / pate	rate / pate	mate / pate	Nate / pate
b		b	tat / bat	day / bay	Kate / bait	gate / bait	late / bait	rate / bait	mate / bait	Nate / bait
t			t	dole / toll	coal / toll	goal / toll	load / toad	road / toad	mode / toad	node / toad
d				d	coal / dole	goal / dole	low / dough	row / dough	mow / dough	no / dough
k					k	goat / coat	lode / code	rote / coat	mote / coat	note / coat
g						g	low / go	row / go	mow / go	no / go
l							l	row / low	mow / low	no / low
r								r	mow / row	no / row
m									m	no / mow
æ	æ									
e	bat / bet	e								
ey	bat / bait	bet / bait	ey							
i	bat / bit	bet / bit	bait / bit	i						
iy	bat / beat	bet / beat	bait / beat	bit / beat	iy					
a	not / gnat	not / net	hot / hate	not / knit	not / neat	a				
ɔ	bought / bat	bought / bet	bought / bait	bought / bit	bought / beat	nought / not	ɔ			
ow	boat / bat	boat / bet	boat / bait	boat / bit	boat / beat	note / not	note / nought	ow		

Consonants

Phonemic	p	b	t	d	k	g	č	j	f	v	θ	ð	s	z	š	ž	m	n	ŋ	l	r	w	y	h
IPA	p	b	t	d	k	g	tʃ	dʒ	f	v	θ	ð	s	z	ʃ	ʒ	m	n	ŋ	l	r	w	j	h

Vowels

Phonemic	i	e	i[14]	ə	æ	a	u	o	ɔ	y[16]	w[17]	h[18]
IPA	I	ɛ	ɪ	ə, ʌ	æ	ɑ	U	e[15]	ɔ	I	U	ə

Diphthongs

Phonemic	iy	ey	ay	aw	ow	uw	ɔy
IPA	i	eI	aI	aU	oU	u	ɔI

Exercise

Complete on a separate sheet the tabulations of vowel phonemes and consonant phonemes begun on page 328, using all the vowels and consonants listed above. First write in the words with ordinary spelling. Then redraw the diagram and repeat the words, this time transcribing them with phonemic symbols.

The Suprasegmental Phonemes

We customarily refer to vowels and consonants as segmental phonemes, since each one consists of an irreducible segment of speech. There are twelve other phonemes which we call suprasegmental, since they are superimposed upon the segmental phonemes. These suprasegmental phonemes include four stress phonemes, one open transition phoneme known as plus juncture, four pitch phonemes, and three clause terminals. In this brief introduction to descriptive linguistics there is time and space for only a token presentation of these, merely by name and illustration.

Stress Phonemes. Stress phonemes are four in number: primary, secondary, tertiary, and weak. Their signs are, in the same order, / ′ ˆ ` ˘ /. The

---

[14] /i̵/ is the vowel used in a certain pronunciation of *just* /ji̵st/ [dʒɪst], often spelled *jist*.

[15] "The New England short *o*," as in *stone* /ston/ [stən], often spelled *stun*.

[16] As in the diphthongs /iy/[i], /ey/ [eI], /ay/ [aI], /ɔy/ [ɔI].

[17] As in the diphthongs /aw/ [aU], /ow/ [oU], /uw/ [u].

[18] Off-glide, as in *cost* /kɔhst/ ['kɔəst].

sign for weak stress is not usually written in. Stress is obviously phonemic, as can be seen by the oft-used minimal pair *pervert'-per'vert* /pərvə́rt-pə́rvərt/, where the meaning is changed when the stress is changed. Examples of primary and weak stress appear in the two words above. Tertiary stress occurs with the third syllable of *appetite* /ǽpətàyt/; secondary stress occurs with the last word of *a green house* /ə gríyn hâws/ as contrasted with *a green-house* /ə gríynhàws/.

Exercise

Transcribe, marking stresses: The presidential white house is called the White House.

Plus Juncture.   Plus juncture appears oftenest as a break, which helps to distinguish meaning and is therefore a suprasegmental phoneme. Its sign is an elevated plus mark /+/. We could have used it in *a green house* to help the stress phonemes to distinguish between /ə gríynhàws/ and /a gríyn+hâws/. Plus juncture is also used to indicate the time value of a long consonant, as in *immobile* /im+mówbəl/ or *rat-trap* /rǽt+trǽp/. Often it is used simply to separate the words of a sentence.

Exercise

Turn back to the exercise about the White House and insert any needed plus.

Pitch Phonemes.   There are four pitch phonemes, viz., low, mid, high, and extra high. They are numbered from low upward as 1, 2, 3, 4. Number four can almost be disregarded, for it is seldom used except for pain or emotional stress, but the other three are in continual use. The sequence 231, or its contraction 31, occurs incessantly, as in:

How do you know it?
/²haw+²dəyə+³nów+¹it/
Stop it.
/³stap+¹it/

It must be understood that a single instance of pitch at a given level is a phoneme, as demonstrated by such minimal pairs as

No. /³nów/ = simple negation.
No! /¹nów/ = incredulity.

But sequences of pitch phonemes (called *intonation contours*) constitute pitch morphemes, such as the instances of 231 above. Such morphemes can be validated by the device of minimal pairs. (See discussion of morphemes later.)

Exercise

Transcribe, marking stress, juncture, and pitch:

> Where *are* you?
> *Is* he? He *is*.
> Come Friday.

Clause Terminals.   A clause, in the sense in which the word is used here, is not necessarily identical with a grammatical clause. It is an utterance containing a primary stress and ending with a break. Its termination is marked by one of the three junctural phonemes called clause terminals, written thus:

> $/\searrow/$ = fading (dying out).
> $/\nearrow/$ = rising.
> $/\rightarrow/$ = sustained.

Examples

I be|lieve|not, but it|can|be.

$/^{2}\grave{a}y^{+}b\text{əlíyv}^{+}n\hat{a}t^{2\rightarrow 2}\text{bət}^{+}it^{+3}k\text{æn}^{+1}biy\searrow/$

Who are|you?

$/^{2}huw^{+}\text{ər}^{+3}yuw\nearrow/$

Who are|you?

$/^{2}huw^{+}\text{ər}^{+3}yuw^{1}\searrow/$

Note minimal pairs:

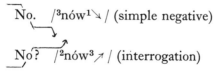

No. $/^{3}n\acute{o}w^{1}\searrow/$ (simple negative)

No? $/^{2}n\acute{o}w^{3}\nearrow/$ (interrogation)

Exercise

Transcribe, using marks for stress, pitch, juncture, and clause terminals. Draw contours on the clauses printed orthographically.

> What country did you visit?
> I mean to say, what state?
> Right now?

The Morpheme

Definitions. We have said that the two foundational units in language structure are the phoneme and the morpheme. The foregoing brief discussion to establish the concept of the phoneme is now followed by an even briefer discussion to establish the concept of the morpheme.

Gleason defines a morpheme as "the smallest unit in the expression system which can be correlated with any part of the content system."[19] If we are willing not to philosophize too much about the meaning of meaning, we may reasonably restate the definition thus: *the morpheme is the smallest portion of an utterance that expresses meaning.* Thus *steely* /stíyliy/ contains two morphemes, /stiyl/ and /iy/, i.e., *steel*, a metal, and *y*, like; *cut*, /kət/, one morpheme, and *cuttingly* /kə́t iŋ liy/ three, viz., /kət/, /iŋ/, and /liy/. Each of these units has meaning; i.e., each correlates with a part of the content system. But though *eel* /iyl/, considered in isolation, has meaning, the *-eel* /iyl/ abstracted from *steely* /stíyliy/ has none. Neither does the *ing* /iŋ/ of *sing*, though the /iŋ/ of /kə́tiŋliy/ does. Clearly a fraction of an utterance, to have meaning, must be considered in its environment.

Components of a Morpheme. On the side of sound, a morpheme is stated in terms of phonemes, from one upward. *Awe* /ɔ/, has one phoneme, *ought* /ɔt/ has two, *bought* /bɔt/ has three, and so on. On the side of word-building elements, a morpheme may be a root, a stem, or an affix.

A root is an uncompounded word or element, without affix. (See below.) *Set* /set/, *act* /ækt/ and *heart* /hart/ are roots, and are morphemes.

A stem is that part of an inflected word which remains unchanged throughout a given inflection. *Reset* /rìysét/, *enact* /enǽkt/, *hearten* /hártən/, *boot* and *shoe* are stems, which may be inflected thus: *resets* /rìyséts/ (three morphemes), *enacted* /enǽktəd/ (three morphemes), *heartened* /hártənd/ (three morphemes), *boots* /buwts/ (two morphemes), and *shoes* /šuwz/ (two morphemes).

Affixes include prefixes, suffixes, and (in some languages) infixes. Typical prefixes are *pre, pro, ad, in*, as in *presume* /priyzúwm/, *propose* /prəpówz/, *admit* /ədmít/, *instruct* /instrə́kt/.

Typical suffixes are *ly, ness, es, ed*, as in *fairly* /fǽrliy/ (two morphemes), *goodness* /gúdnəs/ (two morphemes), *disjointed* /disjóyntəd/ (three morphemes).

Suffixes repeated as inflections are often symbolized. The symbol stands

[19] Gleason, *op. cit.*, p. 54.

for the morpheme as a whole, including its distributional variants, i.e., its allomorphs.[20] For example, plurals are made by /z/, /əz/, /s/, /ən/,[21] as in *buds* /bədz/, *grudges* /grɔ́jəz/, *hats* /hæts/, *oxen* /áksən/. With *deer, sheep,* etc., the allomorph for the plural is zero, written /∅/. The symbol used to include all these allomorphs is $\{-Z_1\}$, always enclosed in braces and referred to as "morpheme Z one."

The allophones of $\{-Z_1\}$ are in complementary distribution. The allophone /s/ is phonologically conditioned to occur only after voiceless sounds, except /s/, /š/, /č/; /z/ only after voiced sounds, except /z/, /ž/, /ǰ/; and /əz/ only after /s/, /z/, /š/, /ž/, /č/, /ǰ/. The allophone ·/ən/ is morphologically conditioned to occur only after *ox*, with close parallels in *children* and *brethren*; and ∅ only with *deer, sheep* and a few others.

In descriptive linguistics, we should go on to develop $\{-Z_2\}$ as the morpheme for the possessive ending, as in *cat's* /kæts/, *lad's* /lædz/, *George's* /džɔ́rdžəz/; $\{-Z_3\}$ for the third person singular ending of verbs, as in *plays* /pleyz/, *passes* /pǽsəz/, *stops* /staps/; $\{-D_1\}$ for the preterite ending of verbs, as in *plowed* /plawd/, *stated* /stéytəd/, *pressed* /prest/; and $\{-D_2\}$ for the participial ending, as in *given* /gívən/. There are numerous others, usually with various allophones. Some are symbolized by their actual spelling, as with {-iŋ} in *coming* /kɔ́miŋ/, {-ər} in *colder* /kówlder/, and {-əst} in *finest* /fáynəst/. But this discussion set out only to give a hint of the nature of the study of descriptive linguistics, and a sample of the elementary methodology of that science.

The Scope of Descriptive Linguistics

A suggestion of what linguistic texts contain will indicate the scope of the discipline. H. A. Gleason's *Introduction to Descriptive Linguistics* has eighteen chapters on phonetics, the phoneme, and the morpheme. In addition to these are chapters on "The Process of Communication," "Variation in Speech," "Writing Systems," "Written Languages," "Language Classification," and "Some Languages and Language Families."

Zellig S. Harris's *Methods in Structural Linguistics*, on the other hand, is essentially in two long parts, phonology and morphology, with 125 closely packed pages devoted to the former, and 205 pages to the latter. There is an

---

[20] Note that throughout descriptive linguistic study, the *eme-allo* pattern repeats itself, as already exemplified in phoneme-allophone, morpheme-allomorph.

[21] Here, as earlier, /ə/ is used in these endings, merely because it is so used in the writer's dialect. Other dialects use /ɨ/, as in /ɪz/ and /in/.

introduction of twenty-five pages on "Methodological Preliminaries" at the beginning and a survey of eighteen pages at the end.

These two books probably stand at the extremes of simplicity (Gleason), and methodological detail (Harris). Other books, such as Charles F. Hockett's *Introduction to Linguistic Structures*, and Archibald A. Hill's *Introduction to Modern Linguistics* (both published in 1958), and most articles in professional journals, fall somewhere between. (See list of pertinent books and of sources for articles, pp. 324–325.)

Linguistic Geography

A relatively recent phase of linguistic work in colleges and universities is linguistic geography or, as it is often called, dialect geography. This has proved to be a very fruitful field. Linguistic geography begins with the gathering of a corpus of phonetic, lexical, and syntactical data in a given area, and culminates in the production of maps delineating the findings.

The Field Workbook

The instrument of field work in linguistic geography is the workbook, a questionnaire designed to elicit the pronunciations, vocabulary, and idioms sought. Field workers trained in the materials and methods of linguistic geography locate informants whose speech is regarded as typical and record this speech in phonetic symbols. Nowadays they often use tape recorders in the field and transcribe the recordings later.

Linguistic Maps

The maps which eventuate from the data are of several kinds:

1. Guide maps showing early migration trends of settlers.
2. Population maps, showing density.
3. Population maps showing special ethnic and cultural groupings.
4. Maps showing communities investigated.
5. Maps showing location of informants.
6. Phonetic maps with the pronunciation of a word or a category of words transcribed directly upon them.
7. Lexical maps with vocabulary features transcribed upon them.

8. Maps containing syntactical features.
9. Maps showing isoglosses (pronunciation boundaries, vocabulary boundaries, syntactical boundaries).

Isoglosses

The tracing of isoglosses has become one of the most important features of linguistic geography study. By means of these, major and minor dialect regions can be located and bounded with an accuracy never achieved by speculation or desultory observation. Some typical illustrative maps showing isoglosses with explanatory notes are shown on pages 336–337.

Linguistic geography work has been pursued in many places. Following is a list of instances where it has been continued to the point of publishing maps:

Atlas Linguistique de la France (Linguistic Atlas of France), J. Gilléron et E. Edmont, 32, fascicules, Paris 1902–1910. Supplement, tome premier, Paris, 1920.

Deutscher Sprachatlas (German Linguistic Atlas), Georg Wenker und Ferdinand Wrede, Lieferung 1–6. Marburg: 1926 ff.

Der Sprach- und Sachatlas Italiens und der Südschweiz (The Linguistic and Topical Atlas of Italy and South Switzerland), K. Jaberg und J. Jud. 4 Bände: I, 1928; II, 1929; III, 1930; IV, 1932.

Atlante Linguistico-Ethnographico-Italiano della Corsica (Linguistic-Ethnographic-Italian Atlas of Corsica), 10 volumes of 200 maps each, Pisa, 1933.

The Linguistic Atlas of the United States and Canada, Hans Kurath. Providence: Brown University, 3 vols. of 2 parts each: I, 1939; II, 1939; III, 1941.

Books based on the *Linguistic Atlas of the United States and Canada*:

Hans Kurath, Handbook of the *Linguistic Geography of New England*, Providence, Brown University, 1939.

Hans Kurath, *Word Geography of the Eastern United States*, Ann Arbor, University of Michigan Press, 1949.

E. Bagby Atwood, *Eastern Verb Geography*, Ann Arbor, University of Michigan Press, 1933.

A list of linguistic atlas projects throughout the world (as of 1933), together with articles on linguistic geography in English, French, German, and Italian, is contained in *Essai de bibliographie linguistic générale*, by Joseph Schrijnen, Nimègue, Belgium, N. V. Dekker & van de Vegt en J. W. van Léeuwen, 1933.

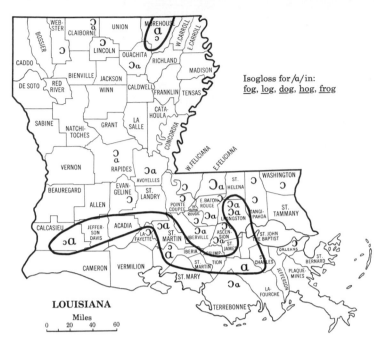

Isogloss for /ɑ/in:
fog, log, dog, hog, frog

LOUISIANA

Miles
0   20   40   60

Figure 72. From Albert Donald George, "Some Louisiana Isoglosses," Unpublished Master's Thesis, Louisiana State University, 1951, p. 34.

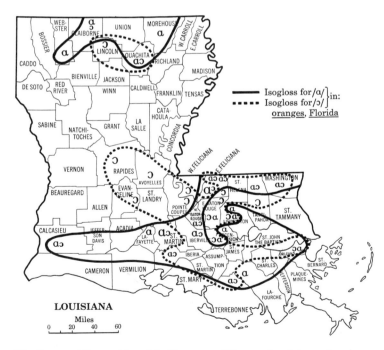

Isogloss for /ɑ/ ⎱ in:
Isogloss for /ɔ/ ⎰
oranges, Florida

LOUISIANA

Miles
0   20   40   60

Figure 73. From Albert Donald George, "Some Louisiana Isoglosses," Unpublished Master's Thesis, Louisiana State University, 1951, p. 42.

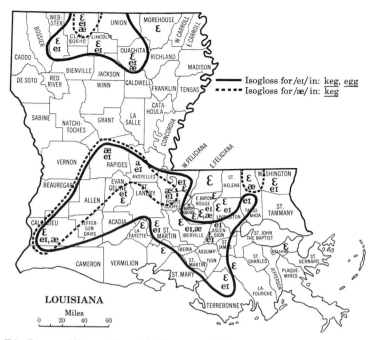

Figure 74. From Albert Donald George, "Some Louisiana Isoglosses," Unpublished Master's Thesis, Louisiana State University, 1951, p. 47.

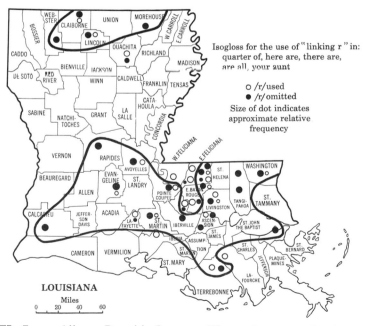

Figure 75. From Albert Donald George, "Some Louisiana Isoglosses," Unpublished Master's Thesis, Louisiana State University, 1951, p. 124.

Languages of the World: Relationships, Families, Classes, Alphabets

We now turn to certain broad considerations, to which are added some facts chosen from linguistic history and from various other divisions and subdivisions of the linguistic field. In a different sort of book this highly selective arrangement of facts would be inappropriate. It is used here because the experience of years shows that a number of loosely related linguistic questions invariably arise in the minds of good students in a speech course. It would seem that such students are entitled to at least elementary answers to questions arising from their spontaneous interests.

The questions that arise in college speech study are usually somewhat like these: When and where did language originate? Do all languages come from a common source? What are the relations of languages to each other? What kinds or classes of languages are there? Whence came our alphabet? How do language changes come about? Are there laws of language change? If so, what are some of them?

The Relations of Languages to Each Other

Perhaps the simplest beginning in answering some of these questions lies in a consideration of the relations of languages to each other at a given time. One answer might be that some languages are neighbors. English and French are neighbors, for example, and as neighbors they borrow from each other. Advertisements in English, playing on the fact that Paris is a fashion center, try to appeal to our vanity and snobbishness by using such words as *chic* [ʃik] and *modiste* (mɔˈdist]. Presently the words will have been permanently borrowed, the pronunciation anglicized into perhaps [tʃik] and [ˈmoʊdəst], and so added to our vocabulary. If these two words have not yet been completely acclimated in English they probably soon will be. At any rate, *garage*, *chauffeur*, and *chassis* have been for some years.

From the Norman Conquest to this day, English has been borrowing from French. Long ago *maintain* came in, derived from French *maintenir*, which in turn comes from Latin *manus* (hand) and *tenere* (to hold). French, on the other hand, borrows from English. *Beefsteak* is interestingly taken into French as *bifteck* [bifˈtɛk].

The word *maintain* suggests another relationship of languages—that some are relatives, children of the same parent. We have noted that the Latin word for *hand* is *manus*. Its parental relation to French *main*, Spanish *mano*, and Italian *mano* may be suspected at a glance. Since we know something of history, we know that Latin is the parent of the other three languages. Did we not know history, we might suspect *maintain* to indicate a child-parent relation of English to Latin—or English to French; but history saves us from this error and proves instead the neighbor-to-neighbor relation already discussed.

Tracing language offspring back to parents shows, in time, that the linguistic changes during the descent have been reasonably regular. After some practice, scholars can often reconstruct old words from their descendants or predict the form in which an old word will reappear in later centuries.

A classic example of simple reconstruction has to do with the Romance words for *horse*. In the four most important languages known historically to have descended from Latin, the word for *horse* appears as follows:

French	*Spanish*	*Italian*	*Portuguese*
cheval	caballo	cavallo	cavalo

By comparison with other Romance words and their Latin sources, it becomes evident that the source of these words in Latin should be *caballus*. It was at first puzzling to find no word in Latin for *horse* except *equus*, which obviously has no relation to the Romance words; but finally in vulgar Latin the missing word was found, and it was *caballus*, possibly from the Celtic.

By similar processes and by reference to history we find a corresponding relationship among German, English, Dutch, Dano-Norwegian, Swedish, and Icelandic, indicating that they are all descendants of the same parent—a primitive Germanic, of which we have, unfortunately, no literary trace, since our Germanic ancestors were illiterate barbarians at the time when the Romans had a high literary culture. Whereas for the sources of Romance words we can always go to the Latin, our only recourse for the sources of Germanic words is a reconstructed primitive Germanic evolved by linguistic scholars.

By such study as is implied in the foregoing we can discover that many of the languages of the earth fit into groups, the members of each group having had a common parent. The question now arises as to the relationship of the parents.

The "Ultimate" Parentage of Languages

Again applying the knowledge gained by examining such known parent-children groups as the Latin-Romance group, we can trace the parents of

LANGUAGE	Modern	Old	Primitive	"Ultimate"

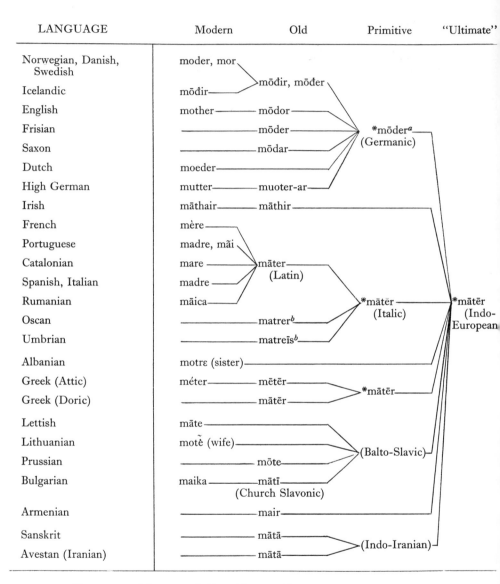

Norwegian, Danish, Swedish — moder, mor
Icelandic — mōðir
English — mother — mōdor
Frisian — mōder
Saxon — mōdar
Dutch — moeder
High German — mutter — muoter-ar
mōðir, mōðer
*mōder[a] (Germanic)

Irish — māthair — māthir
French — mère
Portuguese — madre, mãi
Catalonian — mare
Spanish, Italian — madre
Rumanian — māica
Oscan — matrer[b]
Umbrian — matreīs[b]
māter (Latin)
*mātēr (Italic)

Albanian — motrε (sister)

Greek (Attic) — méter — mētēr
Greek (Doric) — mātēr
*mātēr

Lettish — māte
Lithuanian — motĕ̃ (wife)
Prussian — mōte
Bulgarian — maika — mātī
(Church Slavonic)
(Balto-Slavic)

Armenian — mair

Sanskrit — mātā
Avestan (Iranian) — mātā
(Indo-Iranian)

*mātēr (Indo-European)

a Reconstructed forms are indicated by asterisks.
b Genitive forms of word, corresponding to Latin *māter*. Extant inscriptions contain no nominative form.

some of the various language groups backward toward an ultimate parent. We can even determine approximately what the important words were in this parent language, and thus reconstruct a theoretical vocabulary. This process of reconstructing theoretical primitive forms may be indicated diagrammatically somewhat as is shown on page 340.

This manner of working reveals that a number of groups trace backward to an ultimate parent called Indo-European.[22] Unfortunately for ease of study, Indo-European is not the ancestor of all the languages of the earth. Other groups appear to trace back to other "ultimate" parents of a date comparable perhaps to that of Indo-European.

No one can say, at least at this time, whether all languages have a common source. So far, no original parent language has been found as the ancestor of the parents we have somewhat injudiciously called "ultimate." Sometime one may be found. Although there is some evidence in favor of such an event, it is not now thought very likely. Perhaps language sprang up independently at several places on the earth's surface wherever men were intelligent enough to develop it.

The place of origin of Indo-European is a much discussed question, to which no definite answer is possible. A common statement is that it was probably near the Black Sea. Of the place of origin of other parent languages less is known, but present centers of population give as good a suggestion as any. Indo-European and other parent languages are very old. Little more can be said. But at the dawn of history ages of language had already passed. The birth of language is practically coincident with the birth of intellect. Written records go back much less than 10,000 years; language must go back many times further.

The Languages of the Earth. A view of the important language groups and languages of the earth may be had from the following outline:[23]

Indo-European Family
    Germanic
        West Germanic
            Anglo-Frisian
                English (Earlier forms, Middle English, Old English)
                Frisian (Earlier form, Old Frisian)

[22] Or, considering recent pairing of Indo-European and Hittite as sister languages, to Indo-Hittite.

[23] Derived from Leonard Bloomfield, *Language*, New York, Henry Holt and Company, 1933, chap. IV; Peter Giles, *A Short Manual of Comparative Philology*, New York, The Macmillan Company, 1901, chap. I; Louis H. Gray, *Foundations of Language*, New York, The Macmillan Company, 1939, chaps. XI–XII; and *Columbia Encyclopedia*, New York, Columbia University Press, 1958, pp. 1092–1094.

        Continental West Germanic
            Low German or Plattdeutsch (Earlier form, Old Saxon)
            Dutch-Flemish, Afrikaans (Earlier form, Old Low Franconian)
            New High German (Earlier forms, Middle High German, Old
                High German), Judeo-German or Yiddish
        Lombardian (extinct)
      North Germanic (Scandinavian)
        Norwegian, Icelandic (Earlier form, Old Norse)
        Swedish (Earlier form, Old Swedish)
        Danish, Dano-Norwegian, Faroese
    East Germanic
        Gothic, Vandal, Burgundian (all extinct)
Italic
  Latinic
      French (Earlier form, Old French)
      Provençal
      Catalan
      Spanish, Judeo-Spanish or Ladino
      Italian
      Portuguese
      Ladin (Rhæto-Romanic), Rumanian, Dalmatian (extinct)
  Oscan, Umbrian (both extinct)
Celtic
  Irish; Scotch Gaelic; Manx; Welsh; Breton; Cornish (extinct); Gaulish
    (extinct)
Baltic
  Lithuanian, Lettish, Old Prussian (extinct)
Slavic
  West Slavic
      Lusatian (Wendish, Sorbian); Polabian (extinct); Polish; Bohemian
        (Czech), Slovak
  East Slavic (Russian, including Great Russian, White Russian, and
    Ukrainian)
  South Slavic
      Bulgarian (Older form, Old Church Slavonic); Serbo-Croatian;
        Slovene
Albanian
Hellenic or Greek
Armenian
Indo-Iranian
  Iranian
      Persian (Earlier form, Old Persian); Alfghan (Pushtu); Osetian;

   Caspian; Kurdish; Pamir; Baluchi; Avestan (extinct); Parthian (extinct); Sogdian (extinct); Sakian (extinct)

  Indic (Earlier forms: Prakrit or Middle Indic; Pali; Sanskrit or Old Indic; Vedic)

   Marathi; Gujerati; Panjabi; Rajasthani; Western Hindi; Eastern Hindi; Urdu; Oriya; Bihari; Bengali; Romany (Gipsy); Assamese; Singhalese

  Illyrian (extinct); Venetic (extinct); Messapian (extinct); Thracian (extinct); Phrygian (extinct); Macedonian (extinct); Lingurian (extinct); Sicilian (extinct); Tocharian (extinct).

Basque (Earlier form, Iberian)

Etruscan (extinct)

Hittite (extinct)

Semitic-Hamitic

 Semitic

  Eastern Semitic: Akkadian, also called Babylonian-Assyrian (extinct)

  Western Semitic

   Northern Division: Canaanite (extinct); Moabite (extinct); Hebrew (extinct, but now arbitrarily restored in Israel as New Hebrew); Phœnician (extinct); Aramaic (including Syriac, Mandean)

   Southern Division: South Arabic (extinct); Arabic; Ethiopian (including Tigré, Tigrigna, Gafat, Harari, Guragé, Amharic)

 Hamitic

  Egyptian (extinct) (Later form, Coptic, also extinct)

  Berber (including Tuareg, Kabyle) (Ancient form, Lybian); Riff; Algerian

  Cushite

   Somali

   Galla

North Central African Languages: Wolof; Ful; Grebo; Ewe; Yoruba; Haussa; Nuba; Dinka; Masai

Bantu

 Luganda; Swaheli; Kaffir; Zulu; Tebele; Subiya; Herero

Bushman

Hottentot

Finno-Ugric

 Finnish-Lapponic

  Lappish; Finnish; Esthonian; Carelian; Olonetsian; Ludian; Vepsian; Livonian; Ingrian; Votian

  Mordvine

  Cheremiss

  Permian (including Votyak; Zyrian)

  Obi Ugrian (including Ostyak; Vogul)

  Hungarian or Magyar

Samoyede
Turkic (Turco-Tartar or Altaic—East, West, Central and South)
    Turkish; Tartar; Khirgiz; Uzbeg; Azerbaijani; Yakut
Mongol (East, West)
Tunguse-Manchu
Indo-Chinese (Sino-Tibetan)
    Chinese
        Mandarin (Peiping dialect of Mandarin is official national speech); North
           Chinese; Middle Chinese; West Chinese; Central Coastal Chinese;
           Kiangsi; Cantonese and Hakka
    Thai (including Siamese)
    Tibeto-Burman
        Tibetan; Bodo Naga; Kachin
        Burmese
Japanese
Ainu
Korean
North Causcasian; South Caucasian (including Georgian)
Dravidian
    Tamil; Malayalam; Canarese; Telugu; Brahui
Munda
Mon-Khmer
    Cambodian; Cham
Malayo-Polynesian (Austronesian)
    Malayan (Indonesian)
        Malay; Formosan; Javanese; Sundanese; Borneo; Maduran; Balinese;
           Philippine (Bisayan, Tagalog, Ilocano, Igorot); Malagasy
    Melanesian (North, Central, South)
        Solomon; Fijian
    Micronesian
        Gilbert; Marshall; Caroline; Marianas; Yap
    Polynesian
        Samoan; Tahitian; Tonga; Maori; Hawaiian; Easter (Rapanui); Society;
           Marguesan; Rarotonga, Tuamoto
Papuan
Australian
American Indian (Amerindian)
    Eskimo
    Salishan
        Flathead; Coeur d'Alene; Puyallup; Tillamook
    Algonquian
        Micmac; Montagnais; Cree; Penobscot; Massachusetts; Natick; Narragan-

set; Mohican; Delaware; Ojibwa; Potawatomi; Menomini; Sauk; Fox; Kickapoo; Peoria; Illinois; Miami; Blackfoot; Cheyenne; Arapaho

Athabascan

Chipewayan; Beaver; Dogrib; Sarsi; Hupa; Mattole; Apache; Navaho

Tanoan

Tiwa; Towa; Tewa

Iroquoian

Huron (Wyandot); Mohawk; Oneida; Onondaga; Cayuga; Seneca; Tuscarora; Cherokee (the Iroquoian and Caddoan groups are thought to be related)

Caddoan

Caddo; Pawnee

Natchez-Muskogean

Natchez; Choctaw; Chickasaw; Creek; Seminole

Siouan

Dakota; Teton; Oglala; Assiniboine; Kansa; Omaha; Osage; Iowa; Missouri; Winnebago; Mandan; Crow

Yuman

Yavopai; Havasupai; Yuma; Mohave

Uto-Aztecan

Piman; Shoshonean (Ute; Paiute; Shoshone; Comanche; Hopi); Nahuatlan (including the extinct Aztec)

Mayan

This outline gives only the most important languages of the earth. If subdivisions were included, the names would run into thousands. As the outline stands, there are too many entries for easy comprehension; the following condensation, encompassing only a few important groups, provides a useful summary.

Indo-European

Germanic; Italic; Celtic; Baltic; Slavic; Greek; Indo-Iranian

Semitic-Hamitic

Ethiopian; Arabic; Berber; Hebrew

Bantu

Finno-Ugric

Turkic

Mongol

Indo-Chinese

Malayo-Polynesian

American Indian

These are the principal representatives of groups of related languages. The philologist who discovers positive relations among these groups corresponding to the known relations between members of a given group will be making a step toward possible proof that all languages are related. Some such progress has been made; hence some scholars group the Turco-Tartar and the Mongol and Manchu families together, the Finno-Ugrian and Samoyede together (into a Ural-Altaic group), etc. But since the points of resemblance usually sought for are often lacking—similar numerals, names for members of the family, the verb *to be*—relationships are difficult to establish. As we have implied, no amount of identity of vocabulary of the sort that may be borrowed can prove a relationship. The vocabulary of English is heavily Latinic, yet English is a Germanic, not a Romance, language.

Classes of Languages

We have so far been grouping languages by the kinship shown in their history and preserved in their etymology and syntactical nature. Attempts have been made to classify languages according to various bases discoverable in their intrinsic nature.

One very useful division separates languages into *analytic* and *synthetic* types. An analytic language is characterized by the relative absence of bound forms—word-building prefixes and suffixes, and endings used for conjugation, declension, and grammatical comparison. Such a language uses many helping words, such as prepositions and auxiliary verbs. A synthetic language uses a relatively large number of bound forms (morphemes which cannot stand alone; cf. second paragraph below), and correspondingly few helping words. In Indo-European languages the more primitive the language, the more purely synthetic it is; the more developed, the more analytic. Sanskrit is exceedingly complicated in its synthetic features; Greek, Latin, and old English are still complicated, but less so; modern German and Russian still less; modern English and modern Romance languages, only a little. The change toward analysis rather than synthesis as the guiding principle of a language is a distinct improvement in flexibility and general ease and effectiveness of use.

No entirely satisfactory classification arrangement has been found, for the reason that no language is entirely consistent within itself; any language shows features of other types besides the dominant one. But according to their dominant characteristics, languages have sometimes been divided into some four morphologic varieties. These have been called *inflectional, isolating, agglutinative,* and *polysynthetic.*

Inflectional Languages.[24]   An inflectional language is one wherein the meanings are made clear by the endings. The parts of speech are largely distinguishable from one another by these endings, and the grammatical functions of number, case, gender, voice, mood, tense, comparison, etc., are indicated by them. Such endings have meaning, and are therefore morphemes, but their meaning is conditioned by the stems to which they are attached and, as a consequence, they have no existence as independent words. Inflectional endings are, then, bound forms. Change of word order within a clause in an inflectional language does not greatly affect meaning. For example, *Filia matrem videt* can mean only one thing, namely (*The*) *daughter sees* (*the*) *mother*, no matter what the word order. *Matrem filia videt, videt filia matrem, filia videt matrem, videt matrem filia, matrem videt filia*, all mean the same thing except for varying shades of emphasis. The endings *-a* and *-em* are subject and object signs, no matter what their location.

Latin, Greek, Anglo-Saxon, Russian, and German are predominantly inflectional languages, though in all of them, and in German particularly, word order may on occasion be important. Too, they all make considerable use of helping words, such as prepositions, to add other meanings beyond those expressed by the endings, despite the fact that theoretically such words do not belong to the scheme of an inflectional language. The use, e.g., of both preposition and ending in a phrase like Latin *ex parte* represents a recognition of weakness and ineffectuality in the inflectional scheme. The presence of the analytic *is going*, beside the synthetic *goes*, represents a breaking down of pure inflection.

Isolating Languages.[25]   An isolating language is a language wherein there is no clean distinction between parts of speech; the English word *cut*, for example, may be verb, noun, or adjective interchangeably, with little but context to reveal which is intended. There are no endings in a true isolative language, i.e., none to identify parts of speech and none to express case, person, number, mood, voice, or comparison; indeed, there are no bound forms of any sort. In other words, the root is unalterable, and there is not, as in an inflectional language, a formal distinction between a root and a word. Meanings, in an isolative language, are revealed by word position; hence word order is very important. *Daughter sees mother* would be very much upset

[24] Bloomfield, p. 208; Gray, pp. 300–301; William L. Graff, *Language and Languages*, New York, Appleton-Century-Crofts, 1932, p. 334.
   NOTE: Because of the frequent use of the same references the conventional abbreviation *op. cit.* is omitted throughout this chapter.
[25] Bloomfield, pp. 207–208; Giles, p. 39; Gray, pp. 299, 301, 441; T. L. Papillon, *A Manual of Comparative Philology*, 2nd ed., Oxford, Clarendon Press, 1877, p. 8; J. Vendryes, *Language: A Linguistic Introduction to History*, New York, Alfred A. Knopf, 1931, pp. 349–350.

in meaning if any word were changed from its position. Helping words, such as prepositions, are often necessary in an isolating construction. Whereas in the Latin sentence *Nauta inimicum hastā vincet, The sailor overcomes his enemy with his spear*, the ablative ending *-ā* expresses agency, in English the preposition *with* is necessary.

English has isolating characteristics, yet has numerous inflectional forms. French, Spanish, and Italian are isolating in some aspects, inflectional in others. French may be said to be sometimes inflectional morphologically rather than phonologically, in that many endings, though they are inflectional signals to the eye, are not so to the ear, because they are not pronounced; *ils donnent* and *il donne* are spoken identically, viz., [il dɔn]. Chinese is definitely isolating.

Agglutinative Languages.[26]   An agglutinative language is a language in which parts of "words" which superficially resemble inflectional elements have independent meanings of their own, of importance comparable with what in an inflectional language would be the stem. These "words" are, then, really agglutinations of elements which can be added or subtracted from the word complex at will. Pronouns and articles are usually attached to the stem-like word, frequently at the end. Turkish is the classic example of an agglutinative language. Examples:

> *sev*—love
> *sevmek*—to love
> *sevismek*—to love one another
> *sevdirmek*—to make (someone) love
> *sevilmek*—to be loved
> *sevisdirilmek*—to be made to love one another
> *ne*—not
> *sevnemek*—not to love, etc.

Polysynthetic (Including Incorporative)[27]**Languages.**[28]   A polysynthetic language is one which incorporates with the verb of the simple sentence, as

[26] Bloomfield, pp. 207–208; Gray, pp. 300–301; Hans Oertel, *Lectures on the Study of Language*, New York, Charles Scribner's Sons, 1901, p. 287; Papillon, pp. 4–5.

[27] It is probably as well to consider the incorporative type as a form of the polysynthetic type. J. M. Manly, in a statement to one of the authors, once distinguished it from the general polysynthetic species by saying that an incorporative language, such as Basque, amalgamates the object with the verbal forms, to which the qualifications, explanations, and significations of the incorporated word have to be added. Examples:

   I gave him it, the book.
   I built it, the house.

Still other names are, of course, possible; Gray, pp. 299–300, adds juxtaposing language, which "indicates accessory concepts or grammatical relations by prefixing certain elements (classifiers . . . .) to the word denoting the main concept." He gives Bantu as an example.

[28] Bloomfield, pp. 207–208; Gray, p. 300.

far as possible, the governing and governed parts. This has the effect of making the word and the sentence one and the same thing, a unit complex, no part of which can be taken out and used independently. Eskimo and some American Indian languages have polysynthetic characteristics. Example:

ninacaqua—I flesh eat

ni-tla-qua—I something eat

ni-te-tle-maca—I give somebody something

The Origin of the Alphabet

The origin of our alphabet is better known than many of the facts of linguistics. We borrowed it from the Romans, who had derived it from the Greeks, who had it from the Phoenicians, who had it from the Egyptians— who seem to have invented it. Following the story in the opposite direction, we find that the original Egyptian hieroglyphs had developed at a very early period into an alphabet of some twenty-four characters. However, the Egyptians failed to utilize these alphabetic symbols in the way in which we use them at the present time.

Sometime before the twentieth century B.C., the idea of an alphabet was carried across the Mediterranean by the Semitic peoples who lived in Asia Minor. It is not unlikely that the exodus of the Israelites, about the time of the Hyksos, or Shepherd Kings, was directly connected with this movement; possibly the Phoenician traders (for Phoenicia at that time was the great commercial nation) were instrumental in grafting the principle of alphabetic writing into the civilization of western Asia. At any rate, by the middle of the twentieth century B.C. the Phoenicians had developed, possibly out of the old Egyptian cursive writing known as "hieratic," an alphabet which was to be the forerunner of all the alphabets of western civilization. About the same time, another group of Semitic peoples was forming a somewhat similar alphabet which was to spread to the eastward and come into the possession of the Aryan races of northern India. From these two have been derived all the alphabets in use throughout the Indo-European Old World.

The Greeks did not take over the Phoenician alphabet bodily. At one time they had as many as forty different alphabets. However, early in the fifth century B.C. they more or less officially adopted a single one, the Ionian, which was based upon the old Phoenician. Three of the old Phoenician letters were abandoned and five new ones were added at the end of the alphabet for sounds not occurring in the Semitic.

The Roman alphabet is sometimes thought to have derived directly from the classic Greek. As a matter of fact, it comes from a much earlier Greek alphabet, the Euboean, which first appeared in Italy about the ninth century, probably at Cumae overlooking the Bay of Naples. During the following two or three centuries it spread, with various changes, throughout Italy, differentiating into the several alphabets of the peninsula. The Latin is more like the Phoenician than are any of the other alphabets. Twenty of the Phoenician characters are retained, whereas only nineteen are kept in the Greek.

With the spread of Roman culture throughout western Europe, the Latin alphabet was carried to the farthest reaches of the continent. In the north it came into contact with the old Runic alphabet, and out of those runes took into England two new symbols, the "thorn" (þ) and the "crossed *d*" (ð), which were still in use in Old English days. These letters represented voiced and voiceless *th* [ð, θ] interchangeably. They were used because the Latin had no [θ] and [ð] sounds, and so had no symbols for them. Later *y* was used to a great extent, especially in the word *ye* (the), because of its resemblance to ð. But in time the Latin letters *t* and *h* were combined and used, superseding not merely þ and ð, but this use of *y* as well. This *y*, incidentally, was never pronounced [j], as the pronoun *ye* [ji], but always [ð] as in *the* [ðə, ðɪ].

Among other important systems of writing to develop out of original picture writings have been the ancient Akkadian, the Mayan, and the Chinese. The Akkadians invented the cuneiform writing, transmitting it to the Assyrians, who developed a system containing both sound characters and word characters; the former were syllabic. The Mexicans, through a sort of rebus writing, developed a system which was partly alphabetic (the Mayans had at least twenty-seven alphabetic characters) and partly pictorial. Chinese has not yet fathered an alphabet; but from it grew the Japanese writing, which is syllabic. The Japanese sound system contains only five vowels and fifteen consonants; and since some possible combinations do not actually occur, it is possible to write any Japanese word from a syllabary of not more than fifty characters. In view of the fact that practically all alphabetic systems of writing have at some time passed through the syllabic stage, it is not impossible that the Japanese itself may in time develop into an alphabetic system.

Language Change: Phonetic, Semantic, Miscellaneous

Language, by which we mean speech primarily, is constantly changing.[29] It is dynamic, not static. It is man's invention and it changes as he changes.

[29] E. Prokosch, *An Outline of German Historical Grammar*, New York, Oxford University Press, 1933, p. 22.

The changes may be thought of as of three types: phonetic (phonological, sound) changes, perceptible to the ear; semantic (meaning) changes, perceptible to the intellect; and form (orthographical) changes, perceptible to the eye. Of course these inevitably overlap, as when a phonetic change is reflected in the spelling.

Sometimes changes are rapid, sometimes slow. Sometimes they are anomalous and apparently unexplainable, like the sports which appear in biological annals; more often they are quite explainable by comparison with similar known instances of change; perhaps they would always be explainable if we could but know and apply the phonetic, psychological, and sociological principles which may be in operation. Many scholars believe that all changes are conformable to principle, and that apparently irregular changes are due to the operation of as yet unrecognized principles. Other scholars doubt this. The "laws" of change are, of course, laws only in the sense of being "merely formulas of what happened at one particular time in one particular dialect or language."[30] "They define and describe, but do not explain, the facts of linguistic history."[31]

Causes of Linguistic Change. The causes of linguistic change are matters of perennial speculation. Of those brought forward from time to time, some may be classed as follows:

1. *Somatic*, e.g., (a) limitations of sensory perception, which prevent accurate hearing of sound elements and distinguishing between them[32]; (b) fading of neuromuscular patterns; (c) tendency toward economy of muscular effort[33]; (d) tendency toward simplification[34] or convenience[35]; etc.

2. *Psychological*, e.g., (a) premature production of a sound through anticipation; (b) lack of uniform linguistic experience within a language group; (c) tendency toward analogy; etc.

3. *Sociological*, e.g., (a) geographical separation; (b) political, economic, social and religious influences;[36] (c) language mixtures and substrata; (d) popularity or unpopularity of a dialect; (e) degrees of education; etc.

[30] Otto Jespersen, *Essentials of English Grammar*, New York, Henry Holt and Company, 1933, p. 29.
[31] Prokosch, p. 23.
[32] Gray, p. 85.
[33] *Ibid.*, p. 84.
[34] Bloomfield, p. 370.
[35] Hermann Paul, *Principles of the History of Language*, tr. by H. A. Strong, New York, Longmans, Green & Company, 1891, p. 46.
[36] Gray, pp. 86–87.

Some of these tend to augment or retard changes occurring for mechanical or psychological reasons, by the influence of approval or disapproval.

The paragraphs immediately following touch on some of these suggested causes, particularly those that have to do with hearing and imitative reproduction of sounds. They also touch on certain social influences affecting the adoption or rejection of any change which may set in.

The Sequence of Changes. Sometimes a series of changes occurs in sequence. Such a sequence cannot be disturbed; that is, the events cannot happen in any but their established order—no event can be omitted and no two can be reversed in sequential position.

A case in point is that of a small boy in southern Louisiana who said that his last name was *Moish*. Asked to spell it, he said, "M-a-r-s-h." The evolution of *Marsh* to *Moish* is a very definite process, rigidly governed by the linguistic (in this case phonetic) rules prevalent in this boy's community. Two common phenomena of the speech of that community must be known in order to establish the sequence. One of these is that many of the people of that locality pronounce the stressed orthographic combination *ar*, when not preceded by a *w* sound, as [ɔ], instead of the standard southern [ɑ]; the other is that where [ɔ] is followed by *sh* [ʃ], as in *caution* [kɔʃən], the tongue tends to begin rising too soon from the low [ɔ] position toward the palatal [ʃ] position, and passes through the medium-high-front position of [ɪ], with the result that a supernumerary vowel is introduced, combining with [ɔ] to form the diphthong [ɔɪ]. *Caution* [kɔʃən] thereupon becomes [kɔɪʃən].

Combining these two known tendencies and applying them in their known order of occurrence to the strange pronunciation of *Marsh* as *Moish*, we establish the following sequence:

Marsh is pronounced [mɑʃ] in standard southern speech.

[mɑʃ] becomes [mɔʃ] in provincial southern Louisiana dialect.

The [ɔ] of [mɔʃ] develops under the influence of the approaching final palatal into the diphthong [ɔɪ], and the word becomes [mɔɪʃ].

The evolution is now quite logical as [mɑʃ], [mɔʃ], [mɔɪʃ]; and the unusual pronunciation of *Marsh*, however incorrect it may be and is regarded, no longer seems willful or perverse.

When the nature of the sequences of a change like the preceding is known, the order of events constituting the change can be determined almost infallibly. But the date of these changes cannot always be determined, nor is there any certainty that corresponding changes in a parallel series have taken place simultaneously. We know the *how*, but not the *when*. A reconstructed Indo-

European vocabulary is probably quite accurate as to individual words, but there is no way of knowing whether the several words were contemporaneous.

Literacy Retards Change.   It is almost axiomatic that linguistic changes having an inflection-leveling aspect take place at a speed inversely proportional to the literacy of a people, or directly proportional to the ignorance of a people. A classic example is that of the Anglo-Saxon, which in the tenth century had five grammatical cases, three grammatical numbers (singular, plural, and dual), and a declension of adjectives permitting sixty possible case-gender-number forms of a single word. But the Norman invasion in the eleventh century made French the language of court and government, and Anglo-Saxon was relegated almost exclusively to the use of illiterate peasants. These grammatical complications then fell rapidly away, so that by the fifteenth century English had ceased to be so completely an inflectional, synthetic language and had become to a considerable degree an analytic language. Thenceforward substantives, except for a few pronouns, had only two case forms, nominative-objective and possessive; and the sixty adjective forms had (with a partial exception in the case of two words, *this* and *that*, which have the plurals *these* and *those*) been reduced to one.

Louisiana and Haitian French offer parallel instances. Here, as in the Anglo-Saxon, the change has come about because the language has been freed from the restraints of education over a sufficiently long period of time.

Indeed, it must now be evident that education, with its complement of written forms, books, schools, teachers, and perhaps especially grammars and dictionaries, is a retarding influence in language change. Education, as applied to language, worships precedent; it continually harks back to books, where language has been crystallized into a form which has come to be regarded as the only right form; it frowns upon linguistic experiments and new departures of all kinds; it is linguistically ultraconservative.

Attitudes Toward Linguistic Change.   There is something to be said in justification of conservatism toward language change. If language were permitted to "run wild," with every vagary of pronunciation and syntax welcomed and adopted, it would hardly maintain its identity for even one or two generations. If language had no written form, the catastrophe would be minor, since no close connection with the past could be maintained anyway. But if the people were literate, then spelling too would share in the race for change, and the writings of one century would hardly be intelligible to people of the next. Perhaps it is well, then, that there is always some resistance exerted against any change whatever. Each proposed change must prove itself to be highly useful, completely indispensable, or at least exceedingly popular. If it does so, it will promptly be adopted.

Not all innovations do prove themselves. The once-popular use of the word *macaroni* to designate a fop is now known only to well-read people, and even to them it is merely a historical curiosity. Few of the younger people today know the expression *twenty-three skidoo*, meaning *get out*, common around the turn of the century. These uses of the words did not prove themselves indispensable.

But Hamlet's strained "Saw? Who?" is at long last—after three and a half centuries—being recommended by prominent authorities, who believe that "Who did you see?" has by now proved itself. So with "It's me," apparently, as well as with "It's him, her, and them."

Some bidders for permanency are still being weighed. "Different than" as in "He looks different than he did last week," may be nearing acceptance, judging by the number of educators, not to mention statesmen, who use it. But *this* plus substantive with no previously named referent, is still something less than acceptable. Cf. "As I drove down the highway, I saw this lady trying to change a tire." It appears that writers of fiction and the columns of the *New Yorker* tend to put this locution into the mouths of less literate characters as a way of indicating their low educational and cultural level. But what one hears on campuses (and not solely from students of English zero, we may be sure), implies rapid increase in the prevalence of this expression.

Hardly any innovation is likely to prove stranger than many well-established, and therefore perfectly respectable, strange items. "He's not much of a musician" lacks logic even to a greater degree than does "It's different than it was in my day." "Much of a musician" seems all right to use because we are used to it. We may get used to "different than" and to anecdotes beginning "It seems that this traveling man met this farmer's daughter." It is possible to get used to any language feature, even one so odd as "get used to." But to keep the language from escaping us before our own generation is past, a period of resistance is a good thing. The useless may be sifted out, and the useful may survive.

Along with the tendency toward change, then, is always a strong tendency toward the preservation of the *status quo*—if what already is, is good, it is well; if it is bad, it will be preserved anyway. Thus so good a thing (from the point of view of many other languages) as the fact that English has no rounded front vowels is preserved alongside our atrociously inconsistent spelling. Under these conditions, now that the world is becoming irrevocably literate, we may feel sure that the accepted dialects of the major languages will change grammatically and orthographically much more slowly than when such linguistically fortunate events as the Norman Conquest could occur.

The Fading of Memory Traces.   But there is one type of language change against which even the conservatism of education is powerless. That is the gradual, imperceptible sound change coming from our inaccuracy in remembering motor and auditory images, i.e., changes resulting from the fading of memory traces or neurograms. We pronounce a sound, but before we have occasion to pronounce it again, we forget the precise kinesthesia—the feel of our muscles in pronouncing it; or we hear a sound, but presently forget exactly how it sounded to us; through these two types of forgetting, we lose the capacity to reproduce the sound accurately. Our inaccuracy may be very slight, but it is inevitable.

Of course we continually check up against the pronunciation of other people. As long as equal numbers of a group vary in opposite directions, they will balance each other; and since their influence toward variation upon a single individual of the group will be the resultant of all their individual varyings, the resultant influence will be zero. It will be zero even if the numbers are unequal, provided that the side of the minority contains important individuals whose example or command will balance the influence of several lesser people in the opposite group. But if for any reason the balance of numerical or other potent influence is shaken, the resultant of influences will be greater or less than zero, and a lurch in the direction of the strongest influence toward change will at once be evident.

Examples of such linguistic drift from the *status quo* are plentiful. In the South a small number of white persons living on a plantation with a large number of Negro tenants will sometimes be pushed off balance by sheer numerical force and will adopt certain Negro pronunciations. Young white children are more likely to regard their nurses' version of *door* and *fourteen* as *do'* [do] and *fo'teen* [ˌfotˈtin] equally worthy of imitation alongside their parents' [ˈdoə] and [ˌfoətˈtin].

In the French part of Louisiana, children of non-French parents often speak with a French accent. Here the numerical excess of French neighbors and playmates has overcome the influence of the non-French home.

The uvular [ʀ] of Parisian French and the pronunciation of Castilian *c* and *z* as *th* [θ] instead of *s* are said to have begun as *précieuse* or court affectations. They have been widely adopted by large numbers of the general French and Spanish populations respectively. Here it is clear that the algebraic sum of influence favored the change from [r] to [ʀ] and from [s] to [θ] because the audible example of the few who began the fads was heavily weighted with their social influence as people of courtier class or royal rank.

The drift from [ɛ] to [ɪ] as in [wɪnt] for *went* [wɛnt], or from [ɑ] to [ɔ] as in [ɔtɪst] for *artist* [ˈɑtɪst], is an example of a situation where the resultant of practice has become greater than zero. Hence [ɪ] for [ɛ] and [ɔ] for [ɑ] have increased in currency rapidly in some areas, particularly in the South. With some educational influence being set against it, the predominance of numbers alone may not be sufficient to maintain the drift.

The Lag of Spelling Behind Sound Change.   Evidence of the unwillingness of educational or literate influences to permit change on the one hand, and of the inexorable drift of sound change due to our inaccuracy in remembering our motor and auditory images on the other hand, is present in a legion of our ridiculous modern English spellings. For example, the *k* in *knight* (O.E. *cniht*) was once pronounced; so was the *gh* combination—the word was [knɪçt]. Educational influences, reluctant to permit us to drop any jot of a spelling found somewhere in a book, have compelled us to drag through the centuries the useless silent letters; but by slow degrees, modifications due to faulty memory of motor and auditory images encroached on the sounds [k] and [ç] until they were finally suppressed altogether. [ɪ] changed to [aɪ] as indicated below, and the pronunciation, despite the archaic spelling, became [naɪt].

Probably the best possible illustration of how the "standpat" influences of literacy have held on to symbols whose sounds have changed radically may be seen in the "great vowel change" of the fourteenth and fifteenth centuries. When, by the slow effects of imbalance such as we have been discussing, the changes were in a sense complete,

  a, once pronounced [ɑ], had in many cases become [e] or [eɪ];

  e, once pronounced [e], had in many cases become [i];

  i, once pronounced [i] or [ɪ], had in many cases become [aɪ];
and several other comparable changes had taken place.

But *made* still retained its spelling with *a*, *meet* with *e*, and *knight* with *i*.

Enough has been said to demonstrate the fact that sound changes, both alone and accompanied by grammatical, orthographic, and semantic changes, do take place, and to show that at least some of them occur in orderly fashion, explainable and even predictable. It is little wonder that the rules by which these changes take place are often elevated to the dignity of being called laws or, at any rate, principles. The immediately following portion of this chapter deals with a limited number of these laws or principles, specifically some of those which find application in English.

Phonetic Change

Assimilation.   Assimilation is a sound change resulting from the attraction of a neighboring sound. The position or action of one or more parts of the vocal mechanism used in making a given sound, changes to conform to the position or action used in making the neighboring sound.[37] Assimilation is one of the many sound changes that result from a tendency to simplify the motions of the vocal organs in uttering phonemes. It is a change in the direction of least resistance, hence of greater ease and simplicity.[38] (See illustrations, page 363.) Assimilation functions in several ways:

1. In *progressive assimilation* the assimilative influence reaches forward to affect a sound coming after the dominating sound. Examples: *Opm the door* for *Open the door,*[39] *cup m saucer* for *cup 'n' saucer.* Here the bilabial sound [p] has in each case labialized the succeeding alveolar sound [n] to produce [m]. In *gonna go* and *wanna go* for *goin' to go* and *want to go*, the [n]'s in *want* and in *goin'* completely assimilate the following [t]'s.[40] In *abzorb* and *abzurd* for *absorb* and *absurd*, the voiced sound [b] has, in each case, induced voicing (q.v., page 360) in the succeeding [s] by progressive assimilation, and has thus produced [z]. This is a partial assimilation, or accommodation (q.v., page 359).

2. In the more common *regressive assimilation*[41] the assimilative influence reaches backward to affect a sound preceding the dominating sound. The word *assimilation* itself contains a regressive assimilation, whereby the [s] of Latin *similare* (*simulare*) has reached backward to absorb completely the [d] of *ad*, the elements of the compound being of course, *ad + similare.* In [ðɪʃˈʃoʊ] for *this show* and [hɔrʃˈʃu, hɔʃˈʃu] for *horseshoe* the [ʃ] of the second word has in each case reached backward to absorb the preceding [s] completely. In *dlad* for *glad* (see page 236) the alveolar position of the tongue for [l], supplemented, no doubt, by that of the alveolar final [d], has influenced the velar sound [g] to change to the alveolar sound [d]; in *sam pile* for *san' pile* (sand pile) the bilabial sound [p] has labialized the preceding alveolar sound [n] to produce [m].

3. In the relatively rare *progressive-regressive-reciprocal*[42] assimilation, two adjacent sounds mutually affect each other, both sounds disappearing as such, and a third sound being evolved. Thus after the O.F. *repletion* was borrowed

[37] Bloomfield, p. 372; Albert H. Marckwardt, *Introduction to the English Language*, New York, Oxford University Press, 1942, pp. 39–40.

[38] Papillon, pp. 73–74; Vendryes, pp. 61–62.

[39] John Samuel Kenyon, *American Pronunciation*, 8th ed., Ann Arbor, Mich., George Wahr, 1940, pp. 71–72.

[40] Margaret Schlauch, *The Gift of Tongues*, New York, Modern Age Bks., 1942, p. 172.

[41] Bloomfield, p. 372; Gray, p. 68; Kenyon, pp. 72–73; Schlauch, pp. 173–174.

[42] Gray, p. 68; Markwardt, p. 34.

in the M.E. form *repleccion*, [s] and [j] of the suffix *cion*[43] modified each other reciprocally and disappeared, leaving as residue the [ʃ] of [rɪˈpliʃən]. A great many other words have gone through a similar evolution.[44] In informal speech the same effect can be readily observed in [mɪʃˈʃu] for *miss you*, [ðɪʃˈʃɪr, ðɪʃˈʃɪə] for *this year*, etc. Something very close to reciprocal assimilation occurs when the pedantic [ˈlɪtərəˌtjʊr, ˈlɪtərəˌtjʊə] for *literature* becomes [ˈlɪtərətʃɚ ˈlɪtərətʃə], or when [proˈsidjʊr, proˈsidjʊə] becomes [prəˈsiʤɚ, prəˈsiʤə]; i.e., if [ʧ] and [ʤ] can be regarded as single sounds not analyzable into [t + ʃ] and [d + ʒ], we may say that [t] and [j] have disappeared and left [ʧ], and that [d] and [j] have disappeared and left [ʤ].

4. In *distant (incontiguous, dilated) assimilation*[45] the sound-modifying influence may act progressively or regressively on a sound not adjacent to the dominant sound. Examples in Modern English are not plentiful. However, it is possible to explain some otherwise puzzling plurals, comparatives, and derivatives in English by reference to one form of distant regressive assimilation, prevalent in the Germanic tongues and known by the name *umlaut* (mutation). Umlaut is a sound change effected, typically, through the influence of a vowel in the ending upon the vowel of the stem. An example of this description is *i*-umlaut, as shown in the nominative plurals following:[46] **fōtiz* > O.E. *fēt* (> Mn.E. *feet*). Here the *i* in the plural ending has regressively modified the vowel of the stem. In the singular, we have **fōt* > *foot* without vowel change,[47] since there was no vowel in the ending having the power to change the vowel of the stem. Analogous conditions explain contrasting vowels in *goose—geese, full—fill, foul—filth, mouse—mice, hot—heat, strong—strength, long—length, man—men, old—elder, gold—gild,* etc.[48]

It may be noted that while most of the examples of assimilation are consonant assimilations, umlaut is a vowel assimilation.[49] The examples shown above are of very old date.

---

[43] First, of course, the accent shifted according to English patterns to the syllable *ple*, after which the then unstressed suffix went through some such evolution as [sion > sɪon > sjon > sjən], whereupon the next step would be [ʃən].

[44] A glance at Chaucer's *Canterbury Tales* reveals, e.g., the following, given both with their M.E. and Mn.E. forms: mencion > mention, duracioun > duration, disposicion > disposition, equacion > equation, religioun > religion, pacience > patience, visitacion > visitation, inclinacion > inclination, constellacion > constellation, sauvacion > salvation, discrecion > discretion, dampnacion > damnation, preambulacioun > preambulation, nacion > nation.

[45] Gray, p. 68.

[46] Reconstructed forms are indicated with the asterisk *

[47] That is, without contemporary vowel change. Much later, at the time of the great vowel change, and for different reasons, [o] in the singular form changed to [ʊ].

[48] See Prokosch, pp. 48–52.

[49] Schlauch, p. 174.

Partial and Complete Assimilation.[50]   Using the degree of completeness of the assimilation as a basis for division, assimilations may be classified as either partial (accommodation) or complete (equalization). When the steam engineer pronounces the name of his *Penberthy* injector as *Pemberthy*, the [n] has accommodated itself to the *b* by becoming bilabial; in other words, it has been partially assimilated to the [b]. In *abzurd* and *abzorb* for *absurd* and *absorb*, the [s] in each case has accommodated itself to the preceding [b] by becoming voiced—a concession which makes it partially like the [b]. In [mæŋkaɪnd] for *mankind*, there is partial assimilation of [n] to [k]; in *handker-chief* [ˈhæŋkətʃəf, ˈhæŋkətʃəf], of [n] to [k]; in *raspberry* [ˈræzˌbɛrɪ], of [s] to [b]. When a foreigner says *thiz man* for *this man*, there is a partial assimilation of [s] to [m].

When Latin *in + mobile* became *immobile*, the assimilation of the [n] was a complete one. A Hollander's pronunciation of *this thing* as [ðɪθˈθɪŋ] illustrates complete assimilation; likewise the familiar [ðɪʃːu] for *this shoe*. In *cupboard* [ˈkʌbɚd, ˈkʌbəd], the assimilation is complete and has become standard. The modern pronunciation of *damn, hymn, autumn, column, kiln*[51] represents complete assimilation of final [n] to the preceding consonants. But in some way, the [n] still belongs to each of the morphemes where it is orthographically represented, as may be seen in *damnable, hymnal, autumnal, columnar*. Words containing unpronounced *l, k,* and *w* present analogous assimilations, usually without any such survival as is seen above. However, [l] often survives in *yolk*. Examples: *psalm, calm, palm, half, calf; folk, yolk, talk, walk, calk, balk; would, should; knave, kneel, knead, knight, knit, knock, know; wrath, wrist, wretch, wrench, wring, write, wrought, wrong.*

Attitudes Toward Assimilation.   Taken as a general proposition, assimilation may simply be considered as a fact, an existing phenomenon which, regarded objectively, is neither good nor bad. But the great masses of folk constituting a given speech group are not objective. By their conscious or subconscious attitudes they express either approval or disapproval. The variety of regressive assimilation called nasalization, where a nasal consonant affects a preceding vowel, is a case in point. In French and Portuguese, for example, it has met great approval. The [n] of Latin *manus* has nasalized the preceding vowel to produce French *main* [mɛ̃] and Portuguese *mão*, which have been

[50] Bloomfield, p. 373; Gray, p. 68; Schlauch, pp. 172–173; E. H. Sturtevant, *Linguistic Change: an Introduction to the Historical Study of Language*, New York, G. E. Stechert & Company, 1942, pp. 46–47; Kenyon, p. 73.

[51] Stuart Robertson, *The Development of Modern English*, Englewood Cliffs, N.J., Prentice-Hall, 1938, p. 199.

unreservedly approved and adopted. Perhaps the first experiments in this nasalization were disapproved; it would be an interesting piece of research to find out the attitude of scholars of the transition period.

In contemporary America it is clear that a period is now in progress which may or may not prove to be a transition period, wherein the folk by their practice largely approve of the nasalization of vowels preceding nasal consonants and are well on the way toward developing a set of nasal vowels comparable to those in French and Portuguese, whereas most people who are conscious of the phenomenon are heartily against it. So, incidentally, are most Europeans. It is a striking but hardly unusual fact that a sound characteristic which is acceptable in one language may be unacceptable in another.[52]

Voicing.[53] Voicing (adding vocal band vibration) of unvoiced consonant sounds occurs as a form of assimilation, which may be progressive, regressive, or progressive-regressive (without being reciprocal). In *abzurd* for *absurd* and Mn.E. *partridge* for M.E. *partriche*, it is progressive; in *gosling* ['gɔzlɪŋ] from *goose*, and *husband* ['hʌzbənd] from *house*, it is regressive; in *nodice* for *notice*, *sadisfaction* for *satisfaction*, *shuddup*[54] for *shut up*, *leddup* for *let up*, and *Louisiana* [ˌluɪzɪ'ænə] from *Louis*, it is probably progressive-regressive, being induced by the presence of vowels (which are always voiced, in the nature of the case) on both sides. This type of progressive-regressive assimilation is not reciprocal, because the encasing voiced elements do not affect each other.

A special case of progressive-regressive-nonreciprocal assimilation is the voicing of medial [t] in the usual American conversational pronunciation. Probably the best representation of the resultant sound is the one-tap trill sign, [ɾ]. Hence we have *pity* ['pɪɾɪ], *letting* ['lɛɾɪŋ], *fatty* ['fæɾɪ], *remitted* [rɪ'mɪɾəd, rə'mɪɾɪd], etc. Quite interestingly, some American and British pronunciations thus become homonymous, such as Br. *berry* ['bɛɾɪ]—Am. *Betty* ['bɛɾɪ], Am. *jetty* ['dʒɛɾɪ]—Br. *Jerry* ['dʒɛɾɪ].

Voicing is sometimes used as a device to distinguish parts of speech, as *use* (n.) [jus], *use* (v.) [juz]; *teeth* (n.) [tiθ], *teethe* (v.) [tið]; *mouth* (n.) [maʊθ], *mouth* (v.) [maʊð]; etc. It also appears as an illustration of Verner's addendum to Grimm's law (*q.v.*)[55] in words where the stress *does not* fall on the syllable preceding the consonant or consonants under consideration. Compare *exist*

[52] See p. 359.
[53] Marckwardt, pp. 35–36; Schlauch, p. 176.
[54] See illustrations, Chapter V, p. 272.
[55] Prokosch, pp. 31–38.

[ɪgˈzɪst], *example* [ɪgˈzæmpl̩], *exert* [ɪgˈzɝt, ɪgˈzɜt], etc., with *exit* [ˈɛksət, ˈɛksɪt]; *exercise* [ˈɛksɚˌsaɪz, ˈɛksəˌsaɪz].

The ending *s* of nouns and verbs is voiced by progressive assimilation whenever the final sound of the uninflected word is a vowel or a voiced consonant cluster. Examples: *sees* [siz], *adds* [ædz], *sings* [sɪŋz], *wilds* (waɪldz].

NOTE: The ending *es* is used instead of *s* when the stem ends in [s], [z], [ʃ], or [ʒ], and is pronounced as a separate syllable with the *s* voiced, regardless of whether the stem ends in a voiced or voiceless sound. Examples: *glasses* [ˈglæsəz, ˈglæsɪz], *buzzes* [ˈbʌzəz, ˈbʌzɪz], *ashes* [ˈæʃəz, ˈæʃɪz], *rouges* [ˈruʒəz, ˈruʒɪz], *hitches* [ˈhɪtʃəz, ˈhɪtʃɪz], *bridges* [ˈbrɪdʒəz, ˈbrɪdʒɪz].

Unvoicing.[56]   Unvoicing is the withdrawing of vocal band vibration from a sound. It is a form of assimilation, usually regressive. Thus the voiceless [ʃ] of the suffix *tion* [ʃən] causes [b] to change to [p] in *absorb—absorption*. The voiceless [t] has corresponding effect on the preceding [v] in *have to*, which is often heard as [hæf tu], and on the [z] of *use* in *used to be* [just: ə bi]. It is sometimes said that the unvoicing of originally voiced final plosive and fricative consonants in Russian and German is a regressive assimilation, the silence following the word being thought to act on the final consonant to unvoice it. Thus Russian *muzh* (husband) is pronounced [muʃ]; German *Korb* (basket), [kɔrp]; etc.

The *d* of the ending *ed* in English verbs and participles is unvoiced to [t] by progressive assimilation whenever the final consonant or consonant cluster of the stem is voiceless. Examples: *walked* [wɔkt], *asked* [æskt], *tapped* [tæpt]. Exceptions: Whenever the stem ends in [t] or [d], the ending *ed* is pronounced as a separate syllable with normal voicing. Examples: *batted* [ˈbætəd, ˈbætɪd], *added* [ˈædəd, ˈædɪd].

Dissimilation.[57]   Dissimilation consists in (1) dropping of one of two similar nonadjacent sounds in a word, or (2) replacing one of them with another sound.

Examples of (1): *ar'tic* for [ɑrktɪk, ˈɑktɪk], *su'prise* in General American for *surprise* [səˈpraɪz], [pəˈtɪkjələ] in General American for *particular* [pəˈtɪkjələ], *gover'ment* for *government*, *Feb'uary* for *February*.[58]

---

[56] Schlauch, p. 176.
[57] Gray, p. 70; Ernest Weekley, *The Romance of Words*, London, John Murray, 1912, pp. 52–54; Bloomfield, p. 300; Paul, p. 55; Schlauch, pp. 174–175.
[58] It is possible also to explain [ˈfɛbjuˌɛrɪ] as a pronunciation analogous to *January*.

Examples of (2): *Annabel* and *Arabella* from earlier *Amabel*,[59] *purple* from Latin *purpur*, *irreploachable* (in hurried speech) for *irreproachable*.

Ablaut.   Ablaut (apophony, qualitative gradation, internal inflection)[60] is a system of vowel variation known in various parts of speech, but in English most commonly recognized in verbs, such as *sing, sang, sung*; *drive, drove, driven*; *hang, hung, hung*; etc. There has been a great deal of speculation and some considerable research to find why the changes take place. One very interesting development has been the rise of a theory that the changes grow out of a relationship between pitch and vowel quality.[61] The assumption here is that the pitch which gives the recognizable characteristic quality to any vowel is absolute, and that some vowels therefore lend themselves to being spoken at high pitch, others at low pitch. It would follow, then, that if sentence sense demanded high pitch on a given syllable, a vowel would be chosen which would accommodate itself to that pitch; if low pitch were demanded, then a vowel suitable for low pitch would be selected. Since Indo-European, and after it, Sanskrit, Greek, Slavic, and, more immediate to the present purpose, Germanic, had free stress, which might rest on root, prefix, or suffix, it followed that the stressed syllable of one form of a word might become either a stressed or an unstressed syllable in another form, and so, by reason of its changed pitch, require a different vowel.

Another and related theory[62] is that tension and high pitch go along with interest, that action in the present is more interesting than at any other time, and that therefore front vowels will be used in the present tense, back vowels elsewhere. Still another[63] makes the observation that high vowels are used to express present time, and adds that sounds in the distance are low, hence verbs expressing past (distant) time use low vowels. The whole subject invites still further investigation.

Ablaut becomes a matter of concern here when (a) by analogy weak verbs are fitted into the ablaut series of a strong verb, or (b) when a strong verb of one ablaut series is transferred to another. Examples: (a) *dive, dove*, by the analogy of *thrive, throve*; (b) *fling, flang, flung*, by the analogy of *sing, sang, sung*.

---

[59] [m] and [b] are similar in that both are bilabial.
[60] Vendryes, p. 77.
[61] W. Viëtor, *Elemente der Phonetik*, Leipzig, 1915, p. 28; H. Hirt, *Der Indogermanische Akzent*, Giessen, A. Töpelmann, 1895, p. 16.
[62] That of Prokosch, quoted by Schlauch, p. 162.
[63] That of von der Gabelentz, quoted by Schlauch, p. 162.

Anaptyxis.[64]   Anaptyxis is the appearance of a vowel (usually a form of [ə])
between consonants[65] and alongside a vowel-like consonant, such as [l] or
[r]. It is the result of retarded utterance. Examples: colloquial [ˈɛləm] and
[ˈfɪləm] for *elm* and *film*; western [pəˈrɛrɪ] for *prairie*; seriocomic [pəˈliz]
for *please*; [kəˈræk] for *crack*; [spəˈlæʃ] for *splash*; *Henery*[65] for *Henry*;
Dickens' "sap-pur-IZE" and "sapparised"[66] for *surprise* and *surprised*,
"gan-ger-ene" for *gangrene*.

Word Shrinkage.[67]   Word shrinkage is a product of rapid utterance, which
results first in unstressing of vowels and then in complete loss of some of
them, often with some of their accompanying consonants. Simple examples
are British *library* [ˈlaɪbrɪ] and *secretary* [ˈsɛkrətrɪ], which passed through an
intermediate stage, [ˈlaɪbrərɪ] and [ˈsɛkrətərɪ]. Extreme examples are usually
found among proper names and other often used words: [ˈtʃʌmlɪ] from
Cholmondeley, *bedlam* from *Bethlehem*, *sexton* from *sacristan*, [ˈboʊsən] from
boatswain, [ˈwɛskɪt] from *waistcoat*, [ˈmɔdlən] from *Magdalen* [ˈmægdələn],
[ˈglɔstə] from *Gloucester*, etc.

Simplification of Consonant Clusters.[68]   Both initial and final consonant
clusters are likely to be simplified if difficult to pronounce. Examples of
simplified initial clusters: O.E. *hlaf* > *loaf*, *hlaford* > *lord*, O.E. *hlæfdige* > *lady*,
O.E. *hlystan* > *listen*, O.E. *cniht* [knɪçt] > *knight* [naɪt], O.E. *gnagan* [gnɑgɑn]
> *gnaw*, O.E. *wriðan* > *wrap*, *shrink* > substandard *s'rink*, *shroud* > sub-
standard *s'roud*, O.E. *hnecca* > *neck*, *lecture* > substandard [ˈlɛkʃə-ə], *picture*
> substandard [ˈpɪkʃə-ə] or [ˈpɪtʃə-ə].

Examples of simplified final clusters: substandard [lɪsː] for *lists* [lɪsts],
substandard *ask'* for *asked* [æskt]. For survivals of earlier pronunciation of
final *ng*, *mb*, and *mn*, cf. *stronger-strong*, *longest-long*, *clamber* > *climb*, *columnar-
column*, *solemnity-solemn*.

Aphesis.[69]   Aphesis is the dropping of an unstressed initial vowel or syllable.
Examples: *esquire* > *squire*, *opossum* > *possum*, *escheat* > *cheat*, *estop* > *stop*,
estrange > *strange*, *estray* > *stray*, *assize* > *size*, *ensample* > *sample*, *espice* > *spice*.

---

[64] Bloomfield, p. 384.
[65] Giles, p. 119.
[66] Oertel, p. 221.
[67] Weekley, p. 56.
[68] Bloomfield, pp. 370–371.
[69] Bernard Groom, *A Short History of English Words*, New York, The Macmillan Company,
1935, p. 57.

Prothesis.[70]   Prothesis is the prefixing of a sound designed to break up an undesirable consonant cluster. Spanish appears to have an aversion to using [s] plus a consonant initially. Latin *stare* has accordingly therefore become *estar*; similarly, *scrībere > escribir*, *Stephanus > Esteban*, etc. French has the same aversion for initial [s] plus consonant, with an added aversion for the [s] itself in such clusters. Accordingly, we have *scrībere > écrire*, *Stephanus > Étienne*, *status > état*, etc. Mn.E. has numerous doublets, one of which is based on the O.F. derivative of Latin, and the other on the Latin itself: *estate —state, established—stable*.

Excrescent Sounds.[71]   Words ending in [s] where [s] is not an inflectional ending, sometimes acquire an excrescent [t], developed by allowing the tongue to go from the [s] position to a complete closure and then removing it while the breath pressure is still sufficient for a plosion. Some of these excrescents have been accepted, such as *against* and *betwixt*, from earlier *agains* and *betwix*, as well as the doublets *while-whilst*, *among-amongst*, which have the excrescence on the second of each pair. But *clost* [kloʊst] and *closter* for *close* and *closer* remain unapproved, as well as [wʌnst] for *once*, [twaɪst] for *twice*, [doʊst] for *dose*, etc.

Words ending in [n] may take on an escrescent [d]. Examples: *drownd* for *drown*, *gownd* for *gown*, *sound* from M.E. *soun*.[72] Words ending in [ŋ] may take on an excrescent [g] or [k]. Examples: [lɔŋg] for *long* [lɔŋ], [ræŋk] for *rang* [ræŋ].

Blend-Words (Portmanteau Words, Contamination).[73]   A blend-word is an artificially contrived word made up of parts of two words having some relation in meaning. The purpose of the compound is more often than not satiric or humorous. Examples: *happenstance*, from *happen* and *circumstance*; *bellocution*, from *bellow* and *elocution*; *globaloney* from *global* and *baloney* (from bologna sausage); *quitulate*, from *quit* and *capitulate*; *snerpent*, from *snake* and *serpent*; *ruvershoes*, from *rubber* and *overshoes*. Most such words are "dated" and do not outlive the immediate time of their invention. Occasionally, as in the instance of the often cited *brunch*, from *breakfast* and *lunch*, or *Amerindian*[74] from *American* and *Indian*, a blend-word "catches on" and has a somewhat longer life.

[70] Gray, p. 71.
[71] Marckwardt, p. 34.
[72] Robertson, p. 201.
[73] Gray, pp. 106, 150.
[74] Henry Alexander, *The Story of Our Language*, Toronto, Thomas Nelson and Sons, 1940, p. 166.

Raising and Lowering.   Raising is a vowel change resulting from elevation of the tongue. It, too, is related to assimilation, in that the rise of the tongue, as in the example of *men* below, may be in anticipation of some following sound, such as [n]. It appears as a substandardism in many dialects of English. Examples: Southern [mɪn] for *men* [mɛn], [hɔːd] for *hard* [hɑːd], [goʊn] for *gone* [gɔn]; Eastern *hev*, *hed*, and *thet* for *have*, *had*, and *that*; the universal *git* for *get* and *ketch* for *catch*; the colloquial [eɪg] for *egg*, [leɪg] for *leg*; etc.

Lowering is the opposite of raising. Examples: colloquial *kag* for *keg* and [rʊt] for *root* [rut]; Rocky Mountain [ˈɑdɪənts] for *audience* [ˈɔdɪənts]; Southern *enterest* for *interest*, [lɛntʃ] for *lynch*; *pore* and *shore* for *poor* and *sure*; [rɛntʃ] for *rinse*, etc.

Fronting and Backing.   Fronting is the arching of the tongue near the front of the mouth rather than at the back or center. Examples: the old-fashioned *shet*, *tech*, and *bresh* for *shut*, *touch*, and *brush*; *jist* and *jest* and *sich* and *sech* for *just* and *such*.

Backing is the opposite of fronting: Examples: [ˈtʃʊldrən] for *children* [ˈtʃɪldrən], *cuss* for *curse*, *bust* for *burst*.

Centralizing.   Centralizing is the arching of the tongue in the center of the mouth rather than at the front or back. Examples, *purty* for *pretty*,[75] [ˈprʌzədənt] and [ˈsʌnətɚ, sʌnətə] for *president* [ˈprɛzədənt] and *senator* [ˈsɛnətɚ, ˈsɛnətə]; New York and New Orleans [vɝs] for *voice*; N.E. [mɝɪs] for *mice*.

Vocalization.[76] (**Vowelization.**)   Vocalization is the change of a consonant to a vowel. The vowel-like consonants [l] and [r] lend themselves particularly well to this evolution. Cockney [mɪok] and American (especially Southern) colloquial [mɪək, mɪuk, mɪok] for *milk* are examples. *Will, bill, sale, fail,* and many other words undergo the same change. Southern, Eastern, British *there* [ˈðɛə], *poor* [ˈpʊə], etc., from [ðɛr], [pʊr], etc., can be regarded as carrying along a vowelized residuum of [r] in the form of [ə].

Diphthongization.   Diphthongization is the changing of a single or pure vowel into a gliding combination composed of an infinite number of imperceptibly differing sounds, arranged in sequence between the initial vowel and the closing vowel. These two vowels identify the diphthong. Since the

---

[75] There is, of course, metathesis here also.
[76] Schlauch, pp. 177–178.

intermediate sounds are disregarded, the word diphthong, which means literally two sounds, can by a process of rationalization be considered an appropriate designation. In the principal diphthongs of American English, viz., [eɪ, aɪ, aʊ, ɔɪ, oʊ], the first vowel is stressed and easily recognizable, and the second is unstressed and relatively obscure.

The evolution of single vowels to diphthongs is a constant phenomenon in many languages. M.E. *a* [ɑ], as in *name* ['nɑmə], changed to Mn.E. [e] and took on the off-glide [ɪ], so that it is represented in Mn.E. by the diphthong [eɪ], as in *name* [neɪm]. The added [ɪ] has only irregularly appeared in the spelling; the diphthong is completely spelled out in *day* [deɪ], *lay* [leɪ], *deign* [deɪn], but not in *date* [deɪt], *late* [leɪt], *Dane* [deɪn].

The M.E. [ɔ], as in *holy* ['hɔlɪ], changed to [o] and took on off-glide [ʊ], so that it is represented in Mn.E. by the diphthong [oʊ], as in *holy* ['hoʊlɪ]. The added vowel [ʊ] has only irregularly appeared in the spelling of the many words pronounced with [oʊ]; the diphthong is completely spelled out in *row* [roʊ], *low* [loʊ], *dough* [doʊ], but not in *rote* [roʊt], *lo* [loʊ], *dote* [doʊt].

The sound [i], as in M.E. *devyse* [də'vizə], has taken on the on-glide [a], which has appropriated the major stress of the combination, so that the diphthong [aɪ] has resulted, as in Mn.E. *devise* [dɪ'vaɪz]. The spelling has never changed to keep pace with the sound change and so, even more frequently than in the case of [eɪ] or [oʊ], the two sounds of [aɪ] are represented by the single letters *i* or *y*. In a few loan words such as *aisle* [aɪl], and in occasional native words such as *height* [haɪt], the diphthong is represented by two letters.

The diphthonging process is still continuing in English. In the South generally and in New York City, [ɜ] frequently becomes [ɜɪ], as when *word* [wɜd] becomes [wɜɪd]. In New York City and New Orleans even [ɔɪ] appears occasionally, as in [wɔɪd]. In the South [ɔ] often becomes [ɔo] or [ɔʊ], as when *walk* [wɔk] becomes [wɔok] or [wɔʊk]. Sometimes the basic vowel itself shifts additionally to [o] or [a], as when *on* [ɔn] becomes [oʊn] and *long* [lɔŋ] becomes [laʊŋ]. The shift [ɔ] > [oʊ] is limited to the three words *on* (with its derivatives), *gone* and *want*; the shift [ɔ > aʊ] is more general. Also in the South [æ] before [s] and [n] often shifts to [æɪ], as when *dance* [dænts] and *last* [læst] become [dæɪnts] and [læɪst]. Occasionally [æ] shifts as far as to [eɪ] in the South, as when *can't* [kænt] becomes [keɪnt]. In the General American area and to some degree elsewhere, [ʊ] and [ɔ] before [ʃ] often shift to [ʊɪ] and [ɔɪ], as when *push* [pʊʃ] becomes [pʊɪʃ] and *wash* [wɔʃ] becomes [wɔɪʃ]. In New York City stressed final [i] shifts to [ɛɪ], as when *agree* [ə'gri] becomes [ə'grɛɪ]. In Cockney [i] shifts to [əi], as when *see* [si] becomes [səi]. In the

South any vowel may expand to three or even four sounds, the front vowels drawing on the glide [j] for assistance in the midst of the group, and the back vowels drawing upon the glide [w]. Thus *sat* [sæt] may expand into ['sæjət] or ['sæɪjət], and *call* [kɔl] into ['kɔwəl] or ['kɔowəl]. (See p. 293.)

All of these more recent shifts are strongly resisted by educational influences and may or may not become established, depending on the relative strengths of the trends themselves and of the resistance.

Monophthongization. The reduction of diphthongs to single or pure vowels is as persistent a tendency in language as diphthongization. The antagonism of these two tendencies furnishes another item in the long list of examples of the compensatory tendencies apparent in language, whereby balance in phonemes seems to be maintained. American English exhibits interesting examples: as against [ɔ] > [ɔɪ] in the General American area, we have [ɔɪ] > [ɔ] in some parts of the General American area and the South, as when *boil* [bɔɪl] becomes [bɔl]; and as against [æ] > [æɪ] in the South, we have [aɪ] > [a] (sometimes [ɑ], as when *I* [aɪ] becomes [a] (or [ɑ]), *high* [haɪ] becomes [ha], etc. As against Cockney [i] > [əi] in *see* [si] to [səi], we have Cockney [aʊ] > [ɑ], as when *tower* ['taʊə] becomes [tɑ].

Palatalization.[77] Palatalization results whenever anything causes the tongue to present a broad upper surface in loose contact with the middle part of the hard palate. A high front vowel requires the tongue to assume something like this position, and may palatalize the preceding consonant. Indeed, it may be said that in English [k] and [g] are regularly palatalized by front vowels.[78] The IPA symbol for front [k] is [c], and for front [g], [ɟ]. *Key* and *geese* may then be transcribed [ci] and [ɟis]. The sounds [c] and [ɟ] are non-distinctive, since they occur automatically through the regressively assimilative influence of the succeeding vowels. But in some parts of the United States, e.g., Virginia, the front [c] and [ɟ] are also used with back vowels, whereupon the palatalization takes on the form of an intrusive [j], as in *car* [cjɑ] and *guard* [ɟjɑd].[79]

Many words in modern English represent palatalizations of O.E., such as *drench* from *drencan* ['drɛŋkɑn]. Others have come into English through the French with palatalizations of Latin [k], as *chief* and *chef* from *caput* (head), *gender* from *genus* (kind).

[77] Schlauch, pp. 184–186.
[78] Bloomfield, p. 117.
[79] See corrective exercise, p. 296.

The raising of vowels promotes palatalization in modern American English and produces a change which, because new, is regarded as a serious error. Raised [æ] in *calf* [kæf] superinduces the insertion of the palatal [j], producing [cjæ⁴f]. In children's talk *Indian* ['ɪndɪən] may similarly become ['ɪndʒən]; or British English *endure* [ɪn'djʊə], already containing a palatal, may increase the palatal effect to [ɪn'dʒʊə]. ['dʒutɪ] and [dʒuk] for *duty* and *duke* are not unknown in various English dialects. *Nature* ['neɪtʃə(ɚ)] and *action* ['ækʃən] contain quite well-approved palatals. *Natural* ['nætʃərəl] and *don't you* ['doʊnˌtʃu] are usually better thought of than the pedantic ['nætjurəl] and ['doʊnt ˌju]; *literature* balances between ['lɪtərəˌtjʊə(r)] and ['lɪtərətʃə(ɚ)]; but *enduring* [ɪn'dʒurɪŋ] is taboo.⁸⁰

Unrounding.   The unrounding of rounded vowels is a change resulting from unrounding the lips. In modern English it customarily appears as a substandardism apparently resulting from a languid manner, as if the muscles lacked tonus. Example, *a good book* [ə gʊd bʊk]⁸¹ becomes [ə gɤd bɤk].

Unstressing.   Unstressing is an outstanding phenomenon of Germanic languages, and especially of English. In English the vowel of any unaccented syllable tends to become reduced to [ɪ] or to a light sound equivalent to the French mute *e*, or the last sound in *Cuba*. This sound is usually referred to by the name *schwa*, and is represented by the symbol [ə]. Examples, *open* ['oʊpən]; *Cuba* ['kjubə]; *among* [ə'mʌŋ]; *city* ['sɪtɪ], *reject* [rɪ'dʒɛkt].

Sometimes a vowel (or diphthong) does not level to so great a degree as to become [ə], but instead becomes merely a light, shortened form of itself. Examples, *obey* [o'beɪ]; *orate* ['oʊret]; *event* [i'vɛnt]; etc.

In some of the dialects of English, as southern British and Southern American, many vowels unstress to [ɪ] which in such dialects as General American, Irish, and Scotch, unstress to [ə]. Examples, British *telephone* ['tɛlɪˌfoʊn], Southern American *voices* ['vɔɪsɪz], as compared with General American ['tɛləˌfoʊn] and ['vɔɪsəz].⁸² Faulty unstressing results from confusion as to whether to use [ɪ] or [ə]. In *sody* ['soʊdɪ], *Floridi* ['flɔrədɪ], and *Marthy* [marθɪ], [ɪ] is used where [ə] should be used; in *Missoura* [mɪ'zurə], *Miama* [maɪ'æmə], and [hɪt əm] for *hit him*, [ə] is used where [ɪ] should be used. In some cases both have become standard, as in doublets of both spelling and pronunciation such as *Anna-Annie* and *Laura-Laurie*, and doublets of pronunciation, such as ['fɪlɪs-'fɪləs] for *Phyllis*.

⁸⁰ See Chapter V for exercises on substandard palatalization.
⁸¹ See Chapter V for exercises to correct substandard unrounding.
⁸² See references to unstressing in Chapter V and elsewhere.

Restressing. Restressing is a phenomenon which tends to occur whenever a vowel which has been unstressed to [ə] is for any reason placed in an accented position. Thus *was* and *of*, which in unstressed positions become [wəz] and [əv], are in stressed positions often pronounced [wʌz] and [ʌv].

In song, particularly, restressing is likely to appear when a customarily unstressed syllable has to be stressed by being sung on a sustained note. Thus *when he cometh* [ʍɛn ɪ kʌm-ʌθ], and *through all eternity* [θru ɔl itɜ(ɜ)nʌti], are often heard, the [ʌθ] and the [nʌ] displacing the customary [əθ] and [nə]. Obviously the better practice is to give any restressed vowel the value it originally had before unstressing took place. *Com-eth* and *e-ter-ni-ty* in song would then be [kʌm-ɛθ] and [i-tɜ(ɜ)-nɪ-tɪ]; *was* and *of* would be [wɑz, wɒz] and [ɑv, ɒv].

Usually any restressed form developing [ʌ] from [ə] or [ɪ] is considered substandard. Examples, ['mʌnro] from *Monroe* [mən'roʊ]; ['pʌkˌɒn] from *pecan* [pɪ'kɑn]; etc. For the word *from* [frɑm], however, [frʌm] is accepted as one of the approved pronunciations.

The discussion above recognizes strong (two degrees) and weak stress only, applying to vowels which are in English commonly called merely stressed and unstressed. Further refinement of stress categories seems to have little value in English, except for comparative or illustrative purposes. A native speaker makes all the variations automatically, governed by context. He need be conscious only of two concepts: stressing and unstressing. But a foreigner whose stress patterns are different will profit from a more detailed view of English stress.

Compensatory Lengthening. In Southern American speech the failure to pronounce *r* before consonants and finally in a syllable usually has the effect of quantitatively *lengthening* the preceding vowel. This added length becomes in some cases phonemic, for it is the means of distinguishing what would otherwise be ambiguous homonyms. Compare the following:

cod [kɑd]	card [kɑːd]
cot [kɑt]	cart [kɑːt]
shock [ʃɑk]	shark [ʃɑːk]
dock [dɑk]	dark [dɑːk]
cotter [kɑtə]	Carter [kɑːtə]

Such cases as these present the only important instances in modern English where length is phonemic, i.e., where it has significance in distinguishing meaning. In Eastern and British English the vowels of *cod* [kɒd] and *card* [kɑd] are different, and any added length is nonsignificant.

Obviously extra length is nonsignificant, though indubitably present, in vowels before voiced continuants and plosives, as in *tame* [teɪm], *sale* [seɪl], *made* [meɪd], as contrasted with vowels before voiceless consonants, as in *take* [teɪk], *faith* [feɪθ]. Except in such words as those paired above, changes in length come and go in English, automatically controlled by context, but unimportant in relation to meaning.

Compensatory lengthening may be found throughout language history. In the transition from Latin to French the loss of a nasal consonant had the effect of lengthening (as well as nasalizing) the preceding vowel; e.g., *cantare* —*chanter* [ʃɑ̃ˈte]. The loss of [ç] from O.E. *niht* [nɪçt] was compensated by the lengthening of the vowel, thus [nit], whence *night* [naɪt], which still retains the length of [i] in the combined length of [a] and [ɪ].

Shortening.   A voiced consonant after a vowel lengthens the vowel, as may be seen by comparing *beat* [bit]—*bead* [bid]; it follows that the unvoicing of a consonant shortens the vowel. When the [ð] of *with* [wɪð] becomes [θ] through regressive assimilation, as in *not against Charles, but with* [wɪθ] *Charles*, the [ɪ] automatically becomes shorter. But the change is non-phonemic.[83]

In compounding, long use brings about shortening through unstressing. *Postman*, a word long in use, has a short, unstressed final syllable *man*, thus, [ˈpoʊstmən]. Here the original vowel [æ] has become the obscure [ə]. *Iceman*, because a younger word, with secondary stress, retains the longer [æ], thus, [ˈaɪsˌmæn]. But such reasoning does not explain why Missourians pronounce *yesterday* [ˈjɛstɚdɪ] with a short final syllable, whereas Louisianians pronounce *yesterday* [ˈjɛstəˈdeɪ]; with a long final syllable.

Language Substrata.   Some sound change may result from the learning of a language by people who retain the phonetic patterns of their own tongue.[84] Descendants of such people, if they live close together and in large numbers, will speak with a foreign accent, though they may know no foreign language. The United States offers interesting examples: the Pennsylvania German, the Milwaukee German, the English spoken by the Louisiana French people, the Yiddish dialect of New York, and the speech of many other "speech islands," especially in industrial centers.

These names all designate varieties in English speech. The foreign substratum "shows through" in the form of pure vowels instead of English

---

[83] Unless we recognize the possibility of confusing the preposition *with* the noun *withe*, which seems very unlikely.

[84] Bloomfield, p. 386.

diphthongal vowels, substituted foreign consonants for English consonants unfamiliar to the original immigrants, rhythms and intonations foreign to English, etc. After a long time, some of these characteristics may come to seem normal for a given region (if the region is large enough), and they will thenceforward be thought of as native, not foreign.

Apocope.[85]   Apocope is a term usually confined to the loss of final vowels. This loss readily occurs in English, because of the strong stresses of the language, usually on preceding syllables. Chaucer abounds in final *e*'s which by now have become extinct.

> Whan that Aprille . . .
> > . . . to the roote.
> > . . . He loved chivalrye,
> Faith and honour, fredom and courtesye.

Cf. modern *April, root, chivalry, courtesy. Tomor'* [təˈmɑr:] for *tomorrow,* and [hɑr:] for *harrow* are modern examples. The sequence has doubtless been [təˈmɑro—təˈmɑrə—təˈmɑr:]. The [r] has absorbed the duration value of [ə] and has become long; thus [r:].

Sometimes the scope of apocope is expanded to include the omission of final consonants, syllables, or even longer portions of words. By these definitions, *nex'* for *next, las'* for *last, miss* for *mistress, mob* for *mobile vulgus, cab* for *cabriolet, auto* for *automobile, gas* for *gasoline,* etc. may be included. (See also Clipped Words, page 379.)

Syncope.[86]   Syncope is a similar loss of medial sounds. Cf. Middle English *foules* [ˈfuləs], modern English *fowls* [faʊlz]. *Var'able* for *variable, assoc'ation* for *association, ser'ously* for *seriously,* and in fact most syncopes, involve the loss of a syllable, giving rise to the term syllabic syncope.[87] Sometimes the term is expanded to include the loss of a consonant, as in the modern pronunciation of *glisten, thistle, whistle, listen, often,* without [t].[88] The weakening of medial [t] to [ɾ] or [d] in *better, Kitty, water,*[89] etc., may be regarded as a partial syncope.

---

[85] H. W. Fowler, *A Dictionary of Modern English Usage,* Oxford, Clarendon Press, 1926, p. 599; O. F. Emerson, *The History of the English Language,* New York, The Macmillan Company, 1933, p. 244; Bloomfield, p. 382.

[86] Bloomfield, p. 382.

[87] Oertel, p. 207.

[88] Marckwardt, pp. 29–30.

[89] Bloomfield, p. 374.

Metathesis.[90] Metathesis is the exchange of the position of sounds. Examples, *prespiration* for *perspiration*; *horse* for O.S. *Hros*; etc. Louisiana French-English regularly has *ax* for *ask*. The combination [s] plus a plosive is particularly susceptible to exchange. *Waps* for wasp, *gaps* for gasp, *bax* for bask, etc., are cases in point. *Westren* for *western*, *pattren* for *pattern*, *modren* for *modern*, *aporn* for *apron*, *purty* for *pretty*, etc., involve [r] preceded or followed by a consonant. The transposition of sounds may take place over some distance, i.e., between sounds in different words. This variety is called a "spoonerism." Examples: *dit of bifference* for *bit of difference*, *half-warmed fish* for *half-formed wish*, *well-boiled icicle* for *well-oiled bicycle*.[91] Actually, there is no exchange here, only the shifting of [b].

Haplology.[92] Haplology is a form of syncope involving the loss of duplicative elements. Examples, Latin *nutrix* from *nutritrix*; *Mis'sippi* for *Mississippi*, *miz* for *mistress*, [koʊkˈkoʊlə] for *Coca-Cola*, *Posties* for *Post Toasties*.[93]

Glides. (*Epenthesis*—the insertion of a consonant; intrusion.)   Glides, in the sense of this paragraph, are sounds introduced in liaison between other sounds. Examples: the [b] in *number*, from Latin *numero*; the [b] in *nimble* from M.E. *nimel*; the [p] in *something* [ˈsʌmpθɪŋ]; the [t] in *hence* [hɛnts]; the excrescent [r] in *the idear of it*; the [k] in *strength* [strɛŋkθ]; the [j] in *muse* [mjuz].

Semantic Change

Semantic change, or change of meaning, is a term of many applications. These changes come about because of the impossibility of retaining the original meanings of words through the shifting experiences of life. Here follow a number of the types of semantic change most frequently recognized. Several of them originate as conventional figures of speech which by long use and much repetition have lost their original vividness and have become worn and faded[94] into stereotypes. This dulled condition of once forceful figures is perhaps nowhere better exemplified than in oaths and low name-callings, where the terms are worn so smooth by futile repetition that many

[90] Herbert A. Strong, Willem S. Logeman, and Benjamin Ide Wheeler, *Introduction to the Study of the History of Language*, New York, Longmans, Green & Company, 1891, p. 37; Bloomfield, p. 391.

[91] Gray, p. 73.

[92] Oertel, pp. 207–208.

[93] E. H. Sturtevant, p. 55.

[94] Sturtevant, p. 91.

users and hearers have never actually "translated" them so as to discover their literal meanings. Such expressions are like the casual "good-bye" of daily speech, which has "God be with you [ye]" buried within it.

Connotation.   Connotation, the associations adhering to a word (as opposed to its dictionary definition, or denotation—see Chapter IX, page 512) may change, narrow, or strengthen the meaning of the word. World War II produced many examples. *Dunkirk, Pearl Harbor,* and *Hiroshima* are at the time of writing this paragraph still functioning, though a little worn; of the series *Casablanca, Teheran, Bretton Woods, Dumbarton Oaks, Yalta,* and *San Francisco,* only *Yalta* still has specialized significance. It will be interesting to note how long these words retain their special meanings without explanation. *Quisling* was once spoken of as a familiar new word in many languages. Will it survive? Many similar words have become widely used in their connotative senses. Examples:

> He met his *Waterloo* (defeat).
> The *cross* and the *crescent* (Christianity and Mohammedanism).
> The *stars* and *stripes* (the U.S.A.).
> He went through his *Gethsemane* (period of trial and suffering).

Sometimes connotations may completely obliterate denotations, as in the following colloquy:

> YOUNG MUSIC PUPIL: Yesterday I heard both of Beethoven's symphonies.
> TEACHER: Both?
> PUPIL: Yes. What are you smiling at?
> TEACHER: Just what two symphonies did you hear?
> PUPIL: The Fifth and the Ninth. What others are there?

It seems impossible that even a beginner should so far lose himself in the appreciation of music as to forget the denotation of five and nine; yet most speakers have similarly lost sight of the numeral two in *twilight* and in German *Zwielicht* and Spanish *dos luces,* which mean the same thing; in *twig* and its German equivalent, *Zweig;* and in *doubt* and its German equivalent, *zweifeln.*

Pleonasm [95] **(Redundancy).**   Pleonasm results from the loss or shift of etymological meaning, so that need is felt to strengthen the significance with another word meaning the same thing, usually a contemporary native word. Examples: *love philtre* (philtre < Gr. *phileo,* love); *hound dog* (cf. Ger. *Hund,* dog); *greyhound* (Icelandic *grey* = dog); *crisp curls* (cf. Lat. *crispus,* curly).

[95] Fowler, p. 440.

Metaphor.[96]   A metaphor is a compressed *simile*, or comparison. Where a simile states that something is *like* or *similar to* something else, a metaphor states that it *is* something else. Examples: an *acid* face or disposition; a *wolf* in *sheep's* clothing; the man is a *rat* or *hog* or *fox*; "Words are *silver*, but silence is *golden*"; her heart was *lead*; he had a *quicksilver* (or *mercurial*) temper; he is a *windbag, gourdhead, woodenhead, blockhead, egghead*; an *iron* will.

Synecdoche.[97]   Synecdoche is a figure naming something using a part or quality for the whole or the whole for a part. Examples: hired *hand* for hired *man*; under my *roof* for in my *house*; God's *creatures* for *living things*; fifty *sail* for fifty *ships*; *blade* for *sword*; a huge *sea* (for *wave*) rolled over the deck; "thar she blows—ile!" where *ile* (oil) means *whales*. *Town*, originally *fence* (cf. Ger. *Zaun*), for both the protective enclosure and the buildings within and ultimately, with the disappearance of the enclosure, the buildings only.

Metonymy.[98]   Metonymy is the use of a word for some other word closely related to it in meaning—container for thing contained, the material for that which is made from it, the tool for the act: He likes his *bottle*, for he likes *liquor*, etc. We travel by *rail*, by *motor*, and by *air*. In earlier slang a woman was a *rib*, later a *skirt* or *frail*. We speak of good *rubber* on the car for good *tires*; of resorting to the *knife* for *surgery*; of providing a good *table* for good *food*; of *canvas* for *sails*, of bringing the *sword* for bringing *war*; of living by *bread* alone for living physically to the exclusion of living intellectually, etc.

Widening (Generalization).[99]   *Yankee*, originally of very limited meaning, came to mean, before the Civil War period, a New Englander; during and after the Civil War, any Northerner; during both World Wars, any American. *Cafeteria*, in Spanish a coffee shop, is in American English a self-help restaurant where all sorts of foods can be had. *Frock*, once only a clerical gown, is now applied to any skirted dress. *Victrola*, a trade name originally designating only a single brand of phonograph, has now expanded in the popular language to mean any phonograph. The same widening of application has come about with the trade name *Kleenex*, which now means any facial tissue; and there is nearly as great a generalization for *Frigidaire*, which is

---

[96] Bloomfield, pp. 149, 150, 426–427.

[97] Bloomfield, p. 427; Edward D. Myers, *Foundations of English*, New York, The Macmillan Company, 1940, p. 164; Strong, Logeman, and Wheeler, p. 58; Sturtevant, p. 91.

[98] Myers, p. 163; Bloomfield, p. 427; Robertson, p. 467; Sturtevant, pp. 91–92.

[99] Marckwardt, p. 170; Robertson, pp. 428–429; Schlauch, p. 121; Bloomfield, pp. 151, 426, 430; Alexander, pp. 132–134.

very often applied to any mechanical refrigerator. *Burner*, once narrowed (see below) from one who, or that which, burns to mean a gas jet or comparable object, is again widened to include the heating element of an electric stove. To *ship*, itself consisting of an expansion from a noun to a verb, meant first to send by boat, later by freighter's wagon, overland express, train, truck, and airplane. Incidentally, a steamship or motorship still sets *sail*. *Manufacture* (literally *to make by hand*, from Lat. *manus* and *facere*) now means to make in any way, especially by machinery. From *cork*, a bottle stopper made from the bark of a certain tree, we derive, first the verb *to cork*, meaning *to stop up*, whence such fantastic expansions as *to cork a bottle with a wooden cork*, or a *glass cork*, or a twist of paper made into a *paper cork*. A farmer even corks his water jug with a *corncob cork*, and the spout of his kerosene can with a *potato cork*. By the same process of thinking we may hear of an *aluminium tin-cup*, while parts of a machine may be called *dogs, spider, claw, crowfoot*, etc., according to real or fancied resemblances. By a similar widening, stalks of wheat have *heads*, mountains and trees have *feet*, lakes have *arms* or *branches*, etc.

Narrowing (Specialization).[100] German *sterben* means to die in any manner whatsoever; English *starve*, from the same primitive root, means to die from one cause only, lack of food. Latin *familia* has come into English (family) and German (Familie) with its original meaning of the whole domestic circle; the Russian word *familia* means only a person's last name. *Liquor*, which originally meant liquid, now usually means an intoxicant; even in this meaning it has further narrowed to mean only distilled intoxicants, as may be seen in the common listing, *beer, wines*, and *liquors*. *Burner*, which by construction should mean any person or device that burns things, now means, unless qualified, the part of a stove, lamp, or other utility where the inflammable substance is consumed. A *cultivator*, etymologically one who or that which cultivates, means on a farm only an implement for cultivating row crops. Lat. *corpus* (body), when it reaches English through the French as *corps*, means a group or body of individuals, organized if not militarized; while as *corpse*, it means only a dead body. The German *Gott strafe England* (God punish England) of World War I appears in English as *to strafe* [streɪf], the hortatory subjunctive 3rd person singular of the German having become an English infinitive, used in World War II with the principal meaning of punishing ground forces (or civilians) by machine gunning from low-flying airplanes. *Bed* and *board*, and *aboard* ship (or train, bus, or plane) are strikingly

---

[100] Schlauch, p. 120; Gray, p. 274; Alexander, pp. 130–134; Marckwardt, p. 170.

limited as compared with *board* meaning a *plank*, and *holiday* has all but lost the broader meaning of *holy day*. In folk usage, *doctor* means only M.D., to the exclusion of LL.D., Ph.D., J.D., etc., while *disease* means only bodily sickness, not the earlier dis-ease or discomfort. English *deer* is a particular animal, while the cognate German *Tier* is any animal.

Litotes.[101]   Litotes is the strengthening of meaning by understatement. In gangster slang, *to rub out* means *to kill*. *To snuff out, to liquidate, to purge, to account for*, etc., may also mean to kill. *Boiled, stewed, oiled, squiffed, pifflicated,* etc., may be used to mean *drunk*. *Not bright, not "all there,"* etc., may mean *feeble-minded*. "The late unpleasantness" is a classical substitute for *the war*. A great deal of slang consists in attaching strong meanings to weak words. Many euphemisms operate similarly—*passed on, passed away, gone to his reward, gone beyond*, for *died*; *took some refreshment* for *ate*, etc.

Elevation (Amelioration).[102]   When a word comes to designate a concept of higher rank, value, or satisfaction than originally, it is said to be elevated or ameliorated. Examples: to a child in humorously affectionate vein, *you little rascal* raises an ordinarily negative word to a positive value. *Gospel*, which in O.E. was simply *god spell*, or good tidings, has come to have sacred meaning as containing a plan of salvation. *Angel*, originally a messenger, now means a higher supernatural being. *Fond*,[103] in Shakespeare's time meaning foolish, now means affectionate. *Success*, which Macbeth[104] uses in its etymological sense to signify merely that which follows, either good success or bad success,[105] now means only good success, unless otherwise qualified. *Knight* (O.E. *cniht*), originally a boy or servant (cf. Ger. *knecht*, servant), became a title of nobility.

Degeneration[106] **(Pejoration).**   Degeneration is the lowering of meanings, or the adoption of worse meanings (Lat. *peior*, worse, whence pejoration),

----

[101] Bloomfield, p. 427; Myers, p. 163; Schlauch, pp. 121 f.
[102] Robertson, pp. 437–438; Alexander, pp. 139–140; Gray, p. 260; Schlauch, p. 119.
[103]   "Yea, from the table of my memory
                         I'll wipe away all trivial fond records."
                              Hamlet, Act I, Sc. 5, l. 98–9.
[104]   "If the assassination could trammel up
                        the consequence, and catch with his
                        surcease, success."
                             Macbeth, Act I, Sc. 7, ll. 2–4.
[105] Cf. the Irish imprecation, "Bad 'cess to him!"
[106] Gray, pp. 260, 272; Schlauch, p. 118; Marckwardt, pp. 170–171; Bloomfield, p. 426; Alexander, 128.

through unsatisfactory experiences. *Fool*, which once meant a court jester, has come to mean a numskull, a reckless person, etc. From Lat. *Christianus* (Christian) we have Fr. *crétin* and E. *cretin*, a type of mental imbecile said to be characterized by a gentle, "Christian-like" disposition. *Villein*, once merely a serf, farm laborer, or villager, now *villain*, designates an evil or criminal person. E. *boor* is cognate with Du. *boer* and Ger. *Bauer* (farmer). *Doom*, once meaning only judgment, has come to mean condemnation. From *Bethlehem*, by way of an insane asylum so named, we have *bedlam*; from *John Duns Scotus*, *dunce*; from *Damascus*, *damask*; from *Magdalene*, *maudlin*; from *St. Audrey*, *tawdry*—all epithetologues arrived at by degeneration. *Crafty*, derived from *craft* (skill, cf. Ger. *Kraft*, strength), has degenerated to treacherous. *Knave* (O.E. *cnafa*), originally a boy, servant (cf. Ger. *Knabe*, boy), has degenerated to mean a rascal. *Silly*, which Coleridge used to mean blessed, happy (cf. Ger. *selig*), now means foolish. *Hussy* comes merely from housewife; the earlier meaning of *lewd* was only ignorant.

Hyperbole.[107]   Exaggeration. *Crushed* for *discouraged*; *mortification* (from Lat. *mors*, death), *embarrassment*; *astonished* (cf. Fr. *étonné*), etymologically *thunderstruck*; *awfully* glad for *very* glad; *your humble servant* for *myself; dear sir* for *Mr. Blank*, and *dear sirs* for *gentlemen*; *dead* tired for *very* tired; *sick* of something for *bored*; *in seventh heaven* for *delighted*; etc.

Miscellaneous Changes

Out of the many other formulae of change that the research of a century has disclosed, a few of the more serviceable are listed in the following paragraphs.

Analogy.   Self-defining.[108]   Examples: *Lawr of the Medes and Persians*, analogous to *War of the Roses*; *I heared him*, on the analogy of *I feared him*; *Feb'uary*, on the analogy of *January*; *column* [ˈkɑljəm], on the analogy of *volume*; *these cheese*, on the analogy of, e.g., *these trees*; *I must get me some license* (for *a license*), on the analogy, e.g., of *I must get me some siphons*; *cherubims* and *seraphims*, on the analogy of *arms* and *limbs*—or any regular English plurals, etc. These are auditory analogies. There are also visual or graphic ones. *Whole* (from M.E. *hal*) is modeled on *who*; *island* (from M.E. *iland*, O.E. *igland*) is modeled on Fr. *isle* (from Latin *insula*); *debt* (from M.E.

[107] Bloomfield, p. 427.
[108] Robertson, p. 108.

dette) is modeled on Latin *debitum*; *doubt* (from M.E. *doute*) is modeled on Latin *dubitum*.

Folk Etymology (Popular Etymology).[109]   Folk etymology is a form of analogy. It is the name given to the tendency of people, usually less literate people, to substitute for a strange and difficult word or syllable some familiar word or syllable. Examples: *Westminister* for *Westminster*; *telefoam* for *telephone*; *cold-slaw* for *coleslaw* (from Ger. *Kohl*, cabbage); *Bushway* for *Bourgeois* [ˈburȝwɑ]; *sparrow grass* for *asparagus*; *mad axe* for *mattock*; *broom sage* for *broom sedge*; *flatform* for *platform*, *cow buckle* for *carbuncle*; Fr. *pomme d'amour* (whence E. *love apple*) from It. *pomo dei moro* (*Moor's apple*); *Moros* (Filipino Mohammedans) from *Moros* in Spain (Moors, also Mohammedans); *primrose* from O.F. *primerole* (first little flower); *cockroach* from Sp. *cucaracha*; *gargle-oil* from *Gargoyle motor oil*; *flatypuss* for (duck-billed) *platypus*; *Slumberjay* for *Schlumberger* [ʃlymbɛrˈze] (French pronunciation of German *Schlumberger* [ˈslʊmˌbɛrgər], anglicized in American oil fields); *Smackover* (Arkansas place name derived from French *chemin couvert* [ʃəmɛ̃ kuˈvɛr].

Hyperurbanism (Overcorrection).   A sound change usually made in the mistaken effort to speak correctly. Examples: [ˈkɪtʃɪŋ], for *kitchen* [ˈkɪtʃə(ɪ)n]; [ˈmaʊntɪŋ] for *mountain* [ˈmaʊntən]; [ˈlɪnɪŋ] for *linen* [ˈlɪnən]; [ˌsɪnsəˈnætə] for *Cincinnati* [ˌsɪnsəˈnætɪ] and [mɪˈzʊrə] for *Missouri* [mɪˈzʊrɪ] reveal the speaker's efforts to avoid pronunciations like *sody* for *soda*.

Invention.   Sometimes words are actually invented, even at this date, though derivation is much more common, considering the great number of words already extant. Even so, the *invention* usually has some suggestion—it probably has to have, considering that no neural response can be had without stimulus. *Kodak* is said to have been Mr. Eastman's version of the camera click; *zoom* is onomatopoetic; *Nabisco* is an acrostic from National Biscuit Company. Lewis Carroll's *chortle* (possibly a portmanteau word based on *chuckle*, since the nearby *gallumphing* looks like a blend of *gallop*, *jump* and perhaps *puff*), Gelett Burgess' *blurb* and van Helmont's *gas* have become permanent additions to the language. It is said that during World War II the title *Women's Auxiliary Volunteer Emergency Service* was deliberately constructed so that the acrostic *Waves* would result, as a companion word to *Wac* (Women's Army Corps), and to the Coast Guard *Spar*, made from the initial letters of the Coast Guard motto and its translation, *Semper Paratus*,

[109] Schlauch, pp. 103–104; Bloomfield, pp. 423–424.

Always Ready. Science continually coins words from Latin and especially Greek elements, such as *cardiac, psychoanalysis, hysterectomy, thermometer,* and hundreds of others. *Pericardium* and *altimeter* employ both languages.

Spelling Pronunciation.[110] Self-defining. Examples: [ˈgrinwɪtʃ] for *Greenwich* [ˈgrinɪtʃ(dʒ), ˈgrɛnɪtʃ]; [ˈɔftən] for *often* [ˈɔfən]; [ˈfourˌhɛd] for *forehead* [ˈfɔrəd]; [ˈhɪkˌkɔf] for *hiccough* [ˈhɪkˌʌp]; [ˈkʌpˌbourd, ˈkʌpˌboəd] for [ˈkʌbəd, ˈkʌbəd].

Frequency. Words may live or die according to *frequency* of use. Slang words are good illustrations. *Beau,* once of almost universal currency, is seldom heard now. *Dead pan* as a description of the face of a vaudeville "feeder," or gullible interlocutor, may disappear now that vaudeville houses have given way to the motion pictures. Many sailor's terms are dying out with the passing of sailing ships. But *submarine* appears likely to live a long life. *Home, child, bread,* etc., are so frequently used that they will live indefinitely. Frequently used irregular verbs tend to remain irregular; less frequently used verbs regularize.

Shortening (Clipped Words).[111] Many words have dropped all but the first syllable or two, or a modification thereof. Examples: *gasoline > gas, automobile > auto, cabriolet > cab, mobile vulgus > mob, zoological garden > zoo, medical physician > medico, veterinary surgeon > vet, Captain > Cap, Doctor > Doc.* Most such words retain their original forms beside the shortened forms; *mob* is an exception, *cab* very nearly so.

Other words have lost all but the last syllable or two. Examples: *gator* for *alligator, plane* for *airplane, goo* for *gaspergou* (La. Fr. for freshwater drumfish), *skeeter* (jocular) for *mosquito, coon* for *raccoon, phone* for *telephone.*

This by no means completes even an enumeration of linguistic formulae. But it may point the way toward answering some of the questions to which our perennial linguistic curiosity addresses itself.

---

[110] Kenyon, pp. 113–116.
[111] Gray, p. 150; Schlauch, p. 101.

Chapter VII

The Psychological Basis
of Speech

Introduction

Any consideration of the psychological basis of speech must of necessity be based upon its primary functions. Although in most of its external manifestations speech appears as a patently social activity, involved in the establishment and maintenance of relations among human beings, at the same time it has profound psychological implications. That is, in its capacity as a socializing agent it is also performing an indispensable function in the mental life of the individual himself. It is therefore, impossible to arrive at a satisfactory explanation of the psychological factors involved in speech without an examination of its use in social adaptation and adjustment, social integration, and social control, as well as of its relation to and dependence upon the individual's own mental habits, his attitudes, and feelings.

A living organism is an active organism. Its activity is the result of certain drives, impulses, motives, which lead to basic or acquired goals. The precise forms of this activity are functions of the environment, usually stated in terms of stimuli, or stimulus patterns. Communication is, like all life, a process of stimulation and response, based on these drives and motives, some of which are internal and some external. External stimuli seem to be as powerful in eliciting fundamental response patterns as are internal stimuli.[1] In either case, these impulses, whatever their origin, are potent forces in the initiation and continuance of behavior. Although communication is essentially a social process involving the concerted participation of two or more people, it has likewise many individual aspects arising out of the impulses and

[1] Harry F. Harlow, "Mice, men, monkeys, and motives," *Psychological Review* (1953), *60*: 23–32.

complex behavior patterns of both speaker and listener. Furthermore, because of its symbolic nature, the forms used in communication are also the basic forms employed in most of our thinking processes. It is therefore important that we understand something of the nature of communication itself. For it is as a medium of communication that the social and psychological functions of speech have developed.

In its social application—and this social function is implicit in much of our personal use of language—communication consists of motivated action on the part of one person, providing the stimulus, and motivated reaction on the part of another, responding to that stimulus in accordance with the manner in which that stimulus is related to his own action tendencies. Both action and reaction, in this sense, are the resultant of many contributing factors, some of which, at least, it is the purpose of the present chapter to examine.

The Communicative Situation

It should be obvious that not every situation in which one individual provides a stimulus to which another responds involves communication, except in the broadest meaning of the term. A man is sitting in a room writing; he hears footsteps on the walk outside. He pauses to listen, perhaps looks up to see who is passing. The passerby glances up, sees the man looking at him through the window and goes on without a sign of recognition. The man within turns, perhaps, and makes a comment to someone in the room. He may do any one of a number of things directly as a result of his having observed another man passing his window; but despite the fact that here is a situation providing a stimulus to which there has been a definite response, there has been no communication between the two men.

Suppose, however, the passerby, on looking up, waves a hand in greeting and the one inside responds by a similar gesture. What the latter does subsequently may, so far as can be observed, be identically the same thing that he would have done without the friendly act; actually, though, his movements have been the result of a communicative process. In relation to the individuals involved, both stimulus and response are different; and this difference lies in (1) the nature of the situation, (2) the nature of the stimulus, and (3) the nature of the response, the specific response itself further determined by factors soon to be described.

The Nature of the Situation

In the first instance described above no social relation has been established between the two men. It is true that the behavior of the one has been influenced by something the other has done; one has provided a stimulus to which the other has responded. Yet there has been no *concerted participation*. Any action of the man within the room that has been affected by the passerby has been entirely without purpose or design on the part of the latter. Social coöperation has been entirely lacking.

In the second instance, however, a social situation has been established. The one man's behavior has been influenced by something the other has done; one has provided the stimulus, the other has made a response. But this time there has been a purposely concerted participation; the raising of the hand in a return greeting has been directly the result of the passer's intention in greeting in the first place. He has secured by his action a measure of social coöperation; slight and fleeting it may be, but nevertheless present.

The "situation," as the term is used here, involves considerably more than the mere presence of two persons in some sort of social interaction. A complete analysis of the situation would involve an understanding of the emotional state of each individual at the moment, his motives and attitudes toward his present task, perhaps, as well as toward the other individual, the presence or absence of other people, his general behavior tendencies in similar situations, and so on.

Moreover, he has used a particular type of stimulus. The mere waving of the hand may or may not have communicative significance, depending on the total situation. In and of itself, it "means" no more than waving the hand. But in this particular case it "means" more than that: it has communicative significance. Why?

The Nature of the Stimulus

Stimuli may, in the main, be of two sorts. The first may be illustrated by the example of a loud noise produced close to a newborn baby. A direct, native reaction to this stimulus bears the characteristics of a fear reaction. Not that the child is consciously afraid of the noise; it lacks past experiences which would lead it to be conscious of anything definite. It simply exhibits all the features ordinarily present in a fear response, which may be a somewhat different thing. Similarly, loss of support, or dropping, may elicit the same type of response. We may say, then, that these are *adequate* stimuli for this particular reaction and that the response is a native response to that particular stimulus.

The presence of a puppy or a kitten will not elicit this response; it is an *inadequate* stimulus for the fear reaction. But if, at the same time the animal is presented, or slightly after it, a loud noise is sounded, and this combination is repeated several times, the child will soon come to exhibit the same response to the animal, or one closely resembling it, that it showed to the noise alone. What was originally an inadequate stimulus has come to produce much the same reaction as the adequate stimulus with which it was repeatedly presented. It has become the *substitute stimulus* and the reaction to that stimulus has become an acquired rather than a native reaction; it has become a *substitute response*.

The principle of the substitute stimulus is based upon a physiological law formulated many years ago by Pavlov and discussed in some detail in Chapter IV. The application of this law to association and learning has been developed at considerable length in the literature of psychology. The law, which has been modified since its formulation near the turn of the present century, is essentially a simple schematic design of one of the principal types of learning. Even motives themselves, we are told, may be modified by various types of conditioning.[2] At the same time, the process of conditioning itself is greatly facilitated when strongly motivated. A call to dinner is much more likely to arouse positive reactions when one is hungry than after a hearty meal. Children whose parents anticipate their every want are usually delayed in learning to speak.

The Nature of the Response

Setting up a substitute or conditioned stimulus will at the same time produce a substitute or conditioned response. If an electric shock, producing a sharp leg jerk, is presented immediately following the sounding of a buzzer, the buzzer alone will soon produce the leg jerk without the shock. Not only is the buzzer, then, a substitute or conditioned stimulus for the leg jerk, but the jerk is at the same time a substitute response for the buzzer. It must be noted, however, that the conditioned response is not often of the same quality as the original, native response. Whereas the motion in response to the shock

---

[2] Gardner Murphy, "Social motivation," in *Handbook of Social Psychology*, Gardner Lindzey (ed.), Cambridge, Mass., Addison-Wesley Publishing Company, vol. II, 1954, pp. 601–633. See also Charlotte Buhler, "Maturation and motivation," *Personality* (1951), *1*: 184–211.

will be sudden and jerky, that in response to the buzzer is likely to be smooth, steady, with no wasted energy.[3]

We see a paper bag lying on the sidewalk. It seems to be quite natural, though not necessarily native, for us to kick out of the way any and all objects lying in our course. But previous experiences with similar paper bags on sidewalks, and possibly with bricks inside them, may have led us to modify our response so that instead of kicking it we pass on by. We learn to avoid actions which produce physical discomfort or pain, or which make us appear foolish.

Although loud noises are inherently fear-producing stimuli, we can and do train ourselves not to show such reactions. We hear a loud shot; instead of exhibiting all the characteristics of fear such as are shown by the baby, we may even respond by a curiosity as to what the shooting is about. Partially because of changing motives, we substitute another sort of reaction for the original, native response. Children want things when they want them, and will often fight to get them. But they can be, although they are not always, taught to respond differently, to "socialize" their wants, so to speak, so that as adults they will fit into the social order with less friction. The ancient dictum, "An eye for an eye," has been in general replaced by a different group attitude toward offenders against the social order, a lesson which peoples and nations must learn as well as individuals.

The individual starts out in life with definite and strong desires. His modes of fulfilling these desires are primitive, bordering sometimes on the savage. The wants are powerful stimuli to action, and never entirely disappear. But the individual's modes of satisfaction change; more "civilized" responses come to be substituted for the original.

The Basis of Communication.   It has been said that human speech began when men started to hurl epithets instead of coconuts or stones. Without, for the moment, examining the validity of this statement as explanatory of the origin of speech, let us consider the situation hypothetically to see if we can discover the application of the principle of the substitute stimulus and response to language as a whole. Let us suppose that from his arboreal refuge one of our primordial ancestors hurled a stone or a coconut at his enemy, accompanying the missile with a savage yell. The stone or coconut is a direct attack; it is an adequate stimulus for direct action, and something must be done about it. The yell is as yet inadequate; it can cause no damage. The return volley, another coconut or stone, is also accompanied by a wild cry.

[3] John Frederick Dashiell, *Fundamentals of General Psychology*, 3rd ed., Boston, Houghton Mifflin Company, 1949, pp. 424–425.

In time, as each finds that he can dodge the physical missiles hurled by the other, the adequate stimuli he drops from the affray, and to the substitute stimulus, the first cry, returns a substitute response, the answering yell. And, we may say, the process has been going on from that day to this!

Crude as this example may be, it illustrates the point that herein lies the essence of the nature of communication. As long as organisms, man or animals, were engaged in direct activities, such as attack or defense, in physical contacts, in satisfying their basic needs and wants, and acting alone, there was no such thing as communication; there was no need for it any more than there is need for the child to learn to speak whose every want is anticipated. Only direct stimuli and responses were possible. It was only when substitute stimuli and responses came to be used in place of direct action that communication began. The whole structure of language is based upon this process. Words become words when they can be used as substitute stimuli or substitute responses to satisfy certain needs and desires, and when they mean approximately the same thing to two or more individuals of the group. When these words are used to call forth a response, they are substitute stimuli; when they are used as responses to stimuli, they are substitute responses. When language is used as a stimulus to further language reactions, then words form both substitute stimuli and substitute responses.

As Weiss pointed out many years ago, it is this property of language, the fact that it can function as either a response to a stimulus or a stimulus for a response, that "fits it particularly well as a means for intercommunication and coöperation." [4] It should be pointed out, however, that even though language activities may and do occur as responses, they are significant in communication primarily when they are used as stimuli for further responses, either of action or of still further language. It is not quite correct, as de Laguna argues, that "Men do not speak simply to relieve their feelings or to air their views," but it is true that most of their speaking has as its purpose "to awaken a response in their fellows and to influence their attitudes and acts." [5]

Typical of this sort of situation is ordinary conversation. One participant makes some comment which is answered by his friend. Although the reply is a response to the original remark, it is more significantly a stimulus to further reaction on the part of the first speaker. And so the exchange continues, each stimulus being determined, it is true, by the nature of the

[4] A. P. Weiss, *A Theoretical Basis of Human Behavior*, 1925. Columbus, R. G. Adams & Co., 1925, p. 300. See also Joseph Kirk Folsom, *Social Psychology*, New York, Harper & Brothers, 1931, pp. 94 f.

[5] Grace Andrus de Laguna, *Speech: Its Function and Development*, New Haven, Yale University Press, 1927, p. 19.

stimulus coming from the other speaker. What we have here is a chain of stimulus-response, each response being the stimulus to a further response, until the chain is broken or completed by some outside influence or by direct action.

Factors Determining the Specific Response. The specific response which may be made to any stimulus pattern, or within any given situation, is influenced by three factors: (1) the nature of the organism responding, (2) the past experiences of that organism, and (3) the present situation within which is the specific element that may be termed the stimulus.

THE NATURE OF THE ORGANISM. Because of differences in physical makeup, different organisms will respond differently to the same stimulus, if indeed it is possible ever to present the "same stimulus" to any two organisms. One will be attracted by light, another will be repelled. One lives in the water, another avoids it. A room temperature comfortable for one will be too high or too low for another. Human beings cannot follow a trail by scent, but dogs can. Cats, owls, and other nocturnal animals can see at night when it is so dark that the human eye can barely distinguish objects only a few feet away.

People vary among themselves; individual differences can often be explained on no other basis than that the individuals themselves are simply different; they have dissimilar physical, neuromuscular organizations. Apart from the basic biological urges, their motives are different, their wants are varied. One becomes a salesman, another buries himself in a laboratory. One enjoys the study of music, another mathematics. Only rarely does one find a mathematician who is also a musician like Einstein. In many instances there is no explanation for such variations except that people are inherently different; and no amount of training will make one person preëminent in a field of activity for which he has no aptitude whatever, even though anyone with normal intelligence may develop a certain degree of proficiency in almost anything he undertakes. The mere fact that there is within the human race such a diversity of interests, so many people who have reached high eminence in so many different activities, is evidence that these differences do exist.

THE PAST EXPERIENCES OF THE ORGANISM. The child may show a fear reaction to an animal because sometime in the past the animal has been presented to him simultaneously with a loud noise, or perhaps because it has scratched or bitten him and caused him pain. All associations are based upon previous experiences in which the things associated, or their elements, have been linked together. Furthermore, a repeated association tends to strengthen the bond. It is said that if one uses a new word consciously three times, he has added it permanently to his vocabulary. On the other hand, an association may undergo what is known as *extinction* through disuse. Much of what is learned in classes is "forgotten" for the simple reason that it is never used.

"Any explanation of . . . speech must take into consideration the fact that experiences in some way leave an effect upon the individual and tend to have that effect revived after a passage of time. . . . On the action side, a movement once made in response to a given stimulus tends to be repeated whenever that stimulus presents itself and, when repeated frequently enough, becomes the invariable consequent of that stimulation."[6] This is the natural result of the process of canalization, by which neurograms, sometimes termed engrams, or memory traces, are set up.

THE PRESENT SITUATION.   The term stimulus has been used frequently in the discussion up to the present. It must be pointed out that the word refers not to an isolated stimulus, apart from all context, but to an element in the total situation, or even to the total situation itself, which is a complex, a "configuration," a *Gestalt*, to which and within which we respond in a given way, both the organism and the response being perhaps themselves a part of the total stimulus pattern. There is of course no such thing as an isolated stimulus; that which we so designate always emerges, so to speak, from a background, from a pattern which includes every influence bearing upon the organism at the moment, including the physical and mental status of the organism itself. What we often call the stimulus is the particular element or combination of elements which differentiate two or more complex patterns similar in all significant details except for this one variable. Physiological conditions, impermanent attitudes, and hence the total situation, including the motives for action, vary from time to time in the same individual, so that what seems to be a situation identical with a previous one is actually not the same at all. Arguments which were at one time totally ineffective become, because of such changes in the listeners, strong appeals for action. Brutus and Marc Antony spoke to the "same" mob, with totally opposite results.

We are driving down the road at night. Suddenly we see ahead the red taillight of another car. What we do about it depends on how close it is, on which side of the road it is, how fast we are going, the known efficiency of our brakes in relation to the speed of our car, the condition of the road, the

[6] W. B. Pillsbury and C. L. Meader, *The Psychology of Language*, New York, Appleton-Century-Crofts, 1928, pp. 92–93.

pressure of time in relation to our need for arriving at our destination, and a number of other factors, all of them forming the total situation, and the meaning of the light is made specific by virtue of its relation to all the other elements therein. A change in any one or in any combination of these factors would call for a quite different response.

Similarly, we might say that a stone is a stone; that a given stone would be the same whether it were an obstruction in our path or a geological specimen in the laboratory. The object may be the same, it is true; but its function as a stimulus is determined by its relation to other elements in the total situation, including the particular "frame of mind" in which we happen to be at the moment. What we do about it, how we respond, is fixed by our inherent nature, our past experiences, and the present total situation of which the stone in question, in relation to other aspects of the pattern, is but one element. Later we shall see (Chapter IX) how the total situation, the context, in which words are used has a significant effect on their meanings.

Motivation

Introduction

Much has been made earlier in this chapter of the importance of motives as the basis for activity. It is quite appropriate, therefore, that the problem of motivation be examined, especially as it relates to speech. Dewey has pointed out that activity, rather than inertia, is the normal state of animal existence, including the existence of the human race. "In every fundamental sense," he says, "it is false that a man requires a motive to make him do something. . . . It is absurd to ask what induces a man to activity generally speaking. He is an active being and that is all there is to be said on that score." But whereas "to a healthy man inaction is the greatest of woes," it is when we begin to inquire into the basis for specific acts that the question of reasons and motives arises. "A motive," Dewey goes on to say, "is then that element in the total complex of a man's activity which, if it can be sufficiently stimulated, will result in an act having specified consequences." [7]

The Status of Motivation Knowledge.   Unfortunately, specific knowledge regarding motivation, particularly with reference to the problem of speech, is little advanced beyond its status when Dewey wrote. "With the conclusion of

[7] John Dewey, *Human Nature and Conduct*, New York, Henry Holt and Company, 1922, pp. 118 ff.

total war," wrote Koch in 1951, "psychology seems now to have entered an era of total disorientation. . . . Nowhere is disorientation—old style or new—more evident than in the field of motivation." When we turn to facts, he continues, "what we find is a ridiculously meager set of scattered experimental findings and empirical observations. Moreover, much of this material proves, on close analysis, to be ambiguous, unreliable, of indeterminate generality, or downright trivial." [8] Three years later Atkinson was writing," . . . the theoretical controversy concerning the nature of human motivation is going to require facts for resolution, and the accumulation of the facts to be explained requires the development of suitable methods." [9]

British psychology seems to have fared little, if any, better. Laird and Knight, of the University of Aberdeen, in reviewing the present status of motivational psychology refer to it as "a field which is at once probably the most fertile and the least clearly defined in the whole of psychology." The results of experimental work, they say, has been interpreted "almost according to the particular sympathies of the experimenter." [10]

Perhaps despite these discouraging comments from psychologists themselves something may yet be salvaged. It is doubtful if there is a total vacuum.

Principles of Motivation

In formulating the principles of motivation, areas of agreement and of nonagreement will be found. In the following discussion these areas will not always be designated as of either one or the other.

Sources of Motives.   Among the areas of nonagreement with respect to motives and motivation is the question of the source or sources of the motives themselves. Both the theory that all motives arise from a single drive, such as relief from tensions, and the one which "names practically every observable response in great specificity," each with its many subdivisions, as separate "drives" which form the basis for separate motives, have been generally superseded by a theory which postulates "a middle region of a limited number of relatively flexible tendencies—a few main drives." In general, motives seem

[8] Sigmund Koch, "The current status of motivational psychology," *Psychological Review* (1951), *58*: 147–154.

[9] John W. Atkinson, "Exploration using imaginative thought to assess the strength of human motives," in *Nebraska Symposium on Motivation*," Marshall E. Jones (ed.), Lincoln, University of Nebraska Press, 1954, pp. 56–106.

[10] A. J. Laird and A. R. Knight, "Contemporary studies in motivation," in *Current Trends in British Psychology*, C. A. Mace and P. E. Vernon (eds.), London, Methuen & Co., 1953, pp. 125–137.

to be regarded as "energy sources which keep mechanisms at work." They are characteristically directed broadly toward end results that are desirable, or away from those that are undesirable.[11]

The original motives, those that are active during the earliest months of human life, are either entirely biological, or, after survival has been provided for, hedonistic. As the individual develops in the social environment, however, motives must become socialized, modified in such ways that the motivation of others will have equal room for play; otherwise the conflicting wants and desires of the various members of the group would lead to disorder and anarchy. In the process of enculturation, moreover, additional motives are acquired which have a direct bearing on one's relations with one's associates. The result is that long before adulthood such a structure of motive has been erected that the original drives with which one started out are recognized with difficulty, if at all.

Modification of Motives.   As we grow older and encounter the necessity for coping with our physical and social environment, we find that the motives which direct our general behavior must be modified considerably. We must adjust our behavior patterns in accordance with the physical world about us; there are some aspects of that world that can be molded to satisfy our wants and needs; other aspects cannot be so modified, and we must adjust our wants and needs accordingly. Motives must also be modified in accordance with the social environment as well as the physical.

SOCIAL MODIFICATION OF MOTIVES.   Social modification of motives may be accomplished by one or more of three types of learning: first, by conditioning; second, by intercommunication—that is, motives do not "enjoy sharp physiological isolation, and in time they may become closely connected, so that the arousal of one serves also to arouse the other"; and third, by "progressive increase in the strength of the association between a specific object and a specific type of satisfaction, so that in subsequent behavior the satisfaction is sought by pursuing this particular object rather than some other object which might serve the drive just as well. . . . We develop 'acquired tastes.' "[12]

MATURATION.   In addition to the factor of learning in the modification of motivation is that of *maturation*, as proposed by Buhler.[13] The term matura-

---

[11] Murphy, *op. cit.*
[12] *Ibid.*
[13] Buhler, *op. cit.*

tion refers to the development of the organism and its functions through growth processes. Hence, the fact of growth itself, with its various implications, brings about automatic modification of all the functions of life, including that of motivation. As Buhler herself points out, however, "the difficulty is that maturation and learning are so interwoven that it is hard to isolate the changes of direction due to one or another factor."

Through whatever process such modifications take place, they must be recognized as normal and necessary phenomena in the life of all normal human beings, a fact which must be taken into consideration in a psychological approach to speech. For much if not most of the process of education, both formal and informal, consists in the modification of motivation, which both influences and is influenced by the processes of learning. During the course of development, it should again be emphasized, the modification generally goes so far that the original source of the motive itself is almost completely lost, and the relation is difficult if not impossible to trace.

Some confusion with respect to motives and motivation may perhaps be dispelled by thinking of motives in broad terms of *goals*, or objectives, which are satisfied when and only when these end results are reached. Since it is apparently a characteristic of the human race to set some of these goals quite beyond reach, it is clear that one's satisfactions are attained not always in the ultimate achievement of the objective, but at least partly in striving to reach it, and partly in getting as close as one can. As one ardent sportsman was once heard to say, "I'd rather go fishing than to fish!" And a certain railroad advertises, "Going is half the fun."

UNIVERSALITY OF MOTIVES. Although motives are originally acquired individually, the processes by which they become modified, either biological or cultural, are such that "the probability of certain *common* motives developing in all people is very high. . . . Socialization occurs in all cultures for all individuals and it involves certain common problems in all cultures. Thus the likelihood of certain cues getting associated with reward or punishment is fairly high for all men. . . . The fact remains that *some associations . . .* are laid down in all individuals in all cultures, at all times, simply because with very few exceptions everybody is faced at one time or another with achievement problems." [14] It is this principle that in all probability accounts for what is usually thought of as the universality of motives. The "*forms of learned behavior that are common to all men because of commonly shared environmental*

[14] David C. McClelland, "Notes for a revised theory of motivation," in *Studies in Motivation, op. cit.,* pp. 226–234.

features" (which undoubtedly include modified motivation) are termed *coenotropes* by Dashiell.[15]

Motive and Reason.   Although the terms *motive* and *reason* are often used interchangeably, one's reasons and one's motives for performing a given act are not necessarily the same. The difference was pointed out several years ago by Woodworth:

A reason is thought-out and conscious, which a motive need not be. On the other hand, a reason does not become a motive unless it takes hold of us and arouses a genuine tendency towards the planned result. You may prove to me, logically, the desirability of a course of action, but your reasons do not necessarily make me desire it. You can give a child excellent reasons for studying his lessons, but you have to stir some real motive of child life in order to get action. In the highest type of conduct, to be sure, motive and reason pull together, reason showing the way to the goal at which the motive is aimed.[16]

Motives impel us toward certain end results, certain goals, or certain end reactions; the specific course of action leading to these objectives may be determined by reason. In other words, we have our reasons for choosing a specific line of endeavor, which will in turn lead to the satisfactions of some persistent impulse that constitutes the motive. Assuming that activity in general is a basic characteristic of normal human life, it is motive rather than reason that gives direction to that activity in reaching our goals. Winans defines a motive as "an effective desire. . . . We choose one of two desirable courses because desire is stronger in one direction than in the other."[17]

Motive and Purpose.   Some distinction may also be made between motives on the one hand and purposes on the other. The term *motive* is taken to refer to those impulsions which activate behavior at various levels and in certain general directions, whereas *purpose* refers rather to the specific objectives involved in the selection of a particular mode of satisfaction. Thus one may be activated by a general attitude of sympathy for the unfortunate; this attitude may emerge in overt action in any one or more of several forms, the particular form being determined by the immediate purpose. Conversely, one's purpose may be affected by the form of satisfaction which happens to present itself at the time. One's purpose in acquiring an education may be to

[15] Dashiell, *op. cit.*, p. 153.
[16] R. S. Woodworth, *Psychology, A Study of Mental Life*, New York, Henry Holt and Company, 1921, p. 85.
[17] James A. Winans, *Speech-Making*, New York, Appleton-Century-Crofts, 1938, pp. 304 ff.

achieve a number of different goals, such as improving one's economic status, providing for a lifelong avenue of enjoyment, rendering a positive service to society, or elevating one's social standing. At the same time one chooses a particular college because he feels that there his purpose may be better and more economically accomplished.

The residents of a community may be activated by a desire for esthetically pleasing surroundings; they will attend a special lecture by a prominent landscape architect for the purpose of discovering how they can make those surroundings more beautiful. A group of businessmen are motivated by the desire for acquiring a greater amount of property, or greater profits from their businesses;[18] they will listen attentively to a well-known advertising manager for the purpose of discovering how they can increase sales. Sex and companionship are powerful motives in human life; people choose their mates with the purpose of securing for themselves the maximum satisfaction of these motives.

THE BASIS OF ASSEMBLY.   The motives which may lead people to assemble are essentially the same sort as those which impel them to any other type of behavior. It is unnecessary to do more here than to reiterate that we do not engage in unmotivated activity. Our motives may be either selfish or unselfish, personally or socially oriented; on occasion both kinds may be operative. They are probably rarely in the focus of attention at the time; it may not always be evident just what our motives for a given course of action are. We ourselves do not always know why we do some of the things we do. Whatever the motives currently predominant, they tend to emerge in the form of more or less specific purposes which are related to current issues. Such purposes may themselves be stimulated by the mere announcement of an impending meeting. We see posters announcing a lecture on the political situation in Argentina, or Egypt, or East Germany; and the motive of curiosity, the desire for information, will take the form of a definite intent to hear what the speaker has to say and to acquire such facts as he may be able to present. A mass meeting is called to consider some problem of local significance, and we resolve to attend for the purpose of determining the most appropriate action to be taken to solve the problem. Even temporarily dormant motives may be awakened by the discovery of opportunities for their satisfaction. But

[18] Even the desire to add to one's wealth may have its foundation in some more deeply underlying motive, such as the increased power that wealth may bring, the increased respect which is often accorded to wealth, the providing of better educational and social opportunities for one's children, and so on. Such overlapping of motives illustrates the principle of intercommunication mentioned by Murphy, *op. cit.*, p. 13.

once the opportunity is presented, both motive and purpose become active, especially in relation to the opportunity itself. We are not, for example, constantly engaged in the satisfaction of curiosity; we need time to assimilate and apply the knowledge we already have. But with the announcement of a lecture on some interesting topic our curiosity is stimulated and we proceed to satisfy that desire for information by attending. People are not particularly concerned about the movements of celestial bodies; yet on a certain occasion when Professor Shapley spoke on "The Expanding Universe," he addressed a packed auditorium. Not everyone is continually engaged in the pursuit of esthetic enjoyment, but a concert by an outstanding artist or a famous orchestra will bring out a full house.

MOTIVES AND PROGRAMS.   These purposes and motives cannot be ignored in any consideration of audience psychology, nor can they be neglected in the planning and execution of the program. Some years ago a student convocation was called on a university campus for the purpose of hearing a high official of the government speak on a topic of current moment. The students assembled with considerable interest, even though the convocation was required; they were interested in seeing the speaker and, in the main, genuinely interested in the topic he was to discuss. Unfortunately, the program planners took advantage of the situation to stage a political love feast and arranged to have a number of local politicians appear on the platform and speak. By the time the main speaker arose to address the audience the students were thoroughly disgusted; they felt that they had been assembled under false pretenses, as indeed they had, and they had lost all interest in what they had come to hear. Moreover, the place of assembly had unforgivably bad acoustics, and was unheated despite the fact that the day was cold. As a result the speaker was faced with a situation for which he himself was unprepared, and which he was apparently totally unable to meet. The main fault, however, lay not with him or with the students in the audience, but with the authorities planning the program, for they had completely obscured and largely subordinated the promises which had been held out to the students in justification of requiring their attendance.

Motives and General Ends.   The general ends of the speaker were discussed in Chapter I as an aspect of the social basis of speech. It should be borne in mind, however, that these broader ends, together with the specific purposes of the speaker, both determine and are determined by the motives and purposes of the audience in assembling. In one instance a group will come together to hear what someone has to say upon a given subject; in another the speaker will select his purpose on the basis of the desires of the audience on that particular occasion. The speaker does not always have the choice; what is important is that he align his own purposes with those of the audience, or that he be able to justify with his listeners any significant divergence from their present purposes and motives.

On the whole, it may be said that the general purposes of assembly correspond closely to the objectives of the speaker as they have been classified. People gather to be informed, to be stimulated, to be entertained, to learn the truth about given propositions, or to be advised as to the best courses of action. It is, of course, possible for the speaker to divert his listeners from their original purpose in assembling, but it must be done, as a rule, with considerable care. If a group of people have come together to hear a serious discussion of some weighty problem with the expectation of arriving at some concrete solution, they do not want, and will probably resent, a purely entertaining speech. We go to church on Sunday morning not to be argued with, but to be stimulated, impressed. When the friends and relatives of a deeply loved member of the community not long ago gathered to pay their last respects to his memory, instead of hearing a sermon of sympathy and condolence they were shocked to find themselves being severely castigated for their own transgressions. When we have gone to hear a noted speaker present his solution to some current issues of considerable importance, we feel somehow defrauded if he fails to suggest a course of action intended to solve the problem.

"Selfish" and "Unselfish" Motives. In most discussions of the problem of motives and motivation in relation to speech, it is implied that the "mainsprings of human behavior" lie in the acquisition of some desired pleasure for oneself, the fulfilling of some felt want, the meeting of some need. There is no general agreement as to what the fundamental drives are; almost every writer on the subject has his own list, which may be as good as but probably no better than any other list. Whatever may be included in such classifications, however, it may be observed that they are as a rule based on the assumption that all human behavior is motivated by some desire, want, or need of the individual himself.

At certain levels some of these "inner drives" may be, probably are, primarily organic: self-preservation, direct avoidance of pain; others may be thought of as biosocial; that is, they have to do with the individual in relation to his fellows: ego expansion, or the "wish for worth," gregariousness or the

desire for companionship. Still others may arise from a combination of elemental urges or from others difficult to identify by the time they have become
modified through the processes of enculturation and maturation: construc-
tiveness, curiosity, acquisitiveness, freedom from external restraint, and so
on. Such motives are sometimes thought of as somehow "higher" than the
biological needs. But as Maslow has pointed out, ". . . various 'higher' needs
are as basic, as 'instinctoid,' as characteristic of the whole human species as
are the usually accepted needs for food, sex, sleep, etc. These higher needs are
(1) for safety, (2) for belongingness and love, (3) for importance, respect,
self-esteem, independence, (4) for information, (5) for understanding, for a
frame of reference or values, (6) for beauty, and (7) for self-actualization."[19]
In connection with the need for information, Festinger develops the implication in the assumption that "the human organism expends considerable
energy just finding out about the world in which he lives. He explores, he
tries things out, or is just curious about things."[20]

Hence, according to this point of view, the strongest appeals to induce
action are those which show benefits to be derived from following the course
proposed. These motives have to do, directly or indirectly, with consequences
which reflect back upon the individual and bring to him the satisfaction of
some inner desire. In other words, the implication is that our motives for
acting as we do are entirely selfish. Nor is the expression of this point of view
limited to implication. "The missionary," says West, "is as selfish as the baby,
but he has learned what the baby has not, that he is happiest who serves
himself through serving others."[21] Of course it is doubtful if the motives of
the missionary can readily be traced back to the primarily biological drives of
the infant.

It is true, as West suggests, that these "selfish" motives may be and often
are sublimated, in that in their satisfaction some contribution may be made
to the social good; but the attitude taken seems to be that in such motivation
the social good which may be accomplished is incidental to the satisfaction
that comes to the individual himself. That is, we contribute to the Red Cross
or the Community Chest or the United Givers' Fund, participate in the
activities peculiar to a democratic society, engage in social welfare work, enter
certain professions such as teaching or medicine or nursing or the ministry,
not primarily because of the good we may be able to do, but because by so
doing we are able to satisfy some inner drive, such as winning social approval,

[19] A. H. Maslow, "Higher needs and personality," *Dialectica* (1951), *5*: 257–264.
[20] Leon Festinger, "Motivations leading to social behavior," in *Nebraska Symposium on Motivation, op. cit.,* pp. 191–219.
[21] Robert West, *Purposive Speaking*, New York, The Macmillan Company, 1924, p. 20.

acquiring a respectable living, caring for our families, rising to a certain degree of temporary fame, or simply to enjoy the pleasure of doing good to others— that we belong, in other words, to that class of individuals known rather contemptuously as "professional do-gooders."

It is impossible to deny that such drives are a powerful force in the motivation of human behavior; nor can it be overlooked that all of these basically "selfish" motives can be sublimated, turned to social betterment. The objectives which may be reached through the functioning of such impelling forces are, or may be, entirely legitimate, even highly laudable. No one can reasonably object to anyone's acquiring as much wealth and property as he can so long as the methods which he employs are socially and legally acceptable and the use which he makes of his possessions is worthy. So long as a well-written book is a contribution to knowledge or to literature, we do not inquire too closely into the ultimate motives which led to its writing. We are quite willing to permit our duly elected officers to enjoy their brief moment of authority, provided they use that authority and power according to established principles and for the common good. Certainly there can be no objection when a person takes every available means of prolonging his life, or maintaining his physical health, or of providing for the welfare of his family; on the contrary, such behavior is given every encouragement, and neglect to take such measures meets the strongest social disapproval.

So long as the end results of the behavior springing from the impulsion of these motives is praiseworthy, it should follow that appeals to action on the basis of the motives themselves are justifiable. We encounter such appeals ourselves every day. We are urged to avoid fire hazards because they may result in the destruction of our property. If we use a certain type of automobile tire we will be protected against blowouts which may endanger our lives. The proper deodorant will prevent offensive body odors which repel potential suitors. Our taste will be more pleasantly satisfied if we drink a widely advertised brand of coffee. We should protect our vision by having our eyes thoroughly examined by a competent specialist. The popular magazines are filled with advertisements making entirely valid appeals to such fundamental impelling motives as self-preservation, tastes, the need for companionship, the desire for "getting and having," the "wish for worth," reputation, power, and so on. In a similar manner the speaker is on occasion quite justified in appealing for action from his listeners on the basis of these motives, even though they are "selfish" primarily in that the end results bring benefits, pleasures, satisfactions to the individual himself.

Any attempt, however, to attribute all human behavior to self-interest and motives of personal gain arises from oversimplification, as Dewey has pointed out.[22] To be sure, such motives do exist, as has been recognized, and if held within certain limits they need no excuse. But it can hardly be said with justification that all our acts arise from a desire for personal benefit or aggrandizement, or that every motive which forms the basis for human activity grows, either directly or indirectly, from one or more of the four or five fundamental biological drives. The processes of socialization and maturation are operative in this regard as well as in other aspects of human behavior.

Motives and Habits. It is commonly thought that habits arise from motives, that we acquire certain patterns of behavior in order to satisfy our needs, wants, and desires. It is equally true, however, to say that motives sometimes grow out of habits. Much of the training of children is directed toward the development of such habitual modes of behavior as will give rise to end results, the persistent desire for which constitutes motive. Thus we try to teach our children to have consideration for others, to share their toys, to put their pennies into the contribution plate at church, to submerge their wills in their games to the development of a spirit of team work for the good of the group as a whole. To follow the Golden Rule in our relations with others is not instinctive.

Out of the social consciousness developed from such habits arise interests in the welfare of others, attitudes of generosity, leading to motives which can hardly be characterized as selfish in the common meaning of the term. Such sentiments as pity, sympathy, affection, with the various courses of action to which they give rise, have their bases in these habitual forms of behavior which are acquired, usually, early in life. They are powerful motives when adequately stimulated. The fact that the social behavior thus motivated brings satisfactions to the individual, rather than the unsatisfactions which would result from failure to engage in such activities, is hardly justification for considering all behavior to be motivated entirely by self-interest.

In his analysis of "selfishness" as a factor in motivation Murphy points out that "as the self develops there is identification with other persons in such a way that injury to them is injury to us." Murphy goes on to say:

There are qualitative variations and quantitative differences in the form of sympathy, but sympathy is a powerful motive. If we ask whether such sympathy is basically "selfish" (as basically self-seeking, self-centered), the answer will be affirmative in a formal sense, if one means that all such impulses are brought into relation to the self. It will at the same time become evident ... that this is because

[22] Dewey, *op. cit.*, pp. 120 ff.

the self comprises all the precious things and persons relevant to an individual's life, so that the term selfish loses its original connotation, and the proposition that man is selfish resolves itself into the circular statement that people are concerned with the things that they are concerned with.[23]

The point to be emphasized here, as regards the problem of motivation in relation to speaking and influencing the behavior of others, is that it is not always necessary to appeal to the self-interests of the listeners, or to point out, even indirectly, how they may benefit individually or collectively by following a recommended course of action. In many instances it is equally or even more effective to point out that their conduct may contribute materially to the welfare, the happiness, the safety of others. "Contribute to the United Givers' Fund!" Why? Of course such an act of generosity will give you a personal sense of satisfaction; more important, however, it will help to meet the needs of those unfortunates of the community, children and adults, who depend upon these contributions for their bare subsistence; it will make it possible for such worthwhile enterprises as the Boy Scouts, the Camp Fire Girls, the YMCA and the YWCA, and many others to continue to function for the good of the community as a whole.

It should not be understood that motives of self-interest and those of social significance are necessarily in conflict. Quite the contrary is often the case. One may put a great deal of time and effort into a program to build a new club-house, feeling that it is a community need; at the same time, the fact that one expects to get some of the benefit from that building when it is completed does not detract in the least from the socially oriented motives which direct his efforts to get it built for the good of the entire community. A physician cannot be censured for hoping to make a comfortable living for himself and his family while he is contributing materially to the physical well-being of his patients and to the general health of the community. It not infrequently occurs that one may appeal effectively to both types of motives. On other occasions the strongest appeal may be made to other motives than those of self-interest.

Fluctuation of Motives.   Another factor that must be taken into consideration in the discussion of motives is the fact that they fluctuate in relative strength and effect. They vary from time to time and are of different strengths in different people. Although, as has been pointed out, many of these motives grow out of social situations which are themselves well-nigh universal and hence may be thought of as universal, on the other hand the social habits of different peoples are almost certain to vary significantly; therefore the

[23] Murphy, *op. cit.*

motives growing out of those habits will also vary considerably. Since among different peoples different concepts of social values may and often do lead to the formation of different habits of thought and action, it may be expected that different motives will develop, or at least that they will develop in different degrees of strength. Thus freedom from external restraint, the privilege of choosing one's own course of action, which is so powerful a motive in one people, may appeal so weakly in another that it can hardly be considered a motive at all. Similarly, one nation whose people are trained to the habit of thinking they are "supermen" destined to rule the world may be highly motivated to attempt to enforce its hegemony on less aggressive nations. A person brought up to believe that the world owes him a living can hardly be expected to develop a strong motivation to get out and earn it himself, whereas another, taught that whatever comes to him will come through his own efforts, will provide for his own security.

Among individuals motives change in intensity from time to time and may be stimulated variously by changing internal and external conditions. A businessman, for instance, will give much time and effort to increasing his business and hence his income; but when properly stimulated he will also take time off from his office to participate in some community enterprise, such as a campaign for more and better playgrounds (even though he may have no children himself) which will benefit the whole city. Under normal conditions a person will go to extreme measures to protect his own life; but in emergencies he will offer to sacrifice that life in the interests of his family, his community, his country.

We are activated, in truth, by so many different motives that it would be impossible for all of them to be uppermost at any one time; in any given situation one or more will for that situation be the determining factor.

Conflict of Motives. While there is no essential or inevitable conflict between personally oriented, or "selfish," and socially oriented, or "altruistic," motives, it often happens that conflicts do arise which must be resolved in some way. Not only are there such antagonisms between the so-called "higher" and "lower" motives, but they exist in each general type. Unless hunger is extreme, it will give way before fear. Even animals often sacrifice their own lives to protect their offspring. Young men by the hundreds of thousands face danger and death in battle, in order to "get the job over with." Parents give up comforts and conveniences, even necessities they have long wanted, to send their children to college.

It would be impossible to enumerate all the possible areas of conflict which may arise among the different motives. The truth seems to be that whenever different end results, favorable or unfavorable, are so incompatible that one or more motives must remain unsatisfied, conflicts occur. The choice is made on the basis of the particular motive which is uppermost at the time. So far as the speaker is concerned, he should appeal to those motives that will most probably lead to the response he wants from the audience, observing precautions which will be discussed later.[24]

The selfish or personally oriented motives are strong in all of us. In the beginning they dominate our childish behavior; in later life they aid in the direction of our more mature behavior. As we grow more and more socially conscious we learn that limitations must be placed on the satisfaction of any motive. The necessity for these restrictions gives rise to conflicts between opposing motives. Thus, in an exploratory situation curiosity over the new may conflict with fear of the unknown. In this case, if a choice is made at all, one of the motives must be rejected; but once the choice is made it often becomes a problem to know what to do about the rejected motive. In fact, the resolution of the conflict itself is often a problem. Even without a thorough analysis of the various possibilities, the mention of a few methods of resolution, some wholesome and some not, may be pertinent.

ESCAPE. Sometimes the conflict is so even that the individual finds it difficult if not impossible to make a rational choice. In such cases a not uncommon procedure is to avoid any decision at all and to escape into a mental state where the problem may be ignored. In some cases the individual regresses into an infantile world where he is taken care of, decisions are made for him, and the complexities of adult life are avoided. Typical of this sort of attitude are the utterances of speakers who are constantly bemoaning the fact that "things aren't what they used to be," or urging that society go back to those "good old days" when life was not so complex. This is not to suggest that all reference to the past and its virtues comes under this classification; but it does argue that if the speaker is to urge a revival of earlier forms of social behavior, it should be on the basis of certain elements of superiority in those forms, rather than that human beings are incapable of adjustment to the more complicated society under which we now live.

RATIONALIZATION. Choice of action is not always made on the basis of reason; the fact is that we often decide upon our course and then try to find

[24] See pp. 408–409.

reasons for the choice. This process is known as rationalization. It may further be defined as the assigning of false motives for our actions. As William Jennings Bryan once said, "It is a poor head that cannot find a reason for what the heart wants to do."

It is undoubtedly true that the end results which we seek are determined largely upon an emotional basis. We desire peace, physical well-being, social position, ownership of property, and so on. In themselves, as has been pointed out, these may be entirely worth while. They need no justification in many instances; it is not necessary to seek to get behind them, to discover why they may be desirable, either to the individual or to the group. What does demand examination, however, is the question as to which of these end results is uppermost; what is the real and what is the ostensible motive. Rationalization consists in attributing to our own behavior a false motive, false in the sense that the assigned motive is not the real one. It grows out of a conflict in which the accepted motive, usually a personally oriented one, even though it is the real basis for the ensuing behavior, is replaced in the thinking and the attitudes connected therewith by another, more socially acceptable or more readily explainable, at least to the individual himself. It is a form of self-deception: the person is often if not usually quite unaware that his actual motives are different from those he is convinced lie at the bottom of his behavior. For the speaker, rationalization is a form of deception practiced on the audience as well as on himself.

To have the maximum power of persuasion, not for a single occasion but over an extended period of time, the speaker must first of all analyze his own motives to determine whether he himself is fully aware of his real objectives in speaking. Second, he must in his appeals to his listeners achieve a positive agreement between the logical and the emotional aspects. "Persons can be moved by short-circuiting their critical processes, but the advocate is on much sounder ground, ethically and psychologically, when he uses argument and facts to stir the springs of action. Attitudes reached through thoughtful deliberation are more likely to be active longer and to be more persistent under their influence." [25]

SUBLIMATION. It is not always possible for us to satisfy our wants in exactly the way we would prefer. Conflicts arise which make it impossible always to direct our lives along the precise path we should like to take. But

[25] Waldo W. Braden and Earnest Brandenburg, *Oral Decision-Making*, New York, Harper & Brothers, 1955, p. 504.

motives can be directed into more than one channel and still be satisfied. The rejected motives, or those which it seems must be rejected, can often if not usually be put to useful work. Such a process is called sublimation.

Illustrative of this principle are the numerous instances of women who for one reason or another are denied the privilege of children. Without offspring of their own they often devote their energies to social welfare, teaching, nursing, or other careers in which the "maternal instinct" is turned into useful work. It may not be inappropriate to observe here that the founders of the British and the American branches of the Red Cross, Florence Nightingale and Clara Barton respectively, were unmarried women. The Red Cross itself has often been pictured as the Universal Mother. Other women, at the other extreme, have been known to find an outlet for this fundamental urge in bestowing their affection on a pampered poodle.

Another example can be found in the fact that there is in perhaps most of us more of the exhibitionist than we are willing to admit. The desire for attention is very strong in children and if not satisfied in an acceptable manner may take embarrassing forms. Unless directed into useful channels this urge often may lead into various types of antisocial activity. Many criminals are basically exhibitionists and draw to themselves others whose desire for legitimate attention has been frustrated.

At the other and more hopeful end of the scale may be found scores of people whose urge to be in the public eye has been sublimated and put to useful work. These people play football, become actors, write books, build bridges, run for political office, or become effective public speakers. Sometimes they get themselves elected to the Senate, to a great extent because they enjoy being the "cynosure of neighboring eyes."

Here again a certain amount of rationalization may be involved. At heart exhibitionists, these individuals realize that they are able to attract a considerable amount of highly pleasing attention and at the same time render a distinct public service. So long as one enjoys his work and is making a contribution to the enjoyment, welfare, and progress of society, the rationalization would seem to be of a harmless sort. A good speaker may or may not be basically an exhibitionist; it is probable that many are. But so long as he is speaking for worth-while causes, no one need object to whatever personal enjoyment he is able to derive from the attention he is receiving. The risk comes in his drawing attention to himself personally, to the detriment of the problem he is presenting. When he does that he has not succeeded in completely sublimating his motives.

DAYDREAMING.   Daydreaming may be thought of as a form of escape from reality. It occurs when the individual refuses to accept the reality of a world in which, for one reason or another, some deeply felt want has been denied. Sometimes the want itself is entirely within reason, and could be satisfied with a degree of effort which the person is unwilling to exert. Sometimes the desire is beyond the limits of probable satisfaction, even with great effort. The reasons for the denial of the want or need may be quite within the control of the individual; they may be entirely beyond the control of anyone. But denied either by others or by his own unwillingness to achieve his own satisfactions through normal means, the individual retires into a world of imagination, even of fantasy, in which those satisfactions are fulfilled without effort on his part. So vivid is that imaginary world that it is often difficult to bring the person out of his fantasy into a world of things as they actually are. Instead, he retires further and further into his dreams until he loses all contact with reality.

Constructive imagination is in itself an important aspect of mental life. It is part of the basis for all forward thinking, of science, literature, of social planning. Without it there could be no invention, no creativity, no purpose to education, no program of advancement for either society or the individual. There is no danger involved in the imagination itself; danger arises from the inability or unwillingness of the individual to put forth the necessary effort himself to bring that imagination to fruition in reality. Imagination is necessary; it is equally or more necessary to work to achieve the dreams that one creates. One cannot, for example, become a successful speaker merely by imagining oneself swaying the multitudes; it takes conscious effort over a period of time to develop the ideas and the requisite proficiency to present them with the utmost effectiveness.

The speaker on his part does a disservice when he pictures to his listeners a Utopia, a world of imagination in which their wants and needs are met by some paternalistic company or government, and in which they have only to sit back and wait for rewards for work they do not do. Concepts of unearned support, when carried to extremes, constitute a form of daydreaming, an escape from reality, whether arising from one's own imagination or pictured for one out of the imagination of someone else.

Murphy discusses three types of resolution which may be adopted "to avoid wear and tear when conflict arises." These may readily be adapted to the problem of the speaker. First, we alternate between the possible choices; second, we choose, consciously or unconsciously, throwing out some choices, and integrating others until we "converge upon a few things which are worth

living for and upon some central symbol which stands for the region of
activity which we accept": and third, "we may be lucky enough to find a way
of life which incorporates something good for each of the approved ways of
living. . . . A rather large proportion of our life problems, . . . such as
choosing a mate, a job, a home, a way of living, impose a choice between
alternatives." [26]

The Motivation of the Audience

As has already been pointed out, speech in its social aspects is a two-way
process involving speaker and listener. While it is true that various forms of
symbolic expression occur with little or no reference to the presence, real or
imaginary, of other persons, it is probable that most of our overt speech
is directed toward an audience of one or more. The speaking itself may be
thought of as a function of the total situation, in which the audience is of no
less importance than the speaker. If one accepts the principle stated in
Chapter I that in the typical speaking situation the two most important factors
are what is being said and the person or persons to whom it is being said,[27]
then one must recognize that the audience is of even greater importance than
the speaker, who acts primarily as a medium to bring idea and listener
together.

From a somewhat different point of view, the speech as presented may be
considered as the solution to a problem in human relations, the problem itself
having within it such factors as the occasion, the mental and emotional "set"
of the listeners, their motives, interests, and background of knowledge, as well
as the motives of the speaker and his relation to his auditors.

The Audience Situation. For the present purpose we shall consider
primarily the typical "public speaking" situation, rather than the conversational or conference type of situation. This limitation does not imply that
conversation and conference are of minor importance; it implies rather that
only in the public speaking type of situation may be found what is commonly
known as an audience.[28] The difference seems to be in the degree to which a
single individual is set apart as the "speaker" to whom all the others listen,
and to whom they are "polarized." He dominates the situation for the time
being; he is the focus of attention. The listeners form such a group as may

[26] Murphy, *op. cit.*
[27] See p. 60.
[28] One of the earliest discussions of The Audience as such is that by Charles H. Woolbert,
"The audience," *Psychological Monographs* (1916), *21*: 37–54.

be found in a church service, a public lecture, a student convocation, a
political rally.

THE BASIS FOR ASSEMBLING.   Most analyses of the audience and its
psychology begin with the assembled group and proceed from that point to a
discussion of the group's characteristics, of problems of securing and holding
attention, of establishing a strong impression, and of directing the desired
action. It would seem to be somewhat more reasonable to start with a consideration of the factors which may have led to the coming together of the group
to form an audience in the first place. The subsequent behavior of the group
and of the individuals comprising it is largely conditioned by the very things
that impelled them to assemble. It is just as important, therefore, to know
why a given group has met on a certain occasion as it is to be able to describe
or to influence the group once it has met. In truth, such knowledge is basic
to an understanding of the essential characteristics of any audience or of the
means by which it may most effectively be influenced.

Audiences do not congregate as a rule by mere chance or accident. They
are brought together through the operation of some motivating force which
gives rise to more or less definite purposes. Once assembled, they are likely
to be describable in terms of these purposes, their predominant interests at
the time, their predispositions, anticipations, expectancies, or what Dashiell
calls their "set." [29] These attitudes in turn are largely responsible for such
phenomena as attention, polarization, orientation, and even the ultimate
action which is the main objective of the speaker in addressing the group.
In other words, an assembled audience is not in any sense a *tabula rasa* upon
which the speaker is to make his impressions according to his purposes and
skills. Such a concept of the audience implies a passivity which is by no means
characteristic. On the contrary, the attitudes mentioned above produce a
relatively high order of activity which, however, may as yet be somewhat
diffuse. So far as any specific action in response to the stimulation by the
speaker is concerned, there is already a strong predisposition, a readiness to
act in some as yet undetermined manner. The problem of the speaker, therefore, is not solely to arouse dormant activity; it is first to direct activity which
is already fairly lively, and second, to build upon these predispositions so as
to bring about the desired specific response.

The point to be emphasized here is that this readiness to act, these predispositions, sets, and anticipations, are generally the direct function of the
motives of the listeners, which may even be dormant at the time, but even

[29] Dashiell, *op. cit.*, chap. XIII.

more specifically of the purposes for which they have assembled. To neglect these motives and purposes in an analysis of the audience is to leave out of consideration the very reasons for the existence of the audience itself.

So far as the motives themselves are concerned, they are those which form the basis for human behavior in general; they have already been discussed. An audience may be appealed to by pointing out benefits which may accrue to the individual members of the group as a whole by following the course of action advocated; it may at other times be motivated by pointing out the needs of others. In other words, the people in an audience are no different essentially from the people not so assembled. The presence of others probably influences their individual behavior somewhat in response to the speaker's appeal; but exactly what this influence is has not as yet been fully determined.

STIMULATION OF MOTIVES. In order to make the most effective appeal for the desired response, not only must the speaker know the motives back of the assembling, which may be assumed to be strongest in the minds of the listeners at the time. But if those on which he wishes to base his appeal are momentarily dormant, he must attempt to stimulate them. The classical example of such an attempt is the Gettysburg Address. After pointing out the significance of the occasion on which the address is being given, Lincoln makes his appeal:

It is for us, the living, rather, to be dedicated here to the unfinished work which they who fought here have thus far so nobly advanced. It is rather for us to be here dedicated to the great task remaining before us: that from these honored dead we take increased devotion to that cause for which they gave their last full measure of devotion; that we here highly resolve that these dead shall not have died in vain; that this nation, under God, shall have a new birth of freedom; and that government of the people, by the people, and for the people, shall not perish from the earth.

In a perhaps more dramatic and even desperate situation Winston Churchill, in his famous "Blood, sweat, and tears" speech, stimulated the British people to almost superhuman efforts in repelling the threat of invasion under the Nazi hordes:

Let us therefore brace ourselves to our duties, and so bear ourselves that, if the British Empire and its Commonwealth last for a thousand years, men will still say, "This was their finest hour." [30]

CHOOSING THE MOTIVE APPEALS. In choosing the appeals to stimulate the motives of the listeners a few precautions seem advisable.

[30] Winston Churchill, *Blood, Sweat, and Tears*, New York, G. P. Putnam's Sons, 1941, p. 368.

1. *The motive itself must be "worthy of the deed."* [31] In times of war a man would hardly be urged to join the armed forces solely because of the pay he would receive, or because of the promise of a permanent career. One can often be persuaded to reject an offer of another position with higher remuneration on the basis that in his present situation he can render greater service in his vocation. If generous contributions are to be obtained it must be shown that the cause is worthy of the motive which is being stimulated, and that the motive to which the appeal is being made is in keeping with the importance of the cause itself.

2. *The end result must be shown to be worth the effort it takes to achieve it.* We can more easily motivate a high school graduate to continue with his education if we can convince him that a college degree, with what it represents, is worth four or more years of study. Is the establishment of permanent peace in our own times worth fighting for? If so, then not only is the motive to contribute in whatever manner possible "worthy of the deed," but the end result itself is worth the cost in the money and effort and lives that may be required.

3. *A reasonable probability must be shown that the end result will follow from the course of action recommended.* The student goes to college because he thinks the end result is worth while, but also because he feels that he can actually get the education he wants, and that as a result of having that education he will be in a better position to satisfy other and even more pressing motives. Will a certain labor-saving device actually save labor? If not, there would seem to be little point in urging that it be bought. Will the wage gains obtained by a strike offset the rise in living costs that directly result? Apparent deviations from this principle often occur, however, as in the case of a candidate who enters a campaign knowing that there is very little likelihood of his being elected; but he puts up a strong fight against a strongly entrenched, possibly corrupt political machine. His own stature is thereby increased, incidentally, both in his own estimation and in that of his friends. Such an end result often seems worth the effort and preferable to the comfort and quiet of one's own customary ways of living, which could be maintained merely by permitting the politicians to run the affairs of state as they pleased. Such deviations are, however, as a rule only apparent. The point at issue is not what chance there is of winning, but what course will most certainly gain and hold the good opinion of the world at large. The seemingly hopeless struggle of captive nations to regain their freedom from their captors offers another striking illustration of the point being made here.

[31] Winans, *op. cit.*, p. 315.

4. As Baker pointed out more than three score years ago, it is best to *"Choose the highest motive to which the audience in question will respond. . . .* If, for any reason, [the speaker] feels it necessary in his speech . . . to appeal to motives not of the highest grade, he should see that before he closes he makes them lead to high motives."[32] In other words, if the personally oriented motives, those of self-interest, must be used, it is advisable to link them, if at all possible, to the socially oriented motives, those having to do with the welfare of others.

The Motivation of the Speaker

Thus far the discussion of motivation has centered on the problem of the speaker's appeal to the motives of the listeners. Equally important is the question of the motives of the speaker himself, those urges which lead him to want to influence his hearers at all, or, as was pointed out in Chapter I, to further the processes of social integration and adaptation, or to facilitate his own adjustment to his social environment. The general ends of speech have already been discussed; it has been stated that for the most part, at least, these may be grouped under five types: to inform, to entertain, to stimulate, to convince or arouse belief, and to persuade or to secure action. But the motives of the speaker, the incentives which impel him to speak, lie far beneath these more or less external objectives; for the analysis of the specific response he seeks from his audience may or may not indicate just why he should be interested in securing these responses. He attempts to arrive at certain end results; but how do these end results relate to his own motives for making the attempt in the first place? What is the impulsion which leads him to want to influence the behavior of his listeners, to encourage their social integration, or to make his own social adjustments more complete? What is it to him whether they understand a certain process, accept or reject a given belief, or take one course of action or another?

The Speaker's Motives. In general, it may be said that the speaker is influenced by the same types of motive as those to which he is appealing in his audience. Many of these motives are personally oriented, in that they are aimed at bringing to the speaker himself certain advantages, privileges, social acceptance, or other satisfactions of his own desires, wants, and needs. Others are socially oriented, in that they are directed toward the achieving of

[32] George Pierce Baker, *The Principles of Argumentation*, Boston, Ginn and Company, 1895, p. 351.

certain "goods" for the audience or for the community as a whole, such as police protection, public health, educational advantages, public playgrounds, smoother and more cordial relations, and so on.

PERSONALLY ORIENTED MOTIVES.   Just as in the case of the various motive appeals to the audience, there is nothing inherently reprehensible in the speaker's being interested in the things he wants, so long as what he wants does not interfere with or prevent the satisfaction of like wants of others or the needs of the group. We request from our friends many different kinds of favors; we ask our superiors for certain privileges such as a raise in salary, an extension of vacation, better working conditions, or promotion in rank. We apply for membership in social and professional organizations, hoping to derive some tangible or intangible benefit for ourselves from such member-ships. Our motives are clear, obvious, understandable; and as a rule we make no attempt to conceal, either from ourselves or from the prospective donor, just what those motives are. Furthermore, the clearer we can make those motives, the more openly we are able to state them; and the nearer they come to similar motives on the part of the listener, the more probable will be the success of the request. Not only that: the more nearly our previous behavior has corresponded with the motives implied in the stated purposes, the greater the likelihood of the grant.

In a somewhat similar manner a speaker may be entirely justified in coming before an audience for the express purpose of eliciting a response that will contribute to his own benefit. When a candidate for election to an office asks for the votes of his listeners, he does not by that act violate any code of rational behavior or social ethics; that is his privilege, which cannot be denied him in a democratic society. When a business owner stimulates his salesmen to greater efforts, everyone understands that he is interested in increasing his own profits; normally, there can be no reasonable objection to such a procedure.

At the same time, however, in making such requests it is well to be able to indicate in one way or another that it is not entirely and inevitably a one-way process. A request for a raise in salary is more likely to be successful if the employer can be made to feel that our work, past, present, or future, has been or is going to be worth the increase. On the same principle, the candidate who appeals for the votes of his constituents is asking for what he himself wants; but if he can demonstrate that his election will also be to their advantage, or that they have actually benefited by his election in previous campaigns, his chances of success will be greatly increased. Similarly, the business owner who seeks to increase his own income through greater efforts on the part of his sales force will find himself benefiting if he is also able to show his employees that they will thereby augment their own incomes.

SOCIALLY ORIENTED MOTIVES. Just as people in general are motivated by the interests of others, as has already been pointed out, in the same way the speaker may be and often is motivated by a genuine interest in satisfying the wants, needs, and desires of his listeners. It is no doubt true that the accomplishing of this social good may bring deep satisfactions to him; at the same time it is also true that these personal satisfactions are secondary, that the primary motive has to do with benefits accruing to others.

Furthermore, it not infrequently happens that the speaker, like others, undertakes his task at no inconsiderable sacrifice to himself. When Woodrow Wilson brought his peace treaty back from Versailles in 1919—a historical incident of special significance in view of the more recent United Nations— he sincerely believed that it would set up an international machinery which would make future wars difficult if not impossible. His final appeal to the country, made on his last trip through the West in 1920, was made at the cost of his health and ultimately of his life. Whether the machinery would or would not have achieved its purpose is not the point here; what is significant is that Wilson believed that its acceptance would bring magnificent benefits to the country and to the world as a whole, and that he was willing to make any sacrifice to bring about its adoption. To attribute selfish motives to him in his fight for what he sincerely believed would be for the good of the nation and the world seems to be a misinterpretation of his whole course of conduct with regard to that program.

One reads now and then of an individual who betrays the ethical standards of his profession—ministers, lawyers, physicians, teachers, industrialists. But it is not too idealistic to insist that most people spend a considerable amount of time and effort in acting and speaking in behalf of others. The minister's interest in the moral, ethical, and religious welfare of his listeners is, in the vast majority of cases, genuinely unselfish. What is reprehensible in the relatively few individuals who deviate from the generality is that underneath an ostensible altruism and seeming concern for the welfare of others lies a mass of utterly selfish motives which are in direct opposition to those outwardly professed. So far as a rational idealism is concerned, for that matter, it does not seem to be a matter requiring apology.

AROUSING DORMANT MOTIVES.   Sometimes the major problem of the speaker is one of arousing dormant motives in the listeners, of stimulating desires which, if not entirely absent, may be quiescent or unrealized. A community indifferent to political corruption in its government may be so aroused and motivated by a fearless, outspoken citizen, who himself has nothing to gain other than the benefits shared by all, that the desire for justice, fair play, honesty (to say nothing of lowered taxes) will impel the voters to "clean house" at the next election. The speaker participates in the benefits, it is true; but he might derive even greater material benefits by aligning himself with the corrupt politicians. His own motivation may quite properly be considered as unselfish, socially oriented, in that his primary interest is in the welfare of the community as a whole.

IDENTIFICATION WITH AUDIENCE MOTIVES.   Frequently if not usually a speaker will gain in persuasive power if he succeeds in identifying his own interests with those of his listeners. In urging better school facilities he will be able to project his own point of view into the thinking and attitudes of his hearers if he admits freely that he is desirous of providing improved educational opportunities for his own children as well as theirs. In fact, he may be more successful than another speaker who has no children to educate.

Interests of Third Groups.   Heretofore the discussion has centered about motives in relation to the audience and the speaker. But in still another way the speaker's motives may be important. He may seek to arouse in his listeners a desire to contribute to the welfare of a third group, persons apart from himself or his auditors, and from whom no return can possibly be expected. Let disaster strike in any accessible section of the world, and immediate, effective appeals are made for food, clothing, money, medical supplies. A few short years ago, while the world stood appalled by the degraded savagery with which Soviet Russia was crushing the struggles of the Hungarians for freedom, fruitless appeals were being made to the communists to permit supplies from the free world to enter the stricken country to provide for the barest necessities of existence.

Louis Pasteur had no thought of personal aggrandizement when he appeared before the French Academy with his revolutionary theory of disease and its prevention. His sole interest was to further the means whereby suffering might be alleviated and life preserved. His rejection deterred him not in the least; persistence in his course brought him sacrifice and hardship.

He was far more interested in what his final acceptance meant in terms of combating disease than he was in the plaudits he received.

The Ethics of Motivation.   The motives of the speaker are at all times subject to examination by his listeners. They may be evaluated from various sources, the chief of which is the degree to which his apparent motives correspond to his previous behavior and to his entire known course of conduct. A candidate for office will as a rule win more votes if the voters are convinced that he has as far as is humanly possible lived up to his former campaign promises, or that his conduct prior to his candidacy has shown promise of honesty of purpose in making his pledges. "It is not true," said Aristotle, "as some writers on the art maintain, that the probity of the speaker contributes nothing to his persuasiveness; on the contrary, we might almost affirm that his character (*ethos*) is the most potent of all the means to persuasion." [33]

The motives of the speaker may be revealed in various ways.

1. First, they are revealed by his *known interest in his subject*. In order for this interest to have greatest weight it should be recognized as having persisted over a considerable period of time. While it is possible that the very recency of the speaker's interest in a subject may carry a persuasive force, as a general rule one who has spent a lifetime in the study of a particular field will be credited with higher and more stable motives than one whose interest is recent, temporary, and possibly fleeting.

2. Motives are further revealed by the speaker's *interest in the audience*. In a campaign for better playground facilities, for example, a local speaker, one who knows the audience and is interested in them, will probably have more influence than an equally good speaker brought in from another locality, unless perhaps the latter is a recognized authority on playgrounds. The local speaker's interest in the subject is supplemented by a specific interest in the particular audience to which he is talking, and in the children of the community. As we have seen, the fact that he may have children of his own who will benefit with the children of his listeners, and so can identify his interests with theirs, need have no harmful effect on his persuasive effort.

3. Again, the speaker's motives are revealed by his evident *interest in and enthusiasm for the very act of communication*. It is not enough that he be concerned about a given problem and its relation to his hearers. His interest must be great enough so that he will seek opportunities to present his solution and

[33] Aristotle, *The Art of Rhetoric*, tr. by Lane Cooper, New York, Appleton-Century-Crofts, 1932, p. 9.

try to secure its approval. His interest in a given subject of informative nature may be profound; if he shrinks from imparting that information to others his speaking will carry little weight and his knowledge itself may be of little value. The effective dissemination of knowledge is here seen to be quite as important as its acquisition.

4. Finally, the motives of the speaker are revealed by his *interest in the specific purpose for which he is speaking*. Webster's interest in the maintenance of a strong union among the states persisted throughout his life. This known interest gave his famous "Reply to Hayne" special weight because of the equally well-known motives back of it. President Eisenhower's recognized interest in the preservation of international peace gives special weight to his utterances relative to measures calculated to achieve that objective. When this interest is directed toward the achievement of goals generally agreed upon as highly desirable, it possesses special force.

Although these factors have been presented separately, they are obviously woven into a pattern of honesty of motive and sincerity of purpose having a background of what Aristotle called *ethos*, the components of which are intelligence, character, and good will. For, after all, the problem of the speaker's motives is quite as much a matter of ethics as it is of psychology. "Skillful utterance can be totally destructive unless it is motivated by honest thinking, a feeling for justice, and a genuine concern for the well-being of humanity." [34]

Attention and Interest

In order for the speaker to be able to influence his listeners in any degree, he must secure and hold their attention. Unless the members of the audience will listen, any speech will be so much wasted effort so far as achieving any response is concerned. This conclusion is true regardless of the type of speaking situation, whether it is ordinary conversation or the most exalted kind of oratory, the reading of the minutes of a meeting, or the presentation of a Shakespearean tragedy.

Definition of Attention

Attention may be defined from two points of view. First, it may be thought of as a bodily "set," an adjustment of the sensory apparatus so that we are

[34] Joseph F. Smith, Address to the Speech Association of America, Chicago, December 29, 1944.

more keenly sensitive to certain stimuli out of the great variety of stimuli that assail us. In this sense, attention may be highly selective, in that we are able to isolate, with the proper "set," the particular stimuli we want to respond to at the time. For example, we can often pick out a single instrument from an orchestra or a single voice from the chorus and listen to that one, while all the other instruments or voices fade more or less into the background. We can similarly pick out an odor from a number of mixed odors and adjust our behavior to that one. From the scents emanating from the kitchen we can often know in advance what we are going to have for dinner.

Again, attention may be thought of as an increased awareness of certain stimuli; they come, so to speak, into the "focus of consciousness." Attention thus becomes a phenomenon of consciousness. The things to which we attend seem clearer and more intensified than other objects or sounds or odors that form the background, and the latter become relegated to the "margin" of consciousness. One may not even be aware of the fact that one is attending to the particular stimulus which is at the time in the focus, paradoxical as it may seem.

Stimulation of Attention

Various aspects of the phenomenon being observed may serve to stimulate the attention.

Variations in Stimulus.   Any sudden or intense change in accustomed surroundings may serve to force involuntary attention. We readily become adapted to stimuli which impinge constantly upon our sense organs; that is, stimuli continuously applied for a time cease to have stimulus value, unless they are pain stimuli. We scarcely notice the pressure of our clothing unless it is too tight or otherwise a misfit, producing discomfort. We are constantly being assailed by sounds we never hear and by sights we never see, until some sudden or intense or striking change takes place, whereupon we immediately give attention.

Loud noises, a flash of light, an abrupt touch, or a sudden movement of something within the range of vision will cause an immediate awareness of that stimulus. The hunter may not see the squirrel in the top of the tree, even though he is looking in that direction, until it flicks its tail or moves along the branch. Animals often "freeze" when in danger to avoid attracting the attention of their enemies.

A sudden decrease in the intensity of a stimulus may be just as effective in drawing attention as a sudden increase. People are often awakened at night by the stopping of the clock. Audiences may be aroused to attention by a sudden drop in the loudness of the speaker's voice. The important factor is *change* in the stimulus pattern.

Magnitude.   The magnitude or intensity of a stimulus, even when not sudden, is likewise potent in drawing attention. If we are reading with strong concentration on the printed material the ordinary noises around us do not distract our attention unless they become so loud that they force themselves, so to speak, into our awareness. A full-page advertisement is more likely to be noticed than one of only a quarter-page.

Repetition.   Repetition of a stimulus, up to a certain point, may have a much greater effect than a single stimulus, even if the latter is fairly strong. Noise abatement measures are necessary because of the disturbing effects of long-continued and repeated noises. When repetition is overdone, the effect may be either irritation or adaptation.

Stagner and Karwoski list and describe briefly these "major variations in the physical stimulus which are effective in attracting attention: (1) Intensity of stimulus, including Contrast and Novelty; (2) Movement and Change; (3) Size; and (4) Repetition." [35] Murphy gives a similar list, with only minor deviations: intensity, suddenness, novelty, sharpness of outline, and relevance to our needs. [36]

Attention and Past Experience.   The fifth element listed by Murphy suggests that it is not only by the variations in the physical stimulus itself that attention is aroused. People respond with greater attentiveness to those stimuli which may be related, directly or indirectly, to their own experiences. If we have been a long way from home, the familiar landmarks of well-remembered localities arouse our attention, even though we have enjoyed visiting strange places and have had new experiences during our sojourn in new localities. Even new experiences receive attention partly in proportion as they may be associated with the old. New ideas, also, when connected with older ideas, may have an attention-holding influence which they would not have if they were totally strange.

[35] Ross Stagner and T. F. Karwoski, *Psychology*, New York, McGraw-Hill Book Company, 1952, pp. 195–196.
[36] Gardner Murphy, *An Introduction to Psychology*, New York, Harper & Brothers, 1951, pp. 140–141.

Attention and Interest.   People are also prone to attend to those things in which they are interested. Interest in this sense may be thought of in part in the light of motive, which predisposes the individual to pay attention to certain classes or types of things related to the particular motive. Interest is therefore likely to be more persistent than attention, being more closely related to motives and attitudes. If a geologist and a sociologist, for example, are walking through the country, each will see many things that the other will not see; their interests being different, their attention will be directed to different aspects of the environment. Spectators at a football game rarely see the play of the linemen because they are primarily interested in seeing how far the ball is advanced on each play. A reader may be totally absorbed in a book on some subject in which he is interested, whereas he may find it difficult to give his full attention to another in which he is not at all interested; he may even be thoroughly bored.

"Interest in a stimulus helps to keep it in focus," say Stagner and Karwoski. They report an experiment in which the subjects looked through a stereoscope so arranged that one eye saw a red square, while the other saw a green square. A rhythmic shifting from red to green and back again was observed, until the experimenter marked one of the squares with a white cross. From then on that square stayed in the focus of attention much longer than the other one. "By making that square more interesting, he made it the center of attention. This fact is of importance to the public speaker or the advertiser."[37]

Attention and the Satisfaction of Motives.   As a result of the effect of interest on attention, people are likely to attend to those things which offer some promise of satisfying their motives. If we want to make more money, we are sensitive to discussions on how we can increase our income. If we are collecting old glassware rather than furniture, a display of antique glass will attract us more readily than will a display of chairs, chests, dressers, and beds. A store window showing cameras will cause one person to stop and look, but his companion will gaze longingly upon a complete set of power tools for woodworking, and hardly see the cameras.

Just as our motives, and the interests arising from them, shift in strength from time to time, so also does our attention shift from one detail or set of details to another. A botanist may also be an ardent hunter. When he takes a botanical field trip his motives, and hence his interests, will focus his attention on the various plants which he sees in the field and upon their characteristics. But if he goes hunting in that same field, his motives and interests will be

[37] Stagner and Karwoski, *op. cit.,* p. 199.

entirely different and his attention will be centered on quite different objects. A man may at one and the same time be an excellent businessman and a public-spirited benefactor. During business hours his entire attention will be centered upon the operation and management of his enterprises, but at other times he may be intensely concerned with activities connected with the public welfare. A golfer doesn't hunt four-leaf clovers while trying to find a lost golf ball.

Whatever the interests and motives of a group of people may be at other times, when they have come together as an audience certain interests and motives have led them to assemble on this particular occasion. It is on the basis of these that the speaker will be able to attract and hold their attention.

Attention and Conflict

It has been pointed out that conflicts often arise between and among motives. These give rise to conflicting demands on the attention. It is quite difficult, as we all recognize, to concentrate upon one task which we realize ought to be completed, while all the time we keep thinking about something else that we would rather be doing. When two activities promise to satisfy equally strong motives, our attention is likely to shift from one to the other, at least until we decide which of the two we should undertake first. According to James, what holds the attention determines action. In persuasion, then, the problem of the speaker is to direct and hold the attention of the listeners upon the choice advocated, to the exclusion of other possibilities, if this theory is to be followed.

For an immediate resolution of conflict between motives the James principle may be effective; but for a long-term solution which would be satisfying over a period of time it would seem that a rational balancing of motives and end results, with as careful a weighing as possible of the merits and demerits of each possible choice, would result in a more intelligent decision. James's theory can easily be interpreted as justification for high-pressure methods of persuasion.

Application to Speaking

These various aspects of attention have a direct bearing upon the problem of securing and maintaining the attention of an audience. They are of more than theoretical interest; they have a practical applicability to the task the speaker sets himself when he addresses an audience. He is faced with the necessity of attracting his listeners' attention so that they become "polarized" toward him and to what he is saying; they must focus upon him to such a degree that they will not notice even relatively strong distracting stimuli. A community of interests is developed; their motives become similar. The presence of other members of the group, sometimes even the existence of competing ideas, may become little more than a background, so to speak, relegated to the margin of consciousness. The individuals have assumed a bodily "set," which results in an increased sensitivity to the auditory and visual stimuli emanating from the activities of the speaker. But even these mechanical aspects of the speaking process may become marginal, so that the attention is centered sharply on the *ideas* instead; there is a keener awareness of what is being said, which has been brought into the focus of consciousness.

Attention and the Speaker

Usually the speaker has the attention of the audience the moment he rises to address them. But attention is not immediately polarized, and it does not become so, as a rule, until he has succeeded in arousing a widespread common interest; until he has stimulated motives already operative or aroused others temporarily dormant. Whether attention is polarized or not, the motives which led the group to assemble have generated an interest in the speaker or in what he has to say, or both, and this interest is in turn conducive to that particular "set" which we call attention. An audience will assemble to hear a relatively or completely unknown speaker discuss a subject of vital interest; or they will listen to a well-known and respected, or even a conspicuous, speaker regardless of his subject.

The essential point here is that in the usual case it is not necessary for the speaker to employ special techniques to secure the attention of his listeners; his problem is often one of directing and holding their attention on the subject and its development.

Need to Attract Attention. It occasionally happens, however, that the initial attention of the listeners cannot be so readily assumed, whoever the speaker may be or whatever his subject. The diners seated around a banquet table, for example, may become so engrossed in their own conversation that they do not even notice the toastmaster when he rises to begin the program. Their attention must be drawn in some way to the speaker's place and their immediate interests shifted to him, so that the process of polarization can be facilitated. Any stir or movement or unusual noises about the speaker's area may serve to attract the attention of the listeners; the rapping on the table, the simple rising of the toastmaster from his seat, the rearranging of chairs or reading stand, or other preparations for what is to follow will usually inform the audience that the program is about to begin, and will aid in creating an expectancy on the part of the people present. Often the chairman can take advantage of a temporary lull in the conversation about the table to rise to his feet and open the program. The essential thing is to divert the attention of the audience from their immediate interests and to direct it to the speaker and his subject.

Attention and the Manner of Presentation.   Both the ideas presented and the manner of presenting them should be such as to maintain the attention once it has been secured The ideas themselves should bear a close relation to the purposes of the assembling; if there is any incongruity or conflict, a careful transition and an effort to relate the material of the speech to the motives and interests of the listeners must be made. It is not always necessary for the speaker to choose a subject that is already of great interest to his hearers; but he should be able either to relate his material directly to their interests, or to shift those interests to the topic he proposes to discuss.

SHORT- AND LONG-TERM APPEALS.   What Stagner and Karwoski say about advertising is equally true of speaking. "Advertisers distinguish between short-term and long-term appeals with consideration for [the rapid waning of attention values]. Short-term appeals work satisfactorily for inexpensive or often-needed commodities (food, etc.). Long-term appeals are necessary for infrequent, expensive purchases such as automobiles and radiophonographs." [38]

PROGRESSION OF IDEAS.   The progression of ideas must show movement, advancement, for otherwise the hearers will lose interest and their attention will wander. New and unfamiliar ideas can be presented to hold the attention; but if they are tied in with the old and familiar the effects will be greater. Conflict and antagonism are effective appeals for holding attention, partly because they arouse suspense in the minds of the hearers. Repetition is useful if not carried to the point of adaptation or monotony. Lincoln used this device effectively in his Cooper Union Address by referring repeatedly to "our Fathers who framed the government under which we live . . . ."

THE MODE OF UTTERANCE.   Not only can the content of the speech and its development be so managed as to hold the attention of the audience; the very

[38] *Ibid.*, p. 199.

mode of presentation is also an important phase of the act of speaking. The speaker's behavior on the platform or elsewhere, his movement, his gestures, all serve to maintain his hold on the listeners. The manipulation of the voice, the rise and fall of pitch, the changes in emphasis, the variations in rate of utterance, all provide the variety necessary to keep the attention of one's hearers. "The skillful speaker knows how to hold attention by judicious changes in the pitch of his voice." [39]

It is important to note here that stimulus value depends to a large degree on the nature and the degree of *change* in the vocal elements. The factors listed above by Stagner and Karwoski and by Murphy apply to speaking just as much as they do to any other kinds of stimuli. As Woolbert has pointed out, it is the changes in the pitch, time, force, and quality of the voice which are instrumental in relation to the logical and personal (emotional) meanings of the speech. The careful and thorough student of speech can on any given occasion use most of the psychological determinants of attention in order to insure that the audience will listen attentively to him. [40]

The Problem of Personality

Introduction

People succeed or fail in speaking for many reasons. Up to the past few years attempts to discover the essentials of success or the causes of failure were more or less concentrated on studies of the voice, of speech organization, of the use of language, and so on. More recently, however, investigators have attempted to study those factors within the individual which might contribute to or interfere with his maximum effectiveness as a speaker. [41] Both students of speech *per se* and psychologists in general have taken up the problem in an effort to determine those personal traits which influence our speech as well as our behavior in other types of social intercourse. Since many of the problems of psychology, it has been said, are problems of language, psychologists are becoming interested in the psychological aspects of language, including speech, our most common means of social adaptation and adjustment. These are problems which concern all of us, whether we are students of

---

[39] Dashiell, *op. cit.*, p. 356.

[40] Charles Henry Woolbert, *The Fundamentals of Speech*, rev. ed., 1927. New York, Harper & Brothers, 1927, chap. X. See also Woolbert and Smith, 2nd rev. ed., 1934, chap. VIII.

[41] Franklin H. Knower, "A study of speech attitudes and adjustments," *Speech Monographs* (1938), 5: 130–203.

speech, or psychologists interested in the phenomena of symbolization, or merely people trying to find out how we can best get along with our fellows. And social adaptation and adjustment are to a large extent functions of those individual and personal traits which, taken together, have been called *personality*.

The Concept of Personality

Efforts to correlate personality, or certain aspects of it, with speech have encountered a number of problems. For example, there is as yet no widely accepted understanding of just what is involved in the concept of personality.

Definition. In a very general statement, not intended as a definition, Stagner and Karwoski say that man's "abilites are integrated into a complex pattern of loves, fears, ambitions, and prejudices which we call his *personality*." They go on to point out that "In popular speech, personality is often used rather loosely and in a variety of meanings. Scientific psychology might do better to discard the term entirely. . . . " [42] But they do define the term as referring to "the particular, unique pattern of traits and attitudes character-izing any specific person." In a more precise definition they approach the con-cept from three points of view: first, *as a stimulus*, that is, by the way the individual affects others; second, *as a response*, that is, by the way his responses are interpreted and as they affect others; and third, as an "intervening variable," that is, that personality as *an inner state* can only be inferred from one's observable behavior.

Dashiell defines a man's personality as "the total picture of his organized behavior, especially as it can be characterized by his fellow men in a consistent way." [43] The only attempt at a definition of personality made by Murphy is in the Index to his text: "(1) all the qualities, modes of reaction, etc., which set off an individual as distinct from all others. (2) the integration of these qualities in a unified system." [44]

Eysenck, in referring to the term *personality* in the title of his book, says that "unfortunately it is particularly in relation to this term that agreement as to meaning is almost wholly absent." He cites Allport as having dis-tinguished some fifty different meanings. [45]

Whether specifically defined or not, most writers apparently consider

---

[42] Stagner and Karwoski, *op. cit.*, p. 467.
[43] Dashiell, *op. cit.*, p. 594.
[44] *An Introduction to Psychology, op. cit.*, p. 577.
[45] H. J. Eysenck, *Dimensions of Personality*, Routledge, Kegan Paul, 1948, p. 22.

personality as including, first, one's total behavior patterns, particularly in a social situation, and second, but much less emphasized, the impact which these patterns make on one's associates. Many writers discuss the phenomenon, if it may be so considered, extensively without indicating even generally the sense in which they are using the term.

The Determinants of Personality. What factors in the nature and development of the individual contribute significantly to the establishing of the behavior patterns that constitute what is called the personality? Kluckhohn and Murray distinguish "four classes of determinants (and their interactions) . . . *constitutional, group-membership, role,* and *situational.*" "Constitutional" refers to aspects of personality determined by the physical makeup of the individual at the time; they may be hereditary or environmental. The fact of membership in a group, large or small, and the patterns of behavior resulting from social interaction, some of which may, in fact, through intermarriages, produce a mixture of biological factors, play a significant part in the determination of personality. The functions which one serves within a group, the "roles" which one plays, whether by arbitrary assignment or by having achieved a position through merit or other influence, have a bearing on the individual as he is known to his fellows. Personality is further determined by the events which take place from day to day. "I am a part of all that I have met" is more than a literary phrase. Seemingly insignificant occurrences often initiate a change in the direction of one's development. It will never be known just how many men's attitudes, even vocations, were completely changed by their experiences during either World War or the Korean conflict.[46]

THE BODY-TYPE THEORY.   The oldest attempt to isolate the determinants of personality of which we have any record is that of Hippocrates (fifth century B.C.), who posited two body types, the long-bodied and the round-bodied, each of which was "conceived to be specially linked . . . with certain temperamental peculiarities."[47] His basic theory has been developed further during the past century by a number of investigators, perhaps the best known among them being Kretschmer.[48] All the studies following this theory, according to Eysenck, have recognized the same two types posited by Hippo-

[46] Clyde Kluckhohn and Henry A. Murray, "Personality formation: the determinants," in *Personality in Nature, Society, and Culture,* 2nd ed., Clyde Kluckhohn and Henry A. Murray (eds.), New York, Alfred A. Knopf, 1954, pp. 53–67.

[47] Eysenck, *op. cit.,* p. 22.

[48] Ernest Kretschmer, *Physique and Character,* 2nd (English) ed., tr. by W. J. H. Sprott, New York, The Humanities Press, 1951.

crates, with the usual addition of a third type, intermediate between the two.[49] While any statements of correlation between these body types and personality must be taken with extreme caution, a few studies seem to indicate some correspondence. These relationships, however, are questioned or even denied in other investigations.[50]

THE THEORY OF "HUMORS."   Another attempt to analyze the determinants of personality which has come down to us from antiquity was based on the assumed presence in the blood of certain fluids or "humors." Many of our present terms descriptive of people are derived from the names given to these same humors. Thus persons may be *phlegmatic, choleric, sanguine, melancholy*, and so on, depending, according to ancient theory, on which particular humor is ascendant at the time. One theory of stuttering, advanced during the Renaissance by one Hieronymous Mercurialis, held that the affliction was caused by the presence in the blood of a certain humor, which could be eradicated only by sending the sufferer to a warm, dry climate so that the humor could be evaporated out of the system. It is well known today that excessive or reduced flow of certain glandular secretions has a definite effect on one's attitudes and behavior patterns. But these do not as yet form the basis for any comprehensive catalog of personality traits.

SOCIAL DETERMINANTS OF PERSONALITY.   One's social environment is generally recognized to play a highly significant role in developing the social attitudes and behavior patterns that make up a large part of one's personality. Some of these are analyzed by Dashiell.[51]

1. *The influence of infancy.*   It is becoming more and more widely recognized that the relationship between the infant and the mother, as well as other aspects of family life, have a great influence on the development of the child. Excessive mothering, which usually establishes almost unbreakable ties between parent and child, results in a type of personality incapable of independent initiative in adulthood. At the other extreme insufficient mothering causes damage not only psychologically but physically as well. There is evidence that "children deprived of [affectionate stimulations] by the Spartan training so often given to habituate them to artificial schedules instead of their

---

[49] *Loc. cit.*
[50] See W. H. Sheldon, *The Varieties of Human Physique*, 1940; and *The Varieties of Temperament*, 1942, New York, Harper & Brothers; P. W. Fiske, "A study of relationships to somatotypes," *Journal of Applied Psychology* (1944), *28*: 504–519; David C. McClelland, *Personality*, New York, William Sloan Associates, 1951, pp. 127–128.
[51] Dashiell, *op. cit.*, pp. 617–630.

own natural rhythms, tend to show such behavior traits as tantrums, enuresis, speech defects, sensitiveness, attention-craving, negativism, and other symptoms of personal insecurity, of inability to give or receive affection, of lack of normal responsiveness in general." [52]

2. *Other social influences.* The factors in the social environment that affect the developing personality present a picture of tremendous complexity, so that it is difficult if not impossible to determine just what effect each one of these factors has. The presence in the family of other children; the existence of adequate schools with sympathetic, understanding teachers; the accessibility of recreational facilities, the general economic, cultural, and educational level of the child's associates; the behavior patterns of the parents themselves, together with their attitudes toward the child and his development, all contribute in marked degree to the establishment of the habitual modes of behavior which may be said to contribute to the personality.

The Components of Personality. A part of the difficulty in grasping the concept of personality arises from the fact that there is no general agreement as to what traits, elements, or "dimensions" comprise the personality. Many attempts have been made to isolate these factors, and from many points of view.

"TRAITS" AND "TYPES." Eysenck himself attempts a classification of personality *traits* as differentiated from *types.* He begins with the *specific response,* at which level a given act may occur once, and may or may not occur again. From such specific responses as are likely to recur under similar circumstances is derived the *habitual response,* which constitutes the second level. At the third level these habitual responses are in turn organized into *traits,* such as *persistence, rigidity, autonomic imbalance, accuracy, irritability,* and other response tendencies. At the fourth level these traits become organized into general types, such as *introversion, neuroticism,* or the like. Proceeding from this clarification, and on the basis of the body-type theory and using techniques based on still other theories, his studies of 700 neurotic male soldiers revealed two main types, labeled tentatively "neuroticism" and "extroversion-introversion." These, he seems to think, bear "a close relation to similar factors previously discovered in normal subjects by numerous investigators." [53]

[52] *Ibid.,* p. 621.
[53] Eysenck, *op. cit.,* p. 244.

DYNAMIC COMPONENTS. Among the components which, according to Stagner and Karwoski, must be included to give a worth-while summary of any personality are the *dynamic patterns*—the motives, emotions, that is, the social values and emotional reactions, which impel a person to act as he does; *perceptions*—the way in which persons and things are viewed in relation to the self; *learning*—the patterns of behavior and attitudes acquired through the processes of education, both formal and informal; and *intelligence*—"the ability to think and generalize about one's experiences. . . ." The phenomena to be studied may conveniently be classified according to *temperament*, the characteristic drives and emotions of the individual, and the *social personality*, "the pattern of responses which determines how others will like us." [54]

It is of some interest to observe that, although Stagner and Karwoski discuss at some length "The Expressive Aspect of Personality," they limit their analysis to the visible aspects of expression—facial expression, gestures, and handwriting—with the exception of the noise-making of some children, and the observation that "If one's voice is rasping . . . it is unlikely that he will be able to 'win friends and influence people.'" These expressive movements "do not show hereditary factors of personality. At most they indicate that inherited temperamental traits, such as vigor, speed of response, and persistence, will modify the social side of the personality." [55]

PERSONALITY CLUSTERS AND SECTORS. From a table of some 4504 terms compiled by Allport and Odbert,[56] which were found in literature as relating directly or indirectly to personality, Cattell derived a list of some twenty "Personality Clusters and Sectors." These are outlined, each with its "nuclear clusters" and "overlapping phenomenal clusters." Typical of these clusters are these:

> Fineness of character *versus* Moral defect, non-persistence.
> Realism, emotional integration *versus* Neuroticism, evasion, infantilism.
> Sociability *versus* Timidity, hostility, gloominess.
> Liveliness, instability, verbal expressiveness *versus* Reserve, quiescence, naturalness.
> Bohemian, disorderly *versus* Persevering, pedantic.
> Hypochondriacal, taciturn, retroversion *versus* Eloquence, interest in future.
> Inflexibility, wandering *versus* Adaptableness, ease of settling down.[57]

[54] Stagner and Karwoski, *op. cit.*, pp. 469–470.
[55] *Ibid.*, pp. 476–479.
[56] G. W. Allport and H. S. Odbert, "Trait-names: a psycho-lexical study," *Psychological Monographs* (1936), 47: vii, 171.
[57] Raymond B. Cattell, "Principal trait clusters for describing personality," *Psychological Bulletin* (1945), *42*: 129–161.

Cattell admits, however, that "actual studies dealing with the interrelations of personality variables . . . on an adequate scale and by methods which permit of mutual confirmation of findings, are . . . still distinctly rare. . . ."

OTHER SO-CALLED "TRAITS" OF PERSONALITY.   From time to time still other components of personality have been suggested, and attempts have been made to measure them. Among these may be mentioned the dichotomy of *dominance-submission*, the former of which may be thought of as a social motive rather than a personality trait, although it undoubtedly has a bearing on social adaptability; *self-sufficiency*, which may be related to the commonly considered motive of freedom from restraint; and *hyperkinesis-hypokinesis*. Some of these terms are now found only occasionally in studies of personality.

The Distribution of Types.   Murphy raises the question as to whether there are actually any personality types at all, in the sense that they can be dichotomized, as seems to be an assumption in many attempts to classify personalities.[58]

BIMODAL DISTRIBUTION.   In much of the literature on personality is a more or less tacit assumption that people can be classified into certain rather

Introverts   Extroverts

Figure 76. Bimodal Curve of Distribution.

well-defined "types," in which the curve of distribution is bimodal rather than Gaussian.[59] Suppose, for example, that all people could be classified according to height as either tall or short. We should have, in that case, a large number of tall persons and a large number of short ones, with a relatively small number in between, and the curve representing such a distribution would be something like the one in Figure 76.

Something of the same sort of distribution would result if, in measuring some personality trait, we found certain "types" grouped at or near each end

[58] *An Introduction to Psychology, op. cit.,* p. 507.
[59] This term is often applied to the well-known bell-shaped curve of normal distribution, named for Karl Gauss, nineteenth-century scientist.

of a scale. Individuals would then be classified as *either* one *or* the other:
either introvert *or* extrovert; *either* dominant *or* submissive, according to
formerly prominent classifications.

THE GAUSSIAN DISTRIBUTION. But individual traits or characteristics,
physical, psychological, or otherwise, do not fall into such clearly defined
groups.[60] We cannot say, for example, that there are a large number of introverts and a large number of extroverts, with a relatively small number falling
somewhere between these two types. What we are probably justified in saying
is that such terms as introversion and extroversion merely refer to the extremes
in a distribution of some larger aspect of personality which includes, on either
side of a norm, both "types." Between these two extremes is a large number
of people who may possess something of the characteristics of both and who

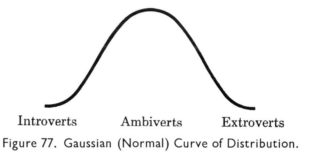

Introverts   Ambiverts   Extroverts

Figure 77. Gaussian (Normal) Curve of Distribution.

might be called "ambiverts." The curve representing the distribution of this
particular trait would be something like that in Figure 77. Much the same
objection could be raised to any attempt to classify personality traits on the
basis of a dichotomy, which assumes an *either-or* principle.

INDIVIDUAL DIFFERENCES.   Still another point should be kept in mind in
a consideration of classifications of personality or behavior patterns, and that
is the simple fact of individual differences. It is this fact that makes anything
like rigid classifications precarious if not impossible. Up to the present time
no generally accepted physiological, neurological, or glandular basis has been
established for those differences that do exist. More is probably known about
the effects of glandular imbalances on the functioning of the various organs of
the body and on general behavior tendencies than about the other two possible
influences. At the same time, an increasingly profound knowledge of the

[60] Dashiell, *op. cit.*, pp. 600 f. See also Hilde T. Himmelweit, "Personality tests as research
tools," in *Current Trends in British Psychology, op. cit.*, pp. 196–204.

nervous system has given us a better understanding of certain aspects of reactions, conditioning, and so on. But it is as yet impossible, on the basis of available data, to assign specific causes for many of the existing individual differences, or for many of the observable deviations from what may be considered norms, or to determine just what the limits of those norms might be, in relation to human behavior.

By way of summary of the results of attempts to catalog personality traits, or factors, or components, one would be justified in saying that *any characteristic behavior pattern or tendency which recurs with fairly reliable consistency may be considered to be a component of personality.* We shall see later how this principle may be applied in the case of speech as a behavior pattern.

The Measurement of Personality

Many types of tests have been devised to study and measure different aspects of personality. Such measurements are essential if studies in this phase of behavior are to have predictive value, for ". . . the precision of predictions about the growth and dynamic interactions of traits is limited by the exactness with which personality can be described and measured in cross-section, i.e., statically." [61] Most tests are of course based upon the particular theory held by the experimenter.

Types of Tests. Four main types of personality tests have been used: inventories and questionnaires, objective testing techniques, projective techniques, and observational and sociometric methods. [62] From whatever point of view they are constructed, practically all of them are designed for the purpose of isolating and measuring specific traits, or aspects, of personality. Some of these are the old *Bernreuter Personality Inventory, Bell's Adjustment Inventory,* the *Guildford-Martin Temperament Profile Chart,* the *Moss Social Intelligence Test,* the *Pressey X-O Test* for investigating emotions, the *Rogers Test of Personality Adjustment,* and so on. It would be impossible to enumerate all the tests, inventories, charts, and schedules that have been devised to measure personality in any or all of its aspects, some of which are today seldom mentioned as components of personality. Perhaps the most widely used and best known of this type of test is the *Minnesota Multiphasic Personality Inventory,* but many of them have been so completely discarded that it is

[61] Raymond B. Cattell, "The description of personality. Foundations of trait measurement," *Psychological Review* (1943), *50*: 559–592.
[62] H. J. Eysenck, "Assessment of personality," *British Medical Bulletin* (1949), *6*: 16–20.

difficult to find even mention of them in the indexes to current texts on psychology or personality.

Commenting on these tests, Ellis remarks, "In general, personality inventories do not show significant group discriminations in the areas in which they are commonly used. . . . When these inventories are effectively used, they tend to be equally as time consuming as alternative psychological procedures." [63] And Eckert has pointed out that "the question of validity in the instruments used in the appraisal of personality continues to be a basic obstacle to valid researches in this field as it does in other areas of personal adjustment." [64] It is not evident that efforts to measure personality have met with increasing success since this conclusion was reached.

Projective Techniques in Measurement. A number of tests have been devised for the purpose of permitting the subject to reveal his own personality, or certain aspects of it, by his reaction to some stimulus, and on the basis of associations and creative activities thereby aroused. The most widely known and used of these are the *Rorschach Inkblot Test* and the *Morgan-Murray Thematic Apperception Test.*[65]

RORSCHACH INKBLOT TEST.   In this test the subject is shown a series of ten inkblot figures, some simple black and white, some shaded into grays, and some having blotches of color. The subject is asked to tell what he sees on the card, or what is represented or suggested there. An elaborate system of recording the responses has been developed, so elaborate, in fact, that the test can be given or scored only after special training. When the responses are analyzed, the experimenter has what is presumed to be a complete picture of the subject's total personality.

The test itself is of such complexity that its use is limited to those thoroughly trained in its administration and interpretation. The multiplicity of variables that enter into the process of testing itself, and which affect significantly the responses of the testee, make it necessary to proceed with the utmost caution in interpreting the responses. These variables make the conditions of testing difficult to standardize fully. Among them may be men-

[63] Albert Ellis, "Recent research with personality inventories," *Journal of Consulting Psychology* (1953), *17*: 45–49.

[64] Ralph G. Eckert, "A mental hygiene approach to speech instruction as a means to personal adjustment," Ph.D. Dissertation, University of California, 1940.

[65] See Hermann Rorschach, *Psychodiagnosis*, tr. by Paul Lemkau and Bernard Kronenberg, New York, Grune & Stratton, 1951; and C. D. Morgan and H. A. Murray, "A method for investigating fantasies: the Thematic Apperception Test," *Archives of Neurology and Psychiatry* (1935), *34*: 289–306.

tioned the personality of the tester, the understanding by the testee of the purposes of the test, interaction tendencies, attitudinal factors (toward the self, the examiner, or other aspects of the external situation), and so on.[66]

Variations in the conditions of testing in turn cause variations in the responses to the test. Furthermore, the results are susceptible of a wide range of interpretation, depending mainly on the clinician's own criteria for scoring. The stimulus materials present

. . . the individual with a relatively novel kind of problem for which he is unlikely to have any specifically taught and overlearned process. From the interaction of the instructions and the stimulus materials one might hypothesize that in the Rorschach situation individuals will differ in the degree to which feelings of indecision, dependence, lack of confidence, and failure will be experienced. Put in another way, *The interaction of instructions and stimulus materials will make the Rorschach situation a stressful one for many individuals.*[67]

It is such considerations as these which no doubt led Cattell to conclude, "Despite the attractions which the Rorschach test has exercised, especially on psychiatrists, it remains a mixture of ill-defined intentions, analogous to a patent-medicine, devoid of clear-cut theoretical basis."[68]

THEMATIC APPERCEPTION TEST. Often used with the Rorschach is the *Thematic Apperception Test*, in which the subject is given a series of pictures and asked to compose a story about each one. With reference to the "*Picture Story Method*" Symonds says,

It is not possible to estimate personality characteristics or life history material with any degree of certainty from picture-story material. . . . Picture-story material, which is on the fantasy level, represents principally unconscious and unexpressed drives, impulses, defenses against anxiety and other dynamic tendencies which may be and frequently are the opposite of expressed personality. It is concluded that content analysis of picture-story (TAT) has little diagnostic (descriptive) significance and that its principal value comes from using it to reveal underlying dynamic trends.[69]

Vernon agrees with Symonds, that the test seems useful in the clinic, "especially when used along with other tests, such as Rorschach," where it

[66] Seymour B. Sarason, *The Clinical Interaction: with Special Reference to the Rorschach*, New York, Harper & Brothers, 1954, chaps. 3–8.

[67] *Ibid.*, p. 114. Italics in the original.

[68] R. B. Cattell, *The Description and Measurement of Personality*, New York, World Book Company, 1946.

[69] Percival M. Symonds, "Interpreting the picture story (TAT) method," *The American Psychologist* (1947), 2: 228–229. (Abstract of a paper read before the American Psychological Association, September 10, 1947.)

may reveal speech and other disturbances.[70] In an investigation of business executives, using the TAT, however, Henry found that the principal differences between executives for whom success was predicted in contrast to those whose future success was somewhat doubtful lay in the area of personality. None of the characteristics of the successful group included any reference to speech or speaking.[71]

Speech and Personality

Just what aspects of speech are to be correlated with what aspects of personality, when and if either is to be measured with any degree of reliability, is another problem which has not as yet been solved. Duyker has suggested that "inadequate concern has been given the effect of language on the developing personality.[72] Not much significance can be attached to such comparisons as personality with grammatical forms, particularly in view of the current ferment among linguists over the value or stability of those grammatical forms. Rate of speaking may be suggestive of impulsiveness-deliberateness, and extroversion may be indicated to some extent by fluency or facility in oral language;[73] but these tell little about speech as a whole. There have been relatively few studies during the past two decades attempting to find definite correlations between speech in general or specific characteristics of speech on the one hand, and personality traits on the other.

Among the traits of personality that have perhaps been most extensively studied in relation to speech are introversion-extroversion, dominance-submissiveness, emotional stability-neuroticism, and self-sufficiency-dependence. These were all measured by the *Bernreuter Personality Inventory*; of this and similar tests McClelland observes that "often they involve a miscellany of correlated responses out of which it is nearly impossible to make any theoretical sense."[74] Any comparisons of speech with measurements from such tools must be evaluated on the basis of the validity of both the personality and the speech scores. It should be kept in mind also that such dual terms as dominance-submissiveness refer to the outer limits in the *distribution* of some more general trait that includes both, and not to any bimodal classification by which people can be assigned definitely to one group or the other.

[70] Philip E. Vernon, *Personality Tests and Assessments*, London, Methuen & Co., 1953, p. 183.
[71] William E. Henry, "The business executive: the psychodynamics of a social role," *American Journal of Sociology* (1949), *54*: 286–291.
[72] H. J. C. Duyker, "Language and psychology," *Acta Psychologica* (1950), 7: 150–173.
[73] Vernon, *op. cit.*, pp. 56–57.
[74] McClelland, *Personality, op. cit.*, p. 185.

In investigating introversion-extroversion in relation to speech Elwood Murray qualified the scale by introducing the facts of egocentricity as opposed to mental objectivity, as measured by the Miller-Henrikson-Murray *Personal Social Adjustment Test for Speech*.[75] When characterized by mental objectivity, neither introversion nor extroversion, according to this principle, needs to interfere with effectiveness in speaking, although "Probably the most effective speakers tend to be objectively minded extroverts."

Up to the present time the results of efforts to correlate personality traits, such as are explored by these tests, with speaking proficiency are conflicting, probably because the techniques of measurement, either of speech or of significant personality characteristics, lack sufficient refinement. It is quite possible, too, that the components which have most to do with effective speaking have not yet been isolated, that the tests which have so far been devised do not actually measure those aspects which enter most significantly into speech behavior. Whatever the reasons, studies on the basis of such personality inventories are either inconclusive or contradictory. Where one investigator finds an existing relation, another finds it either entirely non-existent or functioning in an opposite direction. It seems obvious, then, that in relation to effectiveness in speech, whatever that may mean, the scores made in the older personality tests are little more than indicative, if even that. It would seem that measures of intelligence and educational achievement, together with a background of speaking experiences, from childhood through high school, are much more significant in differentiating good and poor speakers than inventories of speech attitudes and personality traits.[76]

Duncan found that only three factors, none of which appeared on the usual personality inventories, showed significant differences between good and poor speakers: speech training, adequate medical care, and social and cultural status.[77]

Furthermore, "The correlations between 'effective speech' and the various personality traits do not have material meaningfulness because there is no adequate description of what constitutes 'effective speaking.'" That there is a relation between speech and personality can be accepted as a fact, Duncan continues. "But before we can get to the bottom of this relation there are many

[75] Elwood Murray, *The Speech Personality*, rev. ed., Philadelphia, J. B. Lippincott Company, 1944, pp. 78 ff.

[76] See Wilbur E. Moore, "Factors related to achievement and improvement in public speaking," *Quarterly Journal of Speech* (1943), *29*: 213–217; Eugene C. Chenoweth, "The adjustment of college freshmen to the speaking situation," *Quarterly Journal of Speech* (1940), *26*: 585–588.

[77] Melba Hurd Duncan, "An experimental study of some of the relationships between voice and personality among students of speech," *Speech Monographs* (1945), *12*: 47–73.

bridges to cross. . . . What sort of speech should we study if we are hunting for personality; does the individual reveal himself more in written or oral language? In any sample of speech, how much of the response is attributable to the stimulus situation and how much to 'personal determinants'?"[78]

If any conclusions are to be drawn from the evidence thus far found, it would be in part, at least, that much work remains to be done before we shall be able to say with any degree of definiteness just what the relation between personality traits and speech performance really is. Certainly it is unsafe to insist that no aspect of speech is in any way related to "the total picture of [man's] organized behavior, especially as it can be characterized by his fellow men in a consistent way."[79] On the face of it, such a conclusion would seem to be contrary to human experience. Nor can it be said with any assurance that existent measures of those traits which are assumed to enter into man's personality, as it is understood, are indicative of the type of speech performance we may have reason to expect, or that the acquisition of speaking skills results in what is assumed to be an "improvement" in those traits. The present interest in the question, particularly among psychologists, holds some promise of a further approach to a solution of many of the problems involved.[80]

Speech as a Personality Trait.   One possible and partial solution to the problem of the relation of speech to personality is to consider speech *as a distinct personality trait in itself*, rather than to attempt to discover correlations between speech and personality traits. The latter approach is apparently based on the hypothesis that speech and personality are two quite separate phenomena, and that the problem is to discover points of contact and perhaps causal relationship. But it is a matter of common observation that people form their judgments of others' personalities by what they see and hear the others doing. The posture while standing during a speaking performance, either conversation or more formal, the quality of the bodily movement as the speaker shifts from one position to another, the voice—its quality, general rate of utterance, loudness, pitch variations—the manner of dress, of makeup, the facial expression—all these and more enter into the total impression created on one's associates. The ideas one expresses, the consistency—or stubbornness—with which one holds to those ideas, the insistence with which one

---

[78] F. H. Sanford, "Speech and personality," *Psychological Bulletin* (1942), *39*: 811–845.

[79] Cf. p. 53.

[80] See also Keith E. Case, "An investigation into the backgrounds for the study and measurement of personality in speech communication." Unpublished Ph.D. Dissertation, University of Denver, 1948.

imposes those ideas on one's acquaintances on all occasions, all contribute to the composite picture which people inevitably create of one's personality. But these are difficult to measure consistently, and thus far have not been adequately evaluated.

The idea itself is not new. Thirty years ago Sapir suggested much the same thing. He analyzed speech from five levels: the voice, voice dynamics (intonation, rhythm, relative continuity, and speed), pronunciation, vocabulary, and language or style. In getting at one's personality all five of these must be dealt with; but if they were sufficiently described, a fairly accurate description of one's personality would be obtained, particularly with reference to the individual's speech.[81]

Pear discusses research in progress at the University of Manchester, into such problems as "impressions of personality and character from voice and speech, differences in personal attitude towards changes in one's own speech and that of others, social stratification and its effects on behavior. . . . Comparatively little use has been made of the fact that in many countries (more particularly in England) judgements of personality from speech or facial appearance are closely connected with impressions of the person's occupation or social class."[82]

Two difficulties arise in connection with many studies of speech in relation to personality. One of these is the failure to differentiate speech from other forms of verbal communication. The work of Chotlos, for example, is cited as an instance of an analysis of speech characteristics, when as a matter of fact, he studied writing exclusively.[83] When McClelland discusses "Speech and Personality," one is not always certain whether he is writing about speech or language in general. "To illustrate how speech analyses are made," he says, "we can turn to a sample of Karl's *written language* and analyze it according to some of the standard techniques used by psychologists working in this field."[84]

Sanford's study of speech and personality is also cited as presenting a speech characterization which "represents the extent to which a psychologist can place on a quantitative basis characterizations of literary style which critics have arrived at intuitively."[85] McClelland goes on to say that Sanford's

---

[81] Edward Sapir, "Speech as a personality trait," *American Journal of Sociology* (1927), *32*: 892–905.

[82] T. H. Pear, "The social psychology of everyday life," in *Current Trends in British Psychology, op. cit.*, pp. 113–124.

[83] J. W. Chotlos, "A statistical and comparative analysis of written language samples," *Psychological Monographs* (1944), *56*: 77–111.

[84] McClelland, *Personality, op. cit.*, pp. 151–155. Italics added.

[85] F. H. Sanford, "Speech and personality: a comparative case study," *Character and Personality* (1942), *10*: 169–198.

analysis is undoubtedly "excellent so far as Merritt's speech is concerned" (Merritt being one of the two subjects whose "speech" is being analyzed). Actually, Sanford includes in his description of the speech of his two subjects considerably more than "literary style." He uses samples of "oral speech" in his study, analyzing the product from three points of view: (1) "The Mechanics of Speech"; (2) "Grammatical Categories"; and (3) "Composite Categories." The second and third of these contain items that might apply equally to written discourse; Sanford makes no effort to discover the extent to which they were influenced by the fact that the samples were spoken rather than written.

The first of the three, however, consists of such oral characteristics as starting time (after the stimulus is given), length of production (story, etc.), speed of speaking, hesitation sounds (*uh, er*), repetition of words or phrases, rephrasing, contractions (I'll, sha'n't, etc.). In general, he observes that

Though the description of speech at many points reads like a description of the person, there is no attempt in the present paper to look into the relation between the linguistic data and other facts about the two subjects. From what we know of personality we might well expect that the individual's verbal and nonverbal behavior are all of a piece and that we can, if we are clever, see the latter in the former. Studies of style are likely to have diagnostic value. Linguistic traits, however, quite aside from the light they may throw on nonlinguistic behavior, are in themselves important data. The most frequent and most consummately human of human behaviors is speech. When we have characterized the person's speech we have gone a long way toward characterizing the person.[86]

The other difficulty in connection with studies of speech as a distinct trait of personality lies in the tendency to read too much into the analyses that are made. As McCllelland points out, the analysis of Merritt's speech, in the study mentioned, may be very good so far as speech itself is concerned, and may give an excellent picture of that particular aspect of the personality; but it does not necessarily tell us a great deal about the other aspects of the subject's personality, and we must avoid, as Sanford has succeeded in doing, reading into the analysis a great deal that is not there. Whether a complete personality description, normal or abnormal, can be built up solely on the basis of one's speech habits may be open to some question.

At the same time, as Johnson points out,

Generally speaking, the relationship between speech and personality is so close that the two terms can hardly be disentangled. . . . Speech is not only the evidence of personality, but it is also probably the chief means by which it is molded. It

[86] *Ibid.*

seems hardly possible that either term could have any significant meaning in isolation from the other. Communication may be viewed as the interaction of personalities through the medium of speech, and it is when the speaker is his own listener that the closeness of the relationship between speech and personality become (*sic*) strikingly apparent.[87]

Personality and the Speech Defective

With respect to the speech defective, or the otherwise handicapped individual, the picture is somewhat different. Everyone is familiar with the speech of the person severely handicapped by cerebral palsy or often by poliomyelitis. The aphasics and the brain injured present a picture of extreme speech deviation. The personality structure of the stutterer is not as yet clear, if indeed it varies markedly from the nonstutterer. The effect of alcohol on the speech centers, and on speech itself, is likewise well known. Speech disturbances are, in fact, recognized as diagnostic manifestations of neurological and psychological disturbances.

Personality and Stuttering. Walnut studied, by means of the *Minnesota Multiphasic Personality Inventory*, a number of normal speakers, stutterers, crippled, and cleft palate high school students, reporting that all groups fell within the normal range of personality. Compared with the others, the stutterers showed "poor adjustment of the emotional type, with a feeling of uselessness and inability to assume normal optimism with regard to the future"; they were further characterized by "suspiciousness, oversensitivity, and delusions of persecution." The stuttering group also showed inability to handle speech situations—an observation not entirely unexpected. They also "gave slight indications of paranoid and depressive tendencies on the basis of the categories of the MMPI when compared with the control groups. . . . In general, the study did not indicate whether stuttering precipitated abnormal personality or vice versa, since the so-called pathological group showed no significant personality deviations."[88]

Personality and Hearing. In a relatively early study of the relation of personality and hearing, Brunschwig concluded that the general adjustment score, as indicated by the *Personality Inventory for the Deaf*, showed a lower

[87] Wendell Johnson, "Speech and personality," *ETC* (1948), *6*: 84–102.
[88] Francis Walnut, "A personality inventory item analysis of individuals who stutter and individuals who have other handicaps," *Journal of Speech and Hearing Disorders* (1954), *19*: 220–227.

adjustment for those with impaired hearing than for those with normal hearing. Early loss of hearing, within the first year or so, seems to impair adjustment less than a later loss. In general, deaf children do not differ significantly from hearing children.[89]

There is an indication, according to Berlinsky, that the acquisition of speech aids in adjustment; it "helps the deaf behave more like the hearing in their personality adjustment."[90]

As for the Rorschach test, previously referred to, Sheehan concluded that "it could be used to predict psychotherapeutic improvement in the group studied [35 stutterers], but could not be used to predict speech or symptomatic improvement. . . . The Rorschach probably should not be expected to predict changes in overt speech behavior."[91]

Personality and Susceptibility to Persuasion.   The effect of personality characteristics on the individual's susceptibility to persuasion was explored by Janis, who concluded that "(a) persons with low self-esteem tend to be more readily influenced than others. (b) Persons with acute symptoms of neurotic anxiety tend to be more resistant than others."[92]

Speech as Self-Expression

Our first utterances are wholly emotional; that is, they are an aspect of a total bodily reaction to an indeterminate, undifferentiated combination of stimuli impinging upon the as yet undiscriminating sense organs. Although during the process of enculturation we learn a measure of control over our emotional expressions, we never reach a time when they are wholly absent. We all give vent to our feelings at one time or another, although we rarely if ever lose control entirely. The interjection, an expression of emotional behavior, has been considered by many as the principal source for the beginnings of language. Still further, we may and occasionally do "stand up in meeting" and express ourselves vigorously, not so much with the idea of making a significant impression on others, as for the simple purpose of expressing our attitudes. And who has not written a strong letter in which

[89] L. Brunschwig, "A study of some personality aspects of deaf children," *Teachers College Contributions to Education*, No. 687, New York, Columbia University, 1936.

[90] Stanley Berlinsky, "Measurement of the intelligence and personality of the deaf," *Journal of Speech and Hearing Disorders* (1952), *17*: 39–54.

[91] Joseph G. Sheehan, "Rorschach prognosis in psychotherapy and speech therapy," *Journal of Speech and Hearing Disorders* (1954), *19*: 217–219.

[92] Irving L. Janis, "Personality correlates of susceptibility to persuasion," *Journal of Personality* (1954), *22*: 504–518.

a point of view has been stated in the most unrestrained language, only to tear it up without sending it? The feelings have been relieved by merely setting them down in language.

Expressive and Instrumental Utterance

Festinger describes "expressive messages" as "consummatory" rather than "instrumental." "*Instrumental communication* requires feedback from the recipient; the talker wants to know whether or not his message has had an effect. *Consummatory communication*, on the other hand, does not depend upon the effect it has had on others. The talker is usually not interested in secondary information about the effects of his consummatory communication. The expression of the emotion reduces his need to communicate regardless of its effects." [93]

Fearing also differentiates between expression or expressive behavior and communication, although the differentiating criteria may be difficult to establish, and between "planned" and "unplanned" communication. The former are "usually interpreter centered. . . ." A propaganda or political campaign would be an example. Unplanned or unspecific communications tend to be communicator centered, at the extreme becoming entirely expressive. [94]

Affective Elements in Information.   Even in the communication of logical, informative material it is often difficult, even at times undesirable, to avoid some expression of the emotional state, our personal feelings, our attitude toward the subject under discussion. "Feelings cannot be expressed in words," says Thelen; "we can talk about them, but we cannot *talk* them. On the other hand, we can communicate to others how we feel. We do it partly through the nonspecific way we express it: the tone of voice, the inflections, the tempo of a speech. We also use formal elements of speech: the elaborateness of our phrases, the shock we convey through bluntness, the associations of feelings with which people invest particular words, etc. . . ." Thelen goes on to point out that speech is not the only expressive mechanism; posture, facial expression, gestures, especially the involuntary movements, serve also to indicate to others how we feel; "or at least they communicate the fact that our feelings have changed." [95]

[93] Leon Festinger, "Informal social communication," in *Theory and Experiment in Social Communication*, Leon Festinger *et al.* (eds.), Ann Arbor, Institute for Social Research, 1950.
[94] Franklin Fearing, "Toward a psychological theory of communication," *Journal of Personality* (1953), *22*: 71–88.
[95] Herbert A. Thelen, *Dynamics of Groups at Work*, Chicago, University of Chicago Press, 1954, p. 247.

Expression Versus Communication. Even more important than the communication of feelings is simply their expression. The writer of literature is often much less interested in informing others with respect to his attitudes than he is in relieving his tensions.

We have all known the relief that comes from uttering a long and resounding series of impolite vocables under the stress of great irritation. The same releasing of psychological tensions appears to be effected at all levels of affective utterance, if we are to believe what writers themselves have said about the creative process. The novel, the drama, the poem, like the oath or expletive, arise, at least in part, out of internal necessity when the organism experiences a serious tension, whether resulting from joy, grief, disturbance, or frustration.[96]

Révész has pointed out that the role of language cannot be limited to thought and communication; it possesses an "original expressive" aspect. "Emotions appear not only in the form of expressive sounds and gestures enriched by intonation, modulation and rhythm, but also by means of symbolic phonetic signs with expressive value, i.e., words—a correlative conjunction of sound and sense." Thus "The expressive capacity of language as a medium for the display of aesthetic experience and artistic effort appears in literature and in rhetoric and drama."[97]

CATHARSIS IN LITERATURE. Literature does more, however, than express the affective and aesthetic experiences of the writer; it often says for us the things that we would say for ourselves. The writer has, it is true, succeeded in relieving his own tensions whenever he "symbolizes his experiences to himself," as Hayakawa has said.[98] At the same time he has symbolized *our* experiences for and to us. In memorizing and repeating even to ourselves but even more by reciting aloud certain choice passages from literature we are often engaging anew in the processes of purgation; our own tensions are relieved.

CATHARSIS IN CONFESSION. Something of the same phenomenon occurs in certain religious observances. In kneeling we place ourselves in the physical attitude of humbleness and supplication; in repeating the confession we symbolically cleanse ourselves of our transgressions.

It is also well known that when persons accused of crime are finally induced to make a full and voluntary confession, they usually experience a profound

[96] S. I. Hayakawa, *Language in Thought and Action*, rev. ed., New York, Harcourt, Brace and Company, 1949, p. 144.

[97] G. Révész, *The Origins and Prehistory of Language*, tr. by J. Butler, New York, Philosophical Library, 1956, pp. 104 f.

[98] *Loc. cit.*

feeling of relief from tensions, even when they are aware of the fact that a severe penalty awaits them. So far as is known, the phenomenon of confession has not been extensively studied from a psychological point of view. The principal interest in this area has been in the legal validity of the confession in relation to the methods employed in obtaining it.

CATHARSIS IN PSYCHOTHERAPY.   In no area has the principle of catharsis been more effectively and profitably used than in the field of psychotherapy. This is not the place to present a thorough discussion of therapeutic techniques in abnormal psychology and mental hygiene, more than simply to point out that getting the client to bring his difficulties to the surface through freely talking about them is a basic phase of the remedial processes. The therapist goes further than to permit free speech; he encourages, even urges the patient to say whatever comes into his mind, however reluctant the latter may be at first. "As the work proceeds, the patient fearfully recites his thoughts and intentions and awaits the thunderclap of disapproval which he has learned to expect. When it does not come in the course of repeated trials, his fear is extinguished, and the once frightening sentences lose their power to create alarm. As fear is reduced, new thoughts can occur, especially those which have formerly been opposed by anxiety."[99] Needless to say, there is a great deal more to psychotherapy than this, but the essential point is that the patient is led to discuss his situation, and in the discussion gains, with the help and guidance of the therapist, new insights.

The Relation Between Language and Thought

Throughout this chapter the point of view has been taken that language is essentially a means of social adaptation, integration, and control, and that although it is significant in self-expression, its primary function is to influence the behavior of others through the presenting of symbolic stimuli. It has been tacitly assumed that, except for the expressive forms of behavior, at least two persons are involved and are actually and physically concerned in the completed cycle. These two consist of one presenting the stimuli and the other receiving and responding to them. The fact that these two need not be spatially and temporally present has not affected the assumption that they are physically existent.

[99] John Dollard, Frank Auld, Jr., and Alice Marsden White, *Steps in Psychotherapy*, New York, The Macmillan Company, 1953, p. 4.

It has also been pointed out that under certain circumstances the cycle may be broken, in that the response is only an imagined one. In fact, it is altogether possible that the second person in the communication may be entirely imagined. We prepare a speech and rehearse the presentation over and over, imagining the audience and their reactions. In our imagination that audience listens, observes our graceful movements, and makes exactly the appropriate responses—just as we want them to do.

Imaginary Conversation

We hold imaginary conversations with other people; we walk up to the boss (in imagination) and tell him in no uncertain terms just what we think of him, detailing our opinion of his ancestry and ultimate destination—thereby succeeding in relieving ourselves of a certain amount of emotional tension. In these conversations we fulfill all the ends of speech: we may give information, amuse or entertain, convince, persuade, or inspire, as well as give vent to our feelings, and the imagined response completes the cycle. There are present, therefore, all the elements of communication, except for the fact that the second person, the "party of the second part," is no more than a figment of the imagination.

Covert Language Behavior.   Now let us go a step further. In this sort of communication, in which the audience is imaginary, our speech movements may be so slight as not even to be observable; they are "covert" or "implicit," going on inside of us somewhere, unobservable by anyone but ourselves. They do have meanings, however, and communicative significance. By means of them we can and do carry on extended conversations with imagined audiences.

When children are learning to speak they are often discovered talking to themselves. One can hear them and see their lips move. Sometimes they never get beyond this stage; but normally, as they discover through social pressure that it is often inadvisable to reveal these verbalizations, they tend more and more to conceal this type of communicative behavior, with the result that in time it becomes entirely covert. The speech activities themselves become, so to speak, "short-circuited," so that finally there is little or no resemblance between the overt language behavior and the corresponding covert activity. They have become *verbal imagery*. But the communicative significance of this imagery remains just as truly as if the performance were overt speech with an actual listener present. But as Dashiell has pointed out, "When speech has been reduced in intensity to the point of being implicit rather than overt, it is nevertheless still speech."[100]

Conversing with Oneself

It is therefore evident that one can communicate with either an actual or an imaginary audience. So far the assumption has been that this audience is a second person, someone other than the individual initiating the communication. But actually one may provide the stimulus and then *react to it himself.* When children and old people talk to themselves, they do not necessarily have even an imagined audience other than themselves. How many of us are there who have not, at some time or another, held a vigorous argument with ourselves? If we play a musical instrument we may, when thinking over a melody or a harmony or a rhythm pattern, tense our fingers or sway our bodies ever so slightly, but quite perceptibly. Often it is no more than a kinesthetic imagery. (Music is, of course, one kind of symbolic system.)

We do, then, undoubtedly communicate with ourselves. We provide the stimuli and then do our own responding. It is our own behavior that is affected. We consider the facts in the case, reason out conclusions, come to hold beliefs which lead to actions. We make new resolutions to govern our general conduct; we become highly amused at an idea of our own. We daydream and take much pleasure in it; we develop ambitions and lay plans for the future. The resultant behavior may be either implicit or explicit. In most cases our covert communication leads to the latter.

"Thinking." The slight, unobservable muscular contractions by which we hold converse with imaginary persons or with ourselves are just as truly symbolic as if we were actually communicating with some living second person. This process by which we communicate with ourselves, by which we provide symbolic stimuli, usually implicit, and then respond to them ourselves, is one type of *thinking*. It is implicit speech. To the extent, however, that communication may go on in various ways by symbolic movements of various parts of the body, or by the symbolic product of bodily movements, as in writing, to the same extent can thinking proceed by the implicit activities of various parts of the organism—by the symbolic imagery which is called up through the different senses. To the degree that the mechanisms involved in these movements and imagery, overt in communication, covert in thinking, can all be classed under the general term "language mechanisms," to the same

[100] Dashiell, *op. cit.*, p. 539.

degree, and no more, are we justified in saying that thought itself is the implicit action of these same language mechanisms.

The responses to such behavior may be either explicit or implicit, or further implicit symbolic activity, which provides a still further stimulus for either explicit or implicit reactions, and so on, theoretically *ad infinitum*.

Familiar Language Systems.   We think in terms of the symbolic systems with which we are familiar. Most of our thinking is done with the mechanism with which we do most of our communicating: the speech mechanism. Students of foreign languages often arrive at a stage of such familiarity with those symbolic systems that they think in them; one may, for example, think in English, or French, or German, or any other language. To illustrate this point, Chinese students in America, when asked whether they thought in Chinese or in English, replied that when thinking about their school work or about things connected with their life in America, it was in English; but if the subject were China and things Chinese, it was always in that language. The observation has been verified by students from other countries, and speaking widely diverse languages.

Systems Other Than Language.   But we may also do a part of our thinking in systems other than language. If we use a typewriter well, we can occasionally observe ourselves "thinking" in terms of the keyboard and the movements of the fingers in forming the words. If one is an expert telegrapher, he may at times think in dots and dashes and in the movements of the arm and wrist. An artist may think in colors and forms, a musician in terms of melodies, harmonies, and rhythms. A deaf-mute who has not learned speech thinks with his fingers, in terms of the symbolic systems with which he is familiar. He may, however, learn to speak later, in which case he may do his thinking in terms of the newer language system.

One of the most extensively used symbolic systems in which much thinking takes place is that of mathematics, all the way from the simple, fundamental processes to the most abstruse mathematical formulations. It would be impossible to go far in mathematics without thorough familiarity with the symbols and the *relationships which they represent*. Symbolic logic represents still another field of thought in which certain abstract relationships are expressed in an abbreviated symbolism, which in fact makes the science possible. Every student of speech is no doubt familiar with the phonetic alphabet, which makes possible the representation of specific speech sounds; it also makes it possible to think more specifically of those sounds.

Everyone who has driven cross country or ridden any distance on the train knows the value of maps, which represent more or less graphically, as well as symbolically, directions, distances, and significant features of either land or water surfaces; to the geologist and the mariner they represent depths as well. The military strategist must have information regarding contours as well as other natural and artificial features that might affect his planning. These are presented symbolically, and make possible a type of symbolic thinking that would be difficult without the peculiar system of signs and symbols devised for those particular areas of thought and activity.

Blueprints and circuit diagrams of electrical and electronic equipment represent another type of symbolic system, familiarity with which is an absolute essential for efficient work in these fields.

Concrete Thinking

There is another type of thinking, however, which is just as truly thinking as the process we have been describing, although it is generally considered to be on a somewhat lower level. In trying to piece together a particular apparatus, for example, we often think our problem out in terms of that specific object. We try this combination and that, either actually or in imagination, until we finally hit upon one that will accomplish the desired end. If our motor stops, we may search out the cause in some such manner: it may be the ignition—we trace the system from battery to spark plugs. It may be the gasoline feed—we follow the same general procedure. Working out a jigsaw puzzle is a good illustration of this sort of thinking in which concrete objects, rather than abstractions, are dealt with. We look for a piece with a certain form and color pattern, and we may have little or no need for symbolic imagery. A still more primitive form would be that in which we picked up piece after piece, trying to fit it into place without regard to comparisons of form and color pattern. Insistence on putting a square peg into a round hole is much the same type of performance.

In this connection, Weiss holds that "When human achievement is regarded as a form of behavior two relatively distinct types of movements may be discriminated: (a) the manipulation or handling response; (b) the language or speech response. Speaking generally, for the average human individual every stimulus may release either a handling response, a language response, or both." [101]

Pillsbury and Meader say that "it is probable that . . . one thinks in images

[101] Weiss, *op. cit.*, p. 287.

alone when dealing with material that is not easily represented in words, as in musical composition or in designing an instrument of original form. Words alone are most frequently used where the matter is very abstract and images are not at all relevant."[102] It might be added here that Pillsbury and Meader do not, in this particular connection, consider the implicit language activities as "imagery"; it might clarify the difference between these and the type of imagery they discuss, if we always think of the former as "verbal imagery," which may, in fact, include either auditory, visual, or kinesthetic images.

The conclusion of Dashiell, that "faithful imaging of details is not conducive to effective thinking," seems to be applicable to thinking in abstractions; the adult needs the ability "to condense and foreshorten, to organize and reorganize, to abstract and generalize." Inability to advance beyond the concrete to abstract thinking is a characteristic of the schizophrenic's thinking.[103] At the same time, even the normal individual at times does deal in concrete objects and concrete situations, and solves concrete problems in concrete terms applicable to a single instance. Furthermore, one can still include verbal imagery as both a type of symbolization and a type of imagery.

Concrete thinking, then, can and does go on in terms of concrete imagery, or in terms of the objects themselves. In the former the object is present in images, and we manipulate those images much as we would the object itself. This may be true of actions as well as of things. We can study out a tennis or a golf stroke without overtly moving a muscle. Of course, making the muscles actually follow the imagined motions may be quite another thing. There are some things that cannot be learned by correspondence lessons.

"The simplest and most satisfactory view," according to Skinner, "is that thought is simply *behavior*—verbal or nonverbal, covert or overt. It is not some mysterious process responsible for behavior but the very behavior itself in all the complexity of its controlling relations, with respect to both man the behaver and the environment in which he lives."[104]

Abstract Thinking

Abstract thinking, however, must go on in terms of symbolic imagery, because abstract thinking is a matter of determining new relationships between and among concepts. A "concept" is a generalization, a determining of the universal elements or characteristics in a given class of particulars. The

[102] Pillsbury and Meader, *op. cit.*, p. 99.
[103] Dashiell, *op. cit.*, p. 585.
[104] B. F. Skinner, *Verbal Behavior*, New York, Appleton-Century-Crofts, 1957, p. 449.

final step in the process of forming a concept is the giving of a name to that generalization. For example, assume a certain group of particular objects which have elements common to all of them, and we refer to that whole group by the one name "box." There are any number of kinds of boxes, but all boxes have these common characteristics. When we have analyzed the common elements and given a name to that class of objects having these characteristics, we have formed the concept "box."

The importance of the symbol in relation to the concept is recognized and pointed out by a number of writers on the subject. Murphy emphasizes the symbolization process in his definition of the concept: "a symbol which stands for a specific quality possessed in common by a number of stimuli." [105] Although Stagner and Karwoski do not specifically state that the symbol is essential to the generalizations which they term concepts, the generalizations themselves are centered about some symbol or word—"a concept of a chair," "a concept of a triangle," and so on. That is, the application of a symbol, a word, is an essential aspect of the process of conceptualization. [106] Sapir puts the relation even more strongly: "Not until we own the symbol do we feel that we hold a key to the immediate knowledge or understanding of the concept." [107] Miller points out that "our verbal habits are a treasury of abstractions learned" through the strengthening of "associations between certain invariant aspects of the materials [in a complex situation] and the particular response that symbolizes this aspect." [108]

Now if, as Sapir points out, the single elements of speech are symbols of concepts, then the "flow of speech" itself consists in the "setting of these concepts into mutual relations." [109] ". . . one of the main purposes of education, is the building-up of concepts." One might add that among the most important of concepts are those of relationships among other concepts; for the concepts themselves must be organized into patterns representing relationships which correspond to reality. Reasoning consists in the re-arranging and reorganizing of concepts into new but still valid relationships.

But abstract thinking is this same process, carried on implicitly. Sapir says,

Thought may no more be conceivable, in its general and daily practice, without speech than is mathematical reasoning practical without the lever of an appropriate mathematical symbolism. No one believes that even the most difficult mathematical

[105] *An Introduction to Psychology, op. cit.*, p. 291.
[106] Stagner and Karwoski, *op. cit.*, pp. 385–393.
[107] Edward Sapir, *Language*, New York, Harcourt, Brace and Company, 1921, p. 17.
[108] George A. Miller, *Language and Communication*, 1951, New York, McGraw-Hill Book Company, 1951, p. 239.
[109] Sapir, *op. cit.*, p. 12.

proposition is inherently dependent upon an arbitrary set of symbols, but it is impossible to suppose that the human mind is capable of arriving at or holding such a proposition without the symbolism.[110]

The word *name* itself is derived from an ancient root, *gna*, which means to know. From it we get such words as *cognomen*, *agnostic*, *recognize*, and so on.

The first step toward this real knowledge, a step which, however small in appearance, separates man forever from all other animals, is *the naming of a thing*, or the making a thing knowable. . . . It was known . . . that language is a distinguishing characteristic of man; it was known also that the having of general ideas is that which puts a perfect distinction betwixt man and brutes; but that these two were only different expressions of the same fact was not known till the theory of roots had been established as preferable to the theories both of Onomatopoeia and of Interjections. . . . Language and thought are inseparable. Words without thought are dead sounds; thoughts without words are nothing. To think is to speak low; to speak is to think aloud. The word is the thought incarnate.[111]

The Social Nature of Thinking

De Laguna emphasizes the *social* nature of thinking, as she does of speech itself. Thought, or thinking, arises from a form of conversation which "has for its end agreement among the participants regarding some specific conditions of common action." In the earlier forms this discussion had as its end a common assent which led to action. Later, it led more indirectly to conduct.

Thinking is the internalization of this form of conversation and its independent practicing by the individual . . . since it is carried on by the individual himself, the end cannot be agreement as such. . . . This end is the reaching of a belief regarding some doubtful matter. . . . The thinking process reaches its end when a verbal formulation is found which is at once relevant to the point at issue and objectively compatible with the assumed premises and the presumed context from which the process took its start.[112]

The Parallel Growth of Speech and Thought

The relationship between thought and language, which in a sense amounts to identity, may be further described by tracing somewhat their parallel growth.

[110] *Ibid.*, p. 14.
[111] Friederich Max Müller, *The Science of Language,* New York, Charles Scribner's Sons, 1891, pp. 520 ff.
[112] De Laguna, *op. cit.,* pp. 353–353.

The popular notion of learning to speak is that the child first has the idea and then gets from others a sound to use in communicating it; but a closer study shows this is hardly true even of the simplest idea, and is nearly the reverse of truth as regards developed thought. In that the word usually goes before, leading and kindling the idea—we should not have the latter if we did not have the word first. "This way," says the word, "is an interesting thought: come and find it." And so we are led on to rediscover old knowledge. Such words, for instance, as *good*, *right*, *truth*, *love*, *home*, *justice*, *beauty*, *freedom*, are powerful makers of what they stand for.[113]

Even ideas themselves are symbols. "Freiheit ist ein so schönes Wort, dass selbst wenn es nicht wahr ist, muss man daran glauben."[114]

Ayer points out that

. . . the people who talk of having difficulty in putting their thoughts into words are describing something that actually occurs; . . . The thought which we are unable to put into words is vague and inchoate; the symbols in which it is embodied are fragmentary; they do not fit together, or not in any way that satisfies us. As we find more appropriate expression for it the thought itself becomes more definite. In the end one may say, "Yes, this is what I meant all along," but the fact is not that one had a meaning all along, . . . The words say "What we meant all along" because it is they that finally give its sense to the whole previous process of groping; we are satisfied with them in a way that we were not satisfied before.[115]

Révész would not go so far as to identify thought and speech, but he approaches so close that the distinction seems to be little more than a verbal one. "A thorough study of all the varieties of thought . . . does . . . lead to the conclusion that thought, including wordless thought, presupposes the linguistic function in every conceivable instance. Wordlessness does not justify the assumption that thoughts that have not been formulated verbally arise independently of language." He summarizes the relation in four propositions:

1. Human thought presupposes speech.
2. Speech is introduced by thought.
3. Through speech, thought is accompanied by the words and sentences required for the development of ideas.

[113] Charles Horton Cooley, *Social Organization*, New York, Charles Scribner's Sons, 1912, p. 69.
[114] Goethe. Quoted by Dorothy Thompson in "Freedom's back is against the wall!" in *Modern Speeches on Basic Issues*, Lew Sarett and William Trufant Foster (eds.), Boston, Houghton Mifflin Company, 1939, pp. 185–199.
[115] A. J. Ayer, "What is communication?" in *Studies in Communication*, A. J. Ayer *et al.* (eds.), London, Martin Secker & Warburg, 1955, pp. 11–28.

4. Thought and speech are inseparably associated with each other despite their disparity in function, intention and structure.
Speech does not exist without thought, nor thought without speech.[116]

New concepts demand new linguistic embodiment, and we are not satisfied until we have found a distinctive name for the concept. Once it has been found, we can place it in various relations with other concepts and use it in our daily thinking.

Hence the two, explicit language and implicit thought, develop together, new words giving and fixing new concepts, and new concepts being crystallized and made usable by still other new symbols. The educative process is, in a sense, largely a matter of learning these new concepts and of learning how to set them into mutual relations that will bear valid correspondences with realities.

From the neurological point of view, thinking is merely quietly, more or less secretly, as it were, retracing the neurograms laid out by experience— mostly those laid out by the experience of speech. From this point of view, thinking is implicit speaking, a neuromuscular process with the muscular component reduced to slight, perhaps invisible and inaudible, sometimes entirely imperceptible, contractions. It is an all-over-the-body process, not limited to Broca's or any other specific brain area.

Language and Culture

One of the problems of no little interest in a psychological approach to speech is that concerning the relation between language, or speech, and what is known as *culture*. The term *culture* itself refers generally to all the various aspects of a people's manner of living, "the sum total of ways of living built up by a group of human beings, which is transmitted from one generation to another.[117] Many factors are involved in the culture of a given people—their religion, including myths and superstitions as well as rational beliefs, their laws, education, tools, habitations and costumes, maintenance of food supply, marriage customs, arts, and underlying all these and making them possible, language, or speech. "Today we are beginning to realize and to appreciate that the symbol is the basic unit of all human behavior and civilization." White goes on to say that "It was the exercise of the symbolic faculty that brought culture into existence and it is the use of symbols that makes the

[116] Révész, *op. cit.*, pp. 98–102.
[117] *American College Dictionary*, p. 295. See also A. Adamson Hoebel, "The nature of culture," in *Man, Culture, and Society*, Harry L. Shapiro (ed.), New York, Oxford University Press, 1956, pp. 168–181.

perpetuation of culture possible. Without the symbol there would be no culture, and man would be merely an animal, not a human being. Articulate speech is the most important form of symbolic expression."[118]

The language and the culture of a people have grown together, each molding and being molded by the other. That is, the customs, habits, and ways of living have been strongly influential in shaping the language; but at the same time, the language itself, its vocabulary, its structure, its idiom, have had a profound influence on the thinking of the individuals using it, and on their ways of perceiving and interpreting their environment.

The difficulty of translation from one idiom to another is well known. A comparison of translations of the Bible, for example, as it is used in various countries gives considerable insight into the thinking of the different peoples, and we are told that none of the translations of the New Testament currently in use carries the distinctive flavor of the original Aramaic. The difficulty of translating the Bible, or any other literature, into languages not yet even written is exceedingly difficult, largely because unlettered tribes, totally unfamiliar with the culture of the civilized world, simply do not possess the comparable concepts which make translations into their languages possible, and the concepts common to civilization do not apply to their cultures. It has been said that had Aristotle used a language other than Greek, his logic, even if he had written it, would have had a totally different structure. "The very existence of . . . a common stock of conceptions . . . seems to be a necessary concomitant of the communicability of ideas by words."[119]

Whorf maintains that the thinking processes are basically different for peoples whose languages are themselves fundamentally different.[120]

. . . the background linguistic system (in other words, the grammar) of each language is not merely a reproducing instrument for voicing ideas but rather is itself the shaper of ideas, the program and guide for the individual's mental activity, for his analysis of impressions, for his synthesis of his mental stock in trade. Formulation of ideas is not an independent process, strictly rational in the old sense, but is part of a particular grammar, and differs, from slightly to greatly, between different grammars.[121]

[118] Leslie A. White, "The symbol: the origin and basis of human behavior," in *Language, Meaning and Maturity*, S. I. Hayakawa (ed.), New York, Harper & Brothers, 1954, pp. 252–263. See also Harry Hoijer, "Language and writing," in *Man, Culture, and Society, op. cit.*, pp. 196–223; Mischa Titiev, *The Science of Man: An Introduction to Anthropology*, New York, Henry Holt and Company, 1954, pp. 155–163; 410–411; 416–418.

[119] Benjamin Lee Whorf, *Language, Thought and Reality*, New York, John Wiley & Sons, 1956, p. 36.

[120] *Ibid.*, pp. 66–67.

[121] *Ibid.*, p. 212. "Grammar" is not here to be taken in its traditional, formal meaning. See Hoijer, *op. cit.*, p. 199.

On the basis of the theory thus developed, Whorf has formulated his "linguistic relativity principle," which means "in informal terms, that users of markedly different grammars are pointed by their grammars toward different types of observation and different evaluations of externally similar acts of observation, and hence are not equivalent as observers but must arrive at somewhat different views of the world."[122]

Psychologists and anthropologists accept Whorf's extreme views with considerable reservation, but he himself, together with his predecessors and followers, accumulated a very respectable amount of data from languages of both primitive and civilized peoples in support of his general point of view. Whatever may be the details of the relation between language and culture, it is generally agreed that without language the rise of the institutions and habits of thought and behavior which are included in a people's culture would have been utterly impossible.

We are sometimes prone to consider nonliterate peoples as primitive, and their languages as also primitive, and therefore somehow inferior to the literate languages of "civilized" peoples. But as Titiev has pointed out, "One language is as good as another for conveying meaning, and in this sense it can be flatly stated that there is no such thing as an inferior language. On the basis of their experiences with many societies and cultures ethnologists find it impossible to rate languages as better or worse, or more or less effective." Cultural anthropologists no longer attempt to analyze nonliterate languages on the basis of their own tongues; they have come to recognize that "each culture [has] its own vocabulary and grammar for expressing its ideas."[123] One of the most significant phases of the process of enculturation is the acquisition of the language structure of the community in which one is growing up. There can be little question that the language itself is to the individual learning it a highly important carrier of the community's culture.

An illustration of the effect of language on the mode of thought may be noted in the pronoun of direct address in English as compared with German. The English "thou art" has long been obsolete, perhaps because the culture has no place for such distinctions as are indicated by the German "du bist" and "Sie sind," differentiated from the plural "sie sind" by capitalization in writing. The former, "du bist," is permissible only when the persons are on terms of close familiarity. It is an indication of acceptance when a young man is permitted by the young woman of his choice to address her as "du."

If "Sie" is the pronoun of respectful address, a quite different effect is

[122] *Ibid.*, p. 221.
[123] Titiev, *op. cit.*, p. 411.

created by Lessing in his *Minna von Barnhelm*, in the delicate distinctions made by the different people in the play in addressing each other. Persons of social status are regularly addressed by the formal "Sie"; everybody but Tellheim address the servant Just and the sergeant major Werner by "Er"; the landlord is addressed by those of status by "Sie" and by Just and Werner by "Er." Just, Werner, and the Landlord address Francisca by "Sie," but Minna and the Count address her by "du." "The third person singular *er* (Er) and *sie* (Sie) was in former times generally used as a *pronomen reverentiale*. In the course of time it lost its dignity and was used in addressing inferiors, and among persons of a lower rank in life."[124]

In societies where royalty and nobility still exist as social classes, such forms of address as "Your Highness," "Your Lordship," "Your Majesty," are still common. In America these forms are preserved mainly in courts of law, where the judge is addressed as "Your Honor," and in the military establishment, where officers are, at least by regulations, addressed by enlisted men in the third person, "What are the captain's orders?"

That language affects us in our daily living is indicated by Lasswell, Leites, and others:

To an extraordinary degree our well-being depends directly upon words and gestures. If the proper words of greeting are not forthcoming, we are annoyed; and the intonation must be exactly right. We would be hard put to it to describe the more subtle speech claims that we make upon our neighbors, or that they make on us, but "we know what we like," or at least what we don't like, when we meet it. In short, the status of our personality as a whole is involved in a flow of verbal deference from the environment.[125]

All this is a part of the cultural pattern into which we have grown, and to which we have become accustomed.

Confusions may sometimes arise even among people using presumably the same language, when one moves even temporarily into a section of the country where words have somewhat different meanings from what one is accustomed to. Not everyone who has lived all his life in the North is aware of the fact that in much of the South *evening* refers to almost any time in the afternoon. If one is invited for a visit some "evening" it is usually advisable to verify the time by having the hour specified. This point will be further developed in Chapter IX.

The way in which a language may not only reflect but also serve to establish

[124] Lessing, *Minna von Barnhelm*, 5th ed., C. A. Buchheim (ed.), Oxford, Clarendon Press, 1893, p. 136.
[125] Harold D. Lasswell, Nathan Leites, and Associates, *Language of Politics: Studies in Quantitative Semantics*, New York, George W. Stewart, 1949, pp. 4–6.

emotional states and attitudes is shown by Doi, who says, "We assume in interviewing a patient that the words and manner of his speech, intended to convey information, also express his mental status to the experienced observer. That is, in a given individual, we assume a connection between his language and his temperament. Why, then, can we not increase our understanding of the psychology of a whole people through an analysis of their language?"[126] Through the analysis of four Japanese intransitive verbs, *amaeru*, *suneru*, *higamu*, and *kodawaru*, Dr. Doi attempts to show the relation between the language and the modes of thinking of the Japanese people. The difficulty in translation seems to arise from the fact that among English-speaking people these particular emotional states and attitudes, common among the Japanese people, are not sufficiently general to have given rise to specific terms, or have not crystallized as concepts enough to call for some definite word. It is probable that, as in other languages, the concepts themselves grew out of the experiences of the Japanese people, and that the word was applied as the final step in the formation of the concept. Once the term came to be applied to the concept and was widely used, it might even have been instrumental in fixing the concept as well as the attitude or emotion itself as a common experience.

Something of the same principle was expressed a number of years ago by a young Japanese, in attempting to relate the language to the culture and the mode of thinking. The communication is edited only to the extent of putting it into more nearly standard English:

The Japanese language is complex in that it is influenced by Chinese writing and Chinese thought. We have enormous numbers of Chinese characters in our daily vocabulary. From the elementary school on we must spend much time and effort in learning these Chinese characters; otherwise we cannot even read the newspapers. In addition to this, we are obliged to be trained in the "honorific speech," if we aspire to be a gentleman or a lady. Of course, honorific speech has neither truth nor courtesy in it; sometimes it even teaches us to "sell ourselves" for the purpose of winning one's favor.

It may be said that one does not employ the term, but that the term rules one's thought in Japan. The existing ideas of our own language raise great obstacles to our learning a foreign language. The concept and habit of language in the East, that comes from the verbal acceptance and false expression of one's intention, had . . . [caused] us to become a challenge and to break faith with the world.

It is very important that we learn how to reform our abnormal language and all of its evil habits.[127]

---

[126] L. Takeo Doi, "Japanese language as an expression of Japanese psychology," *Western Speech* (1956), *20*: 90–96. Dr. Doi is a psychiatrist.

[127] Personal correspondence, August 14, 1950.

Chapter VIII

The Genetic Basis
of Speech

The Development of Speech in the Race

The Origins of Speech

With an understanding of the functions of speech in social facilitation, social integration, and social control, as presented in Chapters I and VII, we are able to discuss with some appreciation the question of the origins of speech in both the race and the individual. The question of the phylogenesis of language—its beginnings in the human race—has attracted the attention of scholars from the time of the ancient Greek philosophers. A great many ingenious theories have been promulgated, so many that more than a century ago the French Academy announced that it would entertain no more. The arguments gradually subsided, less from the belief that the problem had been solved than that further speculation would be fruitless. Despite the deterring effects of the decree, however, scholars have refused to be entirely discouraged; and every now and then a new theory has been advanced, debated warmly, and allowed to withdraw from the focus of attention and contribute its share to a general understanding of the possible ways in which language, speech, might have developed within the race.

The major difficulty lies in the fact that the beginnings of speech go so far back beyond any recorded history that any attempt at an explanation of just when and how it did begin must be wholly theoretical. According to Bram, it is quite possible that some of our earliest ancestors who lived more than a half-million years ago were capable of speech, whereas "the oldest known systems of graphically recording human speech do not go back beyond the third millennium B.C."[1] There is no record of when man began to speak or of the steps by which he advanced to the stage where even the idea of recording his speech was possible. The most primitive races today are so far advanced beyond those beginnings that they offer little or no information on how speech actually began. It is quite possible that all of the theories that have been advanced contain elements of truth, and that none of them can be entirely ignored in attempting to formulate a single theory that will account for all the probabilities. At the same time, it is equally certain that none of them has satisfactorily told the whole story.

It seems that serious consideration of any theory of the origin of speech is influenced by one's attitude toward a hypothesis of evolution, that is, the development of higher forms of life from lower forms. Some of the theories to be presented are incompatible with any evolutionary hypothesis; others are specifically based upon such a principle. Some consider speech as a direct, conscious invention of man; others that it came about as the result of a fortunate accident; still others that it was an integral part of the long process by which man became a human being. Some of them have been quite ingenuous; others have been the product of careful and thoughtful examination of all the evidence that could be brought to bear on the problem. Most of them seem to consider speech to be entirely a social phenomenon. Only occasionally does some theory contain implications for general or individual psychology. The present section presents a number of these theories; valid or not, they represent the thinking of a number of people on the question at one time or another.

The Divine Origin Theory.   We read, "And out of the ground the Lord God formed every beast of the field, and every fowl of the air; and brought them unto Adam to see what he would call them: and whatsoever Adam called every living creature, that was the name thereof."[2] This account as a complete explanation seems mainly to have been supported by theologians who attempted to attribute all things, even in their more or less completed forms, to a divinity.

But not all ecclesiastics have held to the theory of the divine origin of language. In the fourth century St. Gregory wrote, "Though God has given to human nature its facilities, it does not follow that therefore He produces all the actions which we perform. He has given us the faculty of building a house and doing any other work; but we, surely, are the builders, and not He. In

[1] Joseph Bram, *Language and Society*, Garden City, N.Y., Doubleday & Company, 1955, p. 3.
[2] Genesis 2: 19.

the same manner our faculty of speaking is the work of Him who has so framed our nature; but the invention of words for naming each object is the work of our minds." [3] There seems to have been actually only a small class of philosophers, "more orthodox than the Bible," who accepted the theory of the origin of speech which apparently insists that there could have been only one way a Divine Power could have worked, and that was by instantaneous creation.

The belief in a divine or miraculous origin of speech was not confined to Christian theology. It appears in pagan philosophy as well. To the Norsemen speech was a gift direct from Thor; other races and other tribes had their own legends touching upon the beginnings of language.

In considering the divine origin of language, Whitney points out that there were many who for some reason believed it "derogatory to the honor of the Creator to deny that he devised roots and words, and, by some miraculous and exceptional agency, put them ready-made into the mouths of the first human beings. . . . It is but childish philosophy which can see no other way to make out a divine agency as specially and miraculously efficient in the first stage of the formation of language. We may fairly compare it with the wisdom of the little girl who, on being asked who made her, replied, 'God made me a little baby so high (dropping her hand to within a foot of the floor) and I grew the rest.'" [4]

The Social Pressure Theory: Adam Smith.

Adam Smith's theory, which had first been advanced by the great philosopher John Locke, was a comparatively simple one. It arose from the supposition that primitive men, confronted by the necessity for making "their mutual wants intelligible to each other," would "utter certain sounds whenever they meant to designate certain objects. Those objects only which were more familiar to them and which they had most frequent occasion to mention, would have particular names attached to them. . . . Afterward, when the more enlarged experiences of these savages had led them to observe, and their necessary occasions obliged them to make mention of other caves, and other trees, and other fountains, they would naturally bestow upon each of those new objects, the same name, by which they had been accustomed to express the similar object they were first acquainted with." [5]

[3] Quoted from Friederich Max Müller, *The Science of Language*, New York, Longmans, Green & Company, 1891, vol. I, p. 30.

[4] William Dwight Whitney, *Language and the Study of Languages*, New York, Charles Scribner's Sons, 1868, pp. 399–400.

[5] Adam Smith, "A dissertation on the origin of language," in *The Theory of Moral Sentiments*," 10th ed., London, Cadell, 1804, pp. 343 ff.

When Adam Smith first advanced his theory late in the eighteenth century, biological investigations on the origin of mankind were a half-century in the future. It could hardly have occurred to him that man may have developed little by little to his full physical and intellectual stature. Smith's theory is based upon the supposition that man suddenly appeared fully developed physically, and possessing the mental capacity which characterized the human race at the beginning of the historical era. Speech for him was the product not of a developing human being, but of a *social pressure*. It came into being because of the consciously recognized necessity for social interaction.

Smith's assumption that language begins as definite parts of speech is not borne out by the study of primitive tongues, in many of which separate parts of speech, especially nouns and verbs, are a comparatively late development. According to Willis, Smith's theory "is patently absurd, because it presupposes the existence of the thing which it is invented to explain." [6]

The Onomatopoetic or Echoic Theory. Some of the theories advanced have been given nicknames by their opponents, suggestive of the ridicule which has been heaped upon them. One of these is the so called "bow-wow" theory (named by Müller), or in more dignified language, the onomatopoetic or echoic theory. One of the earlier advocates of this belief was Herder, who later abandoned it to adopt the principle of miraculous revelation.

In brief, the theory assumes that objects were given names which resembled the sounds which those objects made. It refers especially to animal sounds and those made by natural phenomena: man copied the sound of the dog, for example, or the rumbling of the thunder, and thereby obtained the natural word. The bleating of the lamb, perceived as its distinguishing mark, became the name of the lamb. [7]

Such imitation, it might be pointed out, was not confined to primitive man; it goes on even yet, particularly in the developing speech of the child, who might formerly, for example, have called a train a "choo-choo." It is questionable, however, to what extent such imitations are used as *words*, that is, having communicative significance between the child and those about him. But many of the words in our modern language are definitely echoic: *murmur, crash, boom, snap, sough*; a number of names of birds and animals may be traced to such an origin: *whippoorwill, killdeer* or *tildee*. "Through all the stages of the growth of language," says Whitney, "absolutely new words are produced by this method more than any other. . . . The mind pleases itself

---

[6] George Willis, *The Philosophy of Speech*, London, George Allen and Unwin, 1919, p. 17.
[7] Johann Gottfried von Herder, cited by Müller, *op. cit.*, p. 496.

with bringing about a sort of agreement between the sign and the thing signified." [8]

Lefèvre accepts the theory of onomatopoeia, tracing it back to the human cry, which in turn goes back to the animal cry.

Animals possess two of the important elements of language—the spontaneous reflex cry of emotion or need; the voluntary cry of warning, threat, or summons. From these two sorts of utterance man, already endowed with a richer vocal apparatus and a more developed brain, evolved numerous varieties by means of stress, reduplication, intonation. . . . Imitation, direct or symbolical . . . and necessarily only approximative of the sounds of external nature . . . furnished the elements of the attributive roots, from which arise the names of objects, special verbs, and their derivatives. [9]

Müller, in criticizing this theory, traces a number of presumably echoic words back to their origins and shows that they were not, in fact, echoic at all. The word *thunder*, for example, goes back to an Indo-European root which appears in Sanskrit as *tan*, to stretch. From this root we get the words *tonus* and *tone*, as well as *tender* and *thin*. These words have no relation to the "rolling and rumbling noise which the old Germans ascribed to their god Thor playing at ninepins. . . . Most of these onomatopoeias vanish as soon as we trace our own words back to Anglo-Saxon and Gothic, or compare them with their cognates in Greek, Latin or Sanskrit. The number of names which are really formed by an imitation of sound dwindle down to a very small quotum, if cross-examined by the philologist." [10]

As Sapir points out, languages in which such sounds are found have no particular preference for echoic words; there are too many which cannot be traced to such an origin. Furthermore, while onomatopoeia is found in such highly developed and modern languages as English and German, some primitive tribes speak languages in which it is almost entirely absent. The essential nature of speech is but little concerned with mere imitation. Moreover, imitative words, such as "bow-wow," come relatively late in the history of language. "It was only after man had learned the art of speech and was well drilled in its uses that he began to pick up by imitation the sound words which his environment suggested." [11]

Such so-called "imitative" words as are found in the speech of children are hardly to be cited as illustrative of the imitation theory of the origins of speech. In the first place, they are themselves highly conventionalized. "Bow-wow"

[8] Whitney, *op. cit.*, p. 429.
[9] André Lefèvre, *Race and Language*, New York, Appleton-Century-Crofts, 1894, pp. 42–43.
[10] Müller, *op. cit.*, pp. 504, 506.
[11] Edward Sapir, *Language*, New York, Harcourt, Brace and Company, 1921, pp. 5–6.

does not at all resemble the barking of a dog, nor is "cock-a-doodle-doo" even a fair representation of the crowing of a cock. Secondly, they are the result of direct teaching by parents and other attendants rather than the result of any attempt to imitate the sounds that may be brought to the attention of the small child.

The Interjectional Theory. The interjectional theory is based upon the observation that under emotional strain or intense feeling we instinctively give utterance to ejaculations or exclamations. These interjections are interpreted by the hearer as indicative of the emotion itself. The theory seems to have been advanced by a number of philosophers, among them the Frenchman Étienne Bonnot Condillac, and was accepted as a partial explanation by Whitney, who, after pointing out the validity of the imitative (echoic) theory, also argues that it is perfectly natural for the "untaught and undeveloped man to utter exclamations . . . ; and as, in the absence of a voice, the tendency to gesture might have been fruitful in suggesting a language of significant motions, so we most plausibly suppose that the tendency to exclaim was not without value in aiding men to realize that they had in their voices that which was capable of being applied to express the movements of their spirits." [12]
Elsewhere Whitney says,

The tones significant of feeling . . . are fully capable of becoming the effective initiators of language. Spoken language began, we may say, when a cry of pain, formerly wrung out by the real suffering, and seen to be understood and sympathized with, was repeated in imitation, no longer as a mere instinctive utterance, but for the purpose of intimating to another, "I am (was, shall be) suffering"; when an angry growl, formerly the direct expression of passion, was reproduced to signify disapprobation and threatening, and the like. [13]

Whitney thus attempted to harmonize the onomatopoetic and the interjectional theories: These natural cries originally are indicative of emotional states. They are reproduced to indicate to others that such emotional states exist. "The reproduction itself is in a certain way onomatopoetic; it imitates, so to speak, the cries of the human animal, in order to intimate secondarily what these cries in their primary use signified directly. Just as soon . . . as an inkling of the value of communication was gained, and the process began to be performed a little more consciously, the range of imitation would be extended."
Farrar agrees with this harmonization when he says, "The theories of the

[12] Whitney, *op. cit.*, pp. 429 f.
[13] *Ibid.*, p. 288.

interjectional and onomatopoetic origin of language *are not in reality different, and both of them might without impropriety be classed under the latter name*; for, in point of fact, the impulsive instinct to reproduce a sound is precisely analogous to that which gives vent to a sensation by an interjection." [14]

A number of objections have been raised to the interjectional theory. Sapir raises the objection that an expression of this sort, i.e., an interjection or exclamation, is nonsymbolic; it does not

. . . as such, indicate the emotion, it does not stand aloof, as it were, and announce that such and such an emotion is being felt. What it does is to serve as a more or less automatic overflow of the emotional energy; in a sense it is a part and parcel of the emotion itself. Moreover, such instinctive cries hardly constitute communication in any strict sense. They are not addressed to anyone. They are merely overheard, if heard at all, as the bark of a dog, the sound of approaching footsteps, or the rustling of the wind is heard. . . . Interjections are among the least important of speech elements. Their discussion is valuable mainly because it can be shown that even they, avowedly the nearest of all language sounds to instinctive utterance, are only superficially of an instinctive nature. [15]

Jespersen raises the objection that

. . . the most spontaneous interjections often contain sounds which are not used in language proper, as voiceless vowels, inspiratory sounds, clicks, etc., whence the impossibility properly to represent them by means of our ordinary alphabet; the spelling *pooh, pish, whew, tut*, are very poor renderings indeed of the natural sounds. On the other hand, many interjections are now more or less conventionalized and are learnt like any other words, consequently with a different form in different languages: in pain a German and a Seelander will exclaim *au*, a Jutlander *aus*, a Frenchman *ahi*, and an Englishman *oh* or perhaps *ow*. [16]

The theory has been named the "pooh-pooh" theory.

The "Phonetic Type" Theory: Müller.   Müller rejects both the onomatopoetic and the interjectional theories, and adopts one proposed by Heyse of Berlin. After analyzing the various families of languages, he comes finally to the theory of *roots*, which were not mere imitations; nor were they mere interjections. They were "phonetic types," or *basic modes of articulate utterance*.

In his original statement of the theory Müller makes no attempt to go

[14] Frederick William Farrar, *Chapters on Language*, New York, Longmans, Green & Company, 1873, p. 79. Italics are in the original.

[15] Sapir, *op. cit.*, pp. 3–5.

[16] Otto Jespersen, *Language: Its Nature, Development and Origin*, New York, Henry Holt and Company, 1922, p. 415.

further back of these roots than to say that they "are simply ultimate facts." By way of analogy, however, he says,

There is a law, it has been said, which runs through nearly the whole of nature, that everything which is struck rings. Each substance has its own peculiar ring. . . . It is the same, we are told, with man, the most highly organized of nature's work. Man responds. Man rings. Man, in his primitive and perfect state, was not only endowed, like the brute, with the power of expressing his sensations by interjections, but his perceptions by onomatopoeia. He possessed likewise the faculty of giving more articulate expression to the general conceptions of his mind. That faculty was not of his own making. It was an instinct, an instinct of the mind as irresistible as any other instinct. . . . . All that we have a right to assert is that language begins with roots, and that these roots are neither more nor less than phonetic types, or typical sounds. What lies beyond them is no longer, or, if we speak historically, is not yet, language, however interesting it may be for psychological researches. Words are various impressions taken from these phonetic moulds, or, if you like, varieties and modifications, perfectly intelligible in their structure, of those typical sounds which, by means of unerring tests, have been discovered as the residuum of all human speech.[17]

Once the beginnings have been made and have thus removed the need for such instinctive expressions, the instinct itself dies out.

It is manifestly unfair to Müller, however one may disagree with his theory, to charge him with thinking of man as a sort of bell, a kind of resounding drum, as it were, needing to be "struck" in order to bring forth a sound. His point is simply this: Everything in nature responds in some way when it is struck, that is, when physical energy acts upon it. Similarly, man responds, because of his sensory-neuro-muscular makeup, when energy, in the form of stimuli, impinges upon his sense organs. This response is in part vocal. The sounds thus produced fall into certain basic phonetic types which are the roots from which all subsequent language is developed. Müller's theory has been called derisively the "ding-dong" theory.

The essential point of attack lies in the assumption that, as Whitney points out, "a special and exceptional capacity [was] conferred for the purpose upon the first men, and withdrawn again from their descendants. . . . The fatal weakness of such attempts to explain the earliest steps in the formation of language lies in the fact that they would fain discover there some force at work different entirely from that which directs the whole aftercourse of linguistic development."[18]

The "Yo-he-ho" Theory: Noiré. As we have pointed out, Müller made

[17] Müller, *op. cit.*
[18] Whitney, *op. cit.*, p. 428.

no attempt, in his earlier statement of the "ding-dong" theory, to go back of the "ultimate facts" which he called roots, or phonetic types. He made no effort to say whether these phonetic types came from imitation or from inter- jection, or from some other basic or primitive vocalization. For this reason, his "theory," which actually was not a theory of the *origin* of speech and was not presented as such, has been greatly misunderstood.

The lectures in which this principle of roots was propounded were delivered between the years 1861 and 1863. When they were collected and published in 1891, however, Müller wrote a preface in which he presented what to him was an explanation of the source of these phonetic types. For this explanation he borrowed from Noiré, a French philologist.

Briefly stated, the theory is that any strong muscular effort results in an attempt at relief by the forcible emission of breath, which sets the vocal mechanism to vibrating. Different types of exertion would result in different kinds of release, and hence of sound. When a group of primitive men were engaged in labor and uttered these sounds in common, it soon came to pass that the sound itself came to be associated with that particular performance, and hence became a symbol, a name, for it.

Noiré showed that our first concepts arose by necessity from the consciousness of our own repeated or continuous acts. . . . He further showed how these concepts of our own acts might become . . . the sounds which involuntarily accompany the simplest acts of man. . . . When it became clear . . . that what we had obtained as a result of our scientific analysis of language, namely, the roots, were exactly what Noiré postulated, sounds expressive of the simplest acts of man . . . one of the oldest riddles of the world seemed to me solved, and solved without a residue.[19]

Just where either Noiré or Müller would draw the line between these "sounds which involuntarily accompany the simplest acts of man" and the inter- jections is difficult to determine.

The Gesture Theory: Wundt. Wilhelm Wundt was one of the most famous of the nineteenth-century psychologists; he established the first psychological laboratory. The latter part of his life he spent in writing his monumental work, *Völkerpsychologie*, or *Folk-Psychology*, two volumes of which were devoted to language and speech. Wundt based his theory of the origin of speech on the psychological law that every sensation has its peculiar expression, the result of definite neural connections between the "receptor" and the "effector." In time these expressions when observed would come to "mean" that the individual was experiencing the particular sensation with

[19] Müller, *op. cit.*, Preface.

which the expression was neurally connected and which could be used to communicate that fact to others.

Gesture language arises from emotion and the involuntary expressive movements that accompany it. Communication of ideas is accomplished by movements of the hands and arms, supplementing the mimetic movements (expressive of emotions or feelings) of the face. Not only does the action serve as an expression of the individual's own feelings and ideas; it must also evoke the same idea and the same emotion in the minds of others. When the person addressed responds with the same or similar movements, there is developed a common thinking in which voluntary actions gradually replace the impulsive, and ideas enter into the foreground of attention. "By virtue of this ideational content, movements expressive of emotions come to be expressions of ideas; the communication of an individual's experiences results in an exchange of thought—that is, in language." [20]

The ability to hear makes it possible to add to the mimetic and pantomimic movements (expressive of ideas) a third form, namely, articulatory movements. Since these articulatory movements are

. . . more easily perceived, and capable of incomparably more various modifications, it must of necessity follow that they soon exceed the others in importance. . . . Then, too, it is not improbable that articulation was at first aided by accompanying mimetic and pantomimic movements. . . . The development of articulate language is . . . in all probability to be thought of as a process of differentiation, in which the articulatory movements have gradually gained the permanent ascendancy over a number of different variable expressive movements which originally attended them.[21]

While Wundt maintains that gesture is the primitive language, he does not insist that articulate language *develops out of gesture*. "The primitive development of *articulate* language can hardly be thought of except after the analogy of the rise of this natural gesture language." [22] The two were used together, the former (articulate) language gaining the ascendancy because of its greater flexibility and because it could be used in expressing abstractions. It would be extremely difficult to trace a natural transition from visual to auditory stimulus. "The similarities between gesture and early language bespeak the primitive state of the sign-making function underlying both; but they do not explain the transition from manual signification to vocal." [23]

[20] Wilhelm Wundt, *Elements of Folk Psychology*, tr. by Edward LeRoy Schaub, New York, The Macmillan Company, 1916, pp. 60 f.

[21] Wilhelm Wundt, *Outlines of Psychology*, 3rd ed., Leipzig, Kroner, 1907, pp. 339–443.

[22] *Ibid.*

[23] Floyd Henry Allport, *Social Psychology*, Boston, Houghton Mifflin Company, 1924, pp. 192 ff.

Bloomfield seems inclined to question the whole theory of the gestural origin of speech. Gesture, he points out, has so long played a secondary role in communication "that it has lost all traces of an independent character. . . . Doubtless the production of vocal sounds by animals, out of which language has grown, originated as a response-movement (say, contraction of the diaphragm and constriction of the throat) which happened to produce noise. It seems certain, however, that in the further development, language always ran ahead of gesture."[24]

The Vocal Play Theory: Jespersen. Jespersen, the great Danish philologist, attempts to coördinate the theories that have been mentioned and to synthesize them into a hypothesis that will be more completely satisfactory. After drawing his material from three fields of investigation, (1) the language of children, (2) the language of primitive races, and (3) the history of languages, he comes to the conclusion that "primitive speech . . . resembles the speech of the little baby himself, before he begins to frame his own language after the pattern of the grownups; the language of our remote forefathers was like that ceaseless humming and crooning with which no thoughts are as yet connected, which merely amuses and delights the little one. Language originated as play, and the organs of speech were first trained in this singing sport of idle hours." [25]

Jesperson goes on to say,

The genesis of language is not to be sought in the prosaic, but in the poetic side of life; the source of speech is not gloomy seriousness, but merry play and youthful hilarity. And among the emotions which were most powerful in eliciting outbursts of music and song, love must be placed in the front rank. . . . In primitive speech I hear the laughing cries of exultation when lads and lassies vied with one another to attract the attention of the other sex, when everybody sang his merriest and danced his bravest to lure a pair of eyes to throw admiring glances in his direction. Language was born in the courting days of mankind; the first utterances of speech I fancy to myself something between the nightly love-lyrics of puss upon the tiles and the melodious love-songs of the nightingale.[26]

In reply to the possible criticism that such a theory is "a romantic dream of a primitive golden age in which man had no occupation but courting and singing," Jespersen protests a disbelief in the existence of such a golden age; but he maintains that, raw and barbarous as primitive life was, "there were still some moments consecrated to youthful hilarity, and that this gave rise,

[24] Leonard Bloomfield, *Language*, New York, Henry Holt and Company, 1933, pp. 39 f.
[25] Jesperson, *op. cit.*, pp. 433 f.
[26] *Ibid.*

among other merriment, to vocal play of such a character as closely to resemble what we may infer from the known facts of linguistic history to have been a stage of learning earlier than any of those accessible to us."[27]

Jespersen's theory does attempt to bridge the gap between emotional and ideational vocalization. The sounds and combinations were fixed by the "survival of the fittest."

The Oral Gesture Theory: Paget.   One of the most striking of theories is that advanced by Paget, who, like Wundt and Jespersen, brings forward much evidence in support of his views. Paget proceeds from the gesture period to argue that when man developed the use of tools his hands were thereby occupied with the arts and crafts and could no longer be used so freely in communication. Some other mechanism was therefore necessary; and particularly since the use of such tools was a great factor in the development of intelligence and technique, the need for more exact gestures became greater.

Gestures, which were previously made by hand, were unconsciously copied by movements or positions of the mouth, tongue or lips; other gestures were developed, depending on any of the various instinctive methods of gesture formation of which some examples have already been given. . . . The argument . . . runs as follows: Originally man expressed his ideas by gesture, but as he gesticulated with his hands, his tongue, lips and jaw unconsciously followed suit in a ridiculous fashion, "understudying" . . . the action of the hands. The consequence was that when, owing to the pressure of other business, the principal actors (the hands) retired from the stage—as much as principal actors ever do—their understudies—the tongue, lips and jaw—were already proficient in the pantomimic art.

Then the great discovery was made that if, while making a gesture with the tongue and lips, air was blown through the oral or nasal cavities, the gestures became audible as a whispered speech sound. If, while pantomiming with tongue, lips and jaw, our ancestors sang, roared or grunted—in order to draw attention to what they were doing—a still louder and more remarkable effect was produced, namely, what we call voiced speech.[28]

Paget then goes on to show the similarity between "synthetic" sounds and some of the words from primitive languages; that is, he developed a tongue and lip *gesture* which seemed to him to suggest the idea he wanted to represent and accompanied that oral gesture with vocalization. The resulting "synthetic" sound he compared with primitive words, and found what seemed to him a

[27] *Ibid.*, p. 434, footnote.
[28] Sir Richard Paget, *Human Speech*, New York, Harcourt, Brace and Company, 1930, chap. VII.

striking correspondence. For example, after expressing his belief that "[i–i] (made with a little mouth) [ɑ–ɑ] or [ɔ–ɔ] (aw-aw) (made with a big mouth) were the original human words for 'little' and 'big' respectively," he learned that in primitive Polynesian I'I is actually the word for "little," and in archaic Japanese the word for "big" was [ōhō].[29]

Following this lead, Paget examined pantomimic relations existent in Aryan word roots, which confirmed for him his conclusions relative to the East Oceanic languages. This relation he extends even to vowel and consonant symbolism. Furthermore, Paget also found similarities between the Oceanic languages and some of the continental tongues, *ua* in Polynesian meaning *wetting* or *rain*, comparing with Sanskrit *uda*, also meaning *wet*—hence our word *water*.[30]

While to Paget must be given the credit for expanding this theory, it was not original with him. According to Jóhannesson, it was first presented in 1862 by Dr. J. Rae in a treatise on the Polynesian language. "The first Indo-Europeans as well as the first Semitic people began to speak by imitating the signs of the hands with their speech organs."[31] The theory was known (and rejected) by Whitney,[32] who himself claims no authorship for the idea. It was also known—and partially accepted—by Sweet,[33] who considered "symbolic roots" an important element in the beginnings of language: "Sympathetic—at first unconscious—lingual gesture would then accompany the hand-gesture, which by degrees would be dropped as superfluous. . . . Such roots as these contained in English *wind*, German *wehen*, 'blow (of the wind),' may be regarded either as the result of actual blowing with the mouth, or as imitations of the sound of the wind."

Paget may be thought of as continuing and developing Wundt's gesture theory. Wundt makes no attempt to explain the transition from gesture to oral language; Paget's theory is essentially an explanation of this transition.

The evidence in support of Paget's theory is too voluminous to be dismissed lightly, but like nearly all the other theories which have been advanced, there are certain fundamental defects in it. These defects have been analyzed by de Laguna.

[29] *Ibid.*, p. 139.

[30] *Ibid.*, p. 158.

[31] Alexander Jóhannesson, "The gestural origin of languages: Evidence from six 'unrelated' languages," *Nature* (London), *166*: 60–61. Other articles had appeared in *Nature*, *153*: 171; *154*: 466; *157*: 847; *162*: 902. In the first of these Paget's theory is referred to as the one "most probable, and likely, to revolutionize philology." Jóhannesson brings evidence to bear on the theory from various languages.

[32] Whitney, *op. cit.*, p. 430.

[33] Henry Sweet, *The History of Language*, New York, The Macmillan Company, 1900, pp. 37–38.

The first of these is the assumption that speech developed as an individual phenomenon, dependent upon the existence of ideas which needed expression, and that language is the means of expressing or communicating these ideas.

In the first place, language, as a means of expressing or communicating *ideas*, is contrasted with the inarticulate cries of animals, which, it is held, are expressive of mere *feelings* or *emotions*. Thus any theory of the evolution of language from animal cries must first account for the evolution of ideas from mere feelings. In the second place, ideas are tacitly assumed to be prior to their means of expression. But the truth is, of course, that there exists no communicable content except in so far as its mode of expression is already developed.[34]

It is worth considering that instead of the "human race" discovering the voice, it was the use of voice that contributed to making the race human.

The second of these defects, growing out of the first, is the assumption that the beginnings of speech awaited the emergence of the race as human, having certain mental processes which needed expressing or communicating. Such an assumption rests upon a philosophical point of view which conceives of speech "only as an external physical manifestation of inner psychical processes."

These assumptions are easily discernible in the theories of Smith, of Wundt, of Jespersen, and of Paget in particular, and in the other theories only less slightly. Smith, evidently unaware of the continuity of organic development, could not realize that the predecessors of man had for countless generations already been using vocal sounds for purposes of social adaptation and adjustment, social integration, and social control. Wundt's gestures, which have been interpreted as constituting the beginnings of speech, depended upon the existence of ideas which the individual desired to communicate. Jespersen's vocal play theory rests upon an already highly organized and complex society —through what processes this organization came to completion he does not indicate. Paget's oral gesture theory assumes even more: not only was society highly organized, but a fairly high state of culture had been reached.

The Social Control Theory: de Laguna.   De Laguna attempts to throw light on the origin of speech by considering it objectively. "Speech is the great medium through which human coöperation is brought about. It is the means by which the diverse activities of men are coördinated and correlated with each other for the attainment of common and reciprocal ends."[35]

[34] Grace Andrus de Laguna, *Speech: Its Function and Development*, New Haven, Yale University Press, 1927, chap. I.
[35] *Ibid.*, p. 19.

Even animal cries have a social function. The alarm call, for example, which many of us have heard from the brooding hen when a hawk is flying overhead, excites a definite response in the chicks and they scurry for cover. The "social control effected by animal cries is correlated with the relative simplicity of behavior of which the species is capable." [36]

The increasing complexity of life, together with changes in habitat and the constantly enlarged scope of activity, created in turn the necessity for a more concerted coöperation both for defense and for attack. The safety of the group depended more and more upon solidarity. This change in social conditions made necessary the development of a more effective means of social control. It became essential to differentiate between the *proclamation* (the announcing of a disturbing element in the situation) and the *command* (the specifying of the response which the group was to make). Different types of situation would call for different types of response developed in the group, and a more definite means of indicating the particular response needed in the situation became necessary. The mere proclamation of danger or of the proximity of food was no longer adequate; mere announcement was not sufficient. Changes in his mode of living, in other words, placed the emerging human being in such a situation that mere animal cries were inadequate. "What enabled arboreal man to adapt himself to the new environment was his possession of a nervous organization sufficiently complex and flexible to permit him to reassemble on a higher level the elements of simpler and now inadequate responses." [37] Furthermore, with increasing complexity, the organism is more and more sensitive to delicate variations in the stimulus pattern.

When the primitive cry "ceases to be a direct determinant of immediate group action, and comes instead to serve as the conditional determinant of varying group action, to arouse and concentrate attentive preparation for action, it has become a true proclamation. Its indirectness as a means of social control is commensurate with the degree of its independence of emotional expression on the one hand, and its true symbolism, on the other." [38]

The removal of these cries from dependence upon emotional expression makes possible their use in other capacities. De Laguna compares the primitive man's use of vocal sounds with that of the child today. In this she is in agreement with Jespersen, in pointing out that vocal play is an essential element in the beginnings of speech as such. The sounds which are used in such activities are in themselves pleasurable, but there is also pleasure in the

[36] *Ibid.*, p. 34.
[37] *Ibid.*, p. 51.
[38] *Ibid.*, p. 57.

activity itself. When these sounds become "used in a systematic way to control the behavior of others with reference to the objects whose names they are," and with which they have, during the play period, become associated, "they become words and enter as elements into the structure of language. When the hungry baby has learned to call: 'Din-din now!' he has begun to speak in earnest. The play activity has become incorporated in the serious business of living." [39]

De Laguna thus goes further back than Jespersen, in attempting to trace the evolution of speech from the animal cry to its use as speech itself. Furthermore, although incorporating the play theory into her own description, she considers that speech rests basically upon the serious business of living rather than primarily upon "merry play and youthful hilarity." It is possible that these lighter moments contributed to the vocal play activity among primitive men, but only when vocal utterance "became freed from its context and performed a 'free' act, pleasurable in itself." [40]

The "Contact" Theory: Révész. Still another theory of the origins of language is that advanced by Révész, and called by him the "contact" theory. [41] In one particular it resembles the "social pressure" theory of Adam Smith, while in other and more significant aspects it is closer to the "social control" theory of de Laguna. The central principle in the theory is the necessity for "contact" with one's fellows. "When one studies the social relations of living beings one is struck by the unquenchable need among individuals of every species to enter into contact with one another." [42] In the most limited circumstances and on the instinctive level this need is met by merely spatial contact, by physical nearness; but "The more the instinctive life of the person is overlaid by intentionally directed experiences the more likely will the inclination for spatial contact deepen into a desire for emotional contact." [43] At this level one is satisfied by "the emotional proximity of the other person," which leads to understanding, sympathy, to empathy with the other. Emotional contact is essential to the speech act; ". . . the speech act is only possible when personal rapport or emotional contact exists between persons capable of speech." [44]

The final aspect of contact essential to the development of language is

[39] *Ibid.*, pp. 65 ff., 72.
[40] *Ibid.*, p. 67.
[41] G. Révész, *The Origins and Prehistory of Language*, tr. by J. Butler, New York, Philosophical Library, 1956.
[42] *Ibid.*, p. 136.
[43] *Ibid.*, p. 139.
[44] *Ibid.*, p. 145.

intellectual contact. Whereas emotional contact "serves the transfer of emotion," intellectual contact serves "the transmission and exchange of thought. . . . One thing is certain: a human being who has never entered into intellectual contact with others cannot understand language, the intellectual means of communication and influence. This probably also applies phylo-genetically: language could come into being only after the pre-conditions for emotional and intellectual contact were present among the members of primitive society." [45]

Language grows out of expressive sounds which of themselves have no communicative significance. But from these expressive sounds develop the contact sounds, those aimed at established contact with others. The first of these contact sounds is the *cry*, which is directed not at specific individuals, but at the environment in general. It attempts "to establish communication with [the] surroundings, but it is not yet a personal communication." [46] The *call*, on the other hand, which is the next step, is specifically directed to particular individuals. It is uttered "only when the recipient of the communication is within sight or sound of the communication." [47] The final step in the process of the evolution of language is the *word*, to which the call leads us. Thus the initial need for contact somewhat resembles the situation described by Smith of two savages meeting in the forest and being confronted by the need for making their mutual wants known; it resembles de Laguna's theory in that it is evolutionary, and starting with the cry, proceeds through the process of development to the word. But whereas de Laguna attempts to develop a continuous process, Révész admits that he is unable "to form an adequate conception of how the addressed calls were transformed into words. . . . It is a question which cannot be answered without using hypotheses based purely on imagination and without any sort of empirical basis." [48] Although we are apparently no closer to a working hypothesis of how human speech came into being, in many ways the theory as Révész presents it is considerably more satisfying than some of the older ones which start with man as a developed human being, without ever considering how he arrived at that stage other than by direct, instantaneous creation.

Whence came the specific sounds and sound combinations that entered into the structure of language is of comparatively little importance. It is probable that they came from various sources: from the sounds of nature, from emotional expressions, from vocal accompaniments of physical exertion,

[45] *Ibid.*, pp. 147 f.
[46] *Ibid.*, p. 160.
[47] *Ibid.*, p. 161.
[48] *Ibid.*, p. 180.

from mere pleasure in the performance itself. Sweet says that there are three principal ways in which such associations, between sound and "object," can be formed, "yielding the three classes of imitative, interjectional, and symbolic words, all of which have left numerous traces in traditional language."[49] There were numerous possible sources for the sound groups which became the words of speech. It is futile to speculate whether one or another of these sources constituted *the* origin of speech. What is significant is that the growth of language was an evolutionary process, developing as the race developed; that ideas developed also along with the medium for formulating and communicating them; and that whatever there was of the expression or communication of ideas had the essential functions of facilitating social adjustment and integration, of making social interaction possible, and of influencing the behavior of others of the social group. In a very real sense, one cannot say that speech "began," or was "invented"; it was an evolution rather than an invention.

The Development of Speech in the Individual

Racial and Individual Development

It is generally agreed that the course of speech development in the child, or the *ontogenesis* of speech, does not follow in all particulars that in the race. However, as has been mentioned, Jespersen, in seeking an explanation of the racial origins of speech, drew largely for his theory upon his observations of language development in children. Allport points out that "in certain aspects the same conditions and explanatory principles apply to each," while in other aspects there are significant differences.

The points of similarity between racial and individual speech development are (1) that in neither the child nor the aboriginal man is there any inherent tendency or instinct to speak; speech is not an "innate endowment." Furthermore, the biosocial urges and the "laws of learning by which it [speech] had to be acquired are the same for both." (2) Both the child and the primordial man possessed as a basis for language development a rather well-developed "set of laryngeal and articulate utterances."

The two situations are different in that (1) the child comes into an environment in which the vocabulary and grammatical forms are already established, whereas the primitive man had to set up his own; (2) because of the fact that the environment into which the child comes has an already highly organized

[49] Sweet, *op. cit.*, p. 35.

language, he gains a fairly complete mastery of that language within the first few years of his life, whereas it took the race many generations, even millennia, to fix upon word symbols, word order, and the other essential characteristics of a language.[50]

For the learning of speech, certain psychological and physiological factors are essential; in the absence of any of these, speech would be impossible.[51] A reasonably normal speech mechanism must be present, consisting of organs of respiration, phonation, and articulation, with systems of musculature controlling each. An integrating neural system is necessary in order that the whole may work effectively as a unit. "Most important of all, it must be to some degree under control before real speech can be begun." Furthermore, there must be a capacity for ideas, emotions, "and a large amount of spontaneous, playful exercise of the speech mechanism before it can be controlled or used for purposes of voluntary speech."

The baby does not speak for the simple reason that he has nothing to say and could not say it if he had. He lacks the experiences upon which the whole process of symbolization is based. His activities are reflexive, involuntary; and it is only after months, even years, of practice that he gains any measure of control over them. The learning of speech by the child is a tremendously difficult process, even with all the aid he possesses. What must have been the obstacles which primitive man had to overcome, to build his language from the ground up, so to speak!

All that a child has when he comes into the world is a mechanism which is capable of responding to stimuli,[52] and which has the further capacity for the "conditioning" of the responses. Furthermore, even at birth, and, in fact, in prenatal life, the vocal organs are capable of producing sounds, but the auditory and environmental stimuli are not present in the earlier stage.[53]

The capacities with which the child is born are due to the sensory, neural, muscular, and glandular structures and the organization of the body. Energy in its various forms, called stimuli, impinges upon the sense organs (the "receptors": visual, auditory, gustatory, olfactory, tactual, thermal, kinesthetic, pain, hunger, and so on), generating neural impulses in the nerve fibers

[50] Allport, *op. cit.*, pp. 189 ff. See also Révész, *op. cit.*, pp. 44–46.

[51] The point and the quotations in this and the following paragraphs are adapted from Charles W. Waddle, *An Introduction to Child Psychology*, Boston, Houghton Mifflin Company, 1918, pp. 156 ff.

[52] See John Henry Mussen and John Janeway Conger, *Child Development and Personality*, New York, Harper & Brothers, 1956, p. 98.

[53] Dorothea McCarthy, "Language development in children," in *Manual of Child Psychology*, 2nd ed., Leonard Carmichael (ed.), New York, John Wiley & Sons, 1954, pp. 492–630 (p. 505).

and cells (the "conductors"). As outlined in Chapter IV, these impulses are transmitted over "afferent" nerve paths through the conductor system to a central "exchange" and thence out again over "efferent" paths to the muscles or the glands (the "effectors"), where the work of the body is done —digestion, respiration, locomotion, secretion, excretion, vocalization, and so on.

At birth these responses are undifferentiated; there is no capacity for selection of the reactions which the child shall make. It wriggles, twists up its face, moves its arms and legs, and performs the natural biological functions of breathing, eating, and elimination, all as direct, native, inevitable reactions to the stimuli that are striking its sense organs from every side. Of tremendous importance, from the standpoint of its future growth as a talking animal, is the fact that even from the moment of its birth it also cries.

The Speech Mechanism

There has been considerable discussion as to whether there is a "speech mechanism" *per se*, or whether speech is not actually an "overlaid function," that is, whether the mechanisms used for speech were not originally biological mechanisms upon which the function of speech has been superimposed, or overlaid. The implications in the latter theory has been held to be that regardless of the importance, the survival value, of such a superimposition, the mechanisms have undergone no modification thereby, but remain in their original state as, physiologically, vegetative mechanisms. Just what is meant by the term, "overlaid function?" Is it necessary to hold to either of the extreme views implied?

Few writers on the subject will disagree with the principle that all the organs of the body were originally vegetative, and that some of them still are. But it will also be agreed by many that in the course of evolution many of these organs have undergone modifications that permit them to be used in ways other than purely biological. Without destroying their usefulness in fulfilling their original functions, they have become, at least in part, what may be called biosocial. Such a development would be most likely to occur when the biosocial function involved had a significant survival value. Certainly the faculty of communication among human beings would have such a value. And so well adapted for purposes of communication are the mechanisms for producing and modifying the voice that it seems not improbable that a part of the process of becoming a human being might very well have been the development of that apparatus as a more efficient medium of communication.

Certainly the vocal apparatus of the individual is anatomically and physiologically different at the age of twenty from what it was at birth.

The primary purpose of the larynx, as Negus points out, is to keep everything out of the lungs but air," [54] a statement to which there will be no objection. That remains its primary purpose throughout life. But in the same sentence Negus says that the larynx "has, in the course of evolution, acquired other functions." For instance, it has undergone some degeneration as an inlet valve: "at the same time the modifications undergone by the vocal cords have made the valve more adaptable as an organ of voice." [55] "If Man progresses on the path by which he has reached his present state his cords will become more feeble still as inlet valves, and the tones emitted by them will be yet more mellow although less powerful." [56] "Shortening the margins of the glottis gives [Man] assistance in executing the rapid changes necessary for alteration of pitch of the voice in a complicated system of communication. . . ." [57] In the process of evolution the larynx became "freed from the encumbrance of relationship with the palate and allowed [Man] to acquire buccal speech with all the advantages of articulation. . . ." [58] After describing the most favorable type of larynx for phonation, Negus then points out, "Such an organ happens to be possessed by Man, mainly because he does not run fast, is not an eater of herbage, and has allowed the valvular heritage of his arboreal ancestry to fall into degeneration." [59]

Still further in the matter of articulation, which was made possible by the separation of the epiglottis from the palate—for the larynx is not the only mechanism involved in speech—Negus points out that "Man is said to surpass most Mammals in articulation, perhaps by reason of his lips; they project beyond the jaw, and are able to move independently of it." [60] Moreover, "the tongue is large and mobile, primarily for purposes of chewing, but this power of movement is of great advantage in speech, for which function it may have been further developed." [61]

---

[54] V. E. Negus, *The Mechanism of the Larynx*, London, Wm. Heinemann, 1929, p. 7. See also the revised edition, entitled *The Comparative Anatomy and Physiology of the Larynx*, New York, Grune & Stratton, 1949, pp. 4 f.

[55] *Ibid.*, p. 259; *rev. ed.*, p. 188. NOTE: Unless otherwise indicated, references are to the original edition.

[56] *Ibid.*, p. 480; *rev. ed.*, p. 188.

[57] *Ibid.*, p. 472.

[58] *Ibid.*, p. 478; *rev. ed.*, p. 187.

[59] *Ibid.*, p. 372.

[60] *Ibid.*, p. 412.

[61] *Ibid.*, p. 56. In the revised edition Negus omits much material on mechanisms other than the larynx which appeared in the first edition, but which do not bear directly on the development and function of the larynx.

Negus repeatedly insists that the organs now involved in speech, especially the larynx and vocal bands, were not developed *primarily* for speech; but at the same time he points out over and over that many of the changes in the development of those same mechanisms, including the larynx and vocal bands, have in fact taken place in such ways as to contribute greatly to the effectiveness of those organs in the production of speech. In one instance at least, that cited in the last quotation of the preceding paragraph, he suggests that purpose may have played a part in the development.

It would seem, therefore, that there may be some justification for considering that the mechanisms involved in speech, including the larynx, vocal bands, tongue, lips, and other organs, together with the neuromuscular complexes that contribute to intelligence, constitute not only a biological but a biosocial mechanism as well. In the newborn infant these mechanisms are undeveloped, it is true, and are essentially if not exclusively vegetative. But along with the development of the other parts of the body for various functions, not all of which are purely biological, the organs used for speech itself develop also in part as a speech mechanism, while still retaining its essential biological functions. It is in this sense that speech may be thought of as an "overlaid function." [62]

It is then quite unnecessary to take either extreme view, namely, that the mechanisms originating as vegetative mechanisms have continued so without modification throughout all the processes of evolution, regardless of the importance of the supplementary functions they have been called upon to perform; or, as the only alternative, that they have become so completely adapted to the performance of those supplementary functions that they have entirely lost their original vegetative capabilities. The "overlaid function" theory makes no such demands upon credulity.

It has been pointed out by Révész that the first linguistic experience of the child consists not in expression by speech or gesture, but in the *understanding* of language. [63] Others have observed that the child responds to the human voice at a very early age. But how much of these responses arise from an innate tendency so to respond and how much to early conditioning has not been determined. In any event, the two possibilities are not mutually exclusive. It seems certain that after the first year the infant "begins to respond to speech according to the immediate situation in which it occurs." It is also during this first year that "his responses to particular words become

---

[62] See Giles Wilkeson Gray, "A speech mechanism hypothesis," *The Quarterly Journal of Speech* (1936), *22*: 656–660.

[63] Révész, *op. cit.*, p. 44. See also Louis P. Thorpe, *Child Psychology and Development*, 2nd ed., New York, The Ronald Press, 1955, pp. 238 ff.

more specific, more regular, and more frequent," marking the "onset of comprehension" of conventional speech.[64]

Steps in the Development of Speech

Many attempts have been made to analyze the development of speech in the individual into "stages" or "divisions" or "steps." While these analyses are helpful in tracing the growth of language in the child, it must not be thought that the stages named and described are sharply set off one from the other. There is no dividing line between the successive steps, any more than there is between short people and tall people. Furthermore, the particular characteristics of one period may and usually do continue with only slight modifications through later periods. However, such analyses are suggestive and may aid us in understanding the various factors that enter into the development of speech in the individual.

Reflexive Vocalization.   The earliest cries of the baby are no more than a part of his total bodily response to the physical stimuli that suddenly impinge upon his every sense organ. He has just come into a new world, a new environment. Everything is strange. As has already been indicated, physical energy in a multitude of forms is suddenly presented to him in great confusion, and his reactions are equally undifferentiated. This lack of differentiation of both stimuli and response accounts for James's description of the baby's "consciousness" as a "blooming, buzzing confusion."

The response to this new environment is an allover random response, and hence purely emotional. There is as yet none of the particularization, the narrowing down of the responses into smaller reaction systems, which characterizes the "intellectual" activities.

As a part of this general emotional response the musculature of respiration is set vigorously to work, and breathing begins, to continue automatically as long as the individual lives. Other activities take place in the laryngeal musculature, producing tensions in certain muscle groups there, and, incidentally, drawing the vocal bands together. The combination of the two, respiratory and laryngeal, results in the production of the birth cry. It is a reflexive activity in that stimulus and response are inevitably bound together by a causal chain.

At the same time, the child is vigorously moving its arms, legs, and perhaps

[64] M. M. Lewis, *Infant Speech*, New York, The Humanities Press, 1951, pp. 38–42, 44, 47, 105.

its head, contracting its facial muscles, and otherwise engaging in muscular activities of an allover nature. And these too are essentially reflexive. But it is upon such reflexive responses that the whole structure of language is based; upon the vocal reactions is built the verbal language, and on the visible movements of face, arms, hands, and body the expressive gestures. As yet neither has expressive or communicative significance.

During this period are to be noted a number of "instinctive movements which are also expressive and which are the basis for later gestures and words. Among them are the instinctive expressions of pain, weariness, fear, anger, astonishment, joy, desire and pride. These are not all present at birth, but appear before the end of the first year." [65]

It must not be thought that in producing these sounds or movements the child has any specific goal or purpose to communicate. Parents and attendants are prone to read meanings into the early vocalizations of their charges that are far beyond an infant's capacity at that age. When "these vocal responses occur in connection with specific forms of adult behavior, some sounds that the infant produces become symbols for that adult or particular behavior." [66] In other words, the adult reads into these responses meanings and associations which the child could not have possibly intended. "The earlier interpretations of the child's first cry as having intellectual or emotional significance have largely been discarded and are now no longer held in the scientific literature." [67]

Differentiation. Within the first month the cries of the infant begin to differentiate according to the type of stimulation. Variations in pitch, intensity, tempo, and vowel quality are to be observed, expressive of the different physical states felt at the moment. Lewis feels that about all we can distinguish consists of "broad differences between sounds expressing comfort and those expressing discomfort." [68] But differentiation progresses rapidly, so that "by the third month most observers of infant behavior report cooing and babbling, which continue until about the end of the first year, when the first words are heard." [69]

It is during this stage that the child discovers that certain types of cries will produce highly desirable types of attention. According to Allport,

[65] Amy Eliza Tanner, *The Child: His Thinking, Feeling and Doing*, Chicago, Rand, McNally & Company, 1904, p. 312.
[66] Buford J. Johnson, *Child Psychology*, Springfield, Ill., Charles C. Thomas, 1932, p. 192.
[67] McCarthy, *op. cit.*, p. 505.
[68] Lewis, *op. cit.*, p. 22.
[69] McCarthy, *op. cit.*, p. 507.

The sounds . . . take on a social significance which is not innate either in parent or child but a product of experience in reactions between them.

As in the case of infra-human vocalization and human gesture, we find here a transition from a purely individualistic emotional response to expressive behavior, that is, to behavior as a means of communication and social control. The anger cry, if found effective, quickly assumes the role of an infantile imperative.[70]

While this stage begins with the first three or four months of the child's life, it probably never entirely disappears. Meaning itself, as was pointed out in Chapter I, has in many instances a strong emotional content. In the use of language to convey meaning, this emotional component is expressed not so much by the choice of words as by the manner in which they are uttered. The "individualistic emotional responses" have become expressive behavior, and so remain into and through adulthood.

While in the infant this is the first stage of social control through vocalization, it is not yet speech. It is analogous to the degree of development reached by many of the lower animals in their use of different cries in different situations. The clucking of the hen is not the same when calling her chicks to food as it is when a hawk is hovering overhead. The warning bark of a dog at the approach of a stranger changes noticeably when the stranger turns out to be his master.

Even facial expressions are used by animals, as in the case of a dog when he bares his teeth as a sort of danger signal, or of a mule when he lays back his ears preparatory to wheeling and kicking. They are the beginning of gesture; in the animal they never develop further, but in the human race they may become highly refined into a system of language so intricate and conventionalized that extended conversations may be conducted by their exclusive use.

Nonpurposive Articulate Utterance: Vocal Play.   This period, in which comes what the Blantons called "the period of language sounds without association of ideas,"[71] overlaps that of reflexive vocalization and emotional expression. The laryngeal cries contain in them the germ of articulate sounds, but they lack definiteness. It is here that the phonetic elements become more clearly defined, although it will be some time yet before they are finally stabilized and brought under complete voluntary control.

THE ORDER OF APPEARANCE OF SOUNDS.   Many attempts have been made to establish the order in which the various sounds of speech appear. One

[70] Allport, *op. cit.*, p. 180.
[71] Smiley Blanton and Margaret Gray Blanton, *Speech Training for Children*, New York, Appleton-Century-Crofts, 1919, p. 87.

difficulty in the past has been that observers, not being trained phonetically, were unable to make sharp distinctions among many apparently similar sounds. Moreover, lacking an adequate system of phonetic notation, they could not indicate such differences as they may have heard. The early studies based on such inadequate observations and transcription were generally crude and, in the light of more refined techniques, none too reliable. At the same time, it is significant that, although much recent work has been done with improved procedures, some of today's theory regarding the development of language in the child is based on studies made a generation or more ago.

The first utterances are now generally thought to be vowels, rather than those sounds considered easiest to produce. Irwin and Curry found that of the vowels used during the first ten days by forty babies, 92 percent were front vowels, 7 percent were middle vowels, and only 1 percent were back vowels.[72]

Lewis has attempted to show that the appearance of the sounds of speech depends upon the state of comfort or discomfort of the infant. The vowels, for example, are often nasalized in discomfort, whereas in comfort they are rarely nasalized. In discomfort "the semi-consonant $\check{u}$ appears early, followed by h, l and η," and later the nasal consonants m and n. In comfort the indeterminate, nonnasal vowels appear, "interspersed with the back consonants $\mathfrak{g}$, g, x, k, and [uvular] r. Then front consonants appear, mostly nonnasal, p, b, t, and d, together with the corresponding nasals m and n."[73]

According to Poole, by three and one-half years the normal child should have acquired the sounds [p], [b], [m], [w], and [h]. By four and one-half years [d], [t], [g], [n], [k], [ŋ], and [j] should have been added. Only one additional sound, [f], is acquired during the next year, but by six and one-half [v], [ð], [ʒ], [ʃ], and [l] are made correctly. When the child is seven and one-half years old he should have all these plus [z], [s], [r], [θ], and [ʍ]. One child of three used all of these sounds accurately.

Four factors influence the acquisition of these sounds: (1) audition, (2) kinesthetic sensory discrimination, (3) motor exercise, and (4) dentition.[74]

Whatever the order in which the sounds occur, it is generally agreed that within the first few months of the child's life he has produced most if not all of the sounds which he will later use in speech, and many that are not so used. It is in fact often difficult to distinguish in the child's vocalizations which

---

[72] O. C. Irwin and T. Curry, "Vowel elements in the crying vocalization of infants under ten days of age," *Child Development* (1941), *12*: 99–109.

[73] Lewis, *op. cit.*, p. 26.

[74] Irene Poole, "The genetic development of articulation of consonant sounds in speech," *Elementary English Review* (1934), *2*: 159–161.

sounds may be classed as speech sounds and which ones may not. Children use sounds heard not only in the language they will later use, but also in entirely foreign tongues, sounds which later in life will undoubtedly give considerable difficulty when they have to be learned. According to some writers, because of the extreme plasticity of the articulatory organs, the child can make all the sounds required in the learning of any foreign language; one observer reported hearing an infant produce all the sounds of English by the fourth month.[75] Even Arabic and Hebrew gutturals and African clicks are heard. Gesell reports that a six-months-old child used within a period of twenty-four hours no fewer than sixty-four different sounds. Assuming that among these sixty-four were all the sounds that occur in the mother tongue, practically one-third would be entirely discarded as the process of word formation advanced during the next few years.[76]

MATURATION. Writers from Sully to the present time have emphasized the importance of the role played by maturation in the learning of speech. The infant babbling, in which is to be heard the entire repertoire of speech sounds, is probably due to the changes which are taking place in the nervous system as well as in other parts of the speech mechanism. More than fifty years ago Sully was spelling out the nature of these changes:

As the centers of vocalization get developed, motor impulses begin to play on the muscles of throat, larynx, and, later on, lips, tongue, etc., and in this way a larger and larger variety of sound and sound-combination is produced. Such phonation is impulsive. It is instinctive, that is to say, unlearnt, and due to congenital nervous connexions; and at best it can only be said to express in its totality a mood or relatively permanent state of feeling.[77]

These changes in the nervous system and in the structure of the speech apparatus are also pointed out by Miller:

The role of maturation in the development of speech can be seen in many ways. For example, the area in the brain that controls speech (Broca's area) develops later than the other motor centers. . . . Not until 17 months after birth does it reach that degree of anatomical differentiation that can be observed in the other motor centers by the eleventh month. Changes in the structure of the speech apparatus also play a role; the resonating cavities change in size and shape. . . .[78]

[75] McCarthy, op. cit., pp. 507–509.
[76] Arnold Lucius Gesell, The Mental Growth of the Pre-School Child, New York, The Macmillan Company, 1925; cited by B. J. Johnson, op. cit., p. 79.
[77] James Sully, Studies of Childhood, New York, Appleton-Century-Crofts, 1903, p. 137.
[78] George A. Miller, Language and Communication, New York, McGraw-Hill Book Company, 1951, p. 140.

All four of the processes mentioned above by Poole are directly influenced in their development by the processes of maturation.

THE CIRCULAR RESPONSE.   An important phase of this stage of development is emphasized by Allport, namely, the fixation of the *circular response*. Assume that the baby utters the syllable *da*. He receives from that utterance two types of stimuli, one auditory and the other kinesthetic. Of these two the latter is probably significant in *fixing the articulation* of the sound. The former is important in setting up the situation for later conditioning. As the afferent impulse is carried through the central system to the motor outlet, there is a tendency for that impulse to be "redischarged through the same motor pathways as those used in speaking the syllable itself. . . . While the babe is practicing the syllabic elements of his future vocabulary he is therefore also fixating the ear-vocal reflexes through which a spoken sound may directly evoke its enunciation. Articulation has now advanced to a stage where it is capable of being controlled through the auditory receptor." [79] An auditory stimulus coming from another person will have the same effect as if the child himself were to utter the sound.

When the utterance of speech sounds, singly or in combination, results from the child's thus hearing them from another, we have what is called "imitation." The child simply repeats what he has heard from others, just as he has already been repeating what he has been hearing from himself, and for the same reason. The process is "really the touching off of *previously acquired* speech habits by their conditioning auditory stimuli. [80]

A still further step in this conditioning process, and leading, in fact, to the Blantons' division of "language sounds with association of ideas," [81] is taken when, simultaneously with the presentation of the vocal stimulation, an object is also presented as a secondary, as yet inadequate, stimulus. Through this means a substitute stimulus is set up, so that after repeated simultaneous presentations the child learns to respond vocally to the visual stimulus alone.

The diagram (Figure 78) illustrates schematically the process just described. $Voice_1$ is the infant's own voice, the sound of which strikes the ear, providing a stimulus for the voice again, thus setting up the circular response. $Voice_2$ is the voice of the attendant, the sound of which has the same stimulus value as $Voice_1$. The *Object* presented by visual stimulation becomes conditioned

[79] Allport, *op. cit.*, pp. 182 f. The theory is apparently based on Baldwin's hypothesis of the "circular reaction," and is accepted by practically all writers on children's imitation. See M. M. Lewis, *op. cit.*, p. 79.

[80] *Ibid.*, pp. 184 ff. See also Lewis, *op. cit.*, pp. 99, 139 f., chap. X.

[81] *Loc. cit.*

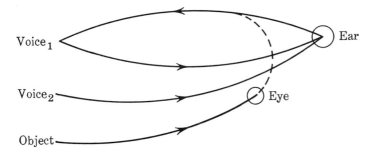

Figure 78. Schema Showing Development of Substitute Response from Circular Response.

upon the circular response, with the result that the sight of the object will come to have the same stimulus value as either *Voice₁* or *Voice₂*.

Comprehension. During the time in which the child is learning to make these vocal responses, and indeed, even preceding it, he has also been forming associations involving an understanding of the words spoken to him. For understanding of speech comes before the use of language by the child; "the passive or 'comprehension' vocabulary is larger than the active or 'speech' vocabulary." [82] Children quite early learn the meaning of "No!" and many similar expressions of direction, or to look about them when asked "Where's dolly?" or "Where's mama?" As Hurlock further points out, however, in many instances it is difficult to know whether the response is to the meaning of the words themselves, or to the manner in which they are uttered, or to the accompanying gesture or facial expression. "Up to the age of eighteen months, words must be reinforced with gestures if the speaker wants to be sure that the child will comprehend what he hears." The precedence of understanding over use of language occurs also in adult learning of new languages, as has been pointed out by Johnson. [83]

Purposive Articulate Utterance. The early articulate utterances which have been set up as a result of conditioning have not as yet any purpose in influencing behavior. They are responses to substitute stimuli and have no significance as stimuli for further responses on the part of others. But the child soon learns to make use of his newly acquired ability to *name* things in making his demands. The acquiring of these associations between object and

[82] Elizabeth B. Hurlock, *Child Development*, New York, McGraw-Hill Book Company, 1942, p. 165.
[83] Johnson, *op. cit.*, p. 196.

sound or sound combination marks the transition between nonpurposive and purposive utterance.

Suppose (the child) sees a new and interesting doll out of reach on a shelf. Manipulative tendencies cause him to reach for it. Failing in this, the usual law of trial and error brings into play all possible movements. One of the readiest and easiest of these movements is the pronunciation of the word "doll"—a reaction which is moreover elicited by its recent association with the sight of an object of that general sort. The word is therefore spoken, and the pleased parent presents the doll as a reward. The manipulative drive now proceeds unhampered, and the arcs involved in this solution of the problem are fixated for future use. By simple vocal expression the child thus learns to control others. He increases vicariously his own stature, his power, and his sagacity by enlisting these attributes of adults in the service of his needs. Little wonder that his linguistic progress is rapid.[84]

Vocabulary.   It is difficult to know when the first word appears, but it seems usually to be near or before the end of the first year.[85] Nor is it easy to say with any degree of reliability or consistency what part of speech is always used. This difficulty arises partly because the earliest utterances are ideas or word sentences; that is, they embody things and actions together without differentiation. Miller thinks that the first word is "almost always a reduplicated monosyllable: 'bye-bye,' 'mama,' 'dada,' 'tick-tick,' etc."[86] Few if any of these represent either a single object or a single action, but usually two together. On the other hand, the earliest meaningful utterance of one of the children of the present authors came upon her locating a missing doll, or ball, "De ti" (There it is).

"True speech has begun when, with a consciousness of the meaning and value of words, the child begins purposively to use them to express or to communicate his thoughts and feelings. When this point is reached all the rest of his immature years are devoted to the perfecting of this power."[87]

From the use of such signs as demands, it is but a short step to their use in pointing out or naming the objects involved, with characteristic actions and gestures. Gradually the necessity for the presence of the specific object grows less; a situation in which the object has been a significant element may become associated with the thing itself so definitely that merely finding himself in such a situation will call forth the verbal response. A child who has been given a toy to play with until he goes to sleep will often, when he is tucked into bed, utter the name of the toy repeatedly. If it is given to him in one

---

[84] Allport, *op. cit.*, p. 187.
[85] McCarthy, *op. cit.*, pp. 523 ff.
[86] Miller, *op. cit.*, p. 149.
[87] Waddle, *op. cit.*, p. 161.

instance, in a short time his utterance takes on the nature of a demand. Later, in case of denial, laryngeal expression is resorted to until either he is given the toy or he goes to sleep in exhaustion. In the former case the arcs are further fixated; in the latter there is a break, so that on succeeding occasions he is less likely to make his demand insistent.

In much the same way the other parts of speech are learned, those having special significance in social control or adaptation usually preceding those of somewhat less immediate importance in satisfying the demands of the child.

With increasing complexity in behavior and the resultant variations in responses, the child begins to differentiate between his demands and his statements—a difference comparable to the primitive distinction between the command and the proclamation. In addition to direct control of others he learns an indirect control, in that a mere statement may result in the desired response without the insistence expressed in the demand. He enters a world of imagination in which his toys take on personal traits. He talks to them and about them. He talks to himself as well as to others, without always being aware of the difference. His concepts (the *meanings* which are attached to the words) become more specific as well as more general, and he now becomes not only a speaking animal, but a thinking one as well.

VOCABULARY GROWTH.   The growth of the child's vocabulary has been studied by a number of investigators. One difficulty in such studies has been that, as has been said, many words are used as complete sentences. For the child "water" may mean "I want water," or any one of a half-dozen other fairly complete ideas. Words are made to do double or triple duty and may, in the same form, be used as two or three different parts of speech—a characteristic of language not confined to children's speech. The number of words, therefore, is not necessarily an indication of the number of ideas which a child may attach to them.

The actual number of words which a child uses is much larger than is commonly thought. Smith reports the averages given on the next page for children of the ages indicated. [88]

A later revision gives figures somewhat higher than these, reporting 1507 words at three years, 2148 at four years, 2527 at five years, and 3054 at six years. [89] It appears from Smith's study that up to the age of four to four and a half years the vocabulary of girls is larger than that of boys; but at about the

[88] M. E. Smith, "An investigation of the development of the sentence and the extent of the vocabulary of young children," *University of Iowa Studies*, 1926, pp. 3, 5.
[89] McCarthy, *op. cit.*, p. 533.

Age (Years)	Number of Children	Average Vocabulary
2	25	272
2½	14	446
3	20	896
3½	26	1222
4	26	1540
4½	32	1870
5	20	2072
5½	27	2289
6	9	2562

age of five the swing is in the opposite direction, and continues at least through the following year. Johnson, however, denies that sex differences are significant.[90]

There are marked individual differences in the size of children's vocabularies. Preyer in 1890 reported that nine two-year-old children had a range of from 173 to 1121 words![91] But Shirley, writing quite a few years later, reported an average vocabulary for two-year-old children of 37 words, with a range of from six to 126.[92] It is not certain that Preyer referred to different words, or to several forms of the same words, in which case the figures might be more nearly comparable.

Waddle's table gives figures in fairly close agreement with those of Smith. Twenty children two years of age had an average vocabulary of 528 words, eight three-year-old children had an average vocabulary of 1407; six four-year-olds, 2171; one five-year-old had a vocabulary of 6837; and one six-year-old, 3590.[93]

Major reported that at the end of the second year his child had a vocabulary of 143 words; from the twenty-fifth to the thirtieth month it increased to 308; and from the thirty-first to the thirty-sixth month, to 564.[94]

The data above refer to the usable vocabularies of children, that is, the words they actually use in speaking. It is generally known, however, that the

[90] Johnson, op. cit., pp. 203–204.
[91] W. Preyer, The Mind of the Child: Part II. The Development of the Intellect, New York, Appleton-Century-Crofts, 1890, p. 237.
[92] M. M. Shirley, The First Two Years, a Study of Twenty-Five Babies: Vol. II, Intellectual Development, Institute of Child Welfare Monograph Series, Nos. 6–8, Minneapolis, University of Minnesota Press, 1931–1933.
[93] Waddle, op. cit., p. 166.
[94] David R. Major, First Steps in Mental Growth, New York, The Macmillan Company, 1906, p. 327.

speaking vocabulary is much smaller than the number of words which have significance when read or heard. M. K. Smith discovered that the average number of words which had such significance for the child in grade one was "16,900, with a range from 5500 to 32,800. . . . For grade twelve the average number of basic words known was 47,300, with a range from 28,200 to 73,200." "Basic words" are those for which separate entries are made in the dictionaries. Derived terms were not considered to be separate words. "For grade one the average number of words in the total vocabulary (basic plus derivative words) was 23,700, with a range from 600 to 48,800. For grade twelve the average number of words in the total vocabulary was 80,300, with a range from 36,700 to 136,500." [95]

Johnson points out that "the acquisition of a vocabulary is a process of distinct importance to the child. . . . The finely differentiated responses possible through speech are essential for the development of symbols that are substituted for complex stimulus patterns and experiences. . . . At an early age other symbols than speech may be developed but word language offers the most rapid acquisition of the many responses essential for quick and efficient thinking." [96]

Gesture Language

Although the psychologist Wundt did not argue that speech developed from gestures, his theory has often been so interpreted, that is, that gesture is the earliest form of communication used by infants, as it was by primitive man. There is no question that it appears very early in life; its precedence as a purposive means of social control or adaptation, however, is open to some question. The head-turning movement, which may be noticed within the first few days, is an innate response to a situation necessitating biologically a refusal of more food. It is of the same order as the ejection of the nipple with the tongue. Even the later conditioning which results in a similar sideward movement of the head has at first no significance in social control. It probably does not precede laryngeal expressions. If the parent or nurse insists upon interpreting such movements as "meaning" refusal, they are still no more language or communication than are those sounds into which meanings are read by parent or nurse.

That animals very low in the scale of organization make use of sound is

[95] Mary Katherine Smith, "Measurement of the size of general English vocabulary through the elementary grades and high school," *Genetic Psychology Monographs* (1941), *24*: 311–345.
[96] Johnson, *op. cit.*, p. 204.

demonstrated by Negus, who carried his investigations down to the invertebrates and crustacea. There is no evidence of a break anywhere along the line of increasing organic complexity in the purposive use of sound for controlling the behavior of others. Negus' illustrations in the field of sound go just as far back into primitive life as do those in the field of sight. The use of visible activity among animals does not occur, apparently, before the use of audible activities.[97]

When primitive man appeared on the scene, there were already countless eons back of him in which both sound and sight had been used for purposes of social interaction. In some instances undoubtedly the one would be most likely to be used; in other instances, the other would have its immediate advantages; while in still others, a combination of the two would have the greatest effect. And so the two developed together. Similarly in the case of the human infant: he has a mechanism by which both sound and sight can be used for influencing the activities of those about him. And as in the case of primitive man, neither takes precedence, but both develop together.

The basic question is not whether *words* or gestures came first; it is whether visual or audible activity precedes in social intercourse. Words *per se* undoubtedly follow; that is, they are subsequent to, gesture; but sounds are used as early as visible actions with communicative significance. As Critchley says, "The two faculties, that of speech and that of gesture, seem to have developed side by side, gesture being comparable with an elder brother of speech."[98]

[97] V. E. Negus, *The Mechanism of the Larynx*, London, William Heinemann, 1929, chap. X.

[98] MacDonald Critchley, *The Language of Gesture*, London, Edwin Arnold & Co., 1939, pp. 116–124.

Chapter IX

The Semantic Basis
of Speech

Introduction

The World of Things and the World of Words

When a child is born into the world he is immediately assailed by a multiplicity of stimuli of all sorts: tactual, olfactory, thermal, visual, auditory, and so on. At first these are so undifferentiated as to give rise to what James, referring to the so-called consciousness of the newborn infant, called a "blooming, buzzing confusion." (See Chapter VIII, p. 477.) But it is not long until he can make distinctions among the stimuli; the responses to these become likewise differentiated, so that the child soon learns to turn his head toward sounds, to cry when hungry, in pain, or in discomfort, to follow with his eyes a moving light. With advancing maturity this differentiation becomes increasingly sharp. The child is learning to react to a world of *things*—his food, clothing, playthings, pets, his parents, brothers, and sisters—a host of objects, actions, and characteristics to be found in his physical environment.

During all this time he is also hearing peculiar sounds, made by the people about him. Certain of these sounds are presented in connection with certain objects, especially those objects which play a part in his daily life. He hears these sounds and sees these objects so often that he ultimately establishes a connection between sound and object. As a result he comes to react to the sounds themselves in very much the same way he has been responding to the objects. Furthermore, partly through imitation and partly through processes described in Chapter VIII, he learns, as his own sound-producing apparatus comes more and more under control, to produce the same or similar sounds in connection with appropriate objects.

489

He has now a new type of stimulus to which to respond, and by applying it to those with whom he comes in contact he can influence their responses. The new stimulus differs from the old in that while the response to it is very much like that to the object itself, it resembles in no particular the original stimulus, which was a material object with weight, dimensions, and appearance, whereas the new one is only sound. But the child has learned to respond to this *substitute stimulus* in much the same way as if it were the original stimulus. The sound, which may now be called a *word*, has become a *symbol* of the thing for which it now stands.

From now on the child lives, in effect, in two worlds—the world of things which he can perceive directly, and the world of symbols, through which he is able to apprehend indirectly those things for which the symbols stand. As his world of things increases in complexity, so also does the world of symbols. He is at the same time learning that the significance of these symbols can take either of two directions, with many shadings of differentiation between the two extremes. On the one hand, he learns, for example, that not every man is to be called "daddy," that this term is to be applied to one and only one person. On the other hand, he learns that the word "ball" may refer not only to the big, round, striped object with which he has been playing, but also to any number of big or small or unstriped or varicolored objects that resemble the old familiar one only in their roundness. Still later he may learn other significances, other things for which these two words may stand. He is learning language and how to use it.

The Reliability of Signification.   In his early experiences with symbols the child has come to place considerable dependence upon the reliability of their signification. If "bye-bye" has been associated with a ride in his carriage, he does not expect to have to go to sleep when he hears the word; he expects his ride. If orange juice is promised he has no reason to expect oatmeal. The story is told that when Tad Lincoln was a very small boy a friend came to visit his father. Tad was quite shy in the presence of the stranger, who, as an inducement to the lad to come and sit on his lap, held out his very fine watch, saying. "If you will come and sit on my knee, I'll give you this watch." The inducement was enough to overcome the shyness, and the boy sat and played with the watch until it was time for the visitor to leave. When the man put the watch back in his pocket, however, Tad set up a protest; he had been promised the watch under certain conditions. He had met those conditions and felt entitled to his reward. Lincoln supported his son's claim; the agreement had been made and entered to in good faith. The watch was accordingly handed over, to the visitor's chagrin.

As the complexity of his two worlds increases, the child learns sooner or later that the reliability of this relation between symbol and reality must often be brought into question. Promises are broken; symbols are used which do not correspond with the world of things in his experience; other symbols apparently have no relation at all to his experiences; they arouse no definite response because there is nothing definite with which they have been associated. As a result he becomes confused. He comes to question not only the validity of the symbols, but the sincerity and honesty of those who use them. This is only one possible result. He may, on the other hand, come to accept the symbol itself without inquiring into its significance; he may have some vague, indeterminate idea of what the symbol stands for, and attach to the symbol itself certain emotional attitudes originally directed toward the object for which it is the symbol.

Any number of unfortunate results may come about through incorrect, inadequate, misleading uses of symbols. It is the purpose of the present chapter to suggest some of the factors involved in the use of language, which after all, consists of no more than an arbitrarily determined system of symbols developed through countless thousands of years into the highly complex code that forms a portion of what may be called our "social heritage."

The Semantic Approach

The examination of these factors is involved in the discipline commonly known as *semantics*, or perhaps more broadly, *general semantics*, which goes further than the linguistic aspects of the relations between words and things, and concerns itself "with the fact that man, as a symbol-creating and symbol-using class of life, reflects the structure of his symbol-systems in the structure of his pattern reactions."[1] That is, so basic an aspect of human life are the phenomena of symbolization and symbolic systems that man's behavior patterns reflect and are influenced by the structure of those systems. Such a point of view is strongly related to the philosophy of Whorf and others, that human nature is largely dependent upon language.[2]

The study of general semantics has increased greatly in the past few years, and like a number of other approaches to studies of human behavior, has many

[1] S. I. Hayakawa, "Reply to Professor Bures" (on criticism of *Language in Thought and Action*), *ETC* (1951), *9*: 43–50.
[2] See Chapter VII, pp. 450–454.

ardent advocates. Many claims have been made for its efficacy in dealing with disorders arising from misunderstandings and confusions because of language difficulties. It is to be suspected that in the warmth of enthusiasm some of these claims may be somewhat exaggerated. As one writer has pointed out,

> It is perhaps worth while saying that semantics as it is conceived in this paper (and in former papers of the author) is a sober and modest discipline which has no pretensions of being a universal patent-medicine for all the ills and diseases of mankind, whether imaginary or real. You will not find in semantics any remedy for decayed teeth or illusions of grandeur or class conflicts. Nor is semantics a device for establishing that everyone except the speaker and his friends is speaking nonsense.[3]

The foregoing quotations from Hayakawa and Tarski may suggest, without definitely stating, the distinction to be made between *general semantics* on the one hand, and *semantics* on the other. The latter discipline is concerned with meaning primarily as a linguistic function. It examines such aspects of language as origins, etymologies, and changes in the meanings of words as they occur in the normal progress of a language. In Chapter VI, for example, "semantic change" is discussed as an aspect of the linguistic basis of speech. Semantics is closely allied with philology, which, however, is concerned as much with language form as with meaning. Essentially semantics is an objective, largely historical approach to language and linguistics, insofar as meaning is concerned.

General semantics, on the other hand, is concerned with language primarily as a behavioral phenomenon. While the discipline makes use of the semantic approach, it is interested even more in such aspects of language as its relation to underlying personal attitudes, and emotional as well as logical adjustments and orientations. It examines language as a basic attribute of human beings, both influenced by and influencing the total environment, social and physical.

Both approaches, semantic and general semantic, are used in the present chapter; but there seems to be so much overlapping that no consistent effort has been made to draw a sharp distinction between the two. It is hoped that where differences are significant they will be obvious from the textual treatment.

---

[3] Alfred Tarski, "The semantic conception of truth and the foundation of semantics," *Philosophy and Phenomenological Research* (1943–1944), *4*: 341–376. It should perhaps be pointed out that the writer has not, in the title, specified *general* semantics.

The Nature of Symbolism

The Basis of Symbolism

In the description of Pavlov's experiments it was suggested that, after repeated trials, the bell had come to "mean" food to the animals. Through the process of substitution of stimuli the sound had become so associated with the food that in time it alone elicited the same flow of saliva that was originally produced by the food itself. There was no basic or essential connection or similarity between the two types of stimuli, food and sound; the choice of a bell instead of a whistle or a red flag or what not as a substitute stimulus was purely arbitrary on the part of the experimenter. He might have used any one of a number of different kinds of stimuli with equal success. The bell was, or came to be, a symbol, a substitute stimulus, which had a certain specific significance to the dogs.

It is, of course, a far cry from such a relatively simple associative process to the complex organization of language; but languages, spoken or written or otherwise constructed, are essentially based on the same process of substitute stimulus and response. Language may be thought of in part as a set of such symbols, arbitrarily chosen but agreed upon by the general population of a given area as having certain more or less definite significances or meanings. They *represent* concepts of things, actions, and attributes of, or relations between the generalized data of experience. "... *all we can ever transform into symbols is some bodily state or other of our very own.*" [4] But language consists of more than a lexicon or vocabulary of isolated words and independent sound combinations, such as might be designated by the term *words*. Equally if not more important is the manner in which these words are put together, structured into a system by which the concepts for which they stand may be placed into various relationships with one another. When these symbolic relationships correspond to the relationships recognized to exist between and among experiences of reality, the language has validity. As Tarski has pointed out, "The sentence 'Snow is white' is true if and only if snow is white." [5]

Symbols as Conventions

That these symbols are mere conventions may be illustrated by the fact that in different languages the same object may be designated by entirely

[4] Wendell Johnson, *Your Most Enchanted Listener*, New York, Harper & Brothers, 1956, p. 67. Italics in the original.

[5] Tarski, *op. cit.*

different symbols. Thus what is called a "horse" in the English language is called *Pferd* in German, *cheval* in French, *hevonen* in Finnish, *konj* in Croatian, *bestiga* in Swedish, *hippos* in Greek, *loshad* in Russian, *equus* in Latin, and *ma* (with a rising inflection) in Chinese. Similarly, many of our common flowers have two or three names, particularly in different localities. The gardenia is also called the cape jasmine; the bachelor's button goes also by the name cornflower, or in the French, *les immortelles*. Camellias are often called japonicas (the japonica being a *species* of the *genus* camellia), and the wild azalea is known by many people as the honeysuckle—a name also given to a quite different flower—and by others as mountain laurel. The "Pope Pius" variety of camellia is also called the "Prince Eugene Napoleon," and the "Chalice" is also listed as the "Mrs. Howard Asper."

The conventional nature of words was recognized by the English philosopher, John Locke, who pointed out, "that they *signify* only men's peculiar *ideas*, and that *by a perfectly arbitrary imposition*, is evident, in that they often fail to excite in others (even that use the same language) the same *ideas* we take them to be the signs of: and every one has so inviolable a liberty, to make words stand for what *ideas* he pleases, that no one hath the power to make others have the same *ideas* in their minds, that he has when they use the same words that he does." [6]

It is futile to inquire what is the "correct" or "real" name for flowers or anything else, for such inquiry is based on the assumption that names are an essential part of the objects for which they stand, rather than a conventionalized symbol. However, such an assumption is not uncommon in our use of language. *We identify the symbol with the object*, or *with the action*, or perhaps *the characteristic of an object or action*, and treat the two as if they were the same thing—as if the name in some way actually belonged to the thing represented. When in 1852 Alvan Bovay was trying to interest Horace Greeley in the new political party which was later to elect Lincoln to the Presidency, he proposed the name "Republican" because of its possible favorable effect on the voters. "Names, Mr. Greeley," he said, "are things to the great mass of mankind." [7] Rejection of such identity is one of the basic tenets of general semantics.

Symbols have significance, meaning, only because of their associations. While many of them have been in our language so long that they *seem* to have inherent meanings, actually they are no more than conventionalized sequences

[6] John Locke, *An Essay Concerning Human Understanding*, Allen & West, 1795, bk. III, chap. 2, sec. 8.

[7] Perrilton Maxwell and Alan Hynd, "Birth of the G.O.P." *Coronet*, September 16, 1944, pp. 117–121.

of sounds or letters or other physical stimuli (such as the dots and dashes of the Morse code or any other prearranged system of signaling) which by general agreement have come to stand for certain objects or experiences. *The meaning itself is a function of the relation between the symbol and the datum of experience.* The smoke signals of the early American Indians, the tom-tom of the African jungles, the cryptic marks of the proofreader—all are symbols which by agreement, tacit or explicit, have come to stand for certain things. To the initiated, that is, to the one who has made the necessary associations, they are quite intelligible. They have semantic significance.

Identity of Words and Things

Much confusion, both in communication with others and in our own thinking, often results from the identification of the symbol with the thing symbolized, as has been emphasized repeatedly in general semantics writings. We are more or less familiar with the habits of primitive peoples who sometimes refuse to speak the names of their children aloud for fear of being overheard by evil spirits who might wish to do the children harm. Frazer tells us that "wine colored amethyst received its name, which means 'not drunken,' because it was supposed to keep its wearer sober."[8] The practice of idol worship was not confined to the heathen or to their bowing before graven images. Many people still avoid the number 13, and hotels often omit a "thirteenth floor," the one immediately above the twelfth being numbered fourteen. Numerologists insist that there is a special virtue in certain numbers, and gullible people sometimes change their names in favor of one having the most favorable number of letters in it. The paper money which many people hoard for its own sake is no more than a symbol of a certain kind of value; it has no intrinsic value of its own, beyond that of any other equal quantity of waste paper that might be remade into some article of utility.

Attitudes Toward Symbols. Typical of the attitude often taken toward words is the feeling many people have that certain words are "ugly" and others are "beautiful." Actually, apart from the fact that some sounds and sound combinations seem to be less pleasant than others,[9] many of the so

[8] Sir James George Frazer, *The Golden Bough*, New York, The Macmillan Company, 1922, chap. 3; cited from Bartlett's *Familiar Quotations*, 11th ed., Boston, Little, Brown & Company, 1938, p. 713. See also Frazer, "Tabooed Words," in *The Language of Wisdom and Folly*, Irving J. Lee (ed.), New York, Harper & Brothers, 1949, pp. 220–223.

[9] Edward L. Thorndike, "Euphony and cacophony of English words and sounds," *The Quarterly Journal of Speech* (1944), *30*: 201–207. See also Jon Eisenson and others, "The affective value of English speech sounds," *The Quarterly Journal of Speech* (1940), *26*: 589–594; and "A second study in the affective value of speech sounds," *ibid.* (1943), *29*: 457–464.

called "ugly" words are unpleasant only because they are associated with unpleasant experiences. Considered only as sequences of sounds, *death* is no more repellent than *breath*, *kill* than *hill* or *mill*; *hell* than *bell*, *cheat* than *sweet*. One of the most "beautiful" words in our language is said to be *mother*; and yet the same sequence of sounds is also applied to a brown, slimy, jellylike mass which is formed in the process of making vinegar. One who knows the word only in the latter significance would hardly be expected to think of it as "beautiful."

We learn to take an attitude toward one object or another, and then transfer the same attitude toward the mere name. As Dashiell has said, "If we will but stop for a moment to ponder the extraordinary degree in which the social life of man is permeated and shot through with his responses to emblems, shibboleths, hackneyed phrases, and epithets, without benefit of first-hand acquaintance and cool-headed analysis of men and issues actually involved, we shall understand the avid interest of the social psychologist and the sociologist in the psychology of attitudes."[10] Since these attitudes affect also our use of language, the student of speech should be no less interested. In his *The American Language* H. L. Mencken has discussed at some length what he calls "forbidden words," and the euphemisms which are or have been substituted for many of them.[11] These are all matters of concern to the general semanticist.

SLOGANS AND LABELS. Another problem of general semantics is the tendency to adhere to slogans and labels, which is recognizable by anyone who gives the matter even cursory attention. Although as early as November, 1916, it was evident that war with Germany was inevitable, Wilson was reëlected on the basis of the slogan, "He kept us out of war." Voters cling to the party label quite regardless of the candidate nominated by the party or the "platform" or set of promises and "principles" proposed for that particular campaign. We extol the virtues of "democracy" without translating those principles into our daily relations with others; and we castigate "communism" without fully, or even partially, understanding the peculiar nature of the politico-socio-economic system for which these terms stand. This is neither an attack on democracy nor a support of opposing types of government; if it is true that "by their works shall ye know them," there is much to

---

[10] John Frederick Dashiell, *Fundamentals of General Psychology*, Boston, Houghton Mifflin Company, 1937, p. 131.

[11] H. L. Mencken, *The American Language*, 4th ed., New York, Alfred A. Knopf, 1938, pp. 300–311.

commend in a democratic form of society and much to condemn in authoritarian forms, as our direct and indirect experiences have led us to associate certain specific practices with the types of society to which these names are given. It seems hardly conceivable that anyone interested in the well-being of humanity could approve of a form of government which would perpetrate the atrocities visited upon the people of Hungary in 1956–1957, whose only crime was that they were struggling for the privilege of managing their own affairs.

At the same time, most of us would be hard put to it to explain the basic tenets of our own form of society, much less those of other forms. To label a proposal intended for the benefit of an underprivileged group as "socialistic" is to arouse, in the thinking and attitude of many, an immediate condemnation. Similarly, the term "economic royalists," when applied to any and all industrialists indiscriminately, arouses, as it is intended to arouse, definite attitudes of opposition, whether justified or not, against everyone profiting from "big business."

The point to be emphasized here is that symbols and the things for which they stand are different entities and that no inherent relation exists between them. "Not everyone that saith unto me Lord, Lord, shall enter into the kingdom of heaven." [12] Patriotism is not to be revealed solely by flag waving, or by joining in the singing of the national anthem, or by insisting that everyone conform rigidly to one's own concept of what constitutes "100 percent Americanism," whatever that may mean. It is recognized that certain ritualistic performances have a value in arousing emotional attitudes which may lead to desirable action; they may with equal effectiveness be used to stimulate people to undesirable forms of behavior. Thomas Mann has Mai-Sachme, the Egyptian jailor, say to Joseph, "Such confusion of the word and the reality is to my way of thinking characteristic of low breeding and lack of education." [13]

Is Is Is? Writers on general semantics have gone so far in their efforts to avoid any suggestion of identity between word and thing that they have attempted to discard for the most part the copulative *is*, as in "This is a pencil." "The common injunction to 'call a spade a spade' has the profoundly misleading implication that we call it a spade because that's what it *is*. . . . To be wary of the 'is' of identity is to guard against confusing words and things, confusing verbal descriptions with actual events." [14]

[12] Matthew 7: 21.
[13] Thomas Mann, *Joseph the Provider*, New York, Alfred A. Knopf, 1944, I, p. 28.
[14] S. I. Hayakawa, "Semantics, general semantics, and related disciplines," in *Language, Meaning and Maturity*, S. I. Hayakawa (ed.), New York, Harper & Brothers, 1954, pp. 19–37.

IDENTIFICATION. It is undoubtedly important to avoid the error of implying an identity between words and events; but it may be equally important to avoid the equal semantic error of considering that the word *is* can have no other signification than to indicate such an identity. In many, if not most, cases it is no more than a connective between subject and predicate, serving the purposes of *identification*, a quite different concept from that of identity. "What is that flower?" "It is a Rosea Superba camellia," is no more an implication that an innate connection exists between either the plant or the flower and the name by which it is known, than to say that "This young man is my son" implies an intrinsic relation between the actual person referred to and either term *man* or *son*. The locution serves to identify the flower or the person, so that we will be able to classify either in the category in which it properly belongs. To say, "I am hungry" would not be understood by an intelligent person as indicating that the acoustic phenomenon, the diphthong *I*, is in any sense identical with the physiological condition known as hunger. The statement serves to identify the gastric condition of the person speaking, for whom the "*I*" is a symbol.

"Is," therefore, cannot always be taken as a term of identity, and in fact, is not always so taken. It is used to establish identification, classification, categorization. If one recognizes the basic principle that words are not things, the presence of the copulative *is* need cause no confusion in one's own orientation. And it is highly probable that it will take much more than the mere avoidance of the word, in speaking with others, to prevent misunderstandings among others who characteristically commit the error in their thinking. At the same time, what Hayakawa is proposing is that one be "wary" of the word, rather than discard it altogether; it is an extremely difficult word to get along without.

Meanings Not "Conveyed"

A further point which should be made with reference to symbols and their meanings is that symbols do not "convey" meanings; they serve only to stimulate meanings or associations in the recipient of the communication. If someone says "pencil" to us, he is not transmitting any meanings to us. He has come to associate that particular sequence of sounds with a certain type of more or less long, slender writing instrument; we have also associated similar sequences, similar enough, that is, for purposes of identification even though they are not identical, with generally similar objects. When we hear the word, experiences in connection with that association are stirred up in our memory which are approximately similar to the experiences in the memory of the one who spoke the word. Meaning, then, is not *in* the symbol; as Weaver says, it "resides in the reactive behavior of the organism itself." And that reactive behavior constitutes the association of which the meaning is the function. "We cannot," he goes on to say, "tell anyone a story: all we can do is to get him to tell himself a story. One reason why we sometimes derive richer meanings from novels than we do from dramatizations and movies made from them is that we have greater freedom in telling the stories to ourselves as we read them than we have when a Broadway or Hollywood producer provides the scenery and the *dramatis personae*."[15]

The Determinants of Meaning

In Chapter I it was pointed out that the principal medium of communication is language, consisting of words in certain relations with each other. In Chapter VII the further point was made that thinking itself, especially the ideational variety, involving abstractions, goes on through the medium of language. The effectiveness of either communication or thinking depends to a great degree on the clarity of our concepts (an essential aspect of which is words) and the extent to which the relationships in which these words are structured correspond to the world of things and events, and the existent relationships among those things and events for which the words are made to stand. Does the language in which we communicate or do most of our thinking make "sense?" Is it semantically sound? Do the meanings which we attribute to our language correspond to realities, to existences and to valid relationships? One brought up in an atmosphere polluted by coal smoke might well insist that snow is black, or at least grey, whereas another reared in a locality where no such pollution prevails would argue that snow is white. The problem of the meanings intended or stimulated by language is a crucial one for both thought and communication.

What, then, determines the meaning of a word as it is used in our daily intercourse with those about us? Perhaps an understanding of these semantic factors may be of some help in the development of more effective language.

The Referent

The first essential in determining the meaning of a word is the definition of its referent, that is, the particular action, object, or relation between actions

[15] Andrew Thomas Weaver, *Speech, Forms and Principles*, New York, Longmans, Green & Company, 1942, p. 319.

or objects, or characteristics of those actions, objects, or relations, for which the word stands.

Meaning a Function of a Relationship.   Let it be remembered that the word is a substitute stimulus or response, its "meaning" depending on its having been associated with the particular experiences for which it has come to stand. Certain phenomena (words), of themselves meaningless, have come to "stand for" certain other phenomena (objects, etc.), and have thereby come to have meanings. For illustration, one may fix one's attention upon any word on this page and hold it for several minutes, completely isolating the word from all context. It will be observed that it may become no more than a group of letters representing or suggesting a sound sequence, and wholly meaningless. One may look at a word from an unknown language, e.g., *sobaka* from the Russian. It is likewise meaningless, even onomatopoeia being insufficient to reveal the meaning without the arbitrary information that the combination "means" *dog*; that is, it is used in Russian to designate the same kind of animal to which we have given the name *dog*. Groups of letters or combinations of sounds become symbols when we can use them in place of objects, actions, relations, or characteristics. We can then manipulate them and place them in various relations with other things, which are in turn represented by other symbols. The "meaning" of a symbol, as has been said, is a function of the association or relationship between the symbol itself and the referent. If no such association or relationship exists the symbol has no meaning; if the referent is nonexistent in either reality or imagination the symbol is meaningless. If to the referent are attached strong emotional attitudes, biases, or prejudices, the meaning of the symbol will be colored by the same attitudes, a phenomenon which goes beyond semantics and becomes one of general semantics. It is essential, therefore, that in either thinking or communication with others these associations be clear and definite if our meanings are to have validity.

Significance of Change in the Referent.   A number of factors affect the nature of these associations and hence of the meanings. We often fail to recognize the fact, for example, that meanings are constantly changing. The word itself, that is, the combinations of letters or the sequences of sounds making up the symbol, is relatively stable; it is particularly so in written language. But the objects, actions, relations, and characteristics designated have a way of changing constantly. These changes are often imperceptible, but they are also often disconcertingly great. Children grow up, their parents grow older, their statures change, their hair thins or falls out almost completely; the Sam Stark you knew ten years ago is not the same Sam Stark today. The pear placed on my desk two days ago now has a large brown spot on one side of it; it is not the same pear. The democracy of Thomas Jefferson is not the same as the democracy of Franklin D. Roosevelt, nor is the Democratic Party of 100 years ago the Democratic Party of today. The Republican Party has undergone parallel changes in the century or so of its existence. The house built several years ago looks much the same today; but the termites have left their mark, the paint is peeling in places, the foundation has settled a little, and the wallpaper in the living room has faded slightly. It is not the identical house that the builders completed, and it will never be the same house again, any more than the children of today will ever again be the same. When these children go to school tomorrow they will be different from what they were when they went this morning.

Even the stone in our path, scientists tell us, is constantly undergoing changes from day to day, though these changes are imperceptible. Streams gradually change their beds, so that the "old swimming hole" which we knew as boys has by now become so completely altered that we can scarcely recognize it. Even the hills over which we hunted in our boyhood have become less steep. In the opening of the second act of *Our Town* the Stage Manager describes the changes that have taken place in Grover's Corners during the previous three years: "Yes, the mountain got bit away a few fractions of an inch; and millions of gallons of water have passed by the mill." [16]

PARALLEL CHANGE IN MEANING.   What we are likely not to recognize, however, is that as things change, the meanings of the symbols by which we refer to them should also change. In other words, of the three factors before us, referent, symbol, and meaning, only the symbol can remain static; the other two must change in parallel, as it were, meaning keeping pace with that to which the symbol refers, that is, to the changing referent. We must beware of violating this continuing parallel and of behaving as if the symbol perpetually designated the referent in its original state. It is irrational to continue to use the symbols as if the things themselves were exactly as they were when the words were first used. We talk about "the" theory of evolution, thinking of it only as Darwin presented it in *The Descent of Man* (or as we *think* he presented it) a century ago. As Lee pointed out, we are prone to wax eloquent

[16] Thornton Wilder, *Our Town*, New York, Coward-McCann and Samuel French, 1939, pp. 37 f.

over "the American way," without reflecting that there have been many changes in the American mode of living since the founding of the nation, and there may have been certain phases in that mode which have not been wholly admirable.[17] Similarly, we continue to speak of "communism" without considering the possibility that the communism of 1957 is somewhat different from the communism of 1918.

Such confusion exists in both our speaking and our thinking. The symbols with which we do our thinking remain fixed, while their referents are in a constant state of change. The result is that the meanings become blurred; there is a lack of correspondence between the word and the reality, and our concepts themselves and hence our thinking become blurred and vague. While semantic change has been a recognized linguistic phenomenon for a long time, its effect on the processes of thought have been given even stronger emphasis through the discipline of general semantics.

Dating.   In discovering the referent for a given word, therefore, it is necessary that the factor of change be recognized. Some writers[18] on this subject have recommended the practice of *dating* the symbol, indicating, for example, that intercollegiate football$_{1958}$ is a somewhat different game from intercollegiate football$_{1920}$. In this particular form such a practice might be unworkable in speech; but it is possible and sometimes necessary, if confusion is to be avoided, to indicate the particular time at which a given reference is or was valid.

CONTINUITY IN CHANGE.   While it is necessary to recognize the factor of change in the meaning of a symbol, it must not be forgotten that through all this change runs a thread of continuity. The stone that lay in our path ten years ago is still, if not removed, just as much of an obstacle today as it was then; its composition and structure have not altered significantly. Although the house built some years ago has undoubtedly undergone some changes, is still, for all practical purposes, just as habitable as it was when it was built. Functionally it is, as a place of dwelling, the same house; and even though it may have to be repainted now and then, and other repairs made from time to time, the owners will probably be still living in the "same" house ten years from now. And in time the grandchildren will play in the "same" yard their parents played in in their childhood.

Sameness.   When one asks, "Is that the 'same' Henry Jones that lived ten

[17] Irving J. Lee, *Language Habits in Human Affairs*, New York, Harper & Brothers, 1941, p. 78.

[18] Korzybski, Lee, Hayakawa, and others.

years ago in the Westbrook Subdivision?" it is no abuse of language to reply in the affirmative, when, as in such instances, the inquiry is solely for the purpose of identification. Of course Henry Jones has changed in the past ten years. Rigid semanticism might insist on saying, "No, that was Henry Jones$_{1948}$ who lived in the Westbrook Subdivision; it is Henry Jones$_{1958}$ who now lives on Hanley Road. They aren't the same men." Then would have to come a long explanation of how Henry Jones$_{1948}$ came to be, because of the processes of change that inevitably overtake any individual, Henry Jones$_{1958}$. Whereupon the inquirer would be quite justified in concluding, "Then it is the same man, after all!"

Fortunately, most of our language does not demand such rigid *dating* in our use of terms. In the great majority of instances no confusion results from considering that some things remain much the same over a period of years; we see the "same" people in our work day after day; we drive the "same" car to school every morning; we park in the "same" place (even though one spot may be ten feet or more removed from another); and despite the fact that 90 percent of the student population of the university changes completely every four years, and there is quite a turnover in the faculty, we continue teaching year after year at the "same" institution.

Notwithstanding all of these practical considerations, it is at the same time often true that the factor of change is significant in a more precise determination of the referent. It is highly important that we recognize the situations in which these more specific meanings are necessary and be able to apply the more precise references in our language.

Abstractions. Another factor in determining the referent is the fact that no symbol can possibly represent all the aspects of reality which we are able to perceive with our senses; nor is it, in fact, possible for us to perceive every detail of any given object. When we associate with such an article a certain symbol, we are engaging in a process of abstracting or generalizing, that is, of selecting certain characteristics and omitting others; the omissions may be just as important as the inclusions. It is often just as necessary, in defining a term, to say what it does not refer to as it is to say what it does. It was Korzybski, generally considered to be the founder of the modern discipline of general semantics, who advocated that statements should be "accompanied by an implicit 'et cetera' to remind one of the premise that 'maps' do not represent all the 'territory,' that no statement about objects or events in the real world can ever be final." [19] ". . . the complete identity [of two objects]

[19] Hayakawa, "Semantics, general semantics, and related disciplines," *op. cit.*, pp. 27–29.

is merely a human contrivance, by which an infinitely diverse creation is comprehended by a finite vocabulary." [20]

More than 250 years ago Locke pointed out the impossibility of knowing every detail of reality:

... it is not to be wondered, that *we have very imperfect* ideas *of substances*; and that the real essences,[21] on which depend their properties and operations, are unknown to us. We cannot discover so much as that *size, figure,* and *texture* of their minute and active parts, which is really in them; much less the different motions and impulses made in and upon them by bodies from without, upon which depends, and by which is formed, the greatest and most remarkable part of those qualities we observe, and of which our complex *ideas* of them are made up.[22]

Ordinarily we do not suffer a great deal of confusion at the lower levels of abstraction and generalization; one does not, as a rule, mistake a Ford for a Rolls-Royce, or a Chevrolet for a Cadillac. But if we group the Ford and the Rolls-Royce together and abstract their essentially similar elements, we may use the general term *automobile* to refer to this higher order of abstraction. If we still further take automobiles and other mechanisms developed for the purpose of carrying people and things from one place to another, and apply a term to refer to the similar elements, we have what might be called *transportation*. Still further, if we group production, transportation, and distribution together, we have something still more abstract to which could be applied the still more general term *commerce*.

Locke describes the process of forming higher abstractions thus:

By the same way that they come by the general name and *idea* of *man*, they easily *advance to more general names* and notions. For observing that several things that differ from their *idea* of man, and cannot therefore be comprehended under that name, have yet certain qualities wherein they agree with *man*, by retaining only those qualities, and uniting them into one *idea*, they have again another and a more general *idea*; to which having given a name, they make a term of more comprehensive extension; which new *idea* is made, not by any new addition, but only, as before, by leaving out the shape, and some other properties signified by the name *man*, and retaining only a body, with life, sense, and spontaneous motion, comprehended under the name *animal*.[23]

It is in these higher orders of abstraction that confusion is most likely to

[20] A. B. Johnson, *A Treatise on Language; or the Relation which Words Bear to Things,* New York: Harper & Brothers, 1836, pp. 72 f.
[21] Locke here uses the term "essence" to refer to "the real internal, but generally in substances unknown, constitution of things, whereon their discoverable qualities depend" (bk. III, chap. 3, sec. 15).
[22] Locke, *op. cit.,* bk. IV, chap. 6, sec. 12.
[23] Locke, *op. cit.,* bk. III, chap. 3, sec. 8.

come. With each higher level of abstraction it becomes more difficult to determine the specific referent for the symbol. So vague is this reference, in fact, that when our speech consists mainly of those higher orders of abstractions, it becomes little more than meaningless jargon. "Watch out for and avoid abstract words one is inclined to capitalize, as they are tending to become shibboleths, empty of precise meaning." [24]

The confusion arising from such vague use of terms was recognized even by Cicero, who raised the question in connection with his discussion of the Attic style of oratory. " 'My aim is,' you say, 'to imitate Attic models.' Which, pray? for they are not all of the same type. Who, for example, are more unlike than Demosthenes and Lysias? Than either of them and Hyperides, than all of these and Aeschines? Whom then are you going to imitate? If one only, do you mean that all the others did not speak pure Attic? If all, how can you imitate them when they are so unlike each other?" [25]

The Atticism of Thucydides, Cicero says, is very good "if you are thinking of writing history, but not if you contemplate pleading cases." In the category of Attic are many qualities: "One must beware not to overlook the gradations and dissimilarities, the force and variety of Attic orators."

ABSTRACTIONS AND IDENTITY. The failure to recognize the significance of abstractions arises, at least in part, from an identity between things which is implied in the identity of terms, and which A. B. Johnson pointed out more than a century ago. "Language implies identities to which nature conforms not," he said. In the field of medicine, he pointed out, "the most skillful physician is often defeated by the individualities of nature. Physicians have long detected these individualities, and deemed them anomalies of nature. The anomaly is, however, in language, which unites under one name, as identities, what is only partially identical." [26] This identity of language refers not only to words, but to propositions as well. "If I assert that George is good, you may assent. Under the verbal identity, I may refer to actions of George that are unknown to you; and you may refer to actions unknown to me. Nay, the actions to which I refer might cause you to reprobate George." [27]

[24] Frank Ford Nesbit, *Language, Meaning and Reality*, New York, Exposition Press, 1955, p. 73.

[25] Cicero, *Brutus*, tr. by G. L. Hendrickson, Loeb Classical Library, Cambridge, Harvard University Press, 1939, LXXXII, secs. 284–291, pp. 247–255. Included in the volume is also Cicero's *Orator*, tr. by H. M. Hubbell.

[26] Johnson, *op. cit.*, pp. 66 f.

[27] *Ibid.*, p. 76. *Reprobate:* "To disapprove with detestation or marks of extreme dislike; to disallow; to reject. . . . We disapprove of slight faults and improprieties; we reprobate what is mean or criminal." (*Webster's Dictionary*, Revised and Enlarged by Chauncey A. Goodrich, Springfield, Mass., G. & C. Merriam, 1849.)

This identity of things which is implied in language, and which leads to complications in abstracting, is further illustrated by Lasswell and his collaborators:

How much "meaning" is there in any given word, slogan, sentence? Suppose, for instance, that we are told by historians of the spread of "Christianity" during the past two thousand years. In what sense is this a meaningful statement in view of the variety of interpretations which have been given to the Old and New Testaments? Does it make much sense to treat of Christianity or Mohammedanism as homogeneous when they are so variously understood? [28]

INDEXING.   A device which has been recommended to aid in avoiding the ambiguity resulting from such abstractions has been called "indexing." [29] For example, one familiar type of organization prominent in economic affairs is known as the "labor union." While there are various types of groups falling under this classification, there are enough points of similarity to enable us to abstract the common characteristics; and so to all groups possessing these characteristics we give the name "labor union." So far, no necessary ambiguity has been created. But the identity among such organizations implied by the identical name given to all exists only in certain of these characteristics. We are likely to neglect an equally important fact that, although there are many common elements that belong to all such groups, there are also many elements which a given group may have that the others do not possess. The "identities" implied in the language simply do not exist among the different labor unions. We can indicate these differences, or that differences do exist, by indexing them as labor union$_1$, labor union$_2$; but despite the differences among them, they still possess many common elements.

Now suppose we want to discuss the practices of labor unions. We read of one which has called what appears to be an unnecessary strike, resulting in enforced unemployment of its own members, and thousands of others in allied industries as well. As a result of this action we may irrationally condemn the practices of labor unions in general, instead of limiting our censure to labor union$_1$ which has called the strike. We forget that labor union$_2$ has succeeded in adjusting its complaint and has continued at work to the profit and satisfaction of everyone concerned. Capitalist$_1$ has engaged in certain nefarious transactions and we blame all capitalists, regardless of the fact that capitalist$_2$ has conducted his business with the utmost honesty and with regard to the highest ethical principles.

[28] Harold D. Lasswell, Daniel Lerner, and Ithiel de Sola Pool, *The Comparative Study of Symbols*, Stanford, Stanford University Press, 1952, p. 9.

[29] Alfred Korzybski, *Science and Sanity*, Lancaster, Pa., Science Press, 1933, p. 135.

In his discussion of the Attic style of oratory, then, Cicero might have indexed his term so as to differentiate

$$Atticism_{Pericles}, Atticism_{Lysias}, Atticism_{Aeschines}, Atticism_{Demosthenes},$$

and so on, to indicate the "gradations and dissimilarities, the force and variety," which he points out are to be discovered among Attic orators, and which make any rigid description impossible.

Both political and economic words are abstractions. They "lift out" or "take out" . . . of the total complex of social activity a certain aspect. In reality these aspects are interrelated and interconnected parts of a single whole, society. But if we are going to talk and think about these different aspects of society clearly and avoid hopeless confusion we must abstract them. That is the nature of the thinking process and one function of symbolization, and we must keep our referents and the words which refer to them separate and distinct. If we do not, we soon arrive at a point where we are calling different things by the same names or the same things by different names, at which time intelligent discussion of opposed theories and points of view becomes impossible and name-calling and vituperation is the only form which the energies of our talking and thinking impulses can take to express themselves.[30]

Abstractions are unavoidable in the use of language; they make language possible. What is important is that in our use of words we should be conscious of the fact that they are abstractions, and that we should also be aware of the level at which we are doing the abstracting. As we go from lower to higher levels more and more of the specific characteristics are omitted until we finally arrive at a level where, unless we are especially conscious of how far we have gone in our abstracting from the actual object or event, our language will be meaningless, even to ourselves.

When we say that a person is an American, just what do we mean? What does it take to be an American? What are the common characteristics of all the people to whom the term can properly be applied? Or are there several different groups of such characteristics so that people possessing any of these various groups can be called American? Did Woodrow Wilson possess them? William Jennings Bryan? Jesse James? Al Capone? If a native of Sweden or of Switzerland or of Hungary or Denmark becomes a naturalized citizen of the United States, does that make him an American? Is every subject of the British Crown British? If an Englishman takes up his permanent residence in Canada, is he still British or is he now a Canadian?

These examples are presented to show something of the difficulties we

---

[30] Nesbit, *op. cit.*, p. 101.

encounter when we place too much reliance upon rigid classifications and attempt to say that a given object belongs categorically in one class or another, or to apply definite and fixed terms to these classes. At the same time there seems to be no necessity for excluding the copulative *is* entirely from our daily vocabulary in making such classifications, particularly for purposes of identification. A strange aircraft flies over the house. "What is that, son?" the father asks. The lad cocks his eyes skyward and with scarcely a pause replies, "That is a B-52, Dad." Now he has never seen a B-52 at a range closer than several thousand feet; he has never looked inside one, probably knows only generally if at all how a jet engine works, and nothing of the details of control; in fact, there is vastly more about the craft that he does not know than there is that he does. He is saying in effect, "From what I can see from this distance, and from the peculiar roar of the engines, it apparently has those characteristics belonging to a particular type of mechanism to which the name B-52 is given." There is more to it than that, of course; but he abbreviates the whole thing into a single, short statement of identification, "That is a B-52." And it is very doubtful if in the abbreviation he has laid the foundation for serious confusion. As a matter of fact, even a strict general semanticist would probably be constrained to say the plane is a B-52, a statement which is true if and only if the plane is in fact a B-52.

Two-Valued Orientation.   Closely related to the problem of abstraction is another question of classification and of evaluation exemplified in the expression "either . . . or." We are accustomed to thinking in terms of opposites, as if events or objects could be definitely and finally placed in the one category or the other. Is a given act good or evil? Is a certain object black or white? Is a certain branch of knowledge useful or useless? Was Lincoln or Washington the greater? In the traditional debate we say, "Resolved, that this program should be adopted," or "Resolved, that this economic principle is wise," and then proceed to discuss the question as if it had only two mutually exclusive sides.

As has been emphasized in general semantics, these inquiries and similar ones are based on the assumption that it is possible to give two and only two values to any given experience. Events are not so easily and so rigidly classifiable. It is quite possible that a given act may have some characteristics that are "good" and some that are "bad," as well as some that are neither. Much depends on one's individual way of looking at it. There are still many people who feel that the playing of a violin in church is sacrilegious. To most people, perhaps, the act in itself is neither good nor evil. There are many shadings between black and white; the psychologist recognizes a multitude of shades of grey.

OPPOSITENESS. As should be quite obvious, there are various types of oppositeness. That between black and white is a different kind from that between, say, life and death, east and west, coming and going, wise and unwise. We tend to treat all these as if they were alike, when as a matter of fact, in many instances the opposites are no more than the extremes in an extended scale of values. In the discussion of personality, as has been pointed out (Chapter VII), one could not assume that people could be fitted into a bimodal distribution of types known as "introverts" and "extroverts"; these were the extremes in a larger Gaussian distribution which recognizes that there is an infinite number of gradations between the one limit and the other.

Much the same principle holds true in many of the two-valued classifications which we express as "either . . . or." Whether one is well or ill depends on many factors: the point of reference, previous condition, one's age, and so on. Without a consideration of these factors the question as to whether one is well or not well is without meaning.

This principle has a direct application in our political, economic, and social thinking. In the minds of many, all labor leaders are rascals and dictators in their own organizations, and would-be dictators for the rest of us. Others apparently cannot rid themselves of the idea that all capitalists are selfish, thoroughly predatory, and without the least concern for their employees or the public. To many Democrats everything connected with or proposed by the Republicans is anathema, and many Republicans feel that all the ills of our present economic status are due to the ineptitude of the Democrats, while Socialists of all varieties can see no good in either. Both Democrats and Republicans view with horror any proposal which they can label as "socialistic" or "communistic," whether the suggested program comes or does not come within any theory or practice held by either the Socialists or the Communists, and despite the fact that many proposals rejected forty years ago as "socialistic" have since been adopted with much acclaim. It could be said, of course, that for Democrat, Republican, or Socialist one could with equal validity substitute the names of any other dissident groups.

MULTIVALUED ORIENTATION. What is necessary in our thinking, as well as in our speech, is to develop a multivalued orientation. In other words, to most questions of policy there are not two but many sides. Terms have not one but many meanings. Between many "opposites" are any number of gradations. Any intelligent public discussion recognizes that very seldom does a single solution represent the only answer to problems of general concern. Formal debate, which seeks a categorical *yes* or *no* answer to the proposition being argued, is in many instances being replaced by a multi-valued consideration of the question at issue. We are learning that neither total condemnation nor unlimited approval is always, or even often, appropriate to the act.

Community of Reference

As a recognized semantic principle, it is not enough that the referent be clear to the person using the symbol. There must be, on the part of all the individuals in the social group concerned, a community of past experiences with which these symbols have been associated. "The bare fact that language consists of sounds which are *mutually intelligible* is enough of itself to show that its meaning depends upon connection with a shared experience. . . . Similar ideas or meanings spring up because both persons are engaged as partners in an action where what each does depends upon and influences what the other does." [31]

Complete Community Impossible. The point made by Dewey has been developed very effectively and interestingly by Lee: "The one thing people tend to take for granted when talking to others is that they understand each other. . . . In the give-and-take of talk things go fast, and one is so busy organizing his reply that he doesn't take the time to make sure he knows what he is replying to. This is unfortunate because it often means that, instead of talking with others, people talk past or by-pass each other." [32] In order for any communication to be intelligible it is essential that the language mean approximately the same thing to all persons involved.

For example, most people in all civilized countries have had experiences with tables. But not all people associate that particular class of objects with the symbol *table*. The word *table*, then, can have reference to such an object only among those people in whose past experiences the two, object and symbol, have been associated. It makes a difference, too, whether the word is an auditory or a visual symbol. The French spoken word, *table*, may be as unintelligible as the German *Tisch* to an American who knows neither French nor German. But the printed word in French is identical in form with the English, and would arouse much the same response if both were isolated.

[31] John Dewey, *Democracy and Education*, New York, The Macmillan Company, 1916, p. 18.
[32] Irving J. Lee, *How to Talk with People*, New York, Harper & Brothers, 1952, chap. II.

Similarly, the form of the German word *Gift* (poison) is the same, except for the capitalization, as that of the English word *gift* (present). But to the German *Gift* is something to be avoided, whereas to the English-speaking person a *gift* is something to be appreciated.

The problem of translation, of finding a word in one language for a word in a different language, is a complicated and difficult one. . . . With simple, concrete words like "house," "tree," "father," "water," which are universal elements in human experience, there is little difficulty. The principal component in these words is their denotation. . . . But with the more abstract words of literature, science, and philosophy, where the component of connotation is more important, the difficulty increases, almost in proportion to the abstractness. These words like "mercy," "justice," "Jehovah," "the Divine Spirit," "atom," "organism," "Zeitgeist," "zenith," "cause," and the like denote ideas or feelings. . . . It is apparent that a perfect translation of many such words is almost impossible. This is the advantage of knowing one or two languages fairly well in addition to one's native tongue. One thus understands many almost untranslatable words. For a Westerner English, French, and German, which have been called by the Germans *die drei Kultursprachen*, are almost indispensable. We have today no common, exact language, as the medieval scholars had in Latin, or the ancient world in Attic Greek, or the Islamic world has in classical Arabic.[33]

No two persons can possibly have had identical experiences. Different people will have had different experiences, for example, with tables, so that when the word is used it will refer to one composite of experiences (or one concept) for one, and to a somewhat different composite of experiences (or one concept) for another. For this reason, words cannot possibly have identical meanings to two or more people; the concepts are inevitably different.

It is for this reason that, as Schlauch has pointed out:

. . . the act [of communication] is and must always be an approximation. . . . The reason is simple. It is impossible for any two persons ever to have learned the same word under precisely the same circumstances; occupying, as it were, the same space in time, and apprehending the new term with precisely the same background. Therefore each will take it into his consciousness ringed about with a special context of associations, differing from the associations of everyone else hearing it.[34]

One can hardly avoid wondering how she found the principle she has so stated operating in her chosen life behind the "Iron Curtain."

General Similarity Essential.   But there is sufficient similarity in the past experiences connected with a given symbol so that ordinarily there is little

[33] Nesbit, *op. cit.*, pp. 84–85.
[34] Margaret Schlauch, *The Gift of Tongues*, New York, Modern Age Books, 1942, pp. 113 f.

difficulty in understanding what we are saying one to another. The general similarity of these experiences, giving rise to the approximate identity of the meanings of the word for the whole group using it, makes up what is called the denotation of that word; while the individuality of experiences, giving rise to differences in concepts, and hence in the meanings of the word among the people who use it, makes up what is called the connotation of that word. It is the denotation of words that give their logical meanings; they are generally understood. It is the connotations that give color, richness, and more subtle suggestion of meaning; they are individual. But it should be understood that not even the denotations of a word can be exactly the same for any two persons.

Because of emotional components usually involved in our experiences, the connotations of words ordinarily imply a fairly strong affective element. Many of the words used daily are employed more for their connotative than for their denotative values. One may *walk, stagger, dash, plunge, creep, drift, stalk, pace, plod, strut, march*; the specific word one uses is not only descriptive of the manner of personal locomotion; it arouses an emotional response depending on the individual attitude that has been built up in connection with these terms. Both speakers and writers often consciously use words "rich in connotation," because they are interested both in arousing ideas and in stimulating emotional responses.

Higher Levels of Abstraction.   At the lower levels of abstraction there is little likelihood of creating confusion, even though there is not always agreement. In the North, "skating," unless qualified, refers to skating on ice; in the South, where ice skating has until recently been almost unknown, the unqualified term refers to roller skating. It would not be difficult to find a number of words habitually used in different senses by different people. On the whole, however, people do manage to understand each other with reasonable satisfaction at the lower levels of abstraction.

Illustrative of the lack of community of reference in the meanings of abstract terms caused by dissimilar associations is the following:

Take, for instance, such a term as liberty. Floating up there in the stratosphere, it can mean all things to all men. Ogden and Richards [*The Meaning of Meaning*] would bring it down to earth by asking, *liberty to do what*? "Your liberty to swing your arms," a great jurist is reputed to have said, "ends where my nose begins." "Liberty," like "freedom," "democracy," and "justice" is only a vague sentiment, amiable or quarrelsome, until a referent is found where the idea can be put to work —liberty to criticize the government, freedom to travel, democracy in elections with secret ballot, the justice of letting an accused person cross-examine his accusers, and so on. Political speeches are normally studded with lofty terms which do not have a referent in a carload. Committees of the United Nations have been trying for two years, without success, to define "aggression." They can try for 200 years with no better luck, unless they start with referents and build cautious generalizations from there. . . .[35]

It is not difficult to understand why differences in concept at the higher levels of abstraction are so likely to cause confusion. With each step upward in the scale of abstraction we get further and further away from our immediate experiences. The result is that, even when two people are clear in their own minds regarding the referents to the terms they individually use, there is less and less likelihood of their having sufficient community of reference to enable one to grasp readily the meaning of the other. When phrases are used to refer to some process or practice, this community of reference is still more remote.

Again referring to the word *democracy*, Stuart Gerry Brown has pointed out that when studied it will be found "to be serving as a sort of mask for a great many quite different things." In any political campaign we are told by both sides that the preservation of democracy is dependent upon the election of certain candidates and the adoption of certain courses of action. "Nothing is easier than to identify events and things in which we have an interest with democracy-as-abstraction, and, in turn, to confuse democracy-as-abstraction with democracy-as-method, that is, government by consent. . . ."[36] If we are willing to agree to Brown's statement that "the controls upon social evolution are determined by free discussion of men, events, and things in the clear light of day, followed by consent to the will of the majority," as "the most useful meaning of democracy," we may have something of a community of reference upon which to base further consideration of proposals having to do with the application of the principle of democracy. We are, of course, equally free to agree upon any other statement which reduces the abstraction *democracy* to things and events in a time-space world.

Our daily speech uses a large number of such terms, the meanings of which are not only vague and undetermined, but are widely different among their users. Capital, capitalist, labor, *laissez faire*, business, government in business, politics, are only a few chosen at random. To some people "religion" means the acceptance of a creed, a set of beliefs; to others it refers to the observance

[35] Stuart Chase, *The Proper Study of Mankind*, rev. ed., New York, Harper & Brothers, 1956, pp. 285 ff.
[36] Stuart Gerry Brown, *We Hold These Truths*, New York, Harper & Brothers, 1941, pp. 2–8.

of certain rites which have been established by authorities in a "church"; to still others it consists in a code of ethics, a general pattern of attitudes and of behavior toward other people. Our discussions are likely to center more about the words themselves than about the things, events, methods, which they should represent. We argue heatedly over some term, only to discover that we are not talking about the same thing at all, that there is no community of reference, no common understanding of the meaning of the term. Not only the connotations but the denotations as well are so different that it is impossible, in many such instances, to arrive at any agreement. Any word can be used arbitrarily in any sense in which we may want to use it, but for any kind of effective communication every party to the process must have a clear understanding of the sense in which it is used on a particular occasion.

Without the postulate that speaker and listener are able to direct their attention to the same thing, the very notion of speech is an absurdity, and any rational theory on the subject becomes impossible. But room must be left for such contingencies as contradiction and differences of feeling as between speaker and listener. . . . It is indispensable for the success of the utterance that Mary should see the thing meant by James in its essential lines, but her own counterpart may reveal a somewhat changed and deepened perspective.[37]

As Locke stated the principle back in the seventeenth century, ". . . unless a man's words excite the same *ideas* in the hearer which he makes them stand for in speaking, he does not speak intelligibly."[38]

"Basic improvement in communication is therefore dependent upon the attainment of a body of signs . . . which have a high degree of similarity of signification to different members of a community, and upon the attainment of skill in using these signs to make clear the particular signification which a given individual intends to communicate in a specific situation."[39]

Context

The third essential in determining the meaning of a word is its place in the context, that is, the total pattern of symbolization, together with all the other factors that enter into the situation in which the word is used, including the interests and previous experiences of the speaker or listener. Definitions of words given in the dictionaries are for the most part their denotations, based

[37] Alan H. Gardiner, *The Theory of Speech and Language*, New York, Oxford University Press, 1932, p. 81.

[38] Locke, *op. cit.*, bk. III, chap. 2, sec. 8.

[39] Charles William Morris, *Signs, Language and Behavior*, Englewood Cliffs, N.J., Prentice-Hall, 1946, pp. 120–121.

on general similarities of association. The connotations of these words are different for every person who has had experiences with these symbols. Most words have several dictionary definitions (denotations), however. For example, the word *get* has no fewer than fourteen different definitions, within each of which are numerous others. This word is used in such senses as *acquiring* (to *get* glory) *suffering* (to *get* a broken arm); *capturing* or *catching* (to *get* a string of fish); *obligation* (you've *got* to do this); *permission* (to *get* to do something); *persuading* (to *get* someone to do something); *removal* of an object (*get* it away from here); *store up* (to *get* the hay in); *donning* of clothes (to *get* one's hat on); *completion* (we'll *get* that done); *arrival* (to *get* home); *become* (to *get* older); *removal* of one's person (to *get* out). And these are not all by any means.

In addition to the numerous denotations of a large number of words in our vocabulary, we have what are called "homonyms," words pronounced alike, but different even in their denotations. Following are examples of such homonyms:

altar	bare	beer	berry
alter	bear	bier	bury
coarse	cast	dear	ferry
course	caste	deer	fairy[40]
foul	flew	haul	laps
fowl	flue	hall	lapse
	flu		
load	mail	nose	plain
lode	male	knows	plane
rite	rein	to	urn
right	rain	too	earn
write	reign	two	
wright			
vain	sole		
vein	soul		

In these illustrations the different words are spelled differently; but the several uses of the word *get*, with its fourteen or more different denotations, as indicated by dictionary definitions, are just as divergent in meaning as are any of the words in the list above, simply because of differences in denotation.

---

[40] Many people pronounce *fairy* and *ferry* differently.

When one studies an unabridged dictionary, such as the *New International*, one cannot but be amazed by the large number of different general senses in which so many of our common words are or have been actually used. It is true that many of these definitions are obsolete or colloquial; the words are no longer used in all of the senses in which they once were used, and in others they have no literary prestige. Yet these words have had at one time references to experiences, and still have, as they are used colloquially. Being obsolete simply means one of three things: (1) certain words have been replaced by other symbols; or (2) in many instances, as the need for such symbolization ceased, the symbols themselves have gradually dropped out of use in connection with those experiences; or (3) the words have undergone either "pejoration" or "amelioration," in that they are no longer used in their former significance. Of seven definitions for the word "silly," six are obsolete or dialectal (which, in this case, means that the word is used in the given sense only among a very limited group of people).

When Hamlet says, "Thus conscience does make cowards of us all," he is not using the word *conscience* with any reference to a sense of guilt or remorse, but rather in the sense of *thoughtful meditation*. "What Hamlet says, therefore," according to Judd, "is that we are all prone to think matters over before taking the risks of a future which we do not know, and as we consider all the hazards involved, we have less and less courage to take the final step." [41]

Illustrative of degeneration (pejoration) in the meaning of words is *hussy*, which is descended directly from *housewife*, an entirely respectable appellation. Many words have within the past few years undergone a similar process of degeneration. *Pious* has become quite altered, at least in connotation, for a great many people, from its former sense of "honestly and sincerely religious," and now carries with it a suggestion of hypocrisy. *Oratory* and *eloquence* have likewise fallen from their once high estate; and *rhetoric*, as has been pointed out, often refers to bombast, the use of flowery language for purposes of effect. *Elocution*, for which no satisfactory substitute has ever been found, is in exceedingly ill repute, except in England, where it is still widely used in the sense of the delivery of spoken discourse.

Such degeneration often, though perhaps not always, results from exaggeration and artificiality, and more attention to form than to substance. *Elocution* died out because of the excesses and artificialities of those who attempted to practice the art without understanding or appreciating its essence.

Schlauch points out other types of semantic change which have taken place

---

[41] Charles Hubbard Judd, *The Psychology of Social Institutions*, New York, The Macmillan Company, 1926, p. 205.

over a period of time. One of these is called "amelioration," which occurs when the meaning is elevated, so to speak. A "bishop" was once merely an overseer; an "angel" was a messenger; "cathedral" is derived from the Greek word meaning *chair*; and a "marshall" was a stableboy—one who looked after the mares.[42]

Another type of change is *narrowing* or *restricting*. A "garage" was originally any place for storing things. "Fruit" and "fruition" both come from "fruor," to enjoy. The latter term now has something of that significance, but the former is largely restricted to such things as apples, peaches, pears, and the like.

Still other types of semantic change are constantly taking place in the meanings of words; but those cited will illustrate the point that meanings are not stable, that in considering the context it is necessary to consider the word in relation to the age or period in which it was or is used.

It might seem that unending confusion would result from such a multitudinous use of words, that there could be no certainty as to the specific referent to be attached to a given symbol. Such bewilderment undoubtedly occurs in many instances. There is just as much confusion resulting from the varied uses of the word *cast*, for example, as from any of the words spelled differently, that is, from any of the homonyms; more, in fact, for there is not even the visual clue by which to differentiate the words. One would not easily mistake *rite* for *right*, or *to* for *two*, if one saw them in print.

While some confusion is experienced occasionally in the case of these homonyms, in general we have little difficulty in determining the particular sense in which a word is used. That form of wit known as the "pun" is an ambiguity based upon the similarity of the sounds of words. We are usually able to fix upon the correct significance of a word by its *context*, its use in relation to the rest of the sentence or the complete discourse. If one speaks, for example, of a *bass* voice, no one is likely, except through willful misinterpretation, to attach the wrong denotation. Similarly, *base*ball has only a remote likelihood of being thought to have any reference to singing, and no intelligent person makes such a reference. The point is that we can and do use this one word (pronounced [beɪs]), and many other such words, in a variety of contexts so that it may have a variety of meanings. The same is true of any kind of stimulus, symbolic or otherwise. Stimuli never appear in isolation, but always in patterns. We may respond to a stimulus pattern containing a given element in one situation, while a similar element in a different pattern would

[42] Schlauch, *op. cit.*, pp. 119 ff. See also Chapter VI of this text, "The Linguistic Basis of Speech."

elicit a quite different reaction. The significance of context in the meaning of words is identical with the significance of the pattern or configuration in which any given element may appear.

It should not be surprising, therefore, that context plays such an important role in determining the signification of any word. There are, as a matter of fact, comparatively few nontechnical words in the English language which do not have more than one referent. This is true not only of the English language, however; Quintilian, writing in the first century A.D., pointed out that "in the opinion of certain philosophers there is not a single word which has not a diversity of meanings." [43]

Just as the function of any stimulus, then, is largely dependent upon its place in a total pattern, in the same way the meaning of a word is to a great degree dependent upon its place in the context. In isolation the word may be well-nigh meaningless because it has so many possible meanings. It covers or refers to such a range of experiences that it is impossible to fix upon any referent. But when that word is placed in a context, as a stone is placed in a total situation—be it the path or the laboratory—then and only then does it come to have specific reference. [44]

Despite the context, however, ambiguity often results from the use of language. Legal phraseology well illustrates this point. In the attempt to set down statements which will be denotatively precise, lawyers and lawmakers frequently leave some loophole through which varied interpretations can be put on the law as it was written, and the evident intention of the framers of the bill is thwarted. Attempts have been made by the courts to determine, from the legislative debates on a given bill, just what the intent of the law-makers was, and decisions have been rendered on the basis of that intent rather than on the wording of the bill itself. Since the lawmakers are unable to know in advance every situation in which the law may be applicable, "technicalities" arise by which criminals are so often able to escape the penalties for their crimes. [45] As of this writing opinion seems to be divided on the question of whether the growing attitude that "The law is what the courts say it is" may not in fact represent a tendency on the part of the courts to by-pass that division of government known as the legislative.

The many interpretations which are placed on literary and Biblical passages

[43] Quintilian, *Institutes of Oratory*, tr. by H. E. Butler, Loeb Classical Library, Cambridge, Harvard University Press, 1921–1922, bk. VII, chap. 9.

[44] See S. I. Hayakawa, *Language in Thought and Action*, New York, Harcourt, Brace and Company, 1949, pp. 60–68.

[45] See Felix S. Cohen, "Transcendental nonsense and the functional approach," in *Language, Meaning and Maturity, op. cit.*, pp. 184–214.

furnish still other examples of the argument. In these, however, the differences are more likely to be the result of variations in connotation rather than in denotation of the words.

The meanings of most of the words we use are learned from context, either verbal or direct or both. No boy has to be told what the word "baseball" means; he learns to associate the word with the game as he plays it or sees it played. It is not necessary to look up the definition of every word in the dictionary in order to discover clues as to its meaning; we get many of those meanings from the context, and the more contexts we encounter in which the word appears, the more extensive grows our understanding of the word itself. For many such words no fine analysis may be necessary, but it is a valuable practice frequently to determine the referent for some of the words as they are used in a particular context.

Manner of Utterance

A fourth determinant of the meanings of words is the manner in which they are uttered. This is particularly operative when words are placed in a context, in which case a change of inflection or of emphasis may entirely alter the meaning of a whole passage. If one reads the well-known line, "All the world's a stage," from *As You Like It*, altering the inflection of each of the three accented words, *all, world's, stage*, from a simple rising to a falling inflection, the line can be read in eight different ways, no two of which have the same meanings. As in this particular instance, context helps in determining the most appropriate inflectional pattern for the line; but even in the same context the same sentence can be read with a variety of logical meanings. No two experienced, trained readers will read a passage in exactly the same way; it does not mean the same to both, and in expressing the differences in meaning the passage has for them they will use a different manner of utterance.

It is because of the significance of inflectional and other patterns in spoken language that quoting the words of another often fails entirely to give an adequate clue to his intent. "I'll get you for that," playfully spoken, may when repeated be so uttered as to indicate that a threat has been made against one's very life. "You said thus-and-so," "Yes, those were the words I used, but that isn't what I said." And in the absence of a recording of the speech, and an objective interpretation of the tonal pattern and its significance, there is no way of recalling those words in order to hear again just how they were spoken and thus to arrive more nearly at a fair understanding of the speaker's meaning. Deliberate, intentional distortion of the mode of utterance is no less reprehensible than willful misquotation by using different words altogether.

Illustrative of the effect of context on the manner of utterance is a German playlet, *Come Here*.[46] In this sketch an actress is applying to a dramatic producer for a role in a play. In order to test her ability he suggests a number of situations to which her verbal response is to consist simply of the words, "come here," to be spoken in the manner appropriate to the specific situation. He suggests no fewer than twenty different types of situational context; and the actress utters those two words in twenty different ways, no one of which would be suitable for any other situation than the one in which it was used, and no two of which mean the same thing.

Personal Attitude

The example given above introduces the matter of the two aspects of meaning. So far we have been discussing denotations primarily. In the playlet *Come Here*, however, no fewer than twenty different meanings are suggested. Wherein lies the difference?

The difference lies to a great extent in the fifth determinant of meaning, the *personal attitude* involved. "Meaning for speech," says Woolbert, "is *always twofold*. . . . It is not enough that a speaker use a type of expression that carries only a logical meaning; he must show the hearer *how he himself feels about the matter*. He must not only let the hearer know *what the idea* is, but *how well or ill he himself thinks of it*."[47]

Psychologists are generally agreed that there is no such thing as a "pure idea" without its emotional aspect, its "affective tone," so to speak. If we *think* about things at all, we also *feel* about them. And while the words we are using may express with some precision what we are thinking, they also have this personal, emotional aspect of meaning.

In his discussion of these two aspects of meaning, Woolbert goes on to show that while "the expression of thought content varies little from one speaker to another," the difference in the personal attitude of different speakers or readers will result in quite different presentations of the same material. When a group reads, the effect is often colorless; but a single individual will put into the reading meanings that the group will leave out. It is this element of personal attitude that "makes a skilled interpreter

[46] Quoted in Alice Evelyn Craig, *The Speech Arts*, New York, The Macmillan Company, 1927, pp. 400–403.

[47] Charles Henry Woolbert, *The Fundamentals of Speech*, rev. ed., New York, Harper & Brothers, 1927, pp. 195 f.

interesting with the very same poem by which the unskilled bores his audience," because different meanings are injected into the same material.

While the number of logical meanings (denotations) of words may be manifold, the number of personal attitudes (connotations)—the ways in which we may feel about the things we think and talk about—are measurable only by the number of experiences with affective content which people may have had with those things. Because the variety of such experiences is well-nigh infinite, these connotations themselves are likewise innumerable.

There is, of course, considerable overlapping in these last two determinants, as indeed there is among all five of them. In the expression of the personal or affective component of meaning the manner of utterance is of extreme importance. But it also happens that, in speech, even the logical aspect of meaning itself often depends largely upon such vocal elements as phrasing, emphasis, and inflection.

The relatively independent attributes of vocal tone (quality or timbre, intensity or "force," time, and pitch) have been analyzed by Woolbert in relation to their influence on the two aspects of meaning, logical and emotional.[48]

Changes in Quality. Changes in the quality or timbre of the voice are most significant in expressing and stimulating the emotional aspect of meaning. It is a matter of common experience that we express different moods differently. Gaiety takes a different kind of vocal quality from gloom. In original speaking, solemn, serious, weighty matters are discussed in tones different from those we use in light, gay, inconsequential affairs. We tell ghost stories in hollow, sepulchral voices and humorous anecdotes in lighter, brighter tones. To use one type of quality when another is demanded would be to alter the essential meaning of the whole discourse; it would create what might be an entirely false atmosphere. Sound and sense would conflict; the listener would be entirely unable to appreciate the mood or to acquire the appropriate attitude. Quality is only slightly concerned in logical meanings.

Changes in Intensity. Although intensity or loudness is significant in the expression of attitudes, it has somewhat more to do with the logical aspects of meaning than does quality. Emphasis may be either logical or emotional or both; in either case it often takes only a slight shading to affect the meaning significantly. Shifting the emphasis on the three accented words in the line "All the world's a stage" will result in quite different readings, and hence quite different meanings.

[48] Woolbert, *op. cit.*, chap. X.

Changes in intensity or loudness can be applied in various ways; in some of these accompanying changes in pitch also occur. First, what is called *accent* consists of increased loudness together, usually, with a rise in pitch, given to a certain syllable of a word to satisfy the convention of correctness in pronunciation.[49] Shifting the accent may also change the meaning of the word. Second, in *emphasis* the increased loudness and raised pitch are applied to certain words or phrases in the sentence. It is concerned with meaning rather than correctness; shifting the emphasis nearly always changes the meaning of the sentence. Third, one may simply speak loudly or softly. Some subjects call for vigorous treatment, introducing the emotional or affective component into the changes in intensity. Others call for milder, softer tones, while in some instances the voice may be lowered almost to inaudibility. The same passage may express, according to the way it is uttered, simple, relatively uncolored information or polite request, or a challenge or strong demand.

Changes in Time. Variations in the time factor may be used to convey both logical and emotional aspects of meaning. Rapid utterance, for example, represents in the speaker, and creates in the listener, a different attitude from slow, measured speech.

Variations in time may be achieved in three ways: first, by using shorter or longer phrases or "thought units," thus varying the number of pauses between them; second, by varying the length of the pauses between phrases; and third, by varying the general rate of speaking, for example, from 120 words per minute to 160. (See also Chapter II, p. 131.)

Emphasis, usually achieved by a change in intensity and a rise in pitch, is usually accompanied by a lengthening of the sounds—the words or syllables to be stressed.

Changes in Pitch. Changes in pitch, according to Woolbert, are primarily instrumental in the expression of the logical aspect of meaning, although they have some emotional significance as well, especially when extremely wide or extremely narrow ranges are used. Lynch found by careful experimentation that both experienced and inexperienced speakers use the widest inflections for anger and the narrowest for grief. One might almost say that excitatory emotional states are expressed in extremely wide variations, whereas inhibitory emotional states are expressed in extremely narrow variations.

[49] See R-M. S. Heffner *General Phonetics*, Madison, The University of Wisconsin Press, 1952, pp. 228–230; Kenneth L. Pike, *The Intonation of American English*, Ann Arbor, University of Michigan Press, 1946, Sections 3 and 4. Authorities are not agreed on whether the pitch changes, when they do occur, are meaningfully significant.

Thus there are, we have learned, no fewer than five determinants which contribute to the meanings of words, apart from the inherent nature of the individual: (1) the experience of the individual in associating the symbol with the object, action, relation, or characteristic; (2) the community of these experiences within the entire group using the symbol; (3) the context in which the symbol is placed; (4) the manner of utterance; and (5) the aspect of meaning involved, whether primarily logical or emotional. It is fairly obvious, from this analysis, that language is a highly complex phenomenon. In his book, *Social Organization*, written almost a half-century ago, Cooley devotes an entire section to communication in relation to the social order.[50] "Language," says Judd, "is a social institution. It has evolved through the coöperation of countless generations. It becomes a guide to the thought and effort of every member of the race. . . . Language is a mode of mental procedure. It is not something which we use from time to time; it is the method of our whole mental existence. An individual can no more get away from language than he can empty his mind of ideas."[51] As de Laguna says, "Human speech has become the most complex and highly specialized of all vital functions. . . . That it has itself become one of the chief human activities which it serves to correlate and coördinate, does not affect its fundamental nature, although it vastly complicates it. . . . It marks in the evolution of life and mind a development as critical as the appearance of the distance receptors."[52]

Extensional and Intensional Use of Language

To have meaning a word or symbol must, as we have seen, have reference; that is, it must stand for some concept which has been built up through the experience of association. As has also been pointed out, the higher the level of abstraction, the further we get from a specific referent; "*The more general our* Ideas *are, the more incomplete and partial they are.*[53] But these abstractions should be traceable back to definite things, actions, relations, or characteristics as they exist in a world of reality. When we make such a use of language, we are using it *extensionally*. In the extensional use of symbols the factor of primary importance is the *fact*, together with the

[50] Charles Horton Cooley, *Social Organization*, 1912, New York, Charles Scribner's Sons, 1912, pt. II, "Communication."

[51] Judd, *op. cit.* By permission of The Macmillan Company, publishers, pp. 207–208.

[52] Grace Andrus de Laguna, *Speech: Its Function and Development*, New Haven, Yale University Press, 1927, p. 20.

[53] Locke, *op. cit.*, bk. III, Chap. 6, Sec. 32.

observation and investigation of events as they actually occur. Once these facts are determined, language can be used to describe them, to discuss them, to put them together into new relations.

The extensional use of language involves much more than mere choice of terms; back of it must be an attitude, a point of view, a willingness to *see* the facts first, and to act on the basis of those facts rather than on the basis of words alone. It involves a recognition that, as Johnson has pointed out, facts themselves are not fixed; they are constantly changing, and they are different for different people. Furthermore, since it is impossible for anyone to know everything about anything, facts are necessarily incomplete, abstractions. At the same time, just as we saw that despite the inevitable changes that take place in the referent for a symbol there is sufficient continuity to permit identification, in much the same way, "Facts change, and yet a semblance of yesterday remains in today's sounds and visions. . . . Generally speaking . . . all the facts within our range do not change so utterly or so suddenly as to leave us dumb with surprise. . . . So long as we remain responsive to the fact of change itself, the ever-changing facts are not, as a rule, unnerving." [54]

"Roughly speaking, to be extensional is to be aware of things, facts, and operations in the way they are related in nature instead of the way they are talked about. The extensionally oriented person differentiates better than the word-minded (intensionally oriented) one." [55]

In *intensional* orientation, on the other hand, we pay more attention to the words themselves than to actual facts; it is the word, rather than the fact, which is of primary importance. We react to the word as if it were the actual thing for which it stands; that is, the word is more than a symbol—it is the thing itself. In general, intensional meanings may be thought of as those which cannot be related to definite referents, which cannot be objectively verified. We hold to untested theories regardless of whether those theories are true to fact, and we use these verbalizations as the basis for proving further theories. Finally, when the actual facts are made known to us, we refuse to modify our attitudes or behavior accordingly. The general semantics discipline attempts to combat all such illogical uses of language.

The history of human thought is filled with illustrations of intensional orientation and its disastrous consequences. Verbal taboos are not limited to primitive peoples by any means. Copernicus incurred the enmity of the clergy of his time by insisting that the earth is not the center of the universe; and

[54] Wendell Johnson, *People in Quandaries*, New York: Harper & Brothers, 1946, pp. 93–99.
[55] Anatol Rapoport, "What is semantics?" in *Language, Meaning and Maturity*, S. I. Hayakawa (ed.), New York, Harper & Brothers, 1954, pp. 3–18.

Galileo was forced to retract his statement of approval because the Copernican theory conflicted with the verbal authority supported by the church. A score or so unfortunates were executed in Salem on the charge of witchcraft. People still plant potatoes in the light (or dark) of the moon; there are relatively few people who do not now and then act upon the basis of some minor or major superstition. Early in the nineteenth century James Rush was insisting that the medical profession followed fancy more than fact in its practice, and even when the facts were available, refused to accept them. Westinghouse had difficulty selling his "air brake" because of the absurdity of believing that "wind" would stop a rapidly moving train.

The theory that higher forms of life develop from lower forms was opposed vigorously on the ground that it conflicted with religious belief. In fact, many relatively recent advances in scientific thought have been opposed on the same basis.

Closely related to the problem of extensional and intensional orientation is the distinction between denotation and connotation. The former may be thought of as having to do with the generally understood referent to the symbol, while the latter may be considered as referring to the individuality of experiences. Connotations usually have a fairly strong affective component. Unfortunately, in many instances we forget the emotional experiences which contributed to the connotations and transfer the emotional attitude directly to the word itself, thereby exhibiting an intensional orientation and use of language. (See page 512.)

Affective attitudes are by no means to be censured; nor does the general semanticist suggest that they are; it would be impossible to avoid them if we would. Their presence does not of itself indicate an unhealthy frame of mind, so long as these attitudes are directed toward the things that aroused them, rather than to the symbols which merely represent those things. Many people, in the earlier years of the Roosevelt administration, favored the "New Deal," quite regardless of the measures proposed under that name. On the other hand, many others opposed the "New Deal," not so much because they objected to every proposal made by its sponsors as because they had transferred their attitude toward measures advocated under the "New Deal" to the term itself. Many people will consistently refuse to vote for a candidate of one political party or the other, regardless of what he may advocate in the interests of social betterment; on the other hand, an appreciable number will support any program to which the label "fair" has been fixed, whether the program justifies the designation or not.

When people reserve their emotional attitudes for the things themselves instead of attaching them to the symbols for those things, a more wholesome frame of mind will ensue and language itself will be more meaningful.

Nothing that has been said should be taken to imply that all language must relate to facts, that it must be based on observation and experimental evidence of verifiable data. To limit ourselves to the purely scientific use of language would be to exclude a vast world of thought and feeling that constitutes a real force in human thought. There is a definite place for the expression of affective states, of ideas not susceptible to objective demonstration in literature, in poetry, essays, fiction, drama, in religion and mythology, in literary criticism, in much of our everyday speaking. So long as such literature is recognized for what it is, and not taken as a description of an observable world of fact, no harm need be done; on the contrary, one may often gain a much deeper understanding and appreciation of many things through the language of literature than through all the scientific descriptions ever written. Wheelwright has made an extended and reasoned differentiation between what he terms *expressive language* or *depth language* on the one hand, and literal language, or *steno-language* on the other.[56] But one who is extensionally oriented will not take the predicaments of Jiggs as a strict biographical account of the episodes in one man's life, or the fantastic adventures of Alley Oop or Li'l Abner as true-to-life narrative. Neither will he take Milton's account of the fall of Lucifer and his cohorts as a verifiable history of events as they occurred before Adam$_1$.

Something of the point of view taken in this discussion of the semantic basis of speech was expressed some sixty years ago by the great teacher of English, George Herbert Palmer:

While we are in training for [precision in language], no word must unpermittedly pass the portal of the teeth. Something like what we mean must never be counted equivalent to what we mean. . . . We have something in mind, yet convey something else to our hearer. And no moral purpose will save us from this untruthfulness unless that purpose is sufficient to inspire the daily drill which brings the power to be true. . . .

But after all, I hope that nobody who hears me will quite agree. There is something enervating in conscious care. Necessary as it is in shaping our purposes, if allowed too direct and exclusive control consciousness breeds hesitation and feebleness. . . . If anybody talking to us visibly studies his words, we turn away. What he says may be well enough as a school exercise, but it is not conversation. Accordingly, if we would have our speech forcible, we shall need to put into it quite as much of audacity as we do of precision, terseness, or simplicity. Accuracy

[56] Philip Wheelwright, *The Burning Bush*, Bloomington, Indiana University Press, 1954.

alone is not a thing to be sought, but accuracy and dash. . . . Pedantry is worse than blundering. . . . Accuracy and dash, then, the combination of the two, must be our difficult aim; and we must not rest satisfied so long as either dwells with us alone.

But are the two so hostile as they at first appear? . . . Supposing we are convinced that words possess no value in themselves, and are correct or incorrect only as they truly report experience, we shall feel ourselves impelled in the mere interest of accuracy to choose them freshly, and to put them together in ways in which they never coöperated before, so as to set forth with distinctness that which just we, not other people, have seen or felt. The reason why we do not naturally have this daring exactitude is probably twofold. We let our experiences be blurred, not observing sharply, or knowing with any minuteness what we are thinking about; and so there is no individuality in our language. And then, besides, we are terrorized by custom, and inclined to adjust what we would say to what others have said before. The cure for the first of these troubles is to keep our eye on our object, instead of on our listener or ourselves; and for the second, to learn to rate the expressiveness of language more highly than its correctness. The opposite of this, the disposition to set correctness above expressiveness, produces that peculiarly vulgar diction known as "school-ma'am English," in which for the sake of a dull accord with usage all the picturesque, imaginative, and forceful employment of words is sacrificed. Of course we must use words so that people can understand them, and understand them, too, with ease; but this once granted, let our language be our own, obedient to our special needs.[57]

As a matter of practical application, the study of the semantic as well as of the general semantic basis of speech should give a better understanding of the principles governing the meanings of the words we employ. It should provide a basis for the avoidance of much of the confusion which results from improper use of language. It should also enable us to detect in the language of others, as well as of ourselves, faulty, inaccurate, vague use of terms. We are assailed on every hand by words whose meanings lack clarity, definiteness; they may even be intentionally misleading. If we know something of how to strip off the abstraction of much of this verbiage and reduce the meanings down to their reference to reality, we may the more easily see how empty of real meaning much of it is.

Illustrative of the abandon with which speakers often broadcast their language is a great deal of political oratory. Relying upon the attitudes held by many if not most people toward the symbols of things instead of the things themselves, some political speakers play upon these attitudes without making any attempt to relate the symbols to a world of reality. While the stimulation

[57] George Herbert Palmer, *Self-Cultivation in English*, Boston, Houghton Mifflin Company, 1909, pp. 14–18. (First published in 1897 by Thomas Y. Crowell.)

of attitudes is not of itself harmful—indeed, it is often necessary to secure acceptance of truth—it should not be mistaken for sound argument and a rational presentation of facts. Neither need the drawing of inferences from these facts be reprehensible, provided the inferences themselves are intelligently and honestly drawn and based on a consideration of as many of the facts as may be available. Reasoning consists of drawing inferences.

In discussing the reasons for the failure to create a lasting peace following the First World War, Raymond Moley points out "fourteen ghastly points of failure." Among these he mentions the following:

... because our leaders' personal honor, pride and prestige became involved in the debate, the true issues were swallowed up by politics. We failed to realize the lack of reality in political thinking, which deals in impressions—in seeming, not being. We put our faith in phrases, in rhetoric, in words. . . . Our learned works on international affairs built a tower of pretentious knowledge upon a conception of the world which belonged to the past.[58]

Thus the neglect of basic semantic principles contributed to a situation which led to the most disastrous conflict the world has ever known.

It could, of course, be pointed out that in this passage Mr. Moley is himself guilty of a gross semantic error in considering *rhetoric* only in the sense of fustian, of bombast, of turgid language "full of sound and fury, signifying nothing," rather than in the classical sense which included, besides effective language, the matter of having something to say. It is said of Aristotle that in his *Rhetoric* his aim was to give effectiveness to truth.

Propaganda

Another use of language which has often been abused is known as *propaganda*. The attempt to influence attitudes and opinion is a matter of everyday experience; we all engage in it nearly every day. Generally, the term may be used to refer to efforts to exert such influence which are persistent, and which are directed toward masses of people rather than toward individuals. Such efforts may or may not be blameless; propaganda itself need not be pernicious. It becomes so when (1) the end results to be attained are unworthy of one's efforts or are opposed to the welfare of humanity; (2) when the methods of persuasion themselves are open to question; (3) when the language used in such persuasive efforts does not represent a world of reality; (4) when the program of persuasion permits no argument; and (5) when the language

[58] Raymond Moley, "The long road ahead," *Vital Speeches* (July 1, 1943), *9*: 567–570.

is rigidly two-valued. As a member of an audience remarked after a particularly vivid portrayal of certain conditions which departed somewhat from known facts, "I feel as if I had been suddenly transported into a new world, for nothing in the world with which I am familiar bears the least resemblance to that which I have just heard described." Of course, all of these methods, and others, are used in the pernicious types of propaganda. Among the many types used may be mentioned the following:

Name-Calling

Name-calling consists generally in the practice of applying opprobrious epithets to the advocates of a given proposal with the intention that the adverse attitude so stimulated will then be transferred to the proposal itself. It often takes the form of applying such epithets to the measure advocated, with the expectation that the attitude generated toward the term by which the measure is known will then be shifted to the measure itself. Designating the Taft-Hartley Law as a "slave-labor law" was such an attempt. Merely labeling a given program or proposal as "radical," or "reactionary," "new-fangled," or "old-fashioned," or attaching to it some other term generally considered to be opprobrious, is often enough to condemn it in many people's minds, regardless of its inherent merits.

It should also be pointed out that the technique of name-calling can be used to build up unjustifiably favorable attitudes as well as unfavorable. One who has acquired, whether earned or not, a reputation for battling against the "interests," or in behalf of the "masses" can often maintain a large and vocal following so long as he can maintain even the fiction of continuing his crusade.

The Red Herring

When former President Truman said that the charges against Alger Hiss were no more than a "red herring," he was saying that these charges were being made in order to draw the attention of the public away from other and more important things that should be taken care of first, things that the accusers might not want brought to public notice. The term may be applied to an attempt to divert the attention from something that, for the time being at least, it may be undesirable to consider. The same technique is used more justifiably by mothers in directing the attention of their children from some mischievous activity to a more constructive one. As it is used in most propaganda, however, the direction is likely to be from the more to the less constructive.

The Repeated Lie

This is a form of propaganda in which the speaker deliberately draws a picture of conditions which is not in accord with reality. The picture may be a total distortion, or it may be made up of elements some of which are true enough to the actuality to give the whole some plausibility. When Hitler charged that all the ills that were besetting Europe, and more particularly the German Reich, were attributable to the Jews, he was drawing a false-to-fact picture of existing conditions, and he repeated the charge over and over. Similarly, when the Communists charge over and over that the Western world is peopled by warmongers, that the laborer there is little if any more than a slave, they are indulging in the form of propaganda known as the repeated lie.

It is not necessary to go back into history to find instances of this type of propaganda. They are heard in every political campaign. When in 1945 the Senate voted to reject the nomination of Aubrey Williams as Rural Electrification Administrator, "The technique of the repeated lie could not have been used more effectively by the Nazis themselves. Day after day United States Senators rose to make charges of 'radicalism,' 'racism,' and 'incompetence' which had been disproved on the same floor in their presence several times before." [59]

Innuendo

Even more reprehensible is the repeated innuendo which suggests, while not specifically stating, that some deplorable or objectionable condition exists, or that a given individual is guilty of something which is never specified; or, if the act or course of conduct is indicated at all, it is only by indirection. It is vicious because defense is impossible: since specific charges have not been made, in specific terms, no one has, it is pointed out, actually said anything at all! A tone of voice in which such innuendoes are cast may be highly expressive; but unfortunately, it is difficult to point out exactly where and how it says one thing while the words spoken would, if written, say something quite different. "Propaganda, even when it sticks to facts, can be slanted by the magic of the human voice. All of which can be accomplished

[59] *The New Republic* (April 2, 1945), *112*: 437.

by emotion and emphasis on words and phrases."[60] Mr. Hoover is in a position to know. But what he has not recognized here is that when so slanted by the voice that false meanings are indicated or conveyed by innuendo, propaganda does not "stick to facts." It should also be pointed out that even written language, as in news reporting, can by choice and arrangement of words so slant the report as to distort the facts completely, or to arouse attitudes quite inappropriate to the situation. One needs only to read the accounts of the same occurrence in two different newspapers (unless taken verbatim from the same news collecting agency) to recognize that news stories are often slanted in accordance with the editorial and political views of the publisher of the paper or magazine.

Propaganda can be appraised adequately if the language used and the manner in which it is used are examined in the light of its reference to a world of reality. Such an evaluation will be materially facilitated if some effort is also made to examine objectively that world of reality so far as possible for oneself, to scrutinize the motives of the speaker, and the social values in the end results to be obtained.

---

[60] Herbert Hoover, "Radio gets a policeman," in "The Early Days of Radio," *American Heritage*, vol. 6, no. 5 (August, 1955), 73–76.

Bibliography

Adams, Harlen M., "Listening," *The Quarterly Journal of Speech* (1938), *24*: 201–211.

Anderson, Harold A., "Teaching the art of listening," *School Review* (1949), *57*: 63–67.

Atkinson, John W., "Exploration using imaginative thought to assess the strength of human motives," in *Nebraska Symposium on Motivation*, Marshall E. Jones (ed.), Lincoln, University of Nebraska Press, 1954, pp. 56–106.

Ayer, A. J., and Others, *Studies in Communication*, London, Martin Secker & Warburg, 1955.

Bailey, Nina Virginia, "Pitch and time variations in certain American regional dialects," Unpublished Master's Thesis, State University of Iowa, 1930.

Baird, A. Craig, *Argumentation, Discussion, and Debate*, New York, McGraw-Hill Book Company, 1950.

Baker, George Pierce, *The Principles of Argumentation*, Boston, Ginn and Company, 1895.

Bales, Robert F., *Interaction Process Analysis*, Cambridge, Addison-Wesley Publishing Company, 1950.

Bavelas, Alex, "Communication patterns in task-oriented groups," *Journal of the Acoustical Society of America* (1950), *22*: 725–730.

Benne, Kenneth D., and Others, "Participation and democracy," *Adult Leadership* (May, 1952), *1*: 25–27.

Berelson, Bernard, "Communication and public opinion," in *Communication in Modern Society*, Wilbur Schramm (ed.), Urbana, University of Illinois Press, 1948, pp. 167–185.

Berlinsky, Stanley, "Measurement of the intelligence and personality of the deaf," *Journal of Speech and Hearing Disorders* (1952), *17*: 39–54.

Berry, Mildred Freburg, and Eisenson, Jon, *Speech Disorders: Principles and Practices in Therapy*, New York, Appleton-Century-Crofts, 1956.

Black, John W., "The quality of a spoken vowel," *Archives of Speech* (July, 1937), *2*: 7–27.

Black, John W., and Moore, Wilbur E., *Speech: Code, Meaning, and Communication*, New York, McGraw-Hill Book Company, 1955.

Bloomer, H. H., "A Roentgenographic study of the mechanism of respiration," *Speech Monographs* (1936), *3*: 118–124.

Bloomer, Harlan H., and Shohara, Hide H., "The study of respiratory movements by Roentgen kymography," *Speech Monographs* (1941), *8*: 91–101.

Bloomfield, Leonard, *Language*, New York, Henry Holt and Company, 1933.

Bogert, B. P., "On the band width of vowel formants," *Journal of the Acoustical Society of America* (1953), *25*: 791–792. (Abstract.)

Bowen, Wilbur Pardon, and Stone, Henry A., *Applied Anatomy and Kinesiology*, 6th ed., Philadelphia, Lea & Febiger, 1949.

Braden, Waldo W., and Brandenburg, Earnest, *Oral Decision-Making*, New York, Harper & Brothers, 1955.

Bradford, Leland P., and Lippitt, Ronald, "Building a work group," *Personnel* (November, 1945), *22*: 142–148.

Bram, Joseph, *Language and Society*, Garden City, N.Y., Doubleday & Company, 1955.

Brown, Donald Pardee, "Auding as the primary language ability," Ed. D. Dissertation, Stanford University, 1954. *Microfilm Abstracts*, *14*: 2281, Publication No. 10,347.

Brown, James I., "The objective measurement of listening ability," *The Journal of Communication* (1951), *1*: 44–48.

Brown, Richard K., "Measurement of the velocity of sound in the ocean," *Journal of the Acoustical Society of America* (1954), *26*: 64–67.

Brunschwig, L., "A study of some personality aspects of deaf children," *Teachers College Contributions to Education*, No. 687, New York, Columbia University, 1936.

Buchanan, A. R., *Functional Neuro-Anatomy*, Philadelphia, Lea & Febiger, 1948.

Buhler, Charlotte, "Maturation and motivation," *Personality* (1951), *1*: 184–211.

Caffrey, John G., "Auding ability as a function of certain psychometric variables," Ph.D. Dissertation, University of California, 1953.

Caffrey, John G., "An introduction to the auding concept," *Education* (1949), *70*: 234–239.

Carlson, Anton J., and Johnson, Victor, *The Mechanism of the Body*, 4th ed. Chicago, University of Chicago Press, 1953.

Cartwright, Dorwin, and Zander, Alvin, *Group Dynamics: Research and Theory*, Evanston, Ill., Row, Peterson and Company, 1953.

Case, Keith E., "An investigation into the backgrounds for the study and measurement of personality in speech communication," Ph.D. Dissertation, University of Denver, 1948.

Cattell, Raymond B., *The Description and Measurement of Personality*, New York, World Book Company, 1946.

Cattell, Raymond B., "The description of personality. Foundations of trait measurement," *Psychological Review* (1943), *50*: 559–592.

Cattell, Raymond B., "Principal trait clusters for describing personality," *Psychological Bulletin* (1945), *42*: 129–161.

Chenoweth, Eugene C., "The adjustment of college freshmen to the speaking situation," *The Quarterly Journal of Speech* (1940), *26*: 585–588.

Chotlos, J. W., "A statistical and comparative analysis of written language samples," *Psychological Monographs* (1944), *56*: 77–111.

Cohen, Felix S., "Transcendental nonsense and the functional approach," in *Language, Meaning and Maturity*, S. I. Hayakawa (ed.), New York, Harper & Brothers, 1954, pp. 184–214.

The Columbia Encyclopedia, 2nd ed., William Bridgewater and Elizabeth J. Sherwood (eds)., New York, Columbia University Press, 1950.

Constans, H. Philip, "An objective analysis of the 'Three Forms of Force' in speech," in *Studies in Experimental Phonetics*, Giles Wilkeson Gray (ed.), *University Studies No. 27*, Baton Rouge, Louisiana State University Press, 1936, pp. 7–36.

Cooley, Charles Horton, *Social Organization*, New York, Charles Scribner's Sons, 1912.

Cowan, Milton, "Pitch and intensity characteristics of stage speech," *Archives of Speech Supplement*, Iowa City, Iowa, 1936.

Critchley, MacDonald, *The Language of Gesture*, London, Edward Arnold & Co., 1939.

Dashiell, John Frederick, *Fundamentals of General Psychology*, 3rd ed., Boston, Houghton, Mifflin Company, 1949.

De Laguna, Grace Andrus, *Speech: Its Function and Development*, New Haven, Yale University Press, 1927.

Dempsey, Edward W., "Homeostasis," in *Handbook of Experimental Psychology*, Herbert S. Langfeld (ed.), New York, John Wiley & Sons, 1951, pp. 209–235.

Dewey, John, *Democracy and Education*, New York, The Macmillan Company, 1916.

Doi, L. Takeo, "Japanese language as an expression of Japanese psychology," *Western Speech* (1956), *20*: 90–96.

Dollard, John and Others, *Steps in Psychotherapy*, New York, The Macmillan Company, 1953.

Drew, R. O., and Kellogg, E. W., "Starting characteristics of speech sounds," *Journal of the Acoustical Society of America* (1940), *12*: 95–103.

Duncan, Melba Hurd, "An experimental study of some of the relationships between voice and personality among students of speech," *Speech Monographs* (1945), *12*: 47–73.

Dunn, H. K., "The calculation of vocal resonance, and an electrical vocal tract," *Journal of the Acoustical Society of America* (1950), *22*: 740–753.

Duyker, H. J. C., "Language and psychology," *Acta Psychologica* (1950), 7: 150–173.

Eckert, Ralph G., "A mental hygiene approach to speech correction as a means to personal adjustment," Ph.D. Dissertation, University of California, 1940.

Eisenson, Jon, and Others, "The affective value of English speech sounds," *The Quarterly Journal of Speech* (1940), *26*: 589–594.

Eisenson, Jon, and Others, "A second study in the affective value of speech sounds," *The Quarterly Journal of Speech* (1943), *29*: 457–464.

Ellis, Albert, "Recent research with personality inventories," *Journal of Consulting Psychology* (1953), *17*: 45–49.

Eysenck, H. J., "Assessment of personality," *British Medical Bulletin* (1949), *6*: 16–20.

Eysenck, H. J., *Dimensions of Personality*, London, Routledge, Kegan Paul, 1948.

Fairbanks, Grant, and Others, "An experimental study in vowel intensities," *Journal of the Acoustical Society of America* (1950), *22*: 457–459.

Farnsworth, D. W., "High-speed motion pictures of the human vocal cords," *Bell Laboratories Record* (1940), *18*: 203–208.

Fearing, Franklin, "Toward a psychological theory of communication," *Journal of Personality* (1953), *22*: 71–88.

Fessenden, Seth A., "Levels of listening: a theory," *Education* (1955), *75*: 288-291.

Festinger, Leon, "Group attraction and membership," in *Group Dynamics: Research and Theory*, Dorwin Cartwright and Alvin Zander (eds.), Evanston, Ill., Row, Peterson and Company, 1953, pp. 72–101.

Festinger, Leon, "Informal social communication," *Psychological Review* (1950), *57*: 271–282.

Festinger, Leon, "Motivations leading to social behavior," in *Nebraska Symposium on Motivation*, Marshall E. Jones (ed.), Lincoln, University of Nebraska Press, 1954, pp. 191–219.

Fiske, P. W., "A study of relationships to somatotypes," *Journal of Applied Psychology* (1944), *28*: 504–519.

Fletcher, Harvey, *Speech and Hearing in Communication*, Princeton, N.J., D. Van Nostrand Company, 1953.

Frazer, Sir James George, "Tabooed words," in *The Language of Wisdom and Folly*, Irving J. Lee (ed.), New York, Harper & Brothers, 1949, pp. 220–223.

Fulton, John Farquhar, *Physiology of the Nervous System*, 3rd ed., New York, Oxford University Press, 1949.

Gardner, Ernest, *Fundamentals of Neurology*, Philadelphia, W. B. Saunders Company, 1948.

Garner, W. R., "A technique and a scale for loudness measurement," *Journal of the Acoustical Society of America* (1954), *26*: 73–88.

George, Albert Donald, "Some Louisiana isoglosses," Master's Thesis, Louisiana State University, 1951.

Grandgent, C. H., "English in America," *Die Neuren Sprachen* (1895), *2*: 443–467; 520–528. (New York, G. E. Stechert & Company.)

Grandgent, C. H., "From Franklin to Lowell," *PMLA* (1899), *7*: 207–239.

Gray, Giles Wilkeson, "American modes of speech," in *Opinions and Attitudes*, rev. ed., Stewart Morgan (ed.), New York, Thomas Nelson and Sons, 1938, pp. 220–232.

Gray, Giles Wilkeson, "Regional predominance in respiration in relation to certain aspects of voice," in *Studies in Experimental Phonetics*, Giles Wilkeson Gray (ed.), *University Studies No. 27*, Baton Rouge, Louisiana State University Press, 1936, pp. 59–78.

Gray, Giles Wilkeson, "A speech mechanism hypothesis," *The Quarterly Journal of Speech* (1936), *22*: 656–660.

Gray, Giles Wilkeson, "Speech Sound Formation," in *Handbook of Speech Pathology*, Lee Edward Travis (ed.), New York, Appleton-Century-Crofts, 1957, pp. 91–108.

Gray, Giles Wilkeson (ed.), *Studies in Experimental Phonetics, University Studies No. 27*, Baton Rouge, Louisiana State University Press, 1936.

Gunderson, Robert Gray, "The group dynamics furor," *School and Society* (August 18, 1951), *74*: 97–100.

Gunderson, Robert Gray, "Group dynamics—hope or hoax," *The Quarterly Journal of Speech* (1950), *36*: 34–38.

Gunderson, Robert Gray, "More dynamics," *The Quarterly Journal of Speech* (1950), *36*: 245–246.

Hackett, Herbert, "A null hypothesis: There is not enough evidence," *Education* (1955), *75*: 349–351.

Haiman, Franklyn H., "Materials in group dynamics," *The Quarterly Journal of Speech* (1954), *40*: 201–206.

Harlow, Harry F., "Mice, men, monkeys, and motives," *Psychological Review* (1953), *60*: 23–32.

Haugen, Einar, "The linguistic development of Ivar Aasen's New Norse," *PMLA* (1933), *48*: 2.

Hayakawa, S. I., *Language in Thought and Action*, rev. ed., New York, Harcourt, Brace and Company, 1949.

Hayakawa, S. I. (ed.), *Language, Meaning and Maturity*, New York, Harper & Brothers, 1954.

Heffner, R-M. S., *General Phonetics*, Madison, The University of Wisconsin Press, 1952.

Heilman, Arthur, "Listening and the curriculum," *Education* (1955), *75*: 283–287.

Henry, William E., "The business executive: the psychodynamics of a social role," *American Journal of Sociology* (1949), *54*: 286–291.

Hill, Archibald A., *An Introduction to Linguistic Structures*, New York, Harcourt, Brace and Company, 1958.

Himmelweit, Hilde T., "Personality tests as research tools," in *Current Trends in British Psychology*, C. A. Mace and P. E. Vernon (eds.), London, Methuen & Co., 1953, pp. 196–204.

Hockett, Charles F., "Biophysics, linguistics, and the unity of science," *American Scientists* (1948), *36*: 558–572.

Hockett, Charles F., *A Course in Modern Linguistics*, New York, The Macmillan Company, 1958.

Hoebel, A. Adamson, "The nature of culture," in *Man, Culture, and Society*, Harry L. Shapiro (ed.), New York, Oxford University Press, 1956, pp. 168–181.

Hoijer, Harry, "Language and writing," in *Man, Culture, and Society*, Harry L. Shapiro (ed.), New York, Oxford University Press, 1956, pp. 196–223.

Hoijer, Harry, "The relation of language to culture," in *Anthropology Today: An Encyclopedic Inventory*, A. L. Kroeber (ed.), pp. 554–573.

Hollien, Harry Francis, "A study of some laryngeal correlates of vocal pitch," Ph.D. Dissertation, State University of Iowa, 1955. *Microfilm Abstracts, 15*: 2340, Publication No. 14,119.

Homans, G. C., *The Human Group*, New York, Harcourt, Brace and Company, 1950.

Hultzén, Lee S., "The pronunciation of monosyllabic form-words in American English," in *Studies in Speech and Drama in Honor of Alexander M. Drummond*, Ithaca, Cornell University Press, 1944, pp. 256–284.

Idol, Harriett R., "A statistical study of respiration in relation to speech characteristics," in *Studies in Experimental Phonetics*, Giles Wilkeson Gray (ed.), *University Studies No. 27*, Baton Rouge, Louisiana State University Press, 1936, 79–98.

Irwin, O. C., and Curry, Thayer, "Vocal elements in the crying vocalization of infants under ten days of age," *Child Development* (1941), *12*: 99–109.

Janis, Irving L., "Personality correlates of susceptibility to persuasion," *Journal of Personality* (1954), *22*: 504–518.

Jespersen, Otto, *Language: Its Nature, Development and Origin*, New York, Henry Holt and Company, 1922.

Jóhannesson, Alexander, "The gestural origin of languages: Evidence from six 'unrelated' languages," *Nature* (London, 1944), *153*: 171; (1945), *154*: 466; (1946), *157*: 847; (1948), *162*: 902; (1950), *166*: 60–61.

Johnson, Alexander B., *A treatise on Language; or The Relation which Words Bear to Things*, New York, Harper & Brothers, 1836.

Johnson, Buford J., *Child Psychology*, Springfield, Ill., Charles C. Thomas, 1932.

Johnson, Wendell, "The fateful process of Mr. A. talking to Mr. B," *Harvard Business Review* (1953), *31*: 49–56.

Johnson, Wendell, *People in Quandaries*, New York, Harper & Brothers, 1946.

Johnson, Wendell, "Speech and personality," *ETC* (1946), *6*: 84–102.

Jones, Daniel, *An English Pronouncing Dictionary*, New York, E. P. Dutton & Co., 1937.

Jones, Marshall E. (ed.), *Nebraska Symposium on Motivation*, Lincoln, University of Nebraska Press, 1954.

Jones, R. Stewart, "A procedure for the appraisal of the mechanics of group discussion," *Progressive Education* (1951), *28*: 96–99.

Kelly, Joseph P., "Studies in nasality," *Archives of Speech* (1934), *1*: 26–42.

Kelman, Herbert C., "Group dynamics—neither hope nor hoax," *The Quarterly Journal of Speech* (1950), *36*: 371–377.

Kenyon, John Samuel, *American Pronunciation*, 8th ed., Ann Arbor, George Wahr, 1940.

Kenyon, John Samuel, *A Pronouncing Dictionary of the English Language*, Springfield, Mass., G. & C. Merriam Company, 1944.

Kluckhohn, Clyde, and Murray, Henry A., "Personality formation: the determinants," in *Personality in Nature, Society, and Culture*, Clyde Kluckhohn and Henry A. Murray (eds.), New York, Alfred A. Knopf, 1954, pp. 53–67.

Knower, Franklin H., "A study of speech attitudes and adjustments," *Speech Monographs* (1938), *5*: 130–203.

Koch, Sigmund, "The current status of motivational psychology," *Psychological Review* (1951), *58*: 147–154.

Kostelyik, P. J., *Theories of Hearing*, Leiden, Univérsitaire Pers Leiden, 1950.

Krieg, Wendell J. S., *Functional Neuroanatomy*, 2nd ed., New York, The Blakiston Company, 1953.

Kroeber, A. L. (ed.), *Anthropology Today: An Encyclopedic Inventory*, Chicago, University of Chicago Press, 1953.

Kurath, Hans, *Handbook of the Linguistic Geography of New England*, Providence, Brown University Press, 1939.

Kurath, Hans, *The Linguistic Atlas of New England*, Providence, Brown University Press, vol. 1, 1939; vol. 2, 1941; vol. 3, 1943.

Kurath, Hans, "Mourning and morning," in *Studies for William A. Read*, Nathaniel M. Caffee and Thomas A. Kirby (eds.), Baton Rouge, Louisiana State University Press, 1940.

Kurath, Hans, *A Word Geography of the Eastern United States*, Ann Arbor, University of Michigan Press, 1949.

Laird, A. J., and Knight, A. R., "Contemporary studies in motivation," in *Current Trends in British Psychology*, C. A. Mace and P. E. Vernon (eds.), London, Methuen & Co., 1953, pp. 125–137.

Langfeld, Herbert S. (ed.), *Handbook of Experimental Psychology*, New York, John Wiley & Sons, 1951.

Lasswell, Harold D., and Others, *The Comparative Study of Symbols*, Stanford, Stanford University Press, 1952.

Lasswell, Harold D., and Others, *Language of Politics: Studies in Quantitative Semantics*, New York, George W. Stewart, 1949.

Lee, Irving J., *How to Talk with People*, New York, Harper & Brothers, 1952.

Lee, Irving J., *Language Habits in Human Affairs*, New York, Harper & Brothers, 1941.

Lee, Irving J., *The Language of Wisdom and Folly*, New York, Harper & Brothers, 1949.

Lefèvre, André, *Race and Language*, New York, Appleton-Century-Crofts, 1894.

Lewis, M. M., *Infant Speech*, New York, The Humanities Press, 1951.

Lippman, Walter, *The Public Philosophy*, Boston, Little, Brown and Company, 1955.

Locke, John, *An Essay Concerning Human Understanding*, 3 vols., London, Allen & West, 1795.

McBurney, James H., and Hance, Kenneth G., *Discussion in Human Affairs*, New York, Harper & Brothers, 1950.

McCarthy, Dorothea, "Language development in children," in *Manual of Child Psychology*, 2nd ed., Leonard Carmichael (ed.), New York, John Wiley & Sons, 1954, pp. 492–630.

McClelland, David C., *Personality*, New York, William Sloan Associates, 1951.

McClelland, David C. (ed.), *Studies in Motivation*, New York, Appleton-Century-Crofts, 1955.

Mace, C. A., and Vernon, P. E. (ed.), *Current Trends in British Psychology*, London, Methuen & Co., 1953.

Marckwardt, Albert H., "Principal and subsidiary dialect areas of the north-central states," *Publication of the American Dialect Society* (April, 1957), No. 27, 2–15.

Maslow, A. H., "Higher needs and personality," *Dialectica* (1951), *5*: 257–264.

Meerloo, Joost A. M., *Conversation and Communication*, New York, International Universities Press, 1952.

Miller, George A., *Language and Communication*, New York, McGraw-Hill Book Company, 1951.

Mitchell, D. A. G., *Anatomy of the Autonomic Nervous System*, Edinburgh and London, E. &. S. Livingstone, 1953.

Moore, Paul, "Motion picture studies of the vocal folds and vocal attack," *Journal of Speech Disorders* (1938), *3*: 235–238.

Moore, Wilbur E., "Factors related to achievement and improvement in public speaking," *The Quarterly Journal of Speech* (1943), *29*: 213–217.

Morgan, C. D., and Murray, H. A., "A method for investigating fantasies: the Thematic Apperception Test," *Archives of Neurology and Psychiatry* (1935), *34*: 289–306.

Morgan, C. T., and Others, "Pitch and intensity," *Journal of the Acoustical Society of America* (1951), *23*: 658–663.

Morgan, Clifford T., and Stellar, Eliot, *Physiological Psychology*, New York, McGraw-Hill Book Company, 1950.

Morris, Charles William, *Signs, Language and Behavior*, Englewood Cliffs, N.J., Prentice-Hall, 1946.

Mudd, Charles S., Jr., "The effect of chest resonance upon the quality of the voice," Master's Thesis, Louisiana State University, 1948.

Müller, Friederich Max, *The Science of Language*, New York, Charles Scribner's Sons, 1891.

Murphy, Gardner, *An Introduction to Psychology*, New York, Harper & Brothers, 1951.

Murphy, Gardner, "Social motivation," in *Handbook of Social Psychology*, Gardner Lindzey (ed.), Cambridge, Addison-Wesley Publishing Company, 1954, pp. 601–633.

Murray, Elwood, *The Speech Personality*, 2nd ed., Philadelphia, J. B. Lippincott Company, 1944.

Mussen, John Henry, and Conger, John Janeway, *Child Development and Personality*, New York, Harper & Brothers, 1956.

Negus, Sir V. E., *The Comparative Anatomy and Physiology of the Larynx*, rev. ed., New York, Grune & Stratton, 1949.

Negus, Sir V. E., *The Mechanism of the Larynx*, London, William Heinemann, 1929.

Nesbit, Frank Ford, *Language, Meaning and Reality*, New York, Exposition Press, 1955.

Nichols, Ralph G., "Factors in listening comprehension," *Speech Monographs* (1948), *15*: 154–163.

Nichols, Ralph G., "Ten components of effective listening," *Education* (1955), *75*: 292–302.

Olson, Harry F., "Frequency range preferences for speech and music," *Journal of the Acoustical Society of America* (1947), *19*: 549–555.

Paget, Sir Richard, *Human Speech*, New York, Harcourt, Brace and Company, 1930.

Pear, T. H., "The social psychology of everyday life," in *Current Trends in British Psychology*, C. A. Mace and P. E. Vernon (eds.), London, Metheun & Co., 1953, pp. 113–124.

Penfield, Wilder, and Rasmussen, Theodore, *The Cerebral Cortex of Man: A Clinical Study of Localization of Function*, New York, The Macmillan Company, 1950.

Peterson, Gordon E., "Phonetics, phonemics, and pronunciation: spectrographic analysis," *Georgetown University Monograph Series on Languages and Linguistics* (July, 1954), *6*: 7–19.

Peterson, Gordon E., "The significance of various portions of the wave length in the minimum duration necessary for the recognition of vowel sounds," Ph.D. Dissertation, Louisiana State University, 1939.

Peterson, Gordon E., "Systematic research in experimental phonetics: 4. The evaluation of speech signals," *Journal of Speech and Hearing Disorders* (1954), *19*: 158–168.

Peterson, Gordon E., and Barney, Harold L., "Control methods used in a study of the vowels," *Journal of the Acoustical Society of America* (1952), *24*: 175–184.

Pike, Kenneth L., *The Intonation of American English*, Ann Arbor, University of Michigan Press, 1946. University of Michigan Publications in Linguistics, Volume I.

Polyak, Stephen L., *The Human Ear*, New York, The Sonotone Corporation, 1946.

Potter, Ralph K., and Others, *Visible Speech*, Princeton, N.J., D. Van Nostrand Company, 1947.

Potter, Ralph K., and Steinberg, J. C., "Toward the specification of speech," *Journal of the Acoustical Society of America* (1950), *22*: 807–820.

Rankin, Paul Tory, "The measurement of the ability to understand spoken language," Ph.D. Dissertation, University of Michigan, 1926. *Microfilm Abstracts*, *12*: 847.

Rapaport, Anatol, "What is semantics?" in *Language, Meaning and Maturity*, S. I. Hayakawa (ed.), New York, Harper & Brothers, 1954, pp. 3–19.

Révész, G., *The Origins and Prehistory of Language*, Tr. by J. Butler, New York, Philosophical Library, 1956.

Richardson, E. G., *Technical Aspects of Sound*, 2 vols., Amsterdam, Elsevier Publishing Company, 1953.

Rorschach, Hermann, *Psychodiagnosis*, Tr. by Paul Kemkau and Bernard Kronenberg, New York, Grune & Stratton, 1951.

Ruch, T. C., "Motor systems," in *Handbook of Experimental Psychology*, Herbert S. Langfeld (ed.), New York, John Wiley & Sons, 1951, pp. 154–208.

Ruch, T. C., "Sensory mechanisms," in *Handbook of Experimental Psychology*, Herbert S. Langfeld (ed.), New York, John Wiley & Sons, 1951, pp. 121–153.

Ruesch, Jurgen, and Kees, Weldon, *Nonverbal Communication*, Berkeley, University of California Press, 1956.

Sanford, F. H., "Speech and personality," *Psychological Bulletin* (1942), *39*: 811–845.

Sanford, F. H., "Speech and personality: a comparative case study," *Character and Personality* (1942), *10*: 169–198.

Sapir, Edward, "Speech as a personality trait," *American Journal of Society* (1927), *32*: 892–906.

Sarason, Seymour B., *The Clinical Interaction: With Special Reference to the Rorschach*, New York, Harper & Brothers, 1954.

Savart, Felix, "Mémoire sur la voix humaine," *Annales de Chimie et de Physique* (1825), *30*: 64–87.

Schramm, Wilbur (ed.), *Communication in Modern Society*, Urbana, University of Illinois Press, 1948.

Segerstedt, Torgny T., *Die Macht des Wortes*, Zürich, Pan-Verlag, 1947.

Shapiro, Henry L. (ed.), *Man, Culture, and Society*, New York, Oxford University Press, 1956.

Sheehan, Joseph G., "Rorschach prognosis in psychotherapy and speech therapy," *Journal of Speech and Hearing Disorders* (1954), *19*: 217–219.

Sheldon, W. H., *The Varieties of Human Physique*, New York, Harper & Brothers, 1942.

Shewmake, E. F., *English Pronunciation in Virginia*, Davidson, N. C., Davidson College, 1927.

Shewmake, E. F., "Laws of pronunciation in Virginia," *Modern Language Notes* (1925), *40*: 479–492.

Shirley, M. M., *The First Two Years, a Study of Twenty-five Babies: Vol. II, Intellectual Development*, Institute of Child Welfare Monograph Series, Nos. 6–8, Minneapolis, University of Minnesota Press, 1933.

Skinner, B. F., *Verbal Behavior*, New York, Appleton-Century-Crofts, 1957.

Smith, Adam, "A dissertation on the origin of language," in *The Theory of Moral Sentiments*, 10th ed., London, Cadell, 1804.

Smith, M. E., "An investigation of the development of the sentence and the extent of the vocabulary of young children," *State University of Iowa Studies*, 1926.

Smith, Mary Katherine, "Measurement of the size and general English vocabulary through the elementary grades and high school," *Genetic Psychology Monographs* (1941), *24*: 311–345.

Smith, Svend, "Remarks on the physiology of the vibrations of the vocal cords," *Folia Phoniatrica* (1954), *6*: 166–178.

Stagner, Ross, and Karwoski, T. F., *Psychology*, New York, McGraw-Hill Book Company, 1952.

Steer, M. D., "A qualitative study of breathing in stutterers," *Speech Monographs* (1935), *2*: 152–157.

Stevens, S. S., "The relation of pitch to intensity," *Journal of the Acoustical Society of America* (1935), *6*: 150–154.

Stevens, Stanley Smith, and Davis, Hallowel, *Hearing, Its Psychology and Physiology*, New York, John Wiley & Sons, 1938.

Symonds, Percival M., "Interpreting the picture story (TAT) method," *The American Psychologist* (1947), *2*: 228–229. (Abstract.)

Tarski, Alfred, "The semantic conception of truth and the foundation of semantics," *Philosophy and Phenomenological Research* (1943–1944), *4*: 341–376.

Thelen, Herbert A., *Dynamics of Groups at Work*, Chicago, University of Chicago Press, 1954.

Thomas, C. K., "American dictionaries and variant pronunciations," *American Speech* (1939), *14*: 175–190.

Thomas, C. K., "The dialectal significance of the non-phonemic low-back variants before R," in *Studies in Speech and Drama in Honor of Alexander M. Drummond*, Ithaca, Cornell University Press, 1944, pp. 244–254.

Thorpe, Louis P., *Child Psychology and Development*, 2nd ed., New York, The Ronald Press, 1955.

Tiffany, William R., "Vowel recognition as a function of duration, frequency modulation and phonetic context," *Journal of Speech and Hearing Disorders* (1953), *18*: 289–301.

Titiev, Mischa, *The Science of Man: An Introduction to Anthropology*, New York, Henry Holt and Company, 1954.

Trimmer, J. S., and Firestone, F. A., "An investigation of subjective tones by means of the steady tone phase effect," *Journal of the Acoustical Society of America* (1937), *9*: 25–29.

Van den Berg, J. W., "On the rôle of the laryngeal ventricle in voice production," *Folia Phoniatrica* (1955), 7: 57–69.

Vernon, Philip E., *Personality Tests and Measurements*, London, Methuen & Co., 1953.

Walnut, Francis, "A personality inventory item analysis of individuals who stutter and individuals who have other handicaps," *Journal of Speech and Hearing Disorders* (1954), *19: 220–227.

Welsh, George Bryan, "An investigation of some predictive factors in auding ability," Ph.D. Dissertation, University of Pittsburgh, 1954. *Microfilm Abstracts*, *14*: 2407, Publication No. 9995.

West, Robert, "The neurophysiology of speech," in *Handbook of Speech Pathology*, Lee Edward Travis (ed.), New York, Appleton-Century-Crofts, 1957, pp. 72–90.

Whatmough, Joshua, *Language*, New York, St. Martin's Press, 1956.

Wheelwright, Philip, *The Burning Bush*, Bloomington, Indiana University Press, 1954.

White, Leslie A., "The symbol: the origin and basis of human behavior," in *Language, Meaning and Maturity*, S. I. Hayakawa (ed.), New York, Harper & Brothers, 1954, pp. 252–263.

Whorf, Benjamin Lee, *Language, Thought, and Reality*, New York, John Wiley & Sons, 1956. (Collected Writings, John B. Carroll, Ed.)

Whorf, Benjamin Lee, "The relation of thought and behavior to language," in *Four Articles on Metalinguistics*, Benjamin Lee Whorf, Washington, D.C., Foreign Service Institute, Department of State, 1950.

Wiener, Norbert, *The Human Use of Human Beings*, Boston, Houghton, Mifflin Company, 1950.

Wiksell, Wesley A., "An experimental study of controlled and uncontrolled types of breathing," in *Studies in Experimental Phonetics*, Giles Wilkeson Gray (ed.), *University Studies No. 27*, Baton Rouge, Louisiana State University Press, 1936, pp. 99–164.

Williamson, Arleigh B., "Diagnosis and treatment of seventy-two cases of hoarse voice," *The Quarterly Journal of Speech* (1945), *31*: 189–202.

Wise, Claude M., *Applied Phonetics*, Englewood Cliffs, N.J., Prentice-Hall, 1957.

Wise, Claude M., "Franklin as a phonetician," *Speech Monographs* (1948), *15*: 99–120.

Wise, Claude M., *Introduction to Phonetics*, Englewood Cliffs, N.J., Prentice-Hall, Inc., 1958.

Wise, Claude M., "ɪz neɪzəl rɛzənənts æktʃuəlɪ neɪzofərɪŋgəl rɛzənənts?" *Le Maître Phonétique*, Janvier-Juin, 1948, pp. 4–5.

Wise, Claude M., and others, "The southern diphthong [aɪ]," *The Southern Speech Journal* (1954), *19*: 304–312.

Woolbert, Charles Henry, "The audience," *Psychological Monographs* (1916), *21*: 4, 37–54.

Woolbert, Charles Henry, "Conviction and persuasion: some considerations of theory," *The Quarterly Journal of Speech* (1917), *3*: 249–264.

Woolbert, Charles Henry, *The Fundamentals of Speech*, rev. ed., New York, Harper & Brothers, 1927.

Wundt, Wilhelm, *Elements of Folk Psychology*, Tr. by Edward LeRoy Schaub, New York, The Macmillan Company, 1916.

Wundt, Wilhelm, *Outlines of Psychology*, 3rd ed., Leipzig, Kroner, 1907.

Index

[a], 249
[ɑ], 249
[ɒ], 249
[æ], 249
Abductor muscles of larynx, 176
Ablaut, 362
Abstraction, confusion resulting from, 504–505, 513; levels of, 504–505, 512, 514
Abstractions, 503, 508, 523; and community of reference, 512; and identity, 505–506; forming, 504; unavoidable, 507
Accent, 522
Acoustic spectrum, 117–121, 123–131
Acquisition of speech sounds, factors affecting, 480
Action, belief and, 28–29; influencing, 28–34; covert and overt, 26; on the screen, 22
Activity, normal in animal existence, 388
Adams, Harlan H., cited, 60
Adaptation, social, function of speech, 380
Adductor muscles of larynx, 176
Adequate stimulus, 230, 231
Adjustments, language and social, 492
Affective elements in information, 439
Affective states, expression of, 526
Afferent nerves in SNS, 211
Afferent neurons, 226
Affixes (prefixes, suffixes, infixes), 332
Affrication, 312
Agglutinative languages, 346, 348
Agnosia (visual, tactile, auditory), 203
Agonists, 176
Aim as factor in communication, 356
Aims of speech, 24–37; overlapping among, 34–35
Air columns as vibrators, 76
Air waves, effect on tympanic membrane, 192
Alexander, Henry, cited, 364, 374, 375, 376
Allen, Kenneth D. A., cited, 153

Allophones in morpheme analysis, 333
Allport, F. H., cited, 26, 464, 473, 482, 484
Allport, G. W., cited, 426
Alphabet, origin of, 349–350
Ambiguity in meaning, 518
Amelioration (elevation), 376
"American Standard Acoustical Terminology," cited, 77
Amplification of sound, 92
Amplitude, 103
Analogical verb forms, false, 273
Analogy, 377; false, 272
Analytic languages, 346
Anaptyxis, 278, 363
Anarchistic groups, 40
Anderson, Harold A., cited, 61
Animation, 57
Antagonists, 176
Anvil (incus) in middle ear, 194
Aphasia, 203
Aphesis, 363
Apocope, 371
Appeals, choosing the motive, 407–409; to selfish motives, 397
Appearance of speech sounds, 479–480
Aqueduct of Sylvius, 215
Argumentative propositions, 31–32
Aristotle, cited, 26, 322, 413
Articulate utterance, nonpurposive, 479–483; purposive, 483–484
Articulation, 188–191; and enunciation, 55–56, 241–252; effect on development of human race, 13; with back of tongue, 190; with lips, 189; with tongue blade and tip, 189–190; with velum, 190–191; with vocal bands, 191
Aryepiglottic folds, 174, 175
Arytenoid cartilages, 173, 174, 177
Arytenoid muscle, 177, 178
Assembling, basis of, 393–394, 406–407

Assimilation, attitudes toward, 359–360; definition, 357; distant, 358; partial and complete, 359; progressive, 357; reciprocal, 357–358; regressive, 357; substandard, 274
Association, and meaning, 494; basis of, 386–387; extinction of, 387
Assumptions as basis of argument, 33
Atkinson, John W., cited, 389
Attention, and change in the vocal elements, 421; and conflict, 418; and interest, 414–421; and progression of ideas, 420; and mode of utterance, 420–421; and the speaker, 419; defined, 414–415; effect of repetition on, 416; in relation to speaking, 418–421; magnitude of stimulus affecting, 416; need to attract, 419–420; past experiences and, 416; stimulation of, 415–421
Attitudes, affective, 525; and language, 492; and meaning, 520–523; in relation to belief, 29; isolation and, 6; toward assimilation, 359–360; toward symbols, 491, 495–497
Atwood, E. Bagby, cited, 335
Auder, ideal, 64
Audible area, 108–109
Audience, basis for assembling, 393–394, 406–417; in radio and television, effect of, 223; motivation of, 405–409; motives, identification of speaker with, 412; motives of, 406–407; response, effect on the actor, 21–22; "set," 406; situation, 405–407; not passive, 406
Auding, primary language ability, 62; substitute for "listening," 61–63
Auld, Frank, Jr., cited, 441
Autocratic groups, 40
Autonomic nervous system (ANS), 209 ff.
Axons, 225, 226
Ayer, A. J., cited, 13, 449

[b], 242–243
Backing, 365
Bailey, Nina Virginia, cited, 132
Baird, A. Craig, cited, 49
Baker, George Pierce, cited, 409
Bales, Robert F., cited, 38, 39, 45, 48
Barnes, John, cited, 139 n.
Barney, Harold L., cited, 127, 130
Barriers to communication, 5–6; attitudes as, 6
Bars as vibrators, 76
Basilar membrane, 196
Bavelas, Alex, cited, 40, 45
Beauty in language, 262–263

Behavior, covert language, 442; expressive, 439
Belief, and action, 28–29; basis of, 28–29; influencing, 28–33; knowledge and, 28–29
Bell tones, 114
Bender, W. R. G., cited, 101 n.
Benne, Kenneth D., cited, 40
Benninghoff, Alfred, cited, 144
Bentley, Madison, cited, 12
Berelson, Bernard, cited, 39
Berlinsky, Stanley, cited, 438
Bernoulli principle, 168–170
Bernreuter Personality Inventory, 432
Bible, cited, 456, 497
Biosocial urges, 472
Black, John W., cited, 119
Blanton, Smiley, and Blanton, Margaret Gray, cited, 482
Blend-words (portmanteau words, contamination), 364
Bloch, Bernard, and Trager, George L., cited, 324
Bloomer, Harlan H., cited, 140, 144, 145, 151
Bloomfield, Leonard, cited, 324, 326 n., 341, 348 n., 351 n., 357 n., 359 n., 361 n., 363 n., 367 n., 370 n., 371 n., 372 n., 374 n., 376, 377 n., 378 n., 465 n.
Blueprints as symbols, 445
Boas, Franz, cited, 322, 323
Body-type theory of personality, 423–424
Bogert, B. P., cited, 126
Bopp, Franz, cited, 322
Bowen, Wilbur Pardon, and Stone, Henry A., cited, 146, 151
Braden, Waldo W., cited, 402
Bradford, Leland P., cited, 40
Brain, 214 ff.; cortex, 220–222
Bram, Joseph, cited, 3, 7–8, 456
Brandenburg, Earnest, cited, 402
Breast bone, 137
Breathiness, 51
Breathing, 135–163; abdominal, 152; amount of air used in, 140; articulation and control of, 162; biological function of, 140–141; clavicular, 154; effective, 159–163; exercises, objectives of, 193; for speech, 141–142; general structure of mechanism of, 136–140; medial, 152; principles of, 154–155; regional predominance in, 152; techniques for studying, 140; thoracic, 152; thought-grouping and, 160–161; types and voice, 152–153; word grouping and, 160–161
Brink, Frank, Jr., cited, 228 n.
British speech, standard Southern, 314–320

"Broad *a*," no use in General American, 265; not used in Southern, 282; use in British, 315; use in Eastern, 300–301

Brodmann, K., cited, 221 n.

Brodmann's numberings of cortical areas, 221–222

Brown, Donald Pardee, cited, 61, 62, 64

Brown, James I., cited, 61

Brown, Richard K., cited, 87

Brown, Stuart Gerry, cited, 513

Brunschwig, L., cited, 438

Bryan, W. J., cited, 23

Buchanan, Archibald R., cited, 101 n.

Buhler, Charlotte, cited, 383, 394

Caffee, Nathaniel M., cited, 266

Caffrey, John G., cited, 61

Cannon, W. B., cited, 212

Carlson, Anton J., 157

Cartilages, cuneiform, 173, 174

Cartwright, Dorwin, 43, 44, 46

Case, Keith E., cited, 434

Catharsis, in confession, 440–441; in literature, 440; in psychotherapy, 441

Cattell, Raymond B., cited, 426, 429, 431

Cavity resonance, 93–95, 185; as maintained vibration, 93

"Central" breathing, 152

Central nervous system (CNS), 209 ff., 214

Centralization, 272, 364

Cerebellum, 215, 217

Cerebral cortex, 220–222

ch [tʃ], 245–246

Change, continuity in, 502–503; in meaning, 501–512; in the referent, 500–503; significance of, 500–501; in vocal elements, attention and, 421

"Change of voice" in boys, 100

Chase, Stuart, cited, 41, 46, 513

Chaucer, Geoffrey, quoted, 358 n.

Chenoweth, Eugene C., cited, 433

"Chest" breathing, 152

Chotlos, J. W., cited, 435

Chromotolysis, 227

Churchill, Winston, cited, 407

Cicero, cited, 505

Circular response, 482–483

City speech, substandard, 271, 309–314

Classes of languages, 346–349

Classification of languages, 341–346

Clause terminal phonemes, 331

Clavicles, 137

"Clavicular" breathing, 154

Clear [l], in British, 317; in Eastern, 316; in Southern American, 287

Clifford, W. K., cited, 29

Clipped words, 379

Closed tube resonation, 94, 185

Clusters, consonant, omission from, 275

Coacting groups, 41

Cochlea (inner ear), 195–198; basilar membrane, 196; ductus cochlearis, 196; endolymph, 196; hair cells, 196; helicotrema, 196; lamina spiralis, 195; membrana spiralis, 196; membrane of Reissner, 196; organ of Corti, 196; perilymph, 196; scala tympani, 195; scala vestibuli, 195; tectorial membrane, 196; windows of, 194

Coenotropes, 392

Cohen, Felix S., cited, 518

Cohesiveness in groups, 44

Collar bone, 137

Colliculi (superior, inferior), 218

Command, proclamation and, 29–31, 469

Communication, 380; as expression, 440; barriers to, 5–6; basis of, 384–388; complete act of, 10–11; consummatory, 439; criteria for, difficult to establish, 439; cycle of, 9–11; essentially social, 380; extension of means of, 8–9; fine distinctions in, 12–13; forms of, 1 f.; four skills, 61; function of, 1; individual aspects of, 380–381; instrumental, 439; interruptions to, 4; inventions and, 8; language in, 1–4; media of, 1–4; proximity in, 22–24; reciprocal, 9; record of, 13–14; response as aim of, 26; senses in, 11–24; speech as universal mode of, 7–9; systems of, 4; transmission in, 13; two-way process, 21; weakening of interpersonal, 8

Communicative situation, 381–384

Communicativeness, 35–37

Community of reference, 510–514; an approximation, 510–512; in abstractions, 512–514

Comprehension of spoken language, 483

Compression and rarefaction, 82; wave of, 82

Concept, definition, 446–447; language and, 493; of personality, 422–423; symbol in relation to, 447

Concrete thinking, 445–446

Condensation and rarefaction, 87

Condillac, Étienne Bonnot de, cited, 460

Conditioned reflex in speech, 232, 383–384

Conditioning, 231

Confession, catharsis in, 440–441

Conflict, attention and, 418; escape as resolution of, 401; normal resolution of, 404–405; of motives, 400–405; rationalization and, 401–402; sublimation and, 402–403

Confrontation, in the group situation, 48; proximity and, 21–23; significance of, 21–24

Conger, John Janeway, cited, 473

Connotation, 373, 512, 521, 525

Consonant clusters, omission from, 275; simplification of, 363

Consonants (description, transcription lists), 241–249

Contact senses, 11

Contact theory of speech origin, 470–471

Contamination (portmanteau words), 364

Context and meaning, 514–519

Control, social, as function of speech, 380

Conversation, 385–386; imaginary, 442; personal, 24; with oneself, 443

Conviction and persuasion, basis of distinction, 29–31; value of distinction, 32

Cooley, Charles Horton, cited, 15, 38, 53, 449, 523

Cooper, Lane, cited, 18, 413

Cornicular cartilages, 173, 174

Corpus collosum, 220

Cortex of brain, 220–222

Cortin, 213

Coupled system, 79–80; vocal mechanism as, 101

Coupling, close, 80; loose, 80

Covert language behavior, 205, 442–443

Cowan, Milton, cited, 102

Crico-arytenoid muscles, lateral, 177–178; posterior, 178

Cricoid cartilage, 173, 174

Critchley, MacDonald, cited, 488

Cruva's disc, 83–84

Culture, based on language, 451–454; defined, 450

Cunningham, D. J., cited, 145

Curry, Robert, cited, 170 n.

Curve, of displacement, 72; representing sound waves, 81, 85–86

Cycle of communication, 9–11; confrontation in, 21–24

Cyto-architecture, 221

Cytoplasm, 226

[d], 244

Damping, 77

Dashiell, John Frederick, cited, 384, 392, 406, 421, 422, 424, 425, 428, 434, 443, 446, 496

"Dating" and change of meaning, 502, 503

Davis, Hallowel, cited, 79, 91, 97, 104, 113, 115, 129

Daydreaming, 404

de Laguna, Grace Andrus, cited, 30 f., 385, 448, 523; theory of speech origin, 468–470

Decibel, 105–109; and loudness, 108; as measure of hearing, 106–107; not absolute unit of measurement, 106

Defective, the speech, and personality, 437–438

Degeneration (pejoration), 376–377, 516

Democratic groups, 40

Dendrites, 225

Denotations, 512, 521, 525

"Depth" language, 526

Descartes, René, cited, 233

Development of speech, in the race, 455–472; steps in, 477

Deviations from standard speech, 307–309; Eastern, 307–309; General American, 268–271; Southern, 287–299

Dewey, John, cited, 388, 398, 510

Dialectal differences, time and, 131–132

Dialects, American, 258–259; English, 254–255

Diaphragm, 137, 143–145; action of, 143–144; excursion of, 145–146, 153; in inhalation, 156; structure of, 143

"Diaphragmatic" breathing, 152

Diction, stage, 260–261

Dictionary as guide to pronunciation, 56–57

Diencephalon, 214, 218–220

Differences, individual, 386

Diffusion, significance of, 16–17

"Ding-dong" theory, see Phonetic type theory

Diphthongization, 365–367; [æ] to [æɪ] in substandard Southern speech, 288

Displacement, in sound wave, 69; curve of, 72, 85

Dissimilation, 361–362; definition, 361; in substandard Southern speech, 292; of [r], 269

Dissyllabication of monosyllables ending in *l*, 270

Distance reception, 11–12

Distance senses, significance of, 15

Distant (incontiguous, dilated) assimilation, 358

Distinctions, significance of fine, 17–18; mechanism for making fine, 13

Distortion in forced vibration, 79

Documentation, recording for, 20–21

Doi, L. Takeo, cited, 454

Dollard, John, cited, 441

Dominance-submission, 427

Drawl, Southern, 293; Western, 270

Drew, R. O., cited, 101, 136

Ductus cochlearis, 196

Duncan, Melba Hurd, cited, 433
Dunn, H. K., cited, 121, 123
Duyker, H. J. C., cited, 432

[e], 249–250
[eɪ, e], 250
[ɛ], 249
[ə], 249, 250
[ɜʊ] for [aʊ] in tidewater Virginia, 284
[ɜʊ] for [oʊ] in British speech, 316
Eastern speech, 56, 299–309
Echoic theory of speech origin, see Onomatopoetic theory
Eckert, Ralph G., cited, 430
Edmont, E., cited, 335
Effectors, 224
Efferent waves in SNS, 212
Elasticity, 68–70; in gases, 68; volume, 87
Elevation (amelioration), 376
Elisions in articulation, 55
Ellis, Albert, cited, 430
Elocutionists, 37
Emerson, O. F., cited, 371
Emotion in relation to speech, 205
Emotional components in experience, 512; reactions, 18
Emphasis, 522; and meaning, 521–522
Enculturation, 438
End correction for resonating tubes, 94 n.
Endocrine system, 206, 212–213
Endolymph, 196–197
Energy, in speech sounds, 104–105; inversely proportional to square of distance, 104; not added by resonance, 93; sources of, 76–77, 135–163
English compared with German, 452–453
Entertainment, aim in speech, 27–28
Enunciation, adequate, 55–56
Epiglottis, 175–176
Erickson, Carl I., cited, 96–101
Escape as resolution of conflict, 401
Ethmoid sinuses, 184
Euphemisms, 496
Eustachian tubes, 188
Excrescent sounds, 364
Exercises, objectives of breathing, 163
Exhalation, 141, 155–163; muscles of, 158–159
Exhibitionism vs. communicativeness, 36–37
Expression vs. communication, 440
Expressive and instrumental utterance, 439
"Extensity" as an aspect of volume, 133
External meatus of the ear, 192
External oblique muscle, 158
Exteroceptors, 223
Eysenck, H. J., cited, 422, 423–424, 425, 429

[f], 243
Fairbanks, Grant, cited, 53, 109
False analogical verb forms, 273
False analogy, 272
Farnsworth, D. W., cited, 166
Farrar, Frederick William, cited, 461
Fear and timidity in speech, 58
Fearing, Franklin, cited, 24, 35, 439
Feedback, 9–11, 21, 23, 35, 47–49; negative and positive, 207–209
Fenestra, ovalis (oval window), 194
Fenestra rotunda, 197
Festinger, Leon, cited, 35, 44, 64, 396, 439
Field workbook, 334
Final [s] voiced in urban substandard, 312
Fine distinctions in communication, 12–13
Firestone, F. A., cited, 115
Fiske, P. W., cited, 424
Fissure, of Rolando, 221; of Sylvius, 221
Fissures of cerebral cortex, 220–222
Fletcher, Harvey, cited, 105, 107, 109, 121
Flexibility in speech, 53–54
Foley, Arthur L., cited, 168
Folk etymology (popular etymology), 273, 378
Folsom, Joseph Kirk, cited, 385
Force, 53–54; restoring, 69
Forced vibration, 78–79; distortion in, 79
Forebrain, 214
Forgetting, 229–230
Formant, 121–131; amplitudes, 129; approximations only, 126–127; of different speakers, 123–124; progression of, 123; summary, 130–131; vowel diagram and, 122–123
Forum as type of group, 41
Foster, William Trufant, cited, 449
Fowler, H. W., cited, 371, 373
Framework of thorax, 136–137
Free vibration, 77; damping and, 77–78
Frequency, 74, 379; a physical phenomenon, 96–97; and pitch, 96–97; and wave length, 89–90; definition, 74; effect of length on, 99–100; effect of mass on, 99; effect of tension on, 100; factors influencing, 99–103; of the wave, 113
Frontal sinuses, 184
Fronting and backing, 365
Fry, D. B., cited, 133
Fulton, John F., cited, 212, 228
Functional relationships in speech control, 201–202
Fundamental, 111–114; and overtones in phonation, 183 ff.

[g], 248
Galambos, Robert, cited, 110
Galileo, 70–71
Gardiner, Alan H., cited, 222, 514
Garner, W. R., cited, 105, 110
Gauss, Karl, 427
Gaussian distribution of personality types, 428
Gemelli, Agostino, cited, 132
General American speech, 56
Generalization (widening), 374–375
George, Albert Donald, cited, 283
Gesell, Arnold L., cited, 481
Gestalt, the situation as, 387–388
Gesture language, 464, 487–488
Gesture theory of speech origins, 463–464
Giles, Peter, cited, 341, 363
Gilléron, J., cited, 335
Gleason, H. A., cited, 232, 326, 333
Glides, 372
Glottal stop in substandard Eastern speech, 312
Glottis, shortening margins of, 475
Glover, William, cited, 22
Goethe, cited, 449
Goss, Charles M., cited, 154 n.
Grandgent, C. H., cited, 277, 303, 308, 313
Gray, Giles Wilkeson, cited, 152, 259, 476
Gray, Henry, cited, 226
Gray, Louis H., cited, 341, 348, 351, 357, 358, 359, 361, 364, 372, 375, 376, 379
"Great vowel change," 356
Green, Harriet C., cited, 120, 123
Grimm, Jacob, cited, 322
Groom, Bernard, cited, 363
Group, definition, 37–39
Group dynamics, definition, 43; evaluations, 46–47; problems in, 44; research centers for, 42; scope of, 43; speech in, 49; summary, 47
Group organization, types of, 40–42
Group situation, 39–40; speech in, 47–49
Groups, characteristics of, 39–40; coacting, 41; learning, 41; policy determining, 41; speaking in, 37–49; types of, 37
Guillemin, A., cited, 183
Gunderson, R. G., cited, 43, 46
Gyri of cerebral cortex, 220

[h], 249
[ʔ], 248–249
Habits, motives and, 398–399
Hackett, Herbert, cited, 65
Haiman, Franklyn H., cited, 43, 45
Hair cells of cochlea, 196
Hammer (malleus, in middle ear), 194
Hance, Kenneth G., cited, 41

Haplology, 372
Harlow, Harry F., cited, 380
Harmonic analysis, 117–131
Harmonic motion, 72–74
Harmonic series, 114
Harmonics, 114
Harris, Zellig H., cited, 324, 325, 333
Harshness, 52
Haugen, Einar, cited, 255, 321
Hayakawa, S. I., cited, 440, 491, 497, 502, 503, 518
Hearing, 191–198; decibel as measure of, 105–109; function of external ear, 192; of inner ear, 195; of middle ear, 194–195; of organ of Corti, 198; personality and loss of, 437; pitch and intensity in relation to, 198–199; theory of, 197–198
Heffner, R.M. S., cited, 522
Hegemony of the CNS, 233
Heilman, Arthur, cited, 60
Helicotrema, 196
Helix, 85
Helmholtz, Hermann L. F. von, cited, 198
Henry, William E., cited, 432
Herder, Johann Gottfried von, cited, 458 n.
Herskowitz, Melville John, cited, 8
Hill, Archibald A., cited, 324, 334
Himmelweit, Hilde T., cited, 428
Hindbrain, 214
Hippocrates, 423–424
Hockett, Charles F., cited, 3, 334
Hoebel, A. Adamson, cited, 450
Hoijer, Harry, cited, 14–15, 451
Hollien, Harry Francis, cited, 103
Homans, G. C., cited, 38
Homeostasis, 212
Homonyms, 515–517
"Honorific" speech, 454
Hoover, Herbert, cited, 531
Horns of thyroid cartilage (inferior, superior), 176
House, Arthur S., cited, 109
Howell, William S., cited, 42
Hultzén, Lee S., cited, 280
Humors theory of personality, 424
Huskiness, 51–52
Huyck, E. Mary, cited, 153
Hynd, Alan, cited, 494 n.
Hyoid bone, 171, 175
Hyperbole, 377
Hyperurbanism (overcorrection), 274, 378
Hypothalamus, 218, 219

[i], 249
[ɪ], 249, 250
Ideas as symbols, 449

Identification, and identity, 498; with audience motives, 412
Identity, abstractions and, 505–506; of words and things, 495
Idol, Harriett R., cited, 139
Imagery in thinking, 446
Imaginary conversation, 442
Imitation, 489
Imitative words, 439
Immediacy of response, 10
Impressiveness as an aim in speech, 34
Impulsions, speech and, 380
Incus (anvil), 194
Indo-European, 341
Inertia, 68–69; law of, 69
Infancy, influence on personality, 424–425; production of sound in, 480
Inflectional languages, 346, 347
Information, affective elements in, 439; primary and secondary, 9; theory, 67
Inhalation, 141–155; theories of, 152–155; thoracic muscles of, 145–151
Inhibition and excitation, 231–232
Inlet valve, degeneration of larynx as, 475
Inner ear (cochlea), 195–198; fenestrae of, 194
Innuendo as propaganda, 530–531
Instrumental communication, 439; language, 26
Insulin, 213
Integration, social, 25; a function of communication, 1–4, 380
Intelligibility of speech, 55–56
Intensional orientation, 524–526
Intensity, 103–109; and loudness, 103–110; and meaning, 521–522; and pitch, 101–110; range, 107; volume and, 133–134; ways of changing, 522
Interaction in groups, 38; need for social, 5–7
Intercalary cells, 226
Interest, attention and, 414–421
Interjectional theory of speech origin, 460–461
Internal oblique muscles, 158
Internuncial cells, 226
Introductions, distinctness in, 55
Introversion, 425
Intrusive [g] or [k] after [ŋ] in urban substandard speech, 312
Intrusive [r] in substandard speech: Eastern, 308; General American, 269; Southern, 290
Intrusive sounds, 274, 290
Invention, 378–379
Irwin, O. C., cited, 480
"Is," as token of identification, 498; the copulative, 497–498

Isoglosses, 335–337
Isolation, 4–7; individual, 6–7
Isolative languages, 346, 347–348

j [dʒ], 246
Jaberg, K., cited, 335
James, William, cited, 489
Janis, Irving L., 438
Japanese language, and modes of thinking in, 454
Jeans, Sir James, cited, 80, 105, 115, 257
Jenkins, David H., cited, 43
Jerome, Eldon K., cited, 100
Jespersen, Otto, cited, 351, 461, 465
Jóhannesson, Alexander, cited, 467
Johnson, A. B., cited, 504, 505
Johnson, B. J., cited, 478, 486, 487
Johnson, Vera Yeteva, 236
Johnson, Victor, cited, 157
Johnson, Wendell, cited, 60, 437, 493, 524
Jones, Arthur Tabor, cited, 45, 77, 115
Jones, Daniel, cited, 300, 314, 316, 326
Joos, Martin, cited, 324
Jud, J., cited, 335
Judd, Charles H., cited, 17, 516, 523
Judson, Lyman S., cited, 143
Juncture phonemes, 330
Junggrammatiker, 322

[k], 249
Karwoski, T. F., cited, 416, 417, 420, 422 426, 447
Kees, Weldon, cited, 9, 11, 49
Keller, Helen, 15 f.
Kellogg, E. W., cited, 101, 136
Kelly, J. P., cited, 52
Kelman, Herbert C., cited, 42, 43, 46
Kenyon, John Samuel, cited, 268, 287, 302, 306, 318, 357, 359, 379
Key words, 236–240
Kinetic energy in speech sounds, 103–105
Kinetoscopic camera, 20
Kirby, Thomas A., cited, 266
Kluckhohn, Clyde, cited, 423
Knight, A. R., cited, 389
Knower, Franklin H., cited, 421
Knowledge and belief, 28–29
Koch, Sigmund, cited, 389
Kopp, George A., cited, 120, 123
Korzybski, Count Alfred, cited, 502, 503, 506
Kretschmer, Ernest, cited, 423
Kurath, Hans, cited, 258, 266, 299, 301, 304, 308, 335

[l], 245

Labialization in substandard Eastern speech, 308–309

Laird, A. J., cited, 389

Lamina spiralis, 195

Language, and culture, 450–454; and emotional states, 453–454; and modes of thinking in Japanese, 454; and personal attitudes, 492; and thought, 441–450; as behavioral phenomenon, 492; as medium of communication, 1–4; basis of, 493; covert behaviour in, 442; change, 350–379; development in child, 3, 472–487; expressive, 526; extensional and intensional use of, 523–528; sounds with association of ideas, 482; structure, criteria and materials for, 325–326; substrata, 370; systems, familiar, 444

Languages of the world, 338–349

Laryngeal measurements, pitch and, 102–103

Laryngeal size and vocal pitch, 102–103

Laryngopharynx, 185

Larynx, 177–183; abductor muscles of, 176; adductor muscles of, 176; cartilages of, 173–174, 177; extrinsic muscles of, 176; freed from epiglottis, 475; intrinsic muscles of, 176–178; primary function of, 475

Lasswell, Harold D., cited, 3, 453, 506

Law of conditioned reflex, 230–232

Leadership in groups, 40

Learning, 229–230

Learning groups, 41

Lee, Irving J., cited, 502, 510

Lefèvre, André, cited, 459

Leites, Nathan, cited, 3, 453

Lenen, Hans von, cited, 165, 166

Lengthening (compensatory), 369–370

Lengthening of vowels, 282

Lerner, Daniel, cited, 506

Lessing, Gotthold Ephraim, cited, 453

Levatores costarum, 150

Lewin, Kurt, 40, 42

Lewis, M. M., cited, 477, 478, 480, 482

Lindsley, C. F., cited, 139 n.

Linguistic change, 7, 350–379; causes of, 351–352; attitude toward, 525

Linguistic geography, 334–337

Linguistics, 321 ff.

Linking [r], omission medially in substandard Southern, 292; use and omission in standard Eastern, 306; in Southern, 286–287; in southern British, 317

Lippitt, Ronald, cited, 40

Lippman, Walter, cited, 24 n.

Lips as articulators, 189

Listening, 60–65; components of, 63; definition, 61–62; difficulties in studying, 61–65; factors conducive to, 63–65; importance of, 65; improvement of, 64–65; skills involved in, 61; levels of, 64; problems of analysis of, 61–65; time spent in, 60

Literacy, universal, 7

Literature, catharsis in, 440

Litotes (understatement), 376

Locke, John, cited, 494, 504, 514, 523

Logarithms, 106

Logical meaning, 521

Longitudinal fissure of cerebral cortex, 220

Loudness, 105–110; and decibel, 108; and intensity, 103–110; correlate of intensity, 105–109; monotony of, 53–54; of sounds of speech, 109; scale, 105; zero, 108
   See also Intensity

Lowering, 365; substandard, 272

Lungs, 137–140; biological function of, 137–138; capacity of, 139; function in speech of, 138–140; structure of, 137–138; relation of capacity to voice, 139

[m], 243

McBurney, James H., cited, 41

McCarthy, Dorothea, cited, 473, 478, 481, 484, 485

McClelland, David C., cited, 391, 424, 432, 435

Magnitude as attention factor, 416

Major, David R., cited, 486

Malleus (hammer), 194

Manly, J. M., cited, 348

Mann, Thomas, cited, 497

Manner of utterance, attention and, 420–421; meaning and, 519–520

Maps as symbols, 445

Marckwardt, Albert H., cited, 258, 357, 360, 364, 371, 375

Maslow, A. H., cited, 396

Mass, effect on frequency of, 99

Mathematics, symbols in, 444

Maturation and motives, 390–391; in learning speech, 481

Maxillary sinuses, 184

Maxwell, Perrilton, cited, 494

Meaning, as function of a relationship, 495–500; ambiguity in, 518; and emphasis, 519; and inflection patterns, 519; and manner of utterance, 519–520; change in, 501–502; determinants of, 499–523; personal attitude and, 520–523

Meanings, and the listener, 19; conveyed by three means, 19; in language, 18; ex-

tensional, 524; intensional, 524; not conveyed, 498–499
"Medial" breathing, 152
Medulla oblongata, 215, 217
Medullary sheath, 227
Meerloo, Joost A. M., cited, 48
Mel, defined, 129 n.
Membrana spiralis, 196
Membrane of Reissner, 196
Membranes as vibrators, 75
Memory trace (neurogram), 229–230
Mencken, H. L., cited, 496
Mesencephalon, 214, 217–218
Metalinguistics, 321
Metaphor, 374
Metathesis, 274, 372
Metencephalon, 214, 217
Metonymy, 374
Metz, Herbert, cited, 288
Metzger, Wolfgang, cited, 166
Microwatt as measure of sound energy, 107
Midbrain, 214, 217–218
Middle ear, 194–195; bones of, 194; muscles of, 194
"Midland," 258
Miller, D. C., cited, 87, 88, 105, 115
Miller, George A., cited, 9, 46, 47, 56, 64, 65, 107, 122, 447, 481, 484
Minimal pairs, 327–328
Momentum, 69–70
Monotony, 53–54; of loudness, 53–54; of pitch, 53; of time, 54
Moore, Paul, cited, 165, 166
Moore, W. E., cited, 152, 433
Morgan, C. D., cited, 430
Morgan, C. T., cited, 110, 219
Morgan, Clifford T., cited, 230
Morgan, Stewart, cited, 259 n.
Morphemes, 332–333; components of, 332; definition, 332
Morris, Charles William, cited, 514
Motivation, 388–414; ethics of, 413–414; of audience, 405–409; of speaker, 409–414; principles of, 389–414
Motivational knowledge, status of, 388–390
Motive, and purpose, 392–393; and reason, 392; stimulation of, 407–409
Motives, and general ends of speech, 394–395; and habits, 398; and programs, 394; and basis of assembly, 393–394; and third groups, 412–413; as basis for activity, 380–381; attention and, 417–418; appeals to selfish, 397, 399; conflict of, 400–405; fluctuation of, 399–400; honesty of, 414; identification with audience, 412; maturation and, 390–391; modification of, 390–392; personally oriented, 400, 410–411; "selfish" and "unselfish," 395–398; social modification of, 390; socially oriented, 400, 411; sources of, 389–390; speaker's, 409–414; stimulation of, 407; universality of, 391–392
Motor neurons, 226
Mudd, Charles S., Jr., cited, 155, 188
Müller, Friedrich Max, cited, 448, 457, 459, 462, 463
Muffled tones, 52
Murphy, Gardner, cited, 383, 390, 393, 399, 405, 422, 427, 447
Murray, Elwood, cited, 433
Murray, Henry A., cited, 423, 430
Muscles, arytenoid, 178; crico-arytenoid, 165, 166; crico-arytenoid, lateral, 177, 178, 180; crico-thyroid, posterior, 179, 180; diaphragm, 144, 145; external oblique, 158; genioglossus, 173; geniohyoglossus, 180; geniohyoid, 180; hyoglossus, 180; internal oblique, 158; levatores costarum, 150; middle constrictor, 180; mylohyoid, 180; of exhalation, 158–159; of larynx, 176–181; pectoralis major, 146; pectoralis minor, 148; quadratus lumborum, 145; rectus abdominis, 158, 159; scaleni, 151; serratus anterior, 151; serratus posterior inferior, 145; serratus posterior superior, 150; sternocleidomastoideus, 148, 173; sternohyoid, 180; striped, 165; styloglossus, 173; subclavius, 148; thoracic (inhalation), 145–151; thyro-arytenoid, 165, 178, 179; thyrohyoid, 180; transversus abdominis, 158; transversus thoracis, 158–159
Muscular antagonism, 155–156
Muscular exertion theory of speech origin, 463
Mussen, John Henry, cited, 473
Myelencephalon, 214, 216–217
Myelin, 216
Myers, Edward D., cited, 374

[n], 245
Name-calling as propaganda, 529
Names of things, 494–495
Narrowing of meaning (specialization), 375–376, 517
Nasality, 52
Nasalization of [aʊ], [æ], 276
Nasopharynx, 185
Negus, V. E., cited, 13, 14, 181, 183, 475, 488
Nerve impulses, 224–225
Nesbit, Frank Ford, 505, 507, 511

Neurofibrils, 226
Neurogram (memory trace), 230
Neurological elements in speech control, 209–233
Neurons, 225–226; afferent, 226; axons, 225–226; cytoplasm, 226; dendrites, 225; efferent, 226; internal structure, 226–227; motor, 226; neurofibrils, 226; Nissl bodies, 226; perifibrillar substance, 226; sensory, 226
Neuroticism, 425
Newton, Law of, 69
Nichols, Ralph G., cited, 61, 63
Nida, Eugene A., cited, 324
Nissl bodies, 226, 227
Nobles, W. Scott, cited, 288
Noiré, speech origin theory of, 463
Noise characteristics in speech sounds, 99
Noises, low pitched and high pitched, 98–99; tones and, 97–99
"North" (American speech region), 258
Nose, 186; bones of, 186; septum, 186; turbinates, 186

[o], 249, 250
[ou, o], 250
[ɔ], 249
Obsolescence, 516
Odbert, H. S., cited, 426
Oertel, Hans, cited, 248, 363, 371, 372
Olson, Harry F., cited, 117
Omissions from consonant clusters, 275, 291, 312, 313
Onomatopoetic theory of speech origin, 458–459
Ontogenesis of speech, 472
Open tube resonators, 93–94, 185
Oppositeness, 509
Optimum pitch, 52–53, 101–102; resonance affecting, 94
Oral gesture theory of speech origin, 466–467
Organ of Corti, 196
Organism, nature of, 386; as determining response, 6–8; past experiences of, 386–387
Orientation, multivalued, 509–510; two-valued, 508–510; extensional and intensional, 524–525
Origin of speech, contact, 470–471; difficulties in establishing, 455–456; divine creation, 456–457; gesture, 463–464; interjection, 460–461; muscular exertion, 463; onomatopoeia, 458–459; oral gesture, 466; phonetic type, 461–462; social control, 468–470; social pressure, 457–458;

theories of, 456–472; vocal play, 465–466
Oropharynx, 185
Ossicular chain, 194
Oval window (fenestra ovalis), 194
-our (for -or suffix), British-Canadian spelling, 286
Overcorrection, 274, 378
"Overlaid function," of speech, 136 n., 474–476
Overtones, 113

[p], 242
Paget, Sir Richard, cited, 466–467
Palatalization, 367–368; in substandard Eastern speech, 309
Palmer, George Herbert, cited, 526–527
Pantomimic relations in Aryan word roots, 467
Papillon, T. L., cited, 357
Parasympathetic nervous system, 212–213
Partials, 113–114
Participation in groups, 39–40, 48
Past experience, attention and, 416
Pastori, Giuseppina, cited, 132
Paul, Hermann, cited, 322, 351, 361
Pavlov, Ivan P., cited, 230, 231, 232, 383
Pear, T. H., cited, 435
Pectoralis major, 146
Pectoralis minor, 148
Pedrey, Charles Paul, cited, 100
Pejoration (degeneration), 376 n., 516
Pendulum, movement of, 70–72; period of, 70, 71
Penfield, W., cited, 221
Perception, centers of, 203; total, 204
Perifibrillar substance, 226
Perilymph, 196–197
Period, definition, 74; of pendulum, 70–71; of vibration, 71
Peripheral nervous system, 209 ff.
Perry, Bliss, cited, 18
Personal Social Adjustment Test for Speech, 433
Personality, and hearing, 437–438; and speech, difficulties in correlating, 435–437; and stuttering, 437; and susceptibility to persuasion, 438; and the speech defective, 437–438; bimodal distribution, 427–428; body-type theory of, 423–424; classes of determinants, 423; clusters and sectors, 426–427; components of, 425–427; concepts of, 422–423; definitions, 422–423; determinants, 423–425; distribution of types, 427–429; dominance and submission as types of, 427; dynamic components

of, 426; expressive aspects of, 426; "humors" theory of, 424; individual differences in, 428–429; influence of infancy on, 424–425; measurement of, 429–432; other traits of, 427; problem of, 421–438; projective techniques of measurement, 430–432; Rorschach test of, 430–431; self-sufficiency as type of, 427; social determinants of, 424–425; social influence on, 425; speech and, 432–437; tests, 429–434; *Thematic Apperception Test of*, 431–432; speech as a trait of, 434–437; "traits" and "types" of, 425; types, bimodal distribution of, 427–428; types, Gaussian distribution of, 428

Persuasion, personality and susceptibility to, 438

Peterson, Gordon E., cited, 119, 120, 121, 127, 129, 130, 132

Pharynx, 185

Phase, and quality, 115–116; calculation of, 75; defined, 75; relations, 75; shift, 75

Phonemes, 250–251; suprasegmental: of clause termination, 331; of juncture, 330; of pitch, 330–331; of stress, 329–330

Phonetic alphabet, need for, 236; symbols of, 238–240, 444

Phonetic reading, 252; transcription, 251–252

Phonetic type theory of speech origin, 461–462

Phonetics, applications to speech improvement, 264; as basic instrument in linguistic study, 325; as instrument for speech improvement, 263–264; relation to general linguistics, 235

Phonograph, invention of, 20

Pike, Kenneth L., cited, 324, 522

Pillars of the fauces, 185

Pillsbury, W. B., cited, 387, 446

Pitch, and frequency, relation between, 96–97; and intensity, 109–110, 198–199; and laryngeal measurements, 102–103; and meaning, 522; dependence on frequency, 97; determined by wave frequency, 113; monotony, 53; phonemes, 330–331; vocal cords as determiners of, 101–102; volume and, 133

Pituitary gland, 218, 219–220

Plates as vibrators, 76

Pleonasm (redundancy), 373

Policy-determining groups, 41

Political oratory, 527–528

Polyak, Stephen L., cited, 197

Polysynthetic (including incorporating) languages, 346, 348–349

Pons, 217

"Pooh-pooh" theory of speech origin, 460–461

Pool, Ithiel de Sola, cited, 506

Poole, Irene, cited, 480

Popular (folk) etymology, 378

Portmanteau words (blend-words, contamination), 364

Pott, August Friedrich, cited, 222

Potter, Ralph K., cited, 120, 123, 128

Poulson principle in recording, 20

Prefixes, 332

Presentation, attention and manner of, 420–421

Pressure, curve of, 85–86; in sound wave, 104

Preyer, W., cited, 486

Primary information, 9

Proclamation and command, 29–31, 469

Programs, motives and, 394

Progression of ideas, attention and, 420

Progressive assimilation, 357

Progressive-regressive-reciprocal assimilation, 357–358

Projection, adequate, 54–55; basis of, 55

Prokosch, E., cited, 350, 351, 358, 360, 362

Pronunciation, archaic (relic), 271; "correct," 56–57; dictionary as guide to, 56–57; of word, 253

Propaganda, 528–531

Proprioceptors, 223, 224

Prothesis, 364

Proximity and confrontation, 21–23; in communication, 22–24; in group, 39

Psychotherapy, catharsis in, 441

Public speaking, speaker's aim in, 26–35

Purpose, motive and, 392–393

Purposive articulate utterance, 483–484

Quadratus lumborum, 145

Quality of voice, and meaning, 521; and phase, 115–116; and resonance, 115–116; and wave complexity, 115; defined, 114 n.

Quintilian, 518

[r], 246–247; r in Eastern speech, 304–306; in General American speech, 267; in Southern speech, 285–287; intrusive, 269

[ɚ], 249

[ɝ], 249

Race, development of speech in the, 455–472

Raising, and lowering, 365; and nasalization of [aʊ], [æ], 276; of vowels before [t], [d], [n], 269; before other front consonants, 279

Rankin, Paul T., cited, 60

Rapoport, Anatol, cited, 524
Rapport in communicativeness, 36
Rarefaction, compression and, 82–83; wave of, 82
Rask, Rasmus, cited, 322
Rationalization, 401–402
Reactions (native, innate, inborn), 229–230
Reading, rapid silent, 17
Reason, motives and, 392
Receptors, 203, 223
Recording, of audible and visible symbols, 13–14; of communication, 13–14; of speech and music, 20–21; Poulson principle in, 20; significance of, 20–21; tape and wire, 20–21
Rectus abdominis, 158
"Red herring," as propaganda technique, 529–530
Redundancy (pleonasm), 373
Reeds as vibrators, 75–76
Reference, community of, 510–514
Reference intensity, 107, 108
Referent, 499–510; change in, 500–503
Reflex arc, 228–229
Reflexive vocalization, 477–478
Regional predominance in breathing, 152
Relic pronunciation, 271
Remembering, 229–230
Repeated lie as propaganda technique, 530
Repetition of stimulus, attention and, 416
Research, centers for group dynamics, 42; in group dynamics, 42
Resonance, 90–95; 183–188; and quality, 115–116; and timbre, 115–116; cavity, 93–95, 185; closed tube, 94, 185; defined, 90; effect on duration of vibration, 93; in flasks, 95; in throat and mouth, 121–126; open tube, 94, 185; sounding board, 91–93, 187–188; sympathetic vibration, 91
Resonating cavities, 122–123
Resonator, tube as, 93–94
Respiration, 135–163; process of, 140–159
    See also Breathing
Response, factors determining specific, 386–388; immediacy of, 10; infant, 474; relation to the cycle of communication, 10–12; nature of, 383–384; substitute, 384–385; aim of communication, 26–27
Restressing, 276, 369
Retracted stress, in substandard speech, 274, 292
Révész, G., cited, 9, 62, 440, 450, 473, 476; speech origin theory of, 470–471
Ribs, 137; rise of, 144–145
Richardson, E. G., cited, 80
Ripple box, 84

Robertson, Stuart, cited, 359, 364, 374, 376, 377
Romanes, cited, 13
Roots, 332
Rorschach, Hermann, cited, 430
Rorschach Inkblot Test, 430–431
Round table as type of group, 41–42
Round window (fenestra rotunda), 197
Ruesch, Jurgen, cited, 9, 11, 49

[s], 246; superfluous before [k], [p], 278
sh [ʃ], 245
Sameness, 502–503
Sanford, F. H., cited, 434, 435, 436
Sanskrit, 459
Santorini, cartilages of, 173
Sapir, Edward, cited, 323, 435, 447, 448, 459, 461
Sarason, Seymour B., cited, 431
Sarett, Lew, cited, 449
Savart, Felix, cited, 183 n.
Scala tympani, 195
Scala vestibuli, 195
Scaleni, 151
Scapulae, 137
Schlauch, Margaret, cited, 357, 358, 359, 360, 361, 365, 367, 375, 376, 378, 379, 511, 517
Schleicher, August, cited, 222
Schramm, Wilbur, cited, 24
Schrijnen, Joseph, cited, 335
Seashore, Carl Emil, cited, 133
Segerstedt, Torgny T., cited, 25
Segmental vibrations, 110–114; and wave complexity, 110–114; tones from, 113–114
Self-expression, speech as, 438
Self-sufficiency as personality trait, 427
"Selfish" motives, 396–399
Semantic approach to symbols, 491–492
Semantic change, 372–377
Semantic soundness, 58–59
Semantics and general semantics differentiated, 491–492
Semicircular canals, 198
Senses, distance and contact, 11–12; in communication, 11–24; significance of distance, 15–16
Sensory neurons, 226
Septuagint, cited, 322
Septum, 186
Serratus, anterior, 151; posterior inferior, 145; posterior superior, 150
"Set," audience, 406
Sheehan, Joseph G., cited, 438
Sheldon, W. H., cited, 424

Shewmake, E. W., cited, 284, 288
Shirley, M. M., cited, 486
Shohara, Hide H., cited, 140
Shortening, of words, 379; of phonetic elements, 370
Shoulder blades, 137
Shrillness, 52
Shrinkage of words, 363
Sight and hearing combined in speech, 11–12, 19
Signification, reliability of, 390–391
Simplification of consonant clusters, 363
Sine curve, 72, 74, 85, 191, 192; construction of, 73; derivation of, 73–74; equation for, 74 n.
Sinuses (frontal, maxillary, ethmoid, sphenoid), 184
Situation, as *Gestalt*, 387–388; communicative, 381–388; nature of, 382; present, 387–388
Skinner, B. F., cited, 446
Skinner, Otis, 22
Slogans and labels, 496–497
Smith, Adam, cited, 457–458
Smith, Alpheus E., cited, 82
Smith, Donald K., cited, 42
Smith, Joseph F., cited, 414
Smith, M. E., cited, 485
Smith, Mary Katherine, cited, 487
Smith, Svend, cited, 168 n.
Social control as aim of communication, 25–35
Social determinants of personality, 424–425
Social influences on personality, 425
Social integration, 25; speech and, 380
Social modification of motives, 390
Social nature of thinking, 448
Social pressure theory of speech origin, 457–458
Social stimulation, 26
Social control theory of speech origin, 468–470
Soft palate, 175
Soliloquy as communication, 36
Somatic nervous system (SNS), 209 ff.
Sound, basic factors of, 95–134; kinetic energy in, 103–105; physicists' and psychologists' concepts of, 66–67; "psychological," 68 n.; range preferences, 116–117; velocity of, 86–89; wave, pressure in, 104
Sound waves, 81–89, 191–199; at tympanic membrane, 192, 193, 194; curves of, 85–86; in air, 191–192; in external ear, 192; in middle ear, 194, 195
Sounding-board resonance, 79, 91–93, 187–188

Sounds, English, 236; minimum perceptible differences in, 132; loudness of speech, 109; order of appearance of, 479–480
"South" (American speech region), 258 n.
Southern drawl, 293; speech, 56
Sparks, Jared, cited, 307
Speaker, attention and, 419; motivation of, 409–414
Speaking, attention in relation to, 418–421
Specialization (narrowing), 375–376
Spectrograph, sound, 120–131
Spectrum, tridimensional, 119
Speech, as social activity, 380; American, future of, 261–262; and freedom of speech, 49–50; and personality, 432–437; and thought, parallel growth of, 448–450; as personality trait, 434–437; as self-expression, 438; as socializing agent, 380; good, characteristics of, 49–59; formulation of, 205; in group dynamics, 49; in group situation, importance of, 47–49; learning, 473; origin, *see* Origins of speech; regions, American, 258–259; sounds, 99, 109, 480
Spelling, inconsistencies, 235–236; and pronunciation, 275–276, 356, 379
Sperry, R. W., cited, 232
Sphenoid sinus, 184
Spinal column, 137; cord, 214–216; reflexes, 214
Stage fright, 58
Stage speech, 314–320
Stagner, Ross, cited, 416, 417, 420, 422, 426, 447
Standard speech, Eastern American, 258, 299–306; European Spanish (Castilian), 255; French (Île de France), 255; General American, 258, 264–268; High German, 255; Norwegian (Landsmaal, Nynorsk), 255; Southern American, 258, 281–287; Southern British, 255, 314–320
Stapedius muscle, 194
Stapes (stirrup), 194
Steer, M. D., cited, 152
Steinberg, J. C., cited, 123
Stems, 332
Sternocleidomastoideus, 148, 173
Sternum, 137
Stevens, Eugene L., 109
Stevens, S. S., cited, 79, 91, 97, 104, 110, 113, 115
Stewart, G. W., cited, 80, 87, 93, 95, 104
Stimmband, Stimmbänder, 165
Stimulation, as aim of speech, 34–35; of attitudes, 415–421; of motives, 407

Stimuli, differentiated, 478–479; external, 380; implicit symbolic, 443; not isolated, 387; undifferentiated, 489

Stimulus, as element in a pattern, 387; function dependent on place in pattern, 387; in total pattern, 517–518; inadequate, 231; sound as auditory, 67; substitute, 384–385, 490; communicative, 382–383; nature of, 381–382; substitute, 383, 384–385, 490, 493; type used in communication, 382–383; variations in, 415–416

Stirrup (stapes) in middle ear, 194

Stone, Henry A., cited, 146, 151

Stress phonemes, 329–330

Stress, primary, advance of in substandard Southern speech, 293; secondary, in British speech, 318; in Eastern, 306; in General American, 268; in Southern, 287

Striate bodies, 218

Strings as vibrators, 75

Strong, Herbert, cited, 372, 374

Strong, Leon H., cited, 178

Sturtevant, E. H., cited, 359, 372, 374

Stuttering, personality and, 437

Styloid processes, 171

Sublimation and conflict, 402–403

Substandard pronunciation (speech), urban, 271, 309–314; common to Eastern, General American, and Southern, 271–281, 293; Eastern, 307–309; Eastern urban, 309–313; General American, 268–271; miscellaneous, 279; Southern, 287–299

Substitutions, substandard, General American, 220, 268, 269, 277, 278; Southern, 289–292, 307–313

Substrata in language, 370–371

Suffixes, 332–333

Sulci of cerebral cortex, 220

Sully, James, cited, 481

Superfluous [s] before [k] and [p], 278; [t], [d], [ə d], 278

Sweet, Henry, cited, 467, 472

Syllabic syncope, 291, 371

Symbol, and object not the same, 494; and reality, 491; in relation to concept, 447; substitute stimulus as, 493

Symbolic movements of the body, 443–444

Symbolic systems, 491

Symbolism, basis of, 493

Symbolization, 491; total pattern of, 514–515

Symbols, as conventions, 493–495; attitudes toward, 495–497; blueprints as, 445; ideas as, 449; in mathematics, 444; maps as, 445; of phonetic alphabet, 444; significance of, 490; vocal, 66; world of, 490

Symonds, Percival M., cited, 431

Sympathetic nervous system, 212, 213

Sympathetic vibration, 91

Symposium as type of group, 41–42

Synapse, 227–228

Syncope, 279, 371; syllabic, 291, 371

Synecdoche, 374

Synthetic languages, 346

Synthetic sounds, 466–467

[t], 244

th [θ], 247

th [ð], 247–248

Taboos, verbal, 525

Tanner, Amy Eliza, cited, 478

Tape recording, 20–21

Tarski, Alfred, cited, 492, 493

Tectorial membrane, 196

Telencephalon, 214, 220–222

Telephone and radio compared, 19–20

Television, closed circuit, 23; programs, recording for, 20–21

Temperature, effect on resonant frequency of tubes, 95; effect on velocity of sound, 88–89

Tempered scale, 97

Tension, effect on frequency, 100

Tensor tympani muscle, 194

Tensors of vocal bands, 176, 178

Thalamus, 218

Thelen, Herbert A., cited, 439

Thematic Apperception Test (of personality), 431–432

Thinking, abstract, 446–448; concrete, 445–446; defined, 443; imagery in, 446; in languages, 444; social nature of, 448

Thomas, C. K., cited, 266, 283, 302

Thompson, Dorothy, cited, 449

"Thoracic" breathing, 152

Thorax, 136–159; decreasing, 156–158; enlarging, 141–155; expanding, 137; increasing horizontal dimensions of, 145

Thorpe, Louis P., cited, 476

Thought-grouping and breathing, 160–161

Thought, language and, 441–450

Thyro-arytenoid muscle, 177

Thyroid cartilage, 173, 174

Thyroxin, 213

Tidal air and voice, 139

Tidewater Virginia, [ɜʊ] for [aʊ], 284; [ɜɪ] for [aɪ], 288

Tiffany, William R., cited, 133

Timbre, and resonance, 115–116; defined, 114 n.; wave complexity and, 110–116
Time, and dialectal differences, 131–132; and meaning, 522; and speech control, 201; and duration of sounds, 131–133; maintained in three ways, 131; monotony in, 54
Titiev, Mischa, cited, 451, 452
Tone-complex, 110
Tones, and noises, 97–99; controlling strength of, 153–154; from segmental vibrations, 113
Tongue, back as articulator, 190; blade and tip as articulators, 189–190
Trachea, 173, 187
Trager, G. L., cited, 324, 326 n.
"Traits" and "types" of personality, 425
Translation, difficulty of, 451; the problem of, 511
Transmissibility, significance of, 19–20
Transmission, media of, 19–20; of audible and visual symbols, 13; of communication, 13
Transversus abdominis, 158
Transversus thoracis, 158–159
Travis, L. E., cited, 101, 208
Trimmer, J. D., cited, 115
Tube, effect of length on resonating, 94; end correction for resonating, 94 n.; frequency of closed, 94; frequency of open, 94; resonance in, 94
Turbinate bones, 186
Twaddell, W. Freeman, cited, 324
Two-valued orientation, 508–510
Tympanic membrane, 192–194

[u], 249
[ʊ], 249
[ʌ], 249
Umlaut, 358
Understanding, as aim of speech, 27; as primary language experience, 476–477
Understatement (litotes), 376
Unrounding, 368
Unstressing, substandard, 273; definition, 368
Unvoicing, substandard, 272, 311
Urban substandardisms (Eastern), 309–313
Utterance, attention and mode of, 420–421
Uvula, 185

[v], 243
Van den Berg, J. W., cited, 183
Velocity, and wave length, 89–90; of sound, 86–89; of sound in air, 87; of sound in different media, 87–88

Velum, 175; as articulator, 190
Vendryes, J., cited, 357, 362
Ventricles of Morgagni, 182–183
Verb forms, analogical, 273
Vernon, Philip E., cited, 432
Vertebrae, 136–137
Vibration, 67–72; cavity resonance as maintained, 93; definition, 70; forced, 78–79; free, 77; maintained, 78; segmental, 110–114; sympathetic, 91; tones from segmental, 113–114; wave complexity and segmental, 111–112
Vibrators, for voice, 163–171; action of, 166–171; housing and musculature of, 171; types of, 75–76
Viëtor, W., cited, 362
Violin and sounding board effect, 92
Viscera, movement of abdominal, 144
Visual, significance of appeal to, 18–19
Visual agnosia, 203
Vital capacity, 139; and voice, 139
Vocabulary, 484–487; growth of, 485–487; and dictionaries, 17
Vocal bands, 163–165; as articulators, 191; as determiners of pitch, 101–102; as vibrators, 77, 136; protection and lubrication of, 182–183; relaxers of, 176, 178; tensors of, 176–178
Vocal folds, 163–165
Vocal mechanism as coupled system, 101
Vocal play, 479–483; theory of speech origin, 465–466
Vocalization (vowelization), 365; reflexive, 477–478
Voice, as a wind instrument, 116; breathing and, 159–163; quality in good speech, 51; pitch range of, 102
Voicing, definition, 360; in urban substandard speech, 312; substandard, 272
Volume, 133–134; and intensity, 133–134; and pitch, 133; attributes of, 133–134; elasticity, 87
von Herder, Johann Gottfried, cited, 458
Vowel diagram, 240–241; and formants, 122–123
Vowelization (vocalization), 365
Vowels, description, 249–250; fronted and raised before front consonants, 279

[ʍ, w] in Eastern speech, 306; in General American speech, 268; in Southern speech, 287
[w], wh [ʍ], 243
Waddle, Charles W., cited, 473, 484, 486
Walker, John, cited, 131
Walnut, Francis, cited, 437

Watson, John B., cited, 198

Wave, complexity and segmental vibrations, 110–114; complexity and timbre, 110–116; form, quality not dependent on, 115; front, 104; length, 89–90; length and frequency, 89–90; length and velocity, 89–90; longitudinal, 81; motion in middle ear, 194, 195; transverse, 81

Wave-to-wave analysis, 117

Weaver, Andrew Thomas, cited, 51, 143, 499

Weber-Fechner Law, 105–106

Weekley, Ernest, cited, 361, 363

Weiss, A. P., cited, 385, 445

Welsh, G. B., cited, 62 n.

Wenker, Georg, cited, 335

West, Robert, cited, 166, 208, 396

Western drawl, 270

Whatmough, Joshua, cited, 321, 324

Wheelwright, Philip, cited, 526

White, Alice Marsden, cited, 441; Leslie, A., cited, 451

Whitney, William Dwight, cited, 457, 459, 460, 462, 467

Whorf, Benjamin Lee, cited, 2, 323, 451, 452

Widening (generalization), 374–375

Wiener, Norbert, cited, 5, 9

Wiksell, Wesley, cited, 61

Wilder, Thornton, quoted, 501

Williamson, A. B., cited, 51

Willis, George, cited, 458

Winans, James A., cited, 35, 392, 408

"Wir-Gefühl," 25

Wise, C. M., cited, 186, 187, 284, 288, 307, 322, 323

Woodworth, R. S., cited, 372

Woolbert, Charles Henry, cited, 18, 21, 28, 405, 421, 520, 521

Word, as substitute stimulus, 490; shrinkage, 363; grouping and breathing, 160–161

Words, as substitute stimulus and response, 385; with a single standard pronunciation, 253; with multiple standard pronunciations, 253

Wrisberg, cartilages of, 173

Writing, dependent on speech, 7–8

Wundt, Wilhelm, cited, 322, 463–465; gesture theory of speech origin, 463–465

y [j], 247

"Yo-he-ho" theory of speech origin, 463

[z], 246

zh [ʒ], 245

Zander, Alvin, cited, 43, 44, 46

Zero loudness, 108

69 70 71 72 73   12 11 10 9 8